MEDICAL ENTOMOLOGY

William B. Herms, Sc.D.

Late Professor of Parasitology, Emeritus, University of California; one-time Lecturer in Tropical Medicine, University of California School of Medicine, San Francisco; late Chairman, Division of Entomology and Parasitology, University of California

Revised by

Maurice T. James, Ph.D.

Professor of Entomology, Washington State University, Pullman

Fifth Edition

THE MACMILLAN COMPANY NEW YORK

Third Printing, 1965

Earlier editions: *Medical and Veterinary Entomology,* copyright, 1915 and 1923 by The Macmillan Company; *Medical Entomology,* copyright, 1939 and 1950 by The Macmillan Company

Library of Congress catalog card number: 60-11814

The Macmillan Company, New York
Collier-Macmillan Canada, Ltd., Toronto, Ontario

Printed in the United States of America

PREFACE TO THE FIFTH EDITION

The past decade has witnessed an extremely rapid development in the science of medical entomology. The impulse given to the study of this subject after the Spanish-American War and, again, after World War I, waned after the immediate problems had reached an apparently satisfactory temporary solution, and after the periods of stern necessity had passed. Fortunately, this trend was not repeated after World War II. The study of the bionomics of arthropods of actual or potential medical or veterinary importance has progressed at an unprecedented rate, as has the related subject of virology, and taxonomic studies have kept pace with biologic investigations. Consequently, we have an ever-increasing fund of information along these lines which has necessitated the revision of any textbook, however thorough the treatment at the time of its publication, that dates back to the days or early aftermath of World War II.

Ten years ago, the "new insecticides" were just becoming established for nonmilitary usage. During the following years we have witnessed the development to an important degree of the use of the chlorinated hydrocarbons, phosphorus compounds, more effective repellents, and synergists; the introduction of systemic insecticides; the recognition of some shortcomings of the "new insecticides," such as special dangers associated with their use and the tendency of many insects to develop resistance to them; the return of certain inorganic chemicals of a previously unknown insecticidal action or in new formulations; and the development of new nonchemical methods, such as new applications of biological control and control through the liberation of sterilized males into a wild population. Our philosophy of insect control has changed in at least two significant ways. First, we have begun to think in terms of eradication as well as suppression. It is true that the idea of eradication antedates the past decade, but our approach to it is now more realistic, based on the possession of better tools and a recognition of the biologic backgrounds that may permit eradication under certain circumstances or make it impossible or unfeasible under others. Secondly, we have a new outlook on the control of pests as such, not necessarily in relation to disease suppression but in terms of improving mental health and raising standards of living. All in all, the control of noxious and dangerous pests, in both objectives and procedure, is quite different from what it was ten years ago.

It has been a privilege and pleasure to attempt to bring up to date a work laid upon the foundation of so many years' experience in teaching and research by one of the truly eminent medical entomologists of our time.

In general, I have attempted to follow Dr. Herms's plan of presentation. Some material has been reduced or deleted in order to strengthen the more purely medical entomologic aspects of the work without increasing its size. The addition of some keys and anatomic material will, I hope, serve to broaden the usefulness of the text, particularly in application to laboratory work. I regret that the veterinary aspects of the subject have had to be further reduced, but that subject could not be treated adequately in a textbook of medical entomology without extending the treatment beyond reasonable textbook length. Such a procedure was feasible in 1915; it is no longer so today.

I am indebted to many persons who have generously made suggestions, lent illustrations, furnished me with reprints, or otherwise made my task of revision easier. I am particularly indebted to the following individuals who have read parts of the manuscript and who have made valuable suggestions about it: W. J. Baerg, S. F. Bailey, Helmut K. Buechner, I. O. Buss, Hahn W. Capps, Deane P. Furman, Willis J. Gertsch, J. D. Gregson, A. B. Gurney, Elizabeth R. Hall, Robert F. Harwood, Melville H. Hatch, Harry Hoogstraal, J. Franklin Howell, A. A. Hubert, William L. Jellison, Carl A. Johansen, Benjamin Keh, Glen M. Kohls, K. V. Krombein, Charles W. McNeil, Torbjorn Moll, Mir S. Mulla, Kellie O'Neill, Richard F. Peters, A. Earl Pritchard, W. C. Reeves, Louis M. Roth, Raymond E. Ryckman, Curtis W. Sabrosky, R. I. Sailer, Arthur C. Smith, M. R. Smith, T. J. Spilman, Harry H. Stage, Alan Stone, H. S. Telford, E. L. Todd, George B. Vogt, Luther S. West, and W. W. Wirth.

M. T. J.

October, 1960

PREFACE TO THE FOURTH EDITION

THE ORIGINAL MANUSCRIPT for this book was prepared about forty years ago, and the first edition, entitled *Medical and Veterinary Entomology,* appeared in 1915. The book was most generously received from the beginning and has been widely and increasingly used in each succeeding edition. It took considerable preseverance to complete another revision for a fourth edition. With the encouragement of long-time users of the work and the assistance of colleagues, graduate students, and others this has now been accomplished.

The science of medical entomology has been fully accepted as one of the important fundamentals for a complete knowledge and understanding of public health operations as well as for an understanding of the health of domestic animals; it is essential to a complete understanding of the epidemiology of disease. Medical entomology is now taught in the entomological curricula of most colleges and universities, as well as in curricula of public health, preventive medicine, and tropical medicine.

The general plan of the book remains essentially unchanged; but owing to the rapid expansion of knowledge pertaining to arthropods as vectors of infections of man and animals and because of changes in control technique due to the discovery of new insecticide, such as DDT, a complete revision of nearly all chapters became necessary. Stress continues to be placed on biology (life history and ecology) as fundamental to rational control and as basic to sound epidemiological procedures.

While it is recognized that the advent of DDT did measurably change arthropod-control concepts, the use of this and other new insecticides precipitated new problems or new phases of old ones, particularly as these newer insecticides affect the public health either directly or indirectly and to some degree also the "balance" in nature. Instead of requiring less knowledge concerning the ecology of living things (so-called "shot-gun" methods of application have too largely prevailed), the wise and successful use of these insecticides requires much more fundamental knowledge of the ecology of the offending organisms as well as of others living in the same niche. Hazards to the health of man and his domestic animals must be well considered. Those in charge of training military personnel for vector control operations (to check malaria, tsutsugamushi disease, etc.) under military conditions must recognize, as do public health officials, that sole reliance on the techniques of chemical control (use of insecticides) and the neglect of knowledge of vectors can lead only to failure in the long run.

Among the many persons to whom I am indebted for assistance I wish to thank Professor E. O. Essig, my successor as head of the Division of Entomology and Parasitology, University of California, for placing clerical and other assistance at my disposal. Thanks are due Professors W. M. Hoskins, M. A. Stewart, R. Craig, and Dean Furman for technical assistance, and to Dr. W. C. Reeves, H. F. Gray, Willis Doetschmann, and Richard Coleman for critical reading of certain chapters. I wish to thank Arve Dahl and Richard Peters of the Bureau of Vector Control of the California State Department of Public Health for many courtesies extended during the preparation of this edition. My thanks go particularly to Mrs. K. E. Frick for the task of typing the manuscript. To my wife for long-continued encouragement I owe more than words can express.

W. B. H.

Berkeley, California
April, 1949

CONTENTS

KEYS

TABLES

MEDICAL ENTOMOLOGY

Chapter 1

INTRODUCTION

Medical entomology may be defined as the science which deals with the relation of insects, arachnids, and other arthropods to the causation of pathological conditions in man or to the transmission of organisms which are responsible for such pathological conditions. The arthropods involved may be the causal agents themselves, e.g., the scabies mites; intermediate hosts, as the crustacean *Cyclops* in its relation to the guinea worm; or vectors, as *Anopheles* mosquitoes in relation to malaria. The science is directly concerned with the biology and control of the offending arthropods and with a recognition of the damage that they do. It contributes to the conservation of both public and individual health and well-being. Its relationship to veterinary entomology is very close, since many of the problems of the two fields broadly overlap or are to a certain extent inseparable, in view of the fact that many arthropods attack both man and domestic (or wild) animals, though sometimes in somewhat different ways or to a somewhat different extent.

The name, medical entomology, as a designation for this field of knowledge apparently did not come into use until about 1909.[26]* Even at that late date there were those in high places who ridiculed the importance of arthropods as vectors of disease in spite of important entomologic discoveries relating to the transmission of plague, malaria, and yellow fever. Today medical entomology is not only recognized as a science in its own right, but also takes equal rank with some of the older sciences contributing to the fields of public health, tropical medicine, preventive medicine, and veterinary medicine.

Training. The medical entomologist must be thoroughly trained in general zoology; he must be particularly well trained in entomology and arachnology; and his training must include protozoology, helminthology, virology, and bacteriology. He must be a parasitologist in the truest and widest sense. He must be well versed in field ecology. Many insect-borne diseases of man and of his domestic animals are maintained in nature in wild mammalian and other reservoir animals; hence, the medical entomologist must have a thorough understanding of vertebrate zoology, particularly mammalogy, and also a wider knowledge of invertebrates (particularly fresh-water forms) than is offered in the usual introductory courses in zoology and entomology. Familiarity with aquatic organisms is also helpful in determining public health implications when these organisms are found in domestic water sup-

* Superior figures in the text refer to the references at the end of each chapter.

plies. Familiarity with insects attacking stored and dried foods, stored grain, and foods in general is valuable. A knowledge of house-invading animals is essential. Entomologic training must be built upon a sound basis of taxonomy and must emphasize immmature stages in the developmental cycle. Foundation work in arthropod toxicology and physiology should be included. Much direct benefit will be derived from many of the courses offered in medical, veterinary, and public health curricula, such as general anatomy, general physiology, epidemiology, pathology, histology, toxicology, hematology, and coprology. If available, training in public health administration should be acquired. A substantial knowledge of chemistry is essential. In order to solve certain field problems involving arthropods, e.g., mosquitoes and flies, knowledge of such phases of engineering as pertain to drainage and sewage disposal is useful. Familiarity with these last-named subjects will enable the medical entomologist to cooperate intelligently with other medical investigators and with engineers, or, on occasion, to make intelligent use of the professional services of physicians, veterinarians, engineers, epidemiologists, and other experts and specialists in the solution of complicated problems. For a more extended consideration of the preparation required for a career as a medical entomologist and of the demands that might be made of him in his chosen field, the student is referred to pertinent articles by Herms[27] and Travis.[79]

Objectives. The aim of medical entomology is the pursuit of knowledge concerning disease vectors and, particularly, the control and prevention of arthropod-borne diseases. There are many notable examples of the service rendered by workers in this fertile field, such as the control of malaria and yellow fever in Cuba and the Panama Canal Zone,[38] and the campaign against rats and fleas in San Francisco in 1907.[78] The latter resulted in the eradication of plague from that city, thus averting the spread of this terrible scourge to the surrounding area. The eradication during 1939–1940 of *Anopheles gambiae* Giles from Brazil after its devastating introduction from tropical Africa[73] and the control of lice and resulting suppression of typhus epidemics in Europe during World War II[12] are excellent more recent examples. The benefit derived by animal industry is well illustrated in the control of the tick vector, *Boophilus annulatus* (Say), of Texas cattle fever in the southern United States. Current campaigns toward the eradication of malaria, yellow fever, and the screw-worm point the way toward what we might hope to accomplish in the future.

Historical. Records from prehistory and early human history indicate man's awareness of medically important arthropods and of the diseases associated with them. The physician Susruta in Chapter XII of the *Susruta Samhita* recorded filarial infections in man in India as early as the sixth century B.C.[55] In approximately 1200 A.D. an American Indian artist unmistakably depicted, on Mimbres, N. Mex., pottery, a swarm of mosquitoes poised for an attack.[63] It is interesting to note that the Flathead Indians of Montana were obviously aware of the fact that fly larvae metamorphosed into flies, since they used the same term, *xelmalten,* to designate both the "white maggot" and the fly.[82]

In the King James version of the Old Testament (Exodus 8:24) we read, " . . . and there came a grievous swarm of flies into the house of Pharaoh, and into his servants' houses, and into all the land of Egypt: the land was corrupted by reason of the swarm of flies." The Douay version reads, "and the land was corrupted by this kind of flies." Whether the term "flies" as used in this passage is coextensive with the modern use of the word may be questioned, but it is interesting to contemplate the implications. As early as 1577 Mercurialis[46] expressed the belief that flies carried the "virus" of plague from those ill or dead of the disease to the food of the well. Although we now know that this is not the usual mode of plague transmission, the principal role that flies play as vectors of disease was correctly interpreted; i.e., they are food contaminators.

In 1587 Gabriel Soares de Souza[74] stated that flies suck poison from sores (*Framboesia tropica*) and leave them in skin abrasions on healthy individuals, thus infecting many persons. In 1769 Edward Bancroft[3] advanced a similar theory, but it was not until 1907 that Castellani[10] demonstrated experimentally that flies do transmit *Treponema pertenue* Castellani, the causal agent of yaws. The role of the house fly as a vector of disease was, however, not fully appreciated until 1898 when, as the result of investigations made during the Spanish-American War, Veeder[80] wrote:

> I have made cultures of bacteria from fly tracks and from the excrement of flies and there seems to be not the slightest difficulty in so doing. Indeed the evidence of every sort is so clear that I have reached the conclusion that the conveyance of infection in the manner indicated is the chief factor in decimating the army. Certainly so far as is known to the writer, nothing adequate has been said about it in current discussions.

Although popular beliefs in many parts of the world had for some time connected mosquitoes with various tropical fevers, no well-formulated ideas were advanced until 1848, when Josiah Nott[51] of New Orleans published his belief that mosquitoes gave rise to both malaria and yellow fever. In 1854 Beauperthuy,[5] a French physician in the West Indies, formulated an excellent theory that mosquitoes were responsible for the transmission of yellow fever. He believed, however, that the unknown disease factor was carried by the insect from certain decomposing matter and in turn was introduced by it into the human body.

While considerable was known by early naturalists and physicians concerning the larger intestinal parasites, such as roundworms and tapeworms, little information relating to microorganisms was available until after the development of the microscope by Anton van Leeuwenhoek (1695),[36] who found that his "material contained many tiny animals which moved about in a most amusing fashion; the largest of these showed the liveliest and most active motion, moving through the water or saliva as a fish of prey darts through the sea." This discovery led to the study of hitherto invisible organisms and eventually to the formulation of the "germ theory" by Pasteur[54] in 1877.

Although according to Howard[28] no standard medical treatise mentioned any specific disease as insect-borne prior to 1871, Raimbert[56] showed in 1869 by experiment (inoculation of proboscides, wings, etc., of nonbiting muscids into guinea pigs) that anthrax (*Bacillus anthracis* Cohn) could be disseminated by flies, which as early as 1776 was believed by Montfils[48] to be the case. The first discovery of primary importance in the field of medical entomology, however, was made in 1878 by Patrick Manson[42] who, working in China, observed the development of *Wuchereria bancrofti* (Cobbold) in the body of a mosquito, *Culex pipiens quinquefasciatus* Say, and eventually, together with Bancroft, Low, and others, proved the mosquito to be the intermediate host and vector of the causal organism of filariasis.

The discovery by Laveran[35] in 1880 of the causal organism of malaria (*Plasmodium malariae*) living parasitically in the red blood cells of man marks an epoch in protozoology, as well as in medical entomology. Taking rank with Laveran's discovery of the malaria parasite is the discovery by Theobald Smith in 1889 (Smith and Kilbourne, 1893[71]) of the causal protozoon (*Babesia bigemina*) of Texas cattle fever, also living parasitically within the red blood corpuscles of the host. Associated with Smith in the investigation of the disease was F. L. Kilbourne, and together in 1893 they made the second great fundamental discovery in the field of medical entomology, namely that the cattle tick, *Boophilus annulatus* (Say), is the necessary intermediate host of the causal agent of the disease. This knowledge, combined with Manson's discovery concerning mosquitoes and filariasis, established a new basis for the control and prevention of disease in both man and domestic animals.

In quick succession there followed a series of famous discoveries. In 1895 Bruce[8] investigated nagana, the fatal tsetse fly–transmitted disease of Africa (Zululand) and established the fact that the infection is conveyed from animal to animal through the agency of *Glossina morsitans* Westwood.

In 1897 Ronald Ross[65] announced that he had found the zygotes of the malaria parasite in two "dapple-winged mosquitoes" (anophelines) which had been bred from the larva and fed on a patient whose blood contained crescents. In the discovery that mosquitoes carry malaria there are linked the names of Ross; Manson;[43] MacCallum;[40] Bastianelli, Bignami, and Grassi;[4] Koch;[32] and Sambon and Low,[67] the last two having demonstrated (1900) beyond a doubt the fact of transmission.

One of the world's outstanding achievements in the field of experimental medicine is that of the United States Army Yellow Fever Commission, consisting of Reed,[57] Carrol, Lazear, and Agramonte, which in 1900 on the island of Cuba proved conclusively that yellow fever is carried by a mosquito, *Aedes aegypti* (Linnaeus), then known as *Culex fasciatus* Fabricius and later as *Stegomyia fasciata* (Fabricius). Carlos Finlay,[19] a Cuban physician, had as early as 1880 propounded the theory and conducted experiments in an attempt to prove it; hence, he, too, amply deserves recognition and great praise.

These two discoveries concerning malaria and yellow fever gave great impetus to the subject of mosquito control, although Howard had already demonstrated the value of kerosene in his experiments in the Catskill Mountains in 1892. Howard's pioneer book, entitled *Mosquitoes: How They Live; How They Carry Disease; How They Are Classified; How They May Be Destroyed,* appeared in 1901.

During almost a third of a century following these fundamental discoveries, little advance was made in knowledge concerning the transmission of malaria and yellow fever, and the complete solution of the problem of control of both diseases seemed to be within reach—that is, simply mosquito control. However, in 1937 malaria was again referred to as a mysterious disease by Hackett[24] in his treatise *Malaria in Europe,* viz.: " . . . under close examination malaria became only more intricate and impenetrable, more protean in its character, more diverse in its local manifestations." The expression "anophelism without malaria" came into use, and malariologists became more interested, as Hackett points out, in the anophelines which did not transmit malaria than in those that did. The discovery by Falleroni[18] in 1926 that *Anopheles maculipennis* Meigen, an important vector of malaria, was in reality separable into races on differences in the egg pattern led Hackett, Martini, and Missiroli[25] (1932) to the discovery that the races of this species differ markedly in their vector relationship to malaria, thus opening new avenues of research. Now what appeared to be a clear-cut situation in 1898 became once more a malaria "puzzle."

Some of the more recent developments toward the solution of this "puzzle" are discussed in a later chapter entitled "Mosquitoes." Studies on the bionomics and taxonomy of mosquitoes have thrown considerable light on the question as to why some species, or supposed species, are much more effective than others in the transmission of malaria. To these aspects of the problem must be added the significant advances made in our knowledge of the parasite and its bionomics, notably the discovery by Huff and his associates of the exerythrocytic cycle of the malaria parasite, and the advances in our knowledge of the epidemiology of the malarias.

Furthermore, the apparently well-solved problem of yellow fever control through the control of *Aedes aegypti* (Linnaeus) was again completely thrown open for further investigation by the discovery of Stokes, Bauer, and Hudson[75] in 1927 that experimental animals (monkeys) can be infected with yellow fever. Now, because of the availability of experimental animals, more than a dozen species of mosquitoes, instead of just one species, are known to have the ability to transmit the infection from monkey to monkey by the bite.

A type of yellow fever designated as jungle yellow fever[72] was first observed in 1932 in the Valle de Chanaan, Espirito Santo, Brazil. It differs from the previously known type of yellow fever, transmitted by *Aedes aegypti,* only in that it occurs under conditions which suggest that infection takes place away from urban habitations and that man may not be an essential factor in the continuity of infection. Indeed, "man may be but an accident in the course of an epizootic in the lower animals, or it may even be due to the persistence of the virus in invertebrate vectors for long periods of time." With the decreasing importance of classical yellow fever resulting from its successful control and the ever-imminent threat of the jungle type, increasing attention is being paid to the latter.

In 1898 Simond[68] succeeded in transmitting plague from a sick rat to a healthy rat through the agency of infected fleas. This discovery was at first discredited, but the experiments were successfully repeated by Verjbitski[81] in 1903 and Liston[39] in 1904. The designation sylvatic (selvatic) plague* has come into use particularly since 1928[29] to specify plague of wild rodents in which fleas play an important role as invertebrate reservoirs as well as vectors.

At this junction of our historical review of the subject, it is appropriate to call attention to the first comprehensive treatise dealing with arthropods as carriers of disease, namely the work of Nuttall[52] entitled, *On the Role of Insects, Arachnids and Myriapods as Carriers in the Spread of Bacterial and Parasitic Diseases of Man and Animals. A Critical and Historical Study.* Nuttall deserves to be called the father of medical entomology.

In 1901 Forde[21] observed certain parasites in the blood of persons suffering from Gambian sleeping sickness, which Dutton[16] recognized as trypanosomes and named *Trypanosoma gambiense;* and in 1903 Bruce and Nabarro[9] showed that *Glossina palpalis* (Robineau-Desvoidy) was the carrier, thus adding another tsetse fly–transmitted disease to the list. Stephens and Fantham[76] in 1910 described *Trypanosoma rhodesiense* as the causal organism of Rhodesian sleeping sickness, and Kinghorn and Yorke[31] in 1912 proved *Glossina morsitans* Westwood to be the responsible vector.

Graham,[23] while working in Syria in 1902, found that dengue, or breakbone fever, a widely distributed disease particularly of warm climates, though frequently occurring elsewhere, is mosquito-borne. He, and later Ashburn and Craig,[1] reported that possibly several species of mosquitoes, notably *Aedes aegypti,* are able to transmit the infection. A related disease is pappataci

* Some investigators of wild rodent plague object to this term. See Chapter 18.

fever, also known as "three-day fever" and "sand fly fever," transmitted by *Phlebotomus papatasii* Scopoli, as proved by Doerr, Franz, and Taussig[14] in 1909.

In 1903 Marchoux and Salimbeni[44] proved that fowl spirochetosis caused by *Borrelia anserina* (Sakharoff) Bergey *et al.* is tick-borne and that *Argas persicus* (Oken), the common fowl tick, is a vector. Another tick-borne disease came to light when Dutton and Todd[17] and Ross and Milne[64] in 1904 discovered that African relapsing fever is carried by the tick *Ornithodorus moubata* (Murray), the causal organism being *Borrelia recurrentis* (Lebert) Bergey *et al.* Furthermore, in 1906 Ricketts,[59] working in Montana, proved conclusively that another tick, which he believed to be *Dermacentor occidentalis* Neumann, but is now known to be *D. andersoni* Stiles, is the principal vector of Rocky Mountain spotted fever. Wolbach[85] named the causal organism *Dermacentroxenus rickettsi.*

Although lice have for centuries been associated with filth and disease, apparently little thought was given these insects as possible carriers of infection, even though Melnikoff[45] had shown in 1869 that the biting dog louse, *Trichodectes canis* De Geer, was an intermediate host of the double-pored dog tapeworm, *Dipylidium caninum* (Linnaeus), which also occasionally occurs in humans. Aubert[2] (1879), according to Nuttall, considered that the pediculi were spreaders of impetigo and the cause of prurigo, pityriasis, etc. Also, in experiments conducted by Dewèvre[13] in 1892, lice were shown to carry the specific microorganisms mechanically on their front legs, and infection was thus accidentally transmitted to healthy persons. Furthermore, Flügge[20] in 1891 and Tictin[77] in 1897 both supposed that disease might be carried by vermin and conducted experiments with bed bugs. In 1907 Mackie[41] working in India found that relapsing fever was transmitted by the body louse, *Pediculus humanus humanus* Linnaeus, in whose body the causal organism, *Borrelia recurrentis,* multiplies.

Nicolle, Comte, and Conseil,[50] working in Tunis in 1909, and Ricketts and Wilder,[60] working independently in Mexico in 1910, proved experimentally that the body louse is a carrier of typhus fever, the causal organism of which, *Rickettsia prowazeki,* was described and named by Da Rocha Lima[62] in 1916.

Members of the bug family Reduviidae have long been known for their bloodthirstiness and for their fierce bites, but it was apparently not until 1909 that insects of this group were experimentally proved to be disease carriers. In that year Chagas,[11] who had already described the causal organism of Chagas' disease, *Schizotrypanum cruzi,* demonstrated that this disease is carried by the conenose bug, *Panstrongylus megistus* (Burmeister). In 1933 Kofoid and Donat[33] showed that the trypanosome of the conenose bug *Triatoma protracta* (Uhler) in California is identical with that found in *Panstrongylus megistus.*

Flies of the family Tabanidae (horse flies, gad flies, deer flies, etc.) were looked upon with suspicion as early as 1776, but apparently no satisfactory evidence against them was forthcoming until 1913, when Mitzmain[47] (Mayne), working in the Philippine Islands, demonstrated transmission of surra of the carabao by *Tabanus striatus* Fabricius, which he regarded as the principal vector. Strong evidence against tabanid flies of the genus *Chrysops* as intermediary hosts of *Loa loa* (Cobbold) was advanced by Leiper,[37] also in 1913.

Bloodsucking gnats belonging to the dipterous family Simuliidae are a terrible scourge to both man and beast in many parts of the world and have long been under suspicion as vectors of disease. In 1926 Blacklock[6] reported *Simulium damnosum* Theobald as the vector of the filarial worm *Onchocerca volvulus* (Leuckart), the causal agent of human onchocerciasis. In 1934 O'Roke[53] reported *Simulium venustum* Say to be the vector of a disease of ducks caused by *Leucocytozoon simondi* Mathis and Léger.

Tularemia, also known as Pahvant Valley plague or deer fly fever, was shown by Francis and Mayne[22] in 1921 to be carried from rodent to rodent by the tabanid fly *Chrysops discalis* Williston, and presumably from rodent to man in the same manner. The causal organism of the disease, *Pasteurella tularensis,* was described in 1911 by McCoy and Chapin as the cause of a plaguelike disease of California ground squirrels. Though transmitted in nature by the deer fly and several other species of arthropods, particularly the tick *Dermacentor andersoni,* which is involved hereditarily, the infection is most commonly contracted by handling infected rabbits.

In 1933 Kelser[30] announced that he had succeeded in transmitting the virus of equine encephalomyelitis from inoculated guinea pigs to a horse by the bite of the mosquito *Aedes aegypti* (Linnaeus). The isolation of the virus from wild *Culex tarsalis* Coquillett by Hammon, Reeves, and their associates in 1941 (see Chapter 11) and the subsequent establishment of that species as the vector of the western equine encephalitis virus was a landmark in the study of the etiology of that disease.

The discovery of the insecticidal value of the compound dichlorodiphenyl trichloroethane (DDT) represents the beginning of a new era in the prevention of insect-borne diseases as pertains to both plants and animals, particularly to such a devastating disease of man as malaria. It also represents the beginning of a new concept in insect control—the use of a *residual* insecticide, with its relatively long-lasting effects, which can be applied in relatively small quantities. DDT was first synthesized by Othmar Zeidler[86] in 1874 at Strasbourg, Germany. Zeidler was apparently ignorant of its insecticidal properties. It was not until about 1939 that Paul Müller,[34] then a member of the scientific staff of Geigy Company in Basle, Switzerland, discovered this remarkable insecticidal value. For this discovery Müller was awarded the Nobel Prize in Medicine for 1948.

A significant discovery that profoundly affects control programs against medically important arthropods was that insects may develop resistance to residual insecticides. This was demonstrated by Speich in house flies in northern Sweden in 1946[84] and by Mosna[49] in the mosquito, *Culex pipiens molestus* Forskål, in Italy in 1947.

A historical review would not be complete without a consideration of the change of attitude which has accompanied the development of medical entomology as a science. As West[83] has pointed out, our early attitude toward the house fly was one of "friendly tolerance"; a few flies "were nice things to have around, to make things seem homelike . . . . Those that were knocked into the coffee or the cream could be fished out; those that went into the soup or the hash were never missed." (Doane, quoted by West.) This attitude prevails today to an extent among primitive peoples, who may look upon head lice, for instance, as something akin to household pets. During the last quarter of the nineteenth century there came a period of incrimination, during which many signal successes in research connected arthropods with the causation or transmission of many diseases.

During the following period, that of "popular education," preceding World War I, the public became aware of the situation through the writings of such men as Howard. The stimulation of the great successes led to some blind alleys, however, such as the attempts to link the transmission of poliomyelitis with the stable fly, that of pellagra with the buffalo gnat, and that of cancer with cockroaches.

Between World Wars I and II there was a diminution of activity resulting from "false security," followed by the period of "stern necessity," during World War II, when the conquest of typhus, scrub typhus, dengue, malaria, and other arthropod-transmitted diseases became an essential part of the war effort. Unlike the aftermath of World War I, the importance of medical entomology is continuing to be recognized to an intense degree and on a world-wide scale. Three aspects of this recognition are particularly important: first, the recognition that problems on the opposite face of the earth are of vital importance to the United States; secondly, the concept of eradication, rather than just control, as applied either to arthropods (e.g., *Anopheles gambiae* Giles in the New World and the primary screw-worm) or to arthropod-transmitted diseases (e.g., malaria, yellow fever, and filariasis); and, thirdly, the recognition that control or even eradication of disease is not sufficient, that we should think also of *pest* control or eradication in terms of improving standards of living, comfort, and mental health. Thus, the trend in attitude has completely reversed itself, from the original idea that a few flies were "nice things to have around," through the idea that they were dangerous carriers of disease, and finally to the modern desire to get rid of them, whether or not they transmit disease, but purely because they are an annoyance.

Literature. The literature of medical entomology has become so voluminous that it is difficult for the worker in one field to keep abreast of even the major developments in other fields. It has been our aim to supply the student with important citations under the individual topics discussed, but such citations have had to be highly selective, and some soon become obsolete with the passage of time. Some of the more important sources and general references are mentioned here.

The *Annual Review of Entomology,* the first volume of which was published in 1956, contains review articles with extensive lists of citations; each of the first five volumes (1956–1960) has included articles which review recent developments in some field of medical entomology, as well as others of pertinent interest. The similar *Annual Review of Microbiology* (first volume, 1947) and the *Annual Review of Medicine* (first volume, 1950) will also repay examination.

For the identification of medically important arthropods, beyond the limits of this text, the student must, for the most part, refer to manuals, monographs, comprehensive reviews, and other important works in the specific fields. A useful general work is that of Smart.[69]

Richardson and Kendall's[58] text in veterinary protozoology is a very useful reference, as are Rivers and Horsfall's[61] *Viral and Rickettsial Infections of Man,* Dubos'[15] *Bacterial and Mycotic Infections of Man,* and Bergey's (Breed *et al.*[7]) *Manual of Determinative Bacteriology.* The last mentioned work has been used here as a guide for standardization of scientific names of bacteria. For scientific and common names of insects, we are following, with few exceptions where special considerations warrant a deviation, the list prepared by the Committee on Common Names of Insects (1955) of the Entomological Society of America.[66] Standardization of names of insecticides is in accordance with the usage of the Entomological Society of America in its publications.[70]

REFERENCES

1. Ashburn, P. M., and Craig, C. F., 1907. "Experimental investigations regarding the etiology of dengue fever," *J. Infect. Dis.,* **4**:440–75.

2. Aubert, 1879. "Les pous et les écoles: Un point d'hygiène scolaire," reviewed in *Ann. de Dermat. et Syph.,* 1880, 2 ser., **1**:292–93.

3. Bancroft, Edward, 1769. *An Essay on the Natural History of Guiana in So. America.* London: T. Becker and P. A. De Houdt. 402 pp.

4. Bastianelli, G.; Bignami, A. E.; and Grassi, B.; 1898. "Coltivazione delle semilune malariche dell' uomo nell' *Anopheles claviger* Fabr.: Note preliminare," *Atti della Reale Accad. del Lincei,* Nov. 28, p. 313. (Cited by Nuttall.)

5. Beauperthuy, L. D., 1854. "Transmission of yellow fever and other diseases by mosquito," *Gazeta oficial de Cumanà,* Año 4, no. 57, May 23. (Cited by Howard, Dyar, and Knab.)

6. Blacklock, D. B., 1926. "Development of *Onchocerca volvulus* in *Simulium damnosum*," *Ann. Trop. Med.*, **20:**1–48 and 203–218.

7. Breed, Robert S.; Murray, E. G. D.; and Smith, Nathan R.; 1957. *Bergey's Manual of Determinative Bacteriology,* 7th ed. Baltimore: Williams and Wilkins Company. 1094 pp.

8. Bruce, David, 1895. *Tsetse-Fly Disease or Nagana in Zululand: Preliminary Report.* Durban: Bennett and Davis. (Cited by Nuttall.)

9. Bruce, D., and Nabarro, D., 1903. *Progress Report on Sleeping Sickness in Uganda.* "Rept. Sleeping Sickness Comm., Roy. Soc. London," no. 1.

10. Castellani, Aldo, 1907. "Experimental investigation on *Framboesia tropica* (Yaws)," *J. Hyg.*, **7:**558–59.

11. Chagas, C., 1909. "Ueber eine neue Trypanosomiasis des Menschen," *Mem. Inst. Oswaldo Cruz,* **1:**159–218.

12. Cushing, Emory C., 1957. *History of Entomology in World War II.* Washington, D. C.: Smithsonian Inst. Publ. 4294. vi + 117 pp.

13. Dewèvre, Doctor, 1892. "Note sur le rôle des pediculi dans la propogation de l'impetigo," *Compt. rend. Soc. de biol.*, **4:**232–34.

14. Doerr, R.; Franz, K.; and Taussig, S.; 1909. *Das Pappatacifieber.* Leipzig u. Wien: Franz Deutiche. 166 pp.

15. Dubos, Rene J., 1958. *Bacterial and Mycotic Infections of Man,* 3rd ed. Philadelphia: J. B. Lippincott Co. 820 pp.

16. Dutton, J. E., 1902. "Note on a Trypanosoma occurring in the blood of man," *Brit. M. J.*, **2:**881–84.

17. Dutton, J. E., and Todd, J. L., 1905. *The Nature of Human Tick Fever in the Eastern Part of the Congo Free State, with Notes on the Distribution and Bionomics of the Tick.* Liverpool School Trop. Med. in Memoir no. 17. 18 pp.

18. Falleroni, D., 1926. "Fauna anofelica italiana e suo 'habitat' (paludi, risaie, canali). Metodi di lotta contro la malaria," *Riv. di Malariol.*, **5:**553–93.

19. Finlay, Carlos J., 1881 *et seq. Trabajos selectos.* Havana: República de Cuba, Secretaría de Sanidad y Beneficencia, 1912. xxxiv + 657 pp.

20. Flügge, C., 1891. *Grundriss der Hygiene.* Leipzig: Veit & Co. x + 560 pp. (Cited by Nuttall.)

21. Forde, R. M., 1902. "Some clinical notes on a European patient in whose blood a Trypanosoma was observed," *J. Trop. Med.*, **5:**261.

22. Francis, Edward, and Mayne, Bruce, 1921. "Experimental transmission of tularaemia by flies of the species *Chrysops discalis,*" U. S. Public Health Service, *Pub. Health Rep.*, **36:**1738–46.

23. Graham, H., 1902. "Dengue: A study of its mode of propagation and pathology," *Med. Rec.*, **61:**204–07.

24. Hackett, L. W., 1937. *Malaria in Europe: An Ecological Study.* Oxford University Press, London: Humphrey Milford. xvi + 336 pp.

25. Hackett, L. W.; Martini, E.; and Missiroli, A.; 1932. "The races of *A. maculipennis,*" *Am. J. Hyg.*, **16:**137–62.

26. Herms, William B., 1909. "Medical entomology. Its scope and methods," *J. Econ. Entomol.*, **2:**265–68.

27. Herms, William B., 1943. "Preparation for a career as a medical entomologist," *J. Econ. Entomol.*, **36:**18–22.

28. Howard, L. O., 1921. "Sketch History of Medical Entomology," in *A Half Century of Public Health,* M. P. Ravenel. New York: Amer. Pub. Health Assn., pp. 412–38.

29. Jorge, Ricardo, 1928. *Les faunes regionales des rongeurs et des puces dans leurs rapports avec la peste.* Paris: Masson et Cie. 306 pp.

30. Kelser, R. A., 1933. "Mosquitoes as vectors of the virus of equine encephalomyelitis," *J. Am. Vet. M. A.,* 82, n.s. **35:**767–71.

31. Kinghorn, A., and Yorke, W., 1912. "On the transmission of human trypanosomes by *Glossina morsitans* Westw., and on the occurrence of human trypanosomes in game," *Ann. Trop. Med.,* **6:**1–23.

32. Koch, R., 1899. "Ueber die Entwicklung der Malariaparasiten," *Ztschr. f. Hyg. u. Infektionskr.,* **32:**1–24.

33. Kofoid, Charles A., and Donat, F., 1933. "Experimental infection with *Trypanosoma cruzi* from intestine of conenose bug *Triatoma protracta," Proc. Soc. Exper. Biol. & Med.,* **30:**489–91.

34. Läuger, P.; Martin, H.; and Muller, P.; 1944. "Über Konstitution und toxische Wirkung von natürlich und neuen synthetischen insektentötenden Stoffen," *Helvet. chimica acta,* **27:**892–928.

35. Laveran, A., 1880. "Note sur un nouveau parasite trouvé dans le sang de plusieurs malades atteints de fievre palustre," *Bull. Acad. de méd.,* Paris, **9:**1235.

36. Leeuwenhoek, Anton van, 1695. *Arcana naturae detecta ope microscopiorum.* Kronevelt: Delphis Batavorum, 568 pp. (Cited by Howard, Dyar, and Knab.) See also *The Select Works of Antony van Leeuwenhoek,* translated by Samuel Hoole, London, 1798.

37. Leiper, Robert R., 1913. "Metamorphosis of *Filaria loa," Lancet,* **1:**51.

38. Le Prince, Joseph A., and Orenstein, A. J., 1916. *Mosquito Control in Panama: The Eradication of Malaria and Yellow Fever in Cuba and Panama.* New York: G. P. Putnam's Sons. 355 pp.

39. Liston, W. G., 1905. "Plague, rats and fleas," *J. Bombay Nat. Hist. Soc.,* **16:**253–73.

40. MacCallum, W. C. 1898. "On the haematozoon infections of birds," *J. Exper. Med.,* **3:**117–36.

41. Mackie, F. P., 1907. "The part played by *Pediculus corporis* in the transmission of relapsing fever," *Brit. M. J.,* **2:**1706–09.

42. Manson, Patrick, 1878. "On the development of *Filaria sanguinis hominis,* and on the mosquito considered as a nurse," *J. Linn. Soc., Zool.,* London, **14:**304–11.

43. Manson, P., 1898. "Surgeon-Major Ronald Ross's recent investigations on mosquito-malaria theory," *Brit. M. J.,* **1:**1575–77.

44. Marchoux, E., and Salimbeni, A., 1903. "La spirillose des poules," *Ann. Inst. Pasteur,* **17:**569–80.

45. Melnikoff, H., 1869. "Ueber die Jugendzustände der *Taenia cucmerina," Arch. f. Naturgesch.,* **25:**62–69.

46. Mercurialis (Hieronymus), 1577 (?). *De pestes in universum, praesertim vero de Veneta et Patavina. Item de morbis cutaneis, et omnibus humani corporis excrementis.* (Not available to the authors.)

47. Mitzmain, M. B., 1913. "The mechanical transmission of surra by *Tabanus striatus* Fabr.," *Philippine J. Sc.*, **8** (ser. B):223–29.

48. Montfils, A. J., 1776. "D'une maladie fréquente connue en Bourgogne sous le nom de Puce maligne," *J. de Méd.*, **45:**500. (Cited by Nuttall.)

49. Mosna, E., 1948. "*Culex pipiens autogenicus* DDT-resistenti e loro controllo con Octa-Klor e esachlorocicloesano," *Riv. Parasit.*, **9:**19–25.

50. Nicolle, Charles; Comte, C.; and Conseil, E.; 1909. "Transmission experimentals du typhus exanthimatique par le pou du corps," *Compt. rend. Acad. d. sc.*, **149:**486–89.

51. Nott, Josiah, C., 1848. "On the origin of yellow fever," *New Orleans M. & Sc. J.*, **4:**563–601.

52. Nuttall, G. H. F., 1899. "On the role of insects, arachnids, and myriapods as carriers in the spread of bacterial and parasitic disease of man and animals. A critical and historical study," *Johns Hopkins Hospital Reports,* **8:**1–154.

53. O'Roke, Earl C., 1934. *A Malaria-like Disease of Ducks Caused by Leucocytozoon anatis Wickware.* Ann Arbor: Univ. Michigan School of Forestry, Bull, no. 4, 44 pp. (5 plates).

54. Pasteur, L., and Joubert, J., 1877. "Chimie physiologique: Etude sur la maladie charbonneuse," *Compt. rend. Acad. d. Sc.*, **84:**900–06.

55. Raghavan, N. G. S., 1957. "Epidemiology of filariasis in India," *World Health Org. Bull.*, **16:**553–79.

56. Raimbert, A., 1869. "Recherches experimentales sur la transmission du charbon par les mouches," *Compt. rend. Acad. d. sc.*, **69:**805–12. (Cited by Nuttall.)

57. Reed, Walter, 1900. "The etiology of yellow fever," *Philadelphia Med. J.*, **6:**790–96.

58. Richardson, U. F., and Kendall, S. B., 1957. *Veterinary Protozoology,* 2nd ed. Edinburgh and London: Oliver and Boyd. 260 pp. (5 plates).

59. Ricketts, H. T., 1906. "The transmission of Rocky Mountain spotted fever by the bite of the wood tick (*Dermacentor occidentalis*)," *J.A.M.A.*, **57:**358.

60. Ricketts, H. T., and Wilder, R. M., 1910. "The transmission of the typhus fever of Mexico (tarbardillo) by means of the louse (*Pediculus vestimenti*), *J.A.M.A.*, **54:**1304–07.

61. Rivers, Thomas M., and Horsfall, Frank L., 1959. *Viral and Rickettsial Infections of Man,* 3rd ed. Philadelphia and Montreal: J. B. Lippincott Co. xviii + 967 pp.

62. Rocha-Lima, H. da, 1916. Untersuchungen über Fleckfieber," *München. Med. Wchnschr.*, **63:**1381–84.

63. Rodeck, Hugo G., 1932. "Arthropod designs on prehistoric Mimbres pottery," *Ann. Entomol. Soc. Amer.*, **25:**688–93.

64. Ross, P. H., and Milne, A. D., 1904. "Tick fever," *Brit. M. J.*, **2:**1453–54.

65. Ross, R., 1897. "On some peculiar pigmented cells found in two mosquitoes fed on malarial blood," *Brit. M. J.*, **2:**1786–88.

66. Sailer, R. I. (Chairman of Committee), 1955. "Common names of insects approved by the Entomological Society of America," *Bull. Entomol. Soc. Amer.*, **1** (no. 4):1–34.

67. Sambon, L. W., and Low, G., 1900. "The malaria experiments in the Campagna," *Brit. M. J.,* **2:**1679–82.

68. Simond, P. L., 1898. "La propagation de la peste," *Ann. Inst. Pasteur,* **12:**625.

69. Smart, John, 1956. *A Handbook for the Identification of Insects of Medical Importance,* 3rd ed. London: British Museum. xi + 303 pp. (13 plates).

70. Smith, Carroll N., 1959. "Common names of insecticides," *J. Econ. Entomol.,* **52:**361–62.

71. Smith, Theobald, and Kilbourne, F. L., 1893. *Investigations into the Nature, Causation, and Prevention of Texas or Southern Cattle Fever.* Washington, D. C.: U. S. Dept. Agric. in Bur. Animal Indust. Bull. no. 1. 301 pp.

72. Soper, Fred L., 1936. "Jungle yellow fever: A new epidemiological entity in South America," *Rev. de Hyg. e saude pub.,* **10:**107–44.

73. Soper, Fred L., and Wilson, D. Bruce, 1943. Anopheles gambiae *in Brazil 1930 to 1940.* New York: The Rockefeller Foundation. xviii + 262 pp.

74. Souza, Gabriel Soares de, 1587. *Tratado descriptivo do Brazil em 1587, orba de Gabriel de Souza.* Rio de Janeiro: Typographia universal de Laemmert, 120 pp. (Cited by França, C., in *Tr. Roy. Soc. Trop. Med. & Hyg.,* **15:**58–60.)

75. Stokes, Adrian; Bauer, J. H.; and Hudson, N. Paul; 1928. "The transmission of yellow fever to *Macacus rhesus:* Preliminary note," *J.A.M.A.,* **90:**253–54.

76. Stephens, J. W. W., and Fantham, H. B., 1910. "On the peculiar morphology of a trypanosome from a case of sleeping sickness and the possibility of its being a new species (*T. rhodesiense*)," *Proc. Roy. Soc.* (London), ser. B, **83:**28–33.

77. Tictin, J., 1897. "Zur Lehre von Rückfalltyphus," *Centralbl. f. Bakt.,* 1 Abt., **21:**179–86.

78. Todd, F. M., 1909. *Eradicating Plague from San Francisco: Report of Citizens Health Committee.* San Francisco: C. A. Murdock Co. Press. 313 pp.

79. Travis, B. V., 1958. "The role of the entomologist in medical and veterinary entomology," *Proc. Tenth Internat. Congr. Entomol.,* **3:**697–701.

80. Veeder, M. A., 1898. "Flies as spreaders of sickness in camps," *Med. Rec.,* **54:**429–30.

81. Verjbitski, D. T., 1908. "The part played by insects in the epidemiology of plague," *J. Hyg.,* **8:**162–208.

82. Weisel, George F., 1952. "Animal names, anatomical terms, and some ethnozoology of the Flathead Indians," *J. Washington Acad. Sc.,* **42:**345–55.

83. West, Luther S., 1951. *The Housefly.* Ithaca: Comstock Publishing Co. 584 pp.

84. Wiesmann, R., 1947. "Untersuchungen über das physiologische Verhalten von *Musca domestica* L. verschiedener Provenienzen," *Mitt. schweiz. entomol. Ges.,* **20:**484–504.

85. Wohlbach, S. B., 1919. "Studies on Rocky Mountain spotted fever," *J. Med. Research,* **41:**1–193.

86. Zeidler, Othmar, 1874. "Verbindungen von Chloral mit Brom und Chlorbenzol," *Ber. d. Deutsch. Chem. Gesellsch.,* **7:**1180.

Chapter 2

HOW ARTHROPODS CAUSE AND CARRY DISEASE

Arthropod and Pathogen. When one considers the fact that man and his domesticated animals are daily closely associated with scores of species of insects* and their kin, the wonder is that there are not more arthropod-caused infestations and insect-borne diseases. Many of the one-time free-living arthropods have in time become parasitic; some now burrow into the skin, as do certain mites (acariasis); others have invaded the alimentary tract, as do larvae of bot flies (myiasis); still others have become bloodsuckers, as are bed bugs, sucking lice, horse flies, mosquitoes, etc. Bloodsuckers, by virtue of their bloodsucking habit, may readily become vectors of pathogenic blood-inhabiting microorganisms. It has been well said that no bloodsucking arthropod can be trusted; eventually many more species will prove to be vectors of disease.

The medical entomologist must acquaint himself with the detailed biology of the disease-producing microorganisms as well as with that of the vectors. In order to know where and how the arthropod acquires the pathogenic agent and how it, the vector, becomes infectious, the behavior of such organisms must be studied; the habitat in the body of the diseased host or reservoir must be known; the gateways of escape must be ascertained; their longevity and virulence when removed from the host as well as many other pertinent factors must be determined. After the pathogenic organism is acquired, its course within the body of the arthropod must be studied in order to know how escape is effected and how it reaches the body of the next host. A knowledge of the feeding habits and mouth parts of arthropods is essential (see mechanism of infection, p. 18).

Bubonic plague, for example, is a bacillary disease caused by *Pasteurella pestis,* of which the rat, among other animals, is an important host. Man readily succumbs to the infection. While the pathogenic organisms may pass from host to host in several ways, it has been found that rat fleas are the most important vectors. The bacilli are found in great abundance in the buboes which are situated largely in the axillary and inguinal regions of the infected rat, and it has been observed that these regions are favored by fleas, which, because of their bloodsucking habits, imbibe the highly infectious fluids. If the rat dies of the plague, the fleas leave the body and seek another host; this interval in the change of hosts raises the question of environmental

* Various estimates as to the number of described species of insects in the world range from about 625,000 to 1,500,000.

resistance and longevity of the bacilli. Do all species of rat fleas lend themselves equally well as hosts? Can the bacilli resist the digestive fluids of the flea, and if so, how long do they remain infective in the body of the flea? In the meantime, what course do these organisms take within the body of the insect, and how do they make their escape? How does the flea find another host, and what animals will it attack? How long can the flea live without food? How are the plague bacilli introduced into the body of the next victim? Will the flea remain infective throughout the rest of its normal life? What is the length of life of a flea, and how does this vary with the species?

Malaria of man, another example, is caused by certain species of plasmodia which live under far more restricted conditions than do the plague bacilli. In the human being these invade the red corpuscles part of the time and, so far as is known, do not live in the blood of other warm-blooded animals. They require certain mosquitoes belonging to the genus *Anopheles* as definitive hosts. Although many other bloodsucking insects imbibe parasitized blood, those do not offer the necessary environment within the alimentary canal for the completion of the life cycle of the parasite.

Relation of the Pathogen to Its Host. When one considers the relation of arthropods to the causation and transmission of disease, one usually deals, in one way or another, with organisms which may, in the broad sense of the word, be considered parasites; that is, usually either the arthropod itself is parasitic, or else it transmits a parasitic infection. It is not within our province to consider the various uses of the term parasite, but in order to understand the facts and principles of arthropod transmission certain definitions are given here.

Parasites which live either temporarily or permanently on the outside of the body are termed *ectoparasites,* e.g., the lice; parasites which live within the body or its cavities are called *endoparasites,* e.g., tapeworms. *Obligatory parasites* are forced to remain during their entire life in or on the body of the host, e.g., both biting and sucking lice. *Facultative parasites* are able to exist as free-living organisms, and they can also live as parasites, e.g., the larvae of certain species of blow flies and flesh flies. Bed bugs are examples of *intermittent parasites* which prey upon the host only at times and are free-living during intervals between meals.

Many other forms of parasitism are recognized, such as *transitory* parasitism, which refers to cases in which the organism is parasitic during only a part of its life history, e.g., bot flies. When two or more hosts are required for the development of an obligatory parasite, that host in which the parasite reaches sexual maturity is termed the *primary* or *definitive* host, while the other, or others if more than one species is required, should be referred to as the *secondary* or *intermediate* host or hosts. This is illustrated in the life history of the malaria *Plasmodium,* which reaches sexual maturity in the body of certain anopheline mosquitoes, the primary or definitive host, while the human being is the secondary host. The lung fluke,

Pathological Conditions Caused by Arthropods. The ways in which arthropods relate to human health and the health and well-being of animals are almost as numerous as the species of responsible arthropods themselves. Each species, however similar to its next of kin, has certain characteristics which affect the host differently. It is nevertheless possible to classify the relationships of arthropods to health by putting them into two divisions, each of which is subject to further segregation. The relationships may be designated as follows:

A. Arthropods as direct agents of disease or discomfort
   1. Entomophobia
   2. Annoyance and blood loss
   3. Accidental injury to sense organs
   4. Envenomization
   5. Dermatosis
   6. Myiasis and related infestations
   7. Allergy

B. Arthropods as vectors or intermediate hosts
   1. Mechanical carriers (transmission being more or less accidental)
   2. Obligatory vectors (involving some degree of development, cyclical or propagative, within the arthropod)
   3. Intermediate hosts (in a passive capacity; some vectors also serve as intermediate hosts)

As our subject develops in the remaining chapters of this book, the student will determine the way or ways in which the particular groups of arthropods fit into the scheme presented in this chapter.

Entomophobia. Insects and spiders, even though they may be wholly innocuous, frequently cause man acute annoyance and worry which may eventually lead to a nervous disorder, sometimes with sensory hallucinations. Such disturbances of long duration are termed entomophobia.

Cases of this nature are from time to time brought to the attention of the medical entomologist either directly or through reference by physicians, or they may be handled by qualified pest control operators, on the basis that one who has knowledge of the control of tormenting insects may either be able to remove the cause of the disturbance or, if the latter is imaginary, may show the patient that such is the case. The subject has been ably reviewed by Pomerantz,[7] with a description of typical case histories.

Entomophobia should not be dismissed as trivial and should not be confused with mere squeamishness. True entomophobia should be viewed sympathetically and may require the help of medical personnel or spiritual advisors.

Annoyance and Blood Loss. It is hard to estimate the importance of annoyance by insects, yet everyone is aware of this source of nuisance and discomfort at one time or another. A blow fly, buzzing through the house, may be very irritating, particularly to small children or to elderly persons, and a swarm of flies alighting on a screen door or hovering in the house can be very annoying to almost anyone. Ants may spoil a picnic; so may the threat of yellow jackets, even though one might not be stung by them. Blood loss from insect bites usually is not of much importance so far as man is concerned (though allergic responses to such bites may be); but in livestock it may cause economic loss, even the death of the animals involved.

Accidental Injury to Sense Organs. Various species of insects, like other minute objects, may accidentally enter the eye; this is most likely to be true of small flying insects. Some of these, notably several species of rove beetles, Staphylinidae, cause extreme pain because of an irritating secretion. Many species of insects discharge odoriferous fluid or vapor, and in some instances the fluid is so forcibly ejected that it may be thrown some distance from the insect. Stewart[9] records the case of a phasmid walking stick, *Anisomorpha buprestoides* (Stoll), squirting fluid a distance of two feet and striking a person in the eye.

> The pain in the left eye was immediately excruciating; being reported to be as severe as if it had been caused by molten lead. Quick, thorough drenching with cool water allayed the burning agony to a dull, aching pain. The pain eased considerably within the course of a few hours. Upon awaking the next morning the entire cornea was almost a brilliant scarlet in color and the eye was so sensitive to light and pressure for the next forty-eight hours that the patient was incapacitated for work. Vision was impaired for about five days. The cornea gradually cleared of congestion and vision improved so that at the end of this time the eye was perfectly normal again. No subsequent ill effects were experienced.

Stewart remarks that, "In Texas there is a rather common belief that devil's horses will spit in human eyes."

Injury to the human eye is often caused by the spiny larvae of the sheep bot fly, *Oestrus ovis* Linnaeus. This fly deposits living young in the nostrils of sheep, and persons working in the field with sheep are occasionally "struck" in the eye by the fly and one or more larvae may be deposited. This indicates that the fly may "strike" sheep similarly at times.

Insects commonly enter the ears of sleeping persons and may cause much pain before they are removed. In the author's (Herms') experience a carpet beetle larva (*Dermestes* sp.) was taken from the ear of an elderly man, and a hyaline grass bug, *Coryzus hyalinus* (Fabricius), family Coreidae, from the ear of a child, having caused much pain in each case. The spinose tick, *Otobius megnini* (Dugés), also invades the ear of man and many animals.

Envenomization. Venoms of insects cause reactions which are remarkably characteristic. The effects may be classified under the following headings: (1) hemolytic; (2) hemorrhagic; (3) neurotoxic; and (4) vesicating. The venoms are introduced in the following ways: (1) by the bite, as of conenose bugs and black widow spiders; (2) by the sting, as of bees, ants, wasps, scorpions; (3) by urticating hair, as by the browntail moth; and (4) by contact, as with vesicating fluids from blister beetles (see Chapter 21).

Dermatosis. Various skin irritations are caused by arthropods, either by bites or by skin invasions. Some of these irritations could be appropriately classified as envenomizations. Skin irritations commonly result from the bites of such insects as mosquitoes, fleas, lice, and bed bugs. Various species of burrowing mites cause skin irritations known as *acariasis.* Among the latter are: the scabies mites, *Sarcoptes scabiei* (Linnaeus); the follicle mites, *Demodex folliculorum* Simon; the chigger mites, *Trombicula alfreddugési* (Oudemans); and others.

Myiasis and Related Infestations. An invasion of organs and tissues of man and beast by the larvae of Diptera is termed *myiasis.* The invading maggots may be specific myiasis-producing forms, i.e., obligatory sarcobionts which invade cutaneous tissues, as does *Dermatobia hominis* (Linnaeus) in man and *Hypoderma bovis* (De Geer), the warble fly of cattle; invading the gastric and intestinal tract are the bot flies of horses, *Gasterophilus intestinalis* (De Geer); and invading the nasal and frontal sinuses are the head maggots of sheep, *Oestrus ovis* Linnaeus. The invading maggots may be necrobionts or facultative sarcobionts, in which case traumatic dermal myiasis may result, as with infestations of the secondary screw-worm, *Callitroga macellaria* (Fabricius). Accidental myiasis may be the result of fly larvae in food, or the result of flies attracted by anal, vaginal, or nasal discharges. The larvae of the house fly, the lesser house fly, certain blow flies and flesh flies, and others may occur in accidental enteric or traumatic myiasis. Related infestations may include invasions by beetle larvae (*canthariasis*), moth larvae (*scoleciasis*), and others.

Allergy Caused by Insects. The condition of being specifically hypersensitive to certain insect proteins is a fairly common and widespread phenomenon among persons working habitually with bees or collections of dead insects, or exposed for longer periods of time to pulverized insect parts, scales of butterflies, moths, and caddisflies. Residents on the shores of lakes where cast skins of mayflies abound are subject to attacks of "asthma" as the result of allergens.[1] Similarly, allergens may complicate the effects of other contacts with insects, e.g., bee stings.

Mechanical (Simple) Carriers of Infection. Many species of insects may accidentally contribute to the transmission of various filth diseases; however, when insects habitually and alternately feed and/or breed in excrement and then feed on human food prepared for the table, they may be classified as food contaminators and a real menace to the public health, e.g., cockroaches and such flies as the house fly. The causal organism of filth diseases such as typhoid fever, cholera, and amebiasis may adhere to the mouth parts and feet of these insects and may be deposited on human food, with resulting infection to the consumer. The mechanical transmission of yaws (a spirochete infection) and of certain eye infections (so-called pink-eye) is similarly effected by flies, particularly *Hippelates*. The eggs of helminth parasites, notably pinworms, may also be so disseminated. Not only do pathogenic bacteria, protozoa, and helminth ova cling to the mouth parts, feet, wings, and other parts of the insect body, but they may also be swallowed by the insect and pass uninjured through its alimentary canal and be deposited on food with the insect's feces or be regurgitated with similar effects.

It has been amply proved that coprohagous fly larvae (maggots), which feed on and develop in human excrement, may transfer bacteria taken up in this stage through the pupal stage to the mature flies. In this manner the infection of anthrax may be disseminated by flesh flies, bred in carcasses of animals that have died of this disease. This is a strong argument in favor of the incineration of dead animals.

Another purely mechanical method of disease transmission is by means of *contaminated* piercing mouth parts, in which these organs in the act of feeding become contaminated with blood-inhabiting pathogenic organisms, and *simple inoculation* may result from the next feeding. Here again, as in the aforementioned cases, the pathogenic organisms undergo no interim developmental changes. Insects that belong to this class of simple carriers generally have strong, piercing mouth parts, capable of drawing considerable blood, and are intermittent feeders, flying readily and quickly from one host to another, e.g., horse flies (Tabanidae), which may be vectors of anthrax in this manner.

Obligatory Vectors. Huff[5] has pointed out that there are three ways in which so-called biological (as opposed to mechanical) transmission by arthropods is effected. These are as follows:

1. *Cyclo-propagative Transmission.* In this type of transmission the causal organisms "undergo cyclical changes and multiply" in the body of the arthropod, as in the transmission of malaria plasmodia by anopheline mosquitoes and in the transmission of *Babesia bigemina* of Texas cattle fever by the Texas fever tick, *Boophilus annulatus.* Of the several ways in which so-called biological transmission by arthropods is effected, this type is one of the most likely to be used to illustrate insect transmission of disease.

2. *Cyclo-developmental Transmission.* When the causal organisms "undergo cyclical change but do not multiply" in the body of the arthropod, transmission may be classified as *cyclo-developmental,* as in the mosquito transmission of the worm *Wuchereria bancrofti,* causal organism of filariasis.

3. *Propagative Transmission.* When "the organisms undergo no cyclical change, but multiply" in the body of the vector, transmission is said to be *propagative* only. The transmission of bubonic plague is probably propagative, since it is known that the causal organism, *Pasteurella pestis,* can multiply in the foregut of the flea. It is also very probable that the transmission of relapsing fever by ticks falls into this category.

Fecal Contamination. The feces of several species of disease-transmitting arthropods are known to be infectious after the insect has fed on infectious animals, for example, the feces of fleas fed on plague-infected rodents, also the feces of conenose bugs, *Triatoma,* after feeding on animals infected with Brazilian trypanosomiasis, Chagas' disease. The feces of infective yellow fever mosquitoes are said to be highly dangerous. The Rockefeller Foundation (Annual Report, 1930) states that a dilution of between one ten-millionth and one-billionth of one cubic centimeter of yellow fever virus has frequently proved fatal to monkeys and that infection through the unbroken skin is readily accomplished. Feces of ticks that are harboring the rickettsial organism of Australian Q fever may be highly infective.

Transovarian Transmission. Transmission of infection through the arthropod egg was discovered by Smith and Kilbourne in 1893 in their investigation of Texas cattle fever. When the cattle tick, *Boophilus annulatus* (Say), reaches maturity on the body of the animal, it drops to the ground, where the female deposits her egg and dies. The young ticks on emerging from the eggs are infective and transmit the causal protozoon, *Babesia bigemina,* to susceptible cattle. The term "hereditary transmission," sometimes applied to the transmission of this disease, is not correct since no hereditary or genetic mechanism is involved; however, it has been widely used and may be permissible under circumstances which would not permit confusion of meaning. "Transovarian transmission" is a more accurately descriptive term and is now in wide use.

Other infections transmitted transovarially are Rocky Mountain spotted fever, caused by *Rickettsia rickettsi* and transmitted by ticks, e.g., *Dermacentor andersoni* Stiles; tularemia caused by *Pasteurella tularensis* and transmitted by the tick *D. andersoni;* relapsing fever, caused by *Borrelia recurrentis* and transmitted by several species of ticks belonging to the genus *Ornithodorus.* Ticks play an important role in the transovarian transmission of infection involving protozoa, rickettsiae, bacteria, and spirochetes. Transovarian transmission of virus diseases is not so clear, although sandfly fever, or pappataci fever, has been produced by the bites of *Phlebotomus papatassii* Scopoli bred from infected parents (Whittingham 1922, according to Hinman[3]).

Arthropods as Intermediate Hosts of Helminths. Numerous arthropods serve as intermediate hosts of many species of parasitic worms. There are at least 150 known species of worms parasitic in vertebrates which have arthropods as intermediate hosts and for which the primary hosts are known. At least 275 species of arthropods are known to serve in this capacity; of these, nearly 200 are insects, about 75 are crustaceans, and the remainder are arachnids and myriapods. No doubt hundreds of such life histories are still to be ascertained. Hall[2] states that only 1 per cent of the life histories of the known tapeworms have been worked out.

The reasons for the frequent host-parasite relationships between arthropods and helminths are no doubt mainly the following: (1) the arthropods are an exceedingly large group of animals; (2) they constitute an important food supply for fish, amphibians, birds, and some mammals; (3) herbivorous animals are sure to ingest arthropods which are habitually present on plants; (4) many species of insects feed on and breed in manures and are thus exposed to infection from eggs and larvae of worms parasitic in hosts responsible for the manure; (5) many arthropods are transient or permanent ectoparasites feeding on blood in which there may be parasitic worms.

Monoxenous worms, such as *Ascaris* and *Enterobius,* during the course of their life histories transfer from one host animal to a similar host animal without the intervention of an intermediate host. According to Hall:[2]

> The heteroxenous worms have life histories in which in most cases the worms pass from mature stages in one host animal to larval stages in a host animal of a different sort, the intermediate host, and then return to a host animal of the first sort or a more or less closely related species and develop in this animal to maturity. In some instances two intermediate hosts are utilized in sequence for larval stages.

As already pointed out, knowledge concerning arthropods serving as intermediate hosts for the Cestoda (tapeworms) is quite fragmentary. Among the better-known instances are the double-pored dog tapeworm, *Dipylidium caninum* (Linnaeus), which requires either the biting dog louse, *Trichodectes canis* De Geer, or a flea, *Ctenocephalides canis* (Curtis), as intermediate host. *Choanotaenia infundibulum* (Bloch), a fowl tapeworm, utilizes the house fly, *Musca domestica* Linnaeus. Stunkard[10] has shown that *Moniezia expansa* (Rudolphi), an important tapeworm of sheep and other herbivores, uses a species of oribatid mite, *Galumna* sp., as intermediate host. Eggs of the tapeworm were fed to these mites, and in time the cysticercoids were recovered in many instances from the body cavities of the mites. More recently Stunkard[11] (1944) reported a similar developmental pattern in oribatid mites for anoplocephaline cestodes of rabbits and for the monkey-human species.

The broad tapeworm of man, *Diphyllobothrium latum* (Linnaeus), has as its first intermediate host a crustacean, *Cyclops* or *Diaptomus.* The parasite, with its crustacean host, is ingested by a fish and is in turn acquired by man if he eats the partially cooked or raw fish.

Numerous trematodes (flukes) of fish, amphibians, reptiles, and other insectivorous animals use arthropods as intermediate hosts. Since many of the vertebrate hosts are aquatic or semiaquatic, so are most of the arthropods, such as dragonflies (Odonata), caddisflies (Trichoptera), mayflies (Ephemeroptera), and stoneflies (Plecoptera). Among the flukes is the

European poultry fluke, *Prosthogonimus pellucidus* (von Linstrow), which uses the nymph of the dragonfly *Libellula quadrimaculata* Linnaeus as an intermediate host. In the United States a similar poultry fluke, *P. macrorchis* Macy, likewise uses dragonfly nymphs in this capacity. The important lung fluke of man, *Paragonimus westermani* (Kerbert), sometimes considered a species complex, requires as its second intermediate host (the first is a snail) a crustacean, namely a river crab or crayfish. Man (and certain carnivores) may acquire the parasite by eating the uncooked or improperly cooked crustacean. This fluke is widely distributed in the Far East.

Among the Nematoda (threadworms) are numerous species that use arthropods as intermediate hosts. These include the *Gongylonema* worms (Spiruridae), such as *G. pulchrum* Molin, which causes an infection of humans (also of the pig, sheep, ox, etc.) known as gongylonemiasis. These worms occur as larvae in such insects as cockroaches (Blattidae), mealworms (Tenebrionidae), and a few other forms. Other nematodes which require arthropods as intermediate hosts are certain species belonging to the family Filariidae, such as *Wuchereria bancrofti* and *Onchocerca volvulus,* the former requiring mosquitoes and the latter, black gnats.

The famous guinea worm of the Nile Valley and equatorial Africa, *Dracunuculus medinensis* (Linnaeus), a worm which as an adult female may measure 70 to 120 cm in length, requires Crustacea belonging to the genus *Cyclops* as intermediate hosts.

The thornheaded worms (Acanthocephala) use beetles (Scarabaeidae) mainly as intermediate hosts, e.g., the thornheaded worm of swine, *Macracanthorhynchus hirudinaceus* (Pallas).

Reservoir Animals. Reservoir animals play an important role in the natural distribution of insect-borne diseases. Since true reservoir animals suffer little or no ill effect from certain microorganisms pathogenic to man, their presence may go unnoticed, as is the case with rabbit reservoirs of Rocky Mountain spotted fever; however, rat epizootics are commonly the forerunners of human plague epidemics. The human being may himself be a reservoir of certain insect-borne infections, even plague. Since there are numerous vertebrates which serve as disease reservoirs, it behooves the medical entomologist to acquaint himself thoroughly with the broad field of vertebrate zoology, particularly the ecological aspects, and with the parasitic ectozoa of wild mammals. Greater attention must be given to the problems of forest sanitation in recreation areas.

There are at least 70 species of mammals which may serve as possible reservoirs of plague, according to Stallybrass.[8] The rickettsial infections are notable for their wild animal reservoirs: Rocky Mountain spotted fever with its rabbits, badgers, woodchucks, field mice, and others; typhus fever with rats; scrub typhus with voles. The spirochete infections are equally noteworthy in that the relapsing fever reservoirs are evidently fairly numerous;

thus, young porcupines, as well as armadillos and opossums, have been listed, and in the western United States certain squirrels and chipmunks. Trypanosome infections are well represented by African sleeping sickness with its numerous big-game reservoirs, and Chagas' disease with its armadillos, opossums, rodents, dogs, and cats.

Hudson[4] calls attention to the fact that the animal reservoir host plays a prime role in tropical medicine. In tropical regions of the earth, as well as in the less highly organized countries of the temperate zone, there is a striking increase in the number of diseases drawn from animal reservoirs. Here huge numbers of human victims are "encompassed by an intricate web of animal and insect life, in a physical environment of extraordinary complexity and variability."

A remarkable suggestion was made by Maldonado[6] that certain plants may act as reservoirs of the causal organism of verruga, a disease of man, and that the species of *Phlebotomus* flies that transmit the disease may feed on the latex. It is also suggested that this would explain why these sand flies are so abundant during the rains (January to April), when this particular plant growth (*Jatropa basiacantha* and *Orthopterygium huancui*) is most luxuriant.

REFERENCES

1. Figley, K. D., 1929. "Asthma due to the may-fly," *Am. J. M. Sc.*, **178:**338–45.

2. Hall, M. C., 1929. *Arthropods as Intermediate Hosts of Helminths.* Washington, D. C.: Smithsonian Institution, in Misc. Coll., vol. 81, no. 15 (Pub. no. 3024). 77 pp.

3. Hinman, E. Harold, 1933. "Hereditary transmission of infections through arthropods," *Am. J. Trop. Med.*, **13:**415–23.

4. Hudson, E. H., 1944. "The role of the reservoir host in tropical disease," *Am. J. Trop. Med.*, **24:**125–30.

5. Huff, Clay, 1931. "A proposed classification of disease transmission by arthropods," *Science*, **74:**456–57.

6. Maldonado, A., 1931. "Rôle probable de quelques plantes caracteristique de la region verruqueuse sur l'etiologie de la verruga du Perou," *Bull. Soc. path. exot.*, **24:**27–28.

7. Pomerantz, Charles, 1959. "Arthropods and psychic disturbances," *Bull. Entomol. Soc. Amer.*, **5:**65–67.

8. Stallybrass, C. O., 1931. *The Principles of Epidemiology and the Process of Infection.* London: C. Routledge & Son. 696 pp. (1 plate).

9. Stewart, Morris A., 1937. "Phasmid injury to the human eye," *Canad. Entomol.*, **69:**84–86.

10. Stunkard, H. W., 1937. "The life cycle of *Moniezia expansa*," *Science*, **86:**312.

11. Stunkard, H. W., 1944. "How do tapeworms of herbivorous animals complete their life cycles?" *Tr. New York Acad. Sc.*, ser. 2, **6:**108–21.

Chapter 3

CONTROL OF MEDICALLY IMPORTANT ARTHROPODS

In the past the control of medically important insects, mites, and ticks, so far as it went, was a relatively simple matter. Today, only a specialist in the area can keep abreast of this rapidly moving field. The reasons for this are chiefly fivefold: (1) instead of one or a very few standard insecticides, the number has multiplied to a hundred or more and is increasing day by day; (2) means and methods of application, once very limited, have likewise increased to the point where exact specifications are now usually necessary; (3) certain complications, such as toxicity to man, crop plants, domestic animals, and wildlife, and the development of resistance to insecticides in insects, have greatly complicated the picture; (4) our increasing knowledge of the bionomics of the organisms involved (e.g., vector, parasite, reservoir, host) has greatly widened the scope of possibilities in control, as well as made the over-all problem more complicated; (5) our realization that the goal of applied medical entomology is not only to remove the threat of disease, but also to increase standards of living through increasing human comfort and mental well-being, has widened the areas where control is necessary or desirable.

Control and abatement involve much more than the application of insecticides. In fact, in many control practices insecticides are not used at all, or their use is limited to supplementary operations. Nevertheless, chemical control, like any other type, must be built upon a firm foundation involving a sound, thorough knowledge of the taxonomy, physiology, and ecology of the organisms involved. The importance of fundamental knowledge may be illustrated by numerous examples which the student will observe as he reads the pages of this book. The need for a sound taxonomic approach may be illustrated by the fact that prior to 1930 vast financial losses, along with much suffering and death in livestock and even man, were incurred annually because it was not recognized that the primary screw-worm, an obligatory parasite, and the secondary screw-worm, a scavenger and facultative parasite, were two distinct species. Successful control of the primary screw-worm is impossible without a thorough knowledge of its bionomics; in fact, as will be shown later, the apparently purely academic fact that the female mates only once has proven to be highly important in the development of a method that is leading to the eradication of this pest over large areas.

Importance of Ecology. The importance of ecologic knowledge in the investigation of insect-borne diseases has long been recognized. As early as 1909 Herms[8] pointed out that "it is essential that the student become familiar with the habits and habitat of the insect in the field, its life history under normal and unusual conditions." Ecology is variously defined, but few of the later proposed definitions define it as well as did Haeckel (1869) when he described it as the "relation of the animal to its organic as well as its inorganic environment." Chapman[6] said, " . . . he [Haeckel] considered oekologie to include the general economy of the household of nature." In many instances man will need to learn how to live in the same world with these now-threatening members of that "household." Pearse[14] in a paper on the ecology of parasites points out that "Man has succeeded by changing the environment or *by changing his own characteristics* as a habitat, in ridding himself of many of his parasites."

In dealing with the importance of ecology in relation to malaria, Strong[15] has stated:

> In addition to these effects of the immediate environment upon the human host, ecological studies must often consider its effects upon the intermediate hosts in instances where they exist. Here, also, climate plays an important rôle, not only in the character of the vertebrate fauna which the region harbors, but especially of the invertebrate fauna. Also, at temperatures below a certain degree, the parasites in the insects which transmit them may be unable to multiply or the insects satisfactorily to breed or even exist, as, for example, the parasites and insects concerned in the transmission of sleeping sickness and of malaria.
>
> . . . .
>
> The epidemic of malaria with its high mortality which has recently been raging in Ceylon, India, is a striking example of the effect that climatic conditions and environment may exert upon a disease. This epidemic has occurred in what has been hitherto regarded as the most healthy and prosperous portion of the island, the southwestern part, in which there has usually been a high annual rainfall and where there has been evidence that the percentage of the population infected with malarial parasites has been but small, and hence the population relatively non-immune to the disease. This year the prevailing rains which are brought so regularly by the southwest monsoon failed to supply the usual amount of water, resulting in a prolonged drought. Then came a few heavy rains and drought again. Thus conditions arose greatly favoring the breeding of the mosquito, *Anopheles culicifacies,* which transmits the disease in this region, as many shallow pools were formed along the river beds and streams. Through these innumerable temporary breeding places, more perfect conditions for the production of mosquitoes could probably not have been devised. The outbreak of malaria was followed by failure of the crops, also due particularly to the lack of rain. Thus the people became further impoverished and the general state of their health reduced, and within five months there were 113,811 deaths, of which 66,704 were estimated to be due to malaria.

The complexity of ecologic factors as pertains to medical entomology is well shown in malaria, in which three animal species are involved, namely, the victim *man,* the vector *mosquito,* and the causal *plasmodium*—each species having characteristic ecologic requirements. The complexity becomes even greater when a reservoir animal enters the epidemiologic picture, as in endemic (tick-borne) relapsing fever in California. In the cycle of this disease *man* is again involved, then there is a *tick* vector, a *spirochete* as the pathogen, and a fourth species, a *chipmunk,* as a reservoir. Meyer[13] has clearly portrayed the complexity of an ecologic approach to the study of plague in his De Lamar lecture, entitled "The Ecology of Plague."

Buxton's[4] article, "The Effect of Climatic Conditions upon Populations of Insects," is well worth reading. In it the author (p. 326) remarks:

> . . . the geographical spread of human diseases and the seasonal occurrence of certain epidemics appear to be directly due to alteration in the numbers of insects which are the essential vectors of these diseases. Our ultimate objective is to know the numbers of particular sorts on insects which are capable of infecting us with the organisms which they carry.

Control of Insect-borne Diseases. The control of insect-borne diseases involves not only the control of the responsible insect vectors, often very difficult or even at times impossible, but depends also upon the control of the fomites from which the arthropod receives its infection.

In the simplest form of insect transmission, i.e., by mechanical contamination of food and drink, the source of infection may be found in human excreta or other dangerous animal wastes, in which case the possibility of spread by insects may be largely overcome by correcting the defect in sanitation. Properly constructed fly-tight privies and septic tanks would aid greatly in preventing the spread of typhoid fever and related filth diseases by flies in rural areas. Rodent control is intended to destroy the natural reservoirs of plague, as the flea is usually only an agent of transmission. The control of plague through flea control alone does not satisfy all requirements.

The handling of persons with infectious diseases is a matter of great importance, as for example the screening of yellow fever and malaria patients against the vector mosquitoes during the critically infectious stages of the diseases. Searching out and adequately treating carriers, although at times beset with many difficulties, should not be overlooked in a program for control of insect-borne diseases. Vector control and carrier prophylaxis must go hand in hand if best results are to be obtained.

In the face of universal rapid transportation by automobile, aircraft, and other means, and in the light of the experiences of World War II, health authorities of states and nations should be thoroughly familiar with the vector potentialities of arthropods within their respective geographic boundaries.[11] Vigilance at the point of departure and proper quarantine measures at the destination should be maintained to avoid the spread of arthropod-borne diseases.[10]

Vector Control. In the control of disease-transmitting arthropods the most vulnerable point in the life history is usually sought, and the most effective control means are then employed. This involves an intimate knowledge of bionomics. The more familiar an investigator is with the life history, habits, and ecology of the vector, the better equipped he will be to cope with the problems of control.

Control measures may be only of a temporary nature for purposes of immediate relief, and hence must be repeated, or they may be intended to have permanent effect. Temporary control measures involve holding a nuisance in check for a short time, a few hours or a few days, and require constant repetition: for example, the use of aerosols to kill adult mosquitoes and flies, the use of mosquito repellents, or even the application of insecticides to mosquito-breeding pools. Permanent control, on the other hand, involves correction of breeding places by mechanical or other means in order to prevent vector breeding: for example, draining or filling unnecessary ponds and pools of standing water in which mosquitoes may breed; the correction of irrigation defects, particularly errors in drainage; the disposal of manures and organic wastes in such a manner as to prevent breeding of house flies, etc. Permanent control measures are usually more economical in the long run.

Permanent control has as its objective the reduction of a vector to a level where it can no longer efficiently transmit a disease-producing organism. It has long been the hope that we can progress one step further, namely to eradication, and that hope is now being realized in certain areas. Two notable examples are the eradication of the important malaria vector, *Anopheles gambiae* Giles, from Brazil, where it had been introduced and had gained a strong foothold, and the eradication of the cattle tick, *Boophilus annulatus* (Say), and consequently of Texas cattle fever, which it transmits, from extensive areas in North America.

Species sanitation implies that control measures aimed at disease vectors must fit the particular offending species. The importance of this procedure is particularly applicable in vector-control operations where closely related species occur in the same general area, but only one is of public health importance. By concentrating appropriate efforts on the proven vector species, good results may be economically obtained.

Natural control implies a planned change in the natural habitat of an offending species, such as a disease vector, so as to make it impossible for the species to continue to breed in effective numbers. For example, *Anopheles albimanus* Wiedemann, a potent vector of malaria in the Caribbean area, breeds abundantly in certain coastal lagoons having a salinity between 15 and 25 per cent sea water. By simply connecting these lagoons with the sea so as to facilitate tidal action and thus increase the salinity in the lagoons to about 75 per cent, breeding of these mosquitoes can be largely eliminated. Such methods have been employed quite extensively in mosquito control, but for their successful application a quite thorough knowledge of the ecology of the offending species is necessary.

Insecticidal Practices. Insecticides must be employed with discretion and understanding. In the first place, when proprietary remedies are to be used, it is good practice to study the labels and then use accordingly. In the United States, federal law requires adequate labeling of all insecticides. These labels are appended both for the protection of the manufacturer and for that of the user as well; they serve not only as a guide to safety but also to aid in getting good results. The entomologist concerned with insect control should have a substantial knowledge of the properties of insecticides, particularly their toxological properties as these pertain to insects, man, useful animals, and crop plants.

Effective use of insecticides depends a great deal on a thorough knowledge of the ecology of the offending insect. No matter how excellent the larvicide, a plague of tree-hole mosquitoes such as *Aedes sierrensis* (Ludlow) or a threat of malaria from the epiphyte-breeding *Anopheles bellator* Dyar and Knab can not be abated by treating stagnant pools on the ground, no matter how thoroughly this is done. Insecticides which have produced spectacular results, such as DDT, are neither foolproof nor infallible. They must be used with care and understanding in order to achieve the greatest good with the least possible chances of injury to man and other animals of all kinds in the immediate treated environment. Knowledge of the ways and means of application is essential.

Dangers attending the improper or careless use of insecticides need to be emphasized,[2] and the student will notice such cautions being given repeatedly in this book, at the risk of too much repetition. Insecticides, with very rare exceptions, are *poisons and should be considered as such.* For a few of them, there is no known antidote, and some are cumulative. Proper use of insecticides is safe, but one sometimes needs to determine with care just what constitutes proper use.

In an editorial entitled "Insecticide or Homicide?" in the *California Vector Views,*[1] the procedure of a foreman in a dairy ranch is described as follows:

> The foreman removed his shoes and socks and stripped to the waist; poured 5% TEPP into a sprinkling can filled with sugar water; mixed it thoroughly with his bare hand and arm; then sprinkled it generously around the milk shed and barn, walking through the wet area with bare feet. When the hazard that he ran was pointed out to him, he replied that he was "tough"! He was still alive at the last report.

Despite his "toughness," it is questionable how long he could continue to use such procedures and survive. Tetraethyl pyrophosphate (TEPP) is absorbed through the skin and is cumulative in its effect, i.e., it is not excreted by normal processes; one pint of it is sufficient to kill 50 men through dermal contact or 235 men through oral dosage.

Most of the criticism of modern chemical methods of insect control arises from the abuse, rather than the use, of insecticides. Workmen should be properly protected. Empty containers should be destroyed promptly by recommended methods, and partially full containers should be placed in a locked storage out of reach of children, pets, and domestic and other useful animals. Residents of areas being treated with insecticides should not be exposed to undue dangers, either real or imaginary. Livestock, honey bees, wildlife, and crop plants should not be endangered. An important aspect of mosquito control, for example, consists of taking care to protect fish and game interests, both in the application of insecticides and in control by other methods.

Good public relations are imperative. Progress in the abatement and control of disease vectors depends very much on public understanding; therefore, education plays an important role in this field. Much of the trouble can be attributed to man's stupidity, carelessness, and ignorance. The medical entomologist must make use of every opportunity to combat ignorance and to secure cooperation on the part of the general public. Oftentimes the ignorance of the well-educated is appalling, and their lack of cooperation is often astounding.

The Nature and Action of Insecticides. Insecticides were at one time classified as stomach poisons, contact poisons, and fumigants, depending upon their mode of entry, to which were later added the categories of residual poisons, repellents and deterrents, attractants, synergists, and systemic insecticides. This method of classification can be used only with limitations, since many insecticides have properties which would fit them into more than one category. It is better, for our purposes, to deal with certain groups of insecticides according to their affinities on the basis of chemical composition. With the ever-increasing number of insecticides and the complexities in their nomenclature, it must serve our purpose to discuss very briefly the properties and action of those with which we will be concerned in this book.

Inorganic Insecticides. This class of insecticides, once very important in the control of medically important arthropods, now has relatively little use for that purpose. *Elemental sulfur,* in the form of small crystals (flowers of sulfur) or in a finely ground form, has long been used to kill and repel mites and certain other noxious arthropods. Most inorganic compounds of use in the control of medically important insects serve as stomach poisons. Among the arsenicals, *Paris green,* a complex of copper metarsenite and copper acetate, has been used extensively in the control of anopheline mosquitoes; though once virtually discarded, it is finding renewed use in a pelleted form that suspends in water long enough to control culicine mosquitoes. Two fluorine compounds, *sodium fluoride* and *sodium fluosilicate,* have been used in poison baits and louse powders, but are now considered too dangerous, in view of the availability of better and safer insecticides. *Borax,* $Na_2B_4O_7$, once widely used for control of fly larvae, is now rarely recommended.

Tarshis[16,17] has recently introduced the use of a silica gel, *SG 77,* and a silica aerogel, *Dri-Die 67,* for cockroach control. The latter compound has proven to be better and is also effective against fleas, conenose bugs, ticks (e.g., dog tick), mites and lice ectoparasitic on domestic and zoo animals, and other noxious arthropods (Tarshis, personal communication). This class of compounds kills by removing the waterproof layer of the epicuticle through a continuous adsorption of its lipid elements or through abrasion, thus bringing about desiccation. Dri-Die 67 is nontoxic to man and to warm-blooded animals, and because it is an amorphous rather than a crystalline compound it will not cause silicosis. It seems unlikely that insects could develop any type of resistance to compounds of this group.

Organic Compounds of Plant Origin. Pyrethrum, obtained from the dried flowers of a plant of the aster family, *Chrysanthemum cinerariaefolium,* and *rotenone,* obtained from the roots of plants of the genera *Derris* and *Lonchocarpus,* are both used in the control of insects of medical importance. Pyrethrum contains at least two insecticidal constituents, pyrethrin I and pyrethrin II, the former being the more effective; two other constituents, cinerin I and cinerin II, are supposed to have some insecticidal value. Pyrethrum has a rapid paralyzing action, and for that reason is often added to slower acting but more toxic substances. *Allethrin,* a related synthetic compound, is often used instead of pyrethrum. *Rotenone* has found its place in medical entomology chiefly in the control of the cattle grub and until recently has been the only insecticide that could be used successfully against that insect. It acts both as a contact and stomach poison.

Synthetic Organic Insecticides. Prior to World War II, a few synthetic organic insecticides were in use, such as: *hydrocyanic acid,* a dangerous fumigant; *formaldehyde,* sometimes used in milk as a fly poison; *paradichlorobenzene,* used in privies for fly maggot control and sometimes for the control of fleas; *cresol* or *cresylic acid,* used for mosquito larviciding and as animal dips; and *benzyl benzoate,* used to kill and repel scabies mites, chiggers, lice, and other ectoparasites.

The advent of DDT introduced a new group in the development of organic insecticides, namely, the residual group. *DDT* is a chlorinated hydrocarbon with high residual value and with great versatility; it is practically insoluble in water, although it can form colloidal solutions, and it is freely soluble in most organic solvents. It may, consequently, be used in liquid or dust form. It is only moderately toxic to man, but it must be remembered that it is a poison, cumulative in fats, and more toxic to some mammals, such as cats, and to aquatic life. Other chlorinated hydrocarbons that are more or less widely used against pests of medical or sanitary importance are: *BHC* and its gamma isomer, *lindane; methoxychlor; TDE* (sometimes called DDD or Rhothane); *chlordane; aldrin; dieldrin;* and *toxaphene*. For more information as to these important insecticides, the student is referred to an up-to-date textbook on this fast-changing subject.

When medically important insects began to show resistance to DDT and the other chlorinated hydrocarbons, medical entomologists turned more toward the organophosphorus compounds. A very large number of these have been developed or tested for insecticidal action within recent years. *Parathion* is very effective against many insects and has attained a distinct place in the control of mosquitoes, for example, in pastures where a quick kill is desired and where no residual effect is needed, or against house flies when used in baits or poison strips. It is *highly toxic to man* and must be used with great precautions. When properly used, it is safe, but no one can expect to handle this substance with his bare hands and come through the experience unscathed. Parathion has little residual effect. *Malathion* is much safer to use and has been employed extensively in mosquito control. Dipterex and Diazinon are other compounds of this group that have been used in fly control.

Sevin, a carbamate (*N*-methyl-1-naphthyl carbamate), has introduced a new group of insecticides in the control of mosquitoes, mites, and other noxious arthropods.

Activators or Synergists. Certain compounds which are themselves not toxic to insects or which may have a low degree of toxicity have been found to increase, often spectacularly, the toxicity of commonly used insecticides. The pyrethrins particularly benefit by this synergistic action, the activators commonly used against lice and various flies and mosquitoes being commonly *piperonyl butoxide* or *MGK 264*. Certain chlorinated hydrocarbons have a synergistic action in partially restoring the effectiveness of DDT against DDT-resistant insects.

Repellents. Man has from early times sought relief from the bites of annoying insects through the use of repellent substances that could be applied to the skin (and, in more recent times, also to the clothing). Some methods of attempting to obtain relief have been little short of heroic. *Oil of citronella* seemed to give the best results (with relatively nonobnoxious qualities) of any repellent used prior to 1940, but since that date a large number of new repellents have been tested, and much more effective and less obnoxious ones have been found. *Ethyl hexanediol* (Rutgers 612) was found to be very effective against mosquitoes, biting flies in general, and some other arthropods; it is used either alone or in combination with *dimethyl phthalate* and *Indalone,* both of which have definite repellent qualities. It is in general nonobjectionable to use, but it should be kept away from the eyes and mouth and must not be permitted to come in contact with plastics, for which it serves as a solvent. The most effective general repellent that has been produced and tested so far is *diethyltoluamide*. This compound is highly effective against mosquitoes, other biting flies, fleas, chiggers, and ticks. A repellent that has been used to give relief to livestock is *butoxy-polypropylene glycol* (Crag fly repellent).

It is a well-known but little-understood fact that individuals differ vastly in their attractiveness or nonattractiveness for insects. It is to be expected, therefore, that the benefits received from repellents will likewise vary greatly from one individual to another.

Systemic Insecticides. Insecticides of this group are introduced either orally or externally as sprays to livestock in order to produce a repellent or toxic effect upon flies, cattle grubs, screw-worm, lice, ticks, and other arthropods that may attack or feed on the animal. Systemic insecticides must have a very low degree of toxicity to the domestic animal but must at the same time be effective against its annoyers. A number of such insecticides are being tested, but *ronnel* (Dow ET-57, Korlan) and *Bayer* 21/199 (Co-ral) have been used with a great deal of success.

Insect Resistance to Insecticides. Insect control by the use of DDT and the other "newer" insecticides received a serious setback with the discovery, in 1947, that house flies and *Culex* mosquitoes could not always be killed by the use of that "miracle" insecticide. Resistance to arsenicals, in the case of the codling moth and other agricultural pests, had been known for a long time, but the reports that DDT was no longer effective under all conditions against the house fly were first received with startled scepticism or even disbelief. Resistance to DDT, BHC, and the other chlorinated hydrocarbons, and even to malathion and parathion, is now a well-established fact. Resistance to one or another of the residual insecticides has been demonstrated among many species of mosquitoes, flies, lice, cockroaches, conenose bugs, ticks, and other arthropods. A good account of the general subject has been given by Brown.[3]

The term "resistance," in its proper sense, refers to resistance (physiologic, behavioristic, or morphologic) which has developed, subsequent to the initial application of an insecticide, through the process of natural selection. Its genetic basis has been the subject of considerable investigation. A type of resistance which may be due to a single gene in one species or strain (e.g., resistance to DDT and its analogs in the house fly) may be polygenic in another species or strain (e.g., the same type of resistance in *Aedes aegypti*). Resistance on the part of one insect to a given insecticide frequently extends to other insecticides of the same group; for example, resistance to DDT may also extend to its analogs but may not involve lindane or the cyclodiene derivatives such as dieldrin or chlordane; or it may extend to all the hydrocarbons but not involve malathion or parathion; or it may even involve, at least to a small degree of resistance, all groups of chemicals.

The development of resistance has led to serious problems in the control of medically important insects, but it has not proven a roadblock to most problems. It must be remembered that an individual insect does not acquire tolerance to an insecticide during its lifetime; it is the already resistant segment of a population that survives which transmits tolerance to their offspring through the selective action of insecticides. Also, most development of resistance among insects of public health importance has been to the chlorinated hydrocarbons. The answer to the problem of resistance must be sought through a consideration of the individual case. No clear general answer is yet available, but some methods which have been suggested to avoid development of resistance are as follows: (1) taking care not to apply sublethal doses which will give less than a complete kill within the circumscribed area; (2) avoiding the use of the same insecticide for both larvae and adults (as in house fly control); (3) alternating the use of insecticides belonging to different chemical groups and showing negative correlation in their action in the hope that cross resistance is not present. It should be emphasized that there is no general agreement as to the efficacy of the above suggestions. Control by sanitation and source reduction is, in the long run, most satisfactory; such measures allow insecticides to be held in reserve for emergency use.

Vital Losses Due to Insects. Comparisons between agricultural and vital losses occasioned by insects, while suggestive, are by their very nature inaccurate and confusing. Because of the intangible nature of the values involved and the changing dollar values, agricultural losses for the United States can only be roughly estimated, but in terms of dollars they would undoubtedly mount into ten figures. Vital losses (human and animal) are still more difficult to judge. Fernald[7] in 1926 estimated these vital losses at $781,450,000; i.e., human, $350,000,000, and animal (inclusive of their products), $431,450,000. Adjusted to present-day values and with allowance for such notable gains as malaria eradication and screw-worm control, these losses would well exceed a billion dollars. In addition to this, it is impossible to place a monetary value on human comfort and well-being and higher standards of living.

Hunter,[12] commenting on agricultural losses as compared with vital losses, states:

> The two branches are radically different in one important respect. One deals with material losses and the other with a reduction in the vital force of a nation. Is it right to compare the loss of a human life with the loss of 28 bales of cotton or 1,700 bushels of corn? The loss in cotton or wheat might be made good in another region or during another season, but for the life that is lost there is no compensation.

Concerning losses due to malaria, a mosquito-borne disease, Carter[5] has well said:

It is not in its death rate that the gravest injury of malaria lies; it is in its sickness rate, in the loss of efficiency it causes rather than in the loss of life. One death from pneumonia ordinarily corresponds to about 125 sick days—work days lost; one death from typhoid fever to 450 to 500 sick days; one from tuberculosis to somewhat more than this among whites. A death from malaria, however, corresponds to from 2,000 to 4,000 sick days. This loss of efficiency may really be doubled or trebled, for the man infected with malaria is frequently "half" sick all the time. The loss of efficiency caused by malaria in the country of the malarious section is beyond comparison greater than that caused by any other disease, or even by any two or three diseases combined, including typhoid fever and tuberculosis.

It is recently becoming evident that malaria control and eradication are playing an important part in permitting formerly dependent nations to take care of their own problems of overpopulation and underproduction. When one or more members of a household are ill, at one time, with malaria, or "half sick" in convalescence, not only the productivity of that household is reduced, but also valuable time and effort are spent caring for the ill. The release of this man power can well mark the difference between financial dependence and independence on a national scale.

In 1919, Herms[9] attempted to estimate the vital losses in terms of "work days lost." Although the data which he used are now obsolete and though his estimate of loss presents only a part of a complex picture, the conclusions and their justification of the relation of loss to the amount justifiably spent on control are valid today. Herms says:

In 1918 there were 5,887 deaths from tuberculosis in California, amounting to a loss of (5,887 × 500) 2,943,500 work days; there were 187 deaths from typhoid, amounting to a loss of (187 × 450) 84,150 work days; and 56 deaths from malaria, with a loss of (56 × 3,000) 168,000 work days; a total loss to California of about 3,200,000 work days. In control work against typhoid fever the State spent between $35,000 and $50,000 in 1918. Assuming that this amount was justified, for such it actually was, because there was a reduction of about 12 per cent in the typhoid rate for 1919, there should have been expended in malaria control between $70,000 and $100,000 because the total number of work days lost is double that of typhoid fever. As a matter of fact, the State spent about $5,000 in malaria control in 1918 and the malaria death rate went up from 1.5 per 100,000 in 1917 to 1.8 in 1918, an increase of about 20 per cent. In the matter of tuberculosis control on the typhoid basis the State should have spent about $1,750,000 in 1918, which was closely approximated, the actual amount being $1,673,000.

REFERENCES

1. Anonymous, 1954. "Insecticide or homicide?" *Calif. Vector Views,* **1** (no. 4):2.

2. Bishopp, F. C., and Horsfall, John L., 1952. "The Safe Use of Insecticides." Washington, D. C.: U. S. Dept. Agric., in *Yearbook of Agriculture,* pp. 271–75.

3. Brown, A. W. A., 1958. *Insecticide Resistance in Arthropods.* Geneva: World Health Organization, in Monograph Ser. No. 38. 240 pp.

4. Buxton, P. A., 1933. "The effect of climatic conditions upon populations of insects," *Tr. Roy. Soc. Trop. Med. & Hyg.,* **26:**325–64.

5. Carter, H. R., 1919. "The malaria problem of the South," U. S. Public Health Service, *Pub. Health Rep.,* **34:**1927–35.

6. Chapman, R. N., 1931. *Animal Ecology.* New York: McGraw-Hill Book Co., Inc. 464 pp.

7. Fernald, H. T., 1926. *Applied Entomology.* New York: McGraw-Hill Book Co., Inc. xiv + 395 pp.

8. Herms, William B., 1909. "Medical entomology. Its scope and methods," *J. Econ. Entomol.,* **2:**265–68.

9. Herms, William B., 1919. "What shall we do with our information concerning malaria in California?" Calif. State Bd. of Health, *Month. Bull.,* **15:**181–89.

10. Herms, W. M., 1946. "Wartime aviation quarantine: Pests and their control," *J. Pest Control Indust.,* **14:**24–25.

11. Herms, William B., 1947. "Vector potentialities with respect to the spread of insect-borne diseases of man in California," *California Med.,* **67:**95–99.

12. Hunter, W. D., 1913. "American interest in medical entomology," *J. Econ. Entomol.,* **6:**27–39.

13. Meyer, K. F., 1942. "The ecology of plague," *Medicine,* **21:**143–74.

14. Pearse, A. S., 1926. "The ecology of parasites," *Ecology,* **7:**113–119.

15. Strong, Richard P., 1935. "The importance of ecology in relation to disease," *Science,* **82:**307–17.

16. Tarshis, I. Barry, 1959. "UCLA tests with desiccant dusts for roach control," *Pest Control,* **27** (no. 6):14, 16–18, 20, 22, 24, 26–28, 30, 32.

17. Tarshis, I. Barry, 1959. "Sorptive dusts for cockroaches," *Calif. Agriculture,* **13** (No. 2):3–5.

Chapter 4

STRUCTURE, DEVELOPMENT, AND CLASSIFICATION OF INSECTS AND ARACHNIDS

THE INSECTA (HEXAPODA)

The Insecta (Hexapoda) constitute the largest class in numbers of species (see footnote, p. 15) in the phylum Arthropoda, which in turn comprises a greater number of species than all other phyla of the animal kingdom combined. As members of the phylum Arthropoda, insects share the following arthropod characteristics: segmented body with paired, segmented appendages; bilateral symmetry; dorsal heart; ventral nerve cord; and chitinous exoskeleton. Insects have the body divided into three more or less distinct parts, the *head,* the *thorax,* and the *abdomen.* There are 18 to 21 segments in the insect body, the variable number resulting from differences in the interpretation of the embryologic evidence, but owing to the specialization of the head and posterior terminal segments, only about 12 or fewer are clearly recognizable. The *head* of the adult insect bears a pair of antennae, the mouth parts, and the eyes. The *thorax* bears the locomotor appendages, namely, three pairs of segmented legs, and in addition usually two pairs of wings (which are morphologically not appendages), one or both of which may be absent or nonfunctional as locomotor structures. The *abdomen* bears no appendages except the terminalia, sometimes cerci, and, in the Collembola, specialized locomotor structures. Respiration is effected by means of a complex system of microscopic tracheal tubules opening through the body wall and carrying air directly to all parts of the body of the insect. Immature insects belonging to many of the orders differ markedly from the mature forms, e.g., maggots of flies, but almost all possess tracheal tubules.

External Anatomy. In order to familiarize himself with the external anatomy of insects, especially with the parts upon which classification is mainly based, the student should study carefully some large hard-bodied insect, such as the horse fly (Fig. 1) or the cockroach. He should give sufficient time to this exercise in the laboratory to become thoroughly informed.

Wings. The earliest systems of insect classification were based on wing characters, which together with mouth parts and metamorphosis afford the major elements in the bases for modern classification. The venation of insect wings is so markedly characteristic for most species that even a part of a wing is sometimes all that is necessary for determination. The winged insects are usually referred to as the *Pterygota* and may be either *Exopterygota*

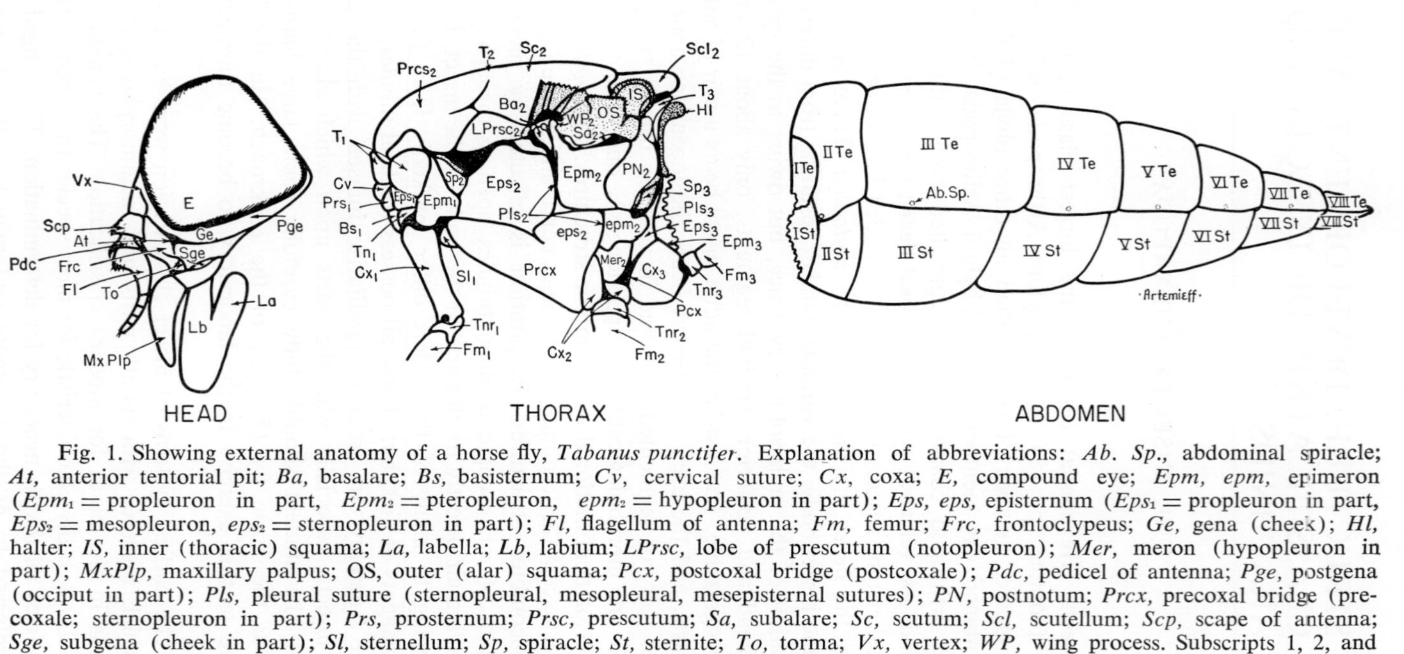

Fig. 1. Showing external anatomy of a horse fly, *Tabanus punctifer*. Explanation of abbreviations: *Ab. Sp.*, abdominal spiracle; *At*, anterior tentorial pit; *Ba*, basalare; *Bs*, basisternum; *Cv*, cervical suture; *Cx*, coxa; *E*, compound eye; *Epm, epm*, epimeron (Epm_1 = propleuron in part, Epm_2 = pteropleuron, epm_2 = hypopleuron in part); *Eps, eps*, episternum (Eps_1 = propleuron in part, Eps_2 = mesopleuron, eps_2 = sternopleuron in part); *Fl*, flagellum of antenna; *Fm*, femur; *Frc*, frontoclypeus; *Ge*, gena (cheek); *Hl*, halter; *IS*, inner (thoracic) squama; *La*, labella; *Lb*, labium; *LPrsc*, lobe of prescutum (notopleuron); *Mer*, meron (hypopleuron in part); *MxPlp*, maxillary palpus; OS, outer (alar) squama; *Pcx*, postcoxal bridge (postcoxale); *Pdc*, pedicel of antenna; *Pge*, postgena (occiput in part); *Pls*, pleural suture (sternopleural, mesopleural, mesepisternal sutures); *PN*, postnotum; *Prcx*, precoxal bridge (precoxale; sternopleuron in part); *Prs*, prosternum; *Prsc*, prescutum; *Sa*, subalare; *Sc*, scutum; *Scl*, scutellum; *Scp*, scape of antenna; *Sge*, subgena (cheek in part); *Sl*, sternellum; *Sp*, spiracle; *St*, sternite; *To*, torma; *Vx*, vertex; *WP*, wing process. Subscripts 1, 2, and 3 refer to the respective somite of the thorax.

(wings developing externally), e.g., cockroaches, or *Endopterygota* (wings developing internally), e.g., beetles. There are typically two pairs of wings present, situated on the mesothorax and metathorax, although in many parasitic insects, such as the bed bugs, lice, fleas, certain louse flies, etc., the wings are absent. The wingless insects just mentioned should, of course, not be included with the *Apterygota,* which are a group of primitively wingless (apterous) forms. The above-mentioned parasitic, wingless insects belong to several distinct orders, of which only one, the Collembola (now considered by many to be distinct from the insects), will be given any consideration here.

In form the wing presents a more or less triangular appearance. The three sides are called margins: the *costal* margin is anterior, the *anal* margin is posterior, and the *apical* (outer) margin is between these. The three angles connecting the margins are *humeral* (at the base), *apical* (apex of wing), and *anal* (between the apical and anal margins). Generally the fore and hind wings differ considerably in size; the fore wing in some groups, such as the mayflies, many butterflies and moths, and the bees and wasps, is larger than the hind wing; while in the grasshoppers, cockroaches, beetles, and some others, the fore wing is narrow and serves largely as a cover to the hind wing, which folds fanlike. In the dragonflies, termites, and antlions the fore and hind wings are nearly equal. In the flies, the hind pair of wings is replaced by club-shaped structures known as *halteres,* leaving consequently only one pair of wings, hence the name Diptera (two-winged). In the calyptrate Diptera and some other flies there are present two pairs of lobes (*squamae,* also called *alulae* or *calypters*) at the junction of the wings and the thorax. One of these squamae, the *thoracic,* is more closely associated with the wall of the thorax; the other, the *alar,* is more closely associated with the base of the wing.

There are some differences in the structure of the wings within the order, although for each order a certain general pattern prevails; e.g., the Neuroptera have thin membranous wings, often quite filmy, and with numerous veins and cells; however, the wings of Diptera and many Hemiptera have the same texture throughout, but possess fewer and differently arranged veins. The Diptera can, of course, be readily distinguished from all but a few insects (such as the male coccids, the Strepsiptera, and the two-winged mayflies) by the presence of but a single pair of wings. The winged Hemiptera of the suborder Heteroptera have the front wings thickened at the base, while the apical portion is membranous. In the winged Hemiptera of the suborder Homoptera, the two pairs of wings are of more or less even texture throughout.

The *venation* of the insect wing is an important element in classification, on account of the great variety of arrangements and the reliability of this character for the identification of the family, genus, and sometimes even the species. The *veins* are hollow, riblike structures which give strength to the wing. The areas of membrane between the veins are called *cells;* they are said to be *open* if the membranous area extends to the wing margin, and *closed* if the cell is surrounded on all sides by veins. By a careful study of the evidence, a fundamental type of wing venation has been constructed by Comstock and Needham and revised by Tillyard. The accompanying figure (Fig. 2) will illustrate this nomenclature as applied to a primitive type of dipterous wing (Fig. 2A) and as modified in the muscoid type (Fig. 2B).

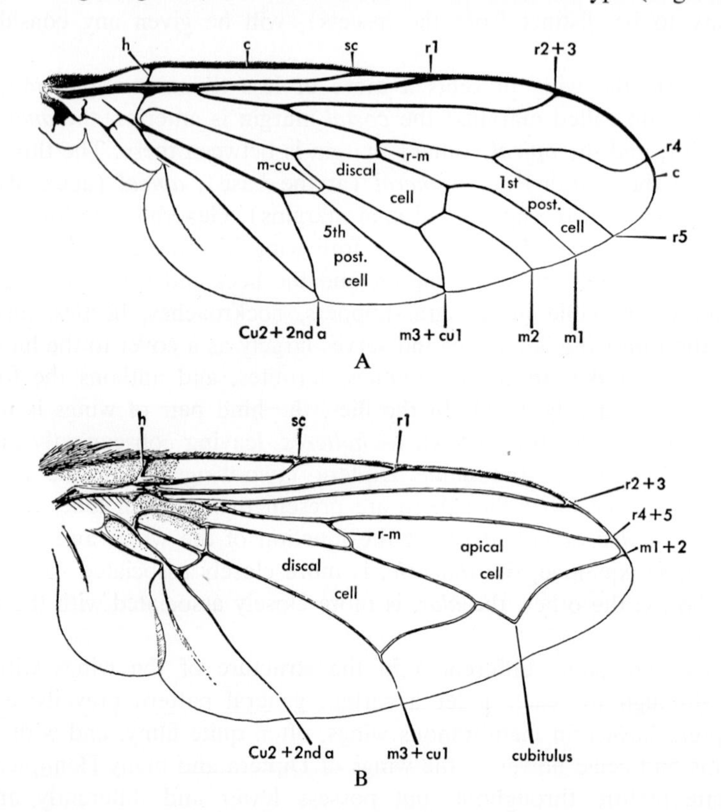

Fig. 2. Application of the Comstock-Needham system of nomenclature to two types of dipterous wing (see also Fig. 40). The longitudinal veins (with the nomenclature used by those dipterists who follow the old system of numbered veins given in parentheses) are as follows: *c,* costa (costal); *sc,* subcosta (auxillary); *r,* radius (r_1 = 1st longitudinal, r_{2+3} = 2nd longitudinal, r_4 and r_5 = 3rd longitudinal) *m,* media (m_1 and m_2 = 4th longitudinal, m_3 = part of 5th longitudinal); *cu,* cubitus (cu_1 = part of 5th longitudinal, cu_2 = part of 6th longitudinal); *2nd a,* 2nd anal (part of 6th longitudinal). The 1st anal vein occurs only as a fold in the membrane. The cross veins are: *h,* humeral; *r-m,* radiomedial (anterior or small cross vein); *m-cu,* mediocubital.

(*A*) Wing of Thereva, illustrative of the more primitive type of venation. (U.S.D.A. photograph.)

(*B*) Wing of *Callitroga hominivorax,* illustrative of the muscoid type. (U.S.D.A. photograph.)

Metamorphosis. In order to achieve the size and development of the parent, the young insect undergoes greater or less change in size, form, and structure. This series of changes is termed *metamorphosis.* The least change is found in the Apterygota (e.g., silverfish), which are primitively wingless insects; hence, the newly emerged young individual is externally unlike the parent in size: this type of development, i.e., *without metamorphosis,* is termed *direct development* (Fig. 3).

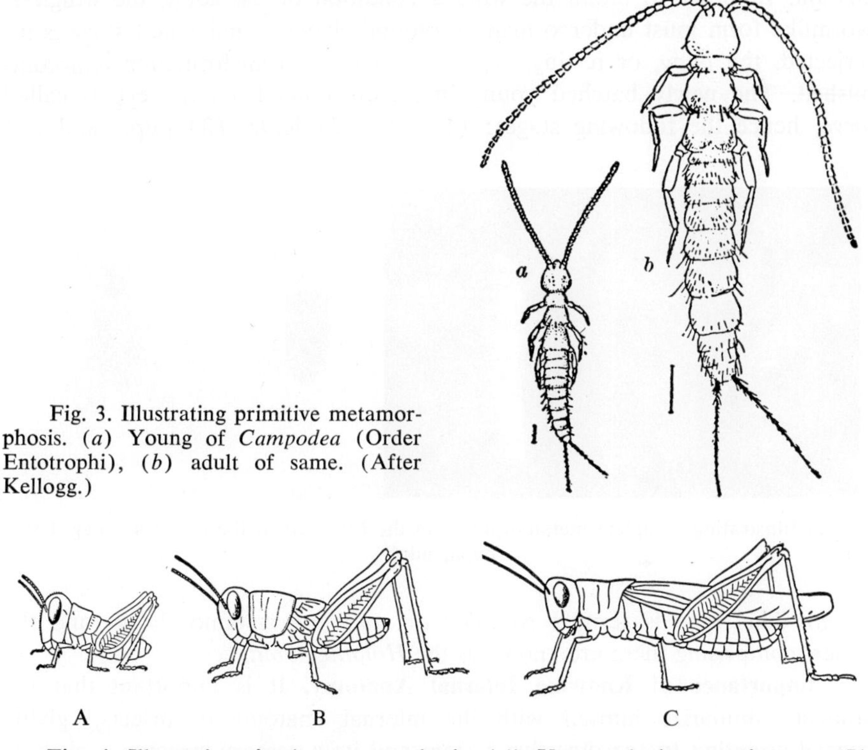

Fig. 3. Illustrating primitive metamorphosis. (*a*) Young of *Campodea* (Order Entotrophi), (*b*) adult of same. (After Kellogg.)

Fig. 4. Illustrating simple metamorphosis. (*A*) Young wingless grasshopper; (*B*) partially developed grasshopper after the appearance of wing pads; (*C*) adult of same. (Redrawn from Packard.)

A low degree of metamorphosis occurs in the grasshopper. There is not only a great difference in size, but also the absence of wings in the young is at once apparent. In order to reach the winged condition, the young individual casts its skin at intervals and with each *ecdysis* achieves longer wings until, after a certain number of molts, the fully developed wings appear. The following stages may be recognized: (1) *egg;* (2) *nymph;* and (3) *imago,* or sexually mature adult. This type of metamorphosis is called *simple* or *incomplete* (Fig. 4), and the orders in which this type occurs are known as the *Heterometabola.*

The greatest difference between the newly hatched young and the parents occurs in such forms as the house fly (Fig. 5) and the butterfly. In these forms the newly hatched insect has no resemblance whatsoever to the adult, but in many cases bears a close resemblance to a segmented worm. However, the internal anatomy and certain other features are distinctly insectan. The fact that the young are mandibulate and the adults haustellate in Diptera and Lepidoptera offers much interesting ground for ecologic discussion. In order to attain the winged condition of the adult, the wingless, wormlike form must undergo many profound changes, and a new stage is interjected, the *pupa,* or resting stage, in which this transformation is accomplished. The newly hatched young insect emerging from the egg is called *larva,* hence the following stages: (1) egg, (2) larva, (3) pupa, and (4)

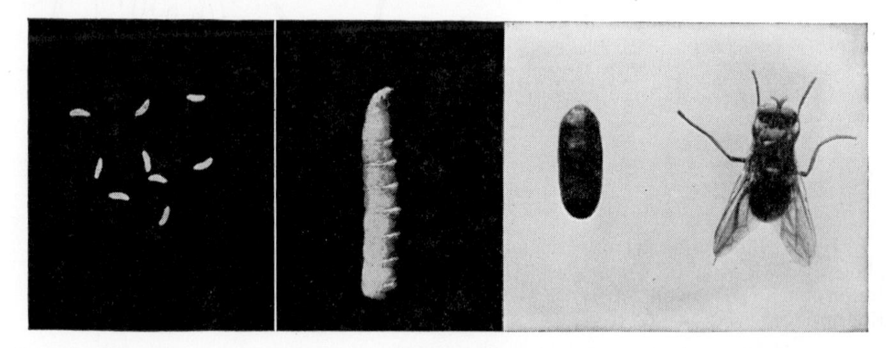

Fig. 5. Illustrating complete metamorphosis in the life cycle of the house fly: egg, larva, pupa, adult.

imago. This type is termed *complex* or *complete* metamorphosis, and the orders comprising these are known as the *Holometabola.*

Importance of Knowing Internal Anatomy. It is important that the student familiarize himself with the internal anatomy of insects,[4] giving special attention to the digestive system and its accessory structures, such as the salivary glands. The following two cases illustrate the reason for this.

Firstly, the simplest condition in which internal organs of insects are involved in disease transmission is in the case of the common house fly, in which pathogenic organisms may be sucked up with infectious dejecta from those ill with cholera or typhoid fever and pass out with the feces of the fly, which may be deposited on human food, either in their original virulent condition or more or less attenuated. Regurgitation on the part of the insect may be equally effective. Simple passage through the digestive tract is involved, and not much knowledge of its special anatomy is required.

Secondly, a more complicated situation exists in the case of the *Anopheles* mosquito, which sucks up pathogenic organisms (plasmodia) with its meal of human blood, whereupon these parasites undergo vital sexual changes within the body of the insect, eventually finding lodgment in the salivary glands before final introduction by the "bite" into the next human victim. The insect in this case is the essential natural vector. An understanding of the part of the cycle of the plasmodium within the mosquito requires at least a basic knowledge of the digestive system of the insect and its spatial relation to other parts of the body.

Digestive System. There are three distinct regions to the insect intestine (Fig. 6); namely, (1) the *foregut,* consisting of the mouth, pharynx, esophagus, crop, and proventriculus; (2) the *midgut,* comprising the stomach; and (3) the *hindgut,* consisting of the ileum, colon, rectum, and the anus. In bloodsucking insects, such as the conenose bug and the mosquito, the pharynx, including its pumping organ, becomes associated with the sucking tube of the proboscis. In the mosquito the esophagus has three diverticula which serve as food reservoirs. The crop presents merely a widened portion of the esophagus in the more generalized forms and serves as a food receptacle. In the more specialized groups, such as the Diptera and Lepidoptera, the crop is expanded into a capacious pocket or pouch. In such forms as the cockroach and grasshopper the proventriculus consists of a highly muscular dilation provided internally with sclerotized teeth for grinding or straining food. The stomach is a simple sac into which open *gastric ceca,* generally few in number, which give rise to certain digestive fluids. At both ends of the stomach are located valves which control the flow of the food. There is much variation in the length and the degree of convolution of the hind intestines, but usually the three regions mentioned, namely, ileum, colon, and rectum, can be located. Emptying into the ileum are the excretory or *Malpighian tubules,* varying in number and length in the several groups of insects.

The *salivary system* consists of a pair of salivary glands which may be lobed; they are situated within the head, often extending into the thorax. Usually each gland empties into a *salivary duct,* the two ducts discharging into a common duct which opens into the mouth at the base of the labium. In many species of insects there is present a pair of *salivary reservoirs;* these may be located near the opening of the common duct and then present a compound condition, or may be situated on either side of the esophagus at the end of a long slender duct.

Insect Larvae. When insect larvae, parasitic or accidental, are encountered in the body of man or beast, confusion may arise because of the wormlike appearance of the invaders, which may be incorrectly mistaken for worms, e.g., muscoid fly larvae. These larvae are short and plump and have 11 or 12 well-marked segments. Microscopic examination of fragments will reveal tracheal tubules, which are not present in worms. The student of medical entomology must be thoroughly familiar with the immature stages of those arthropods which are or may become pathogenic.

Although the larvae of insects belonging to the order Diptera (flies,

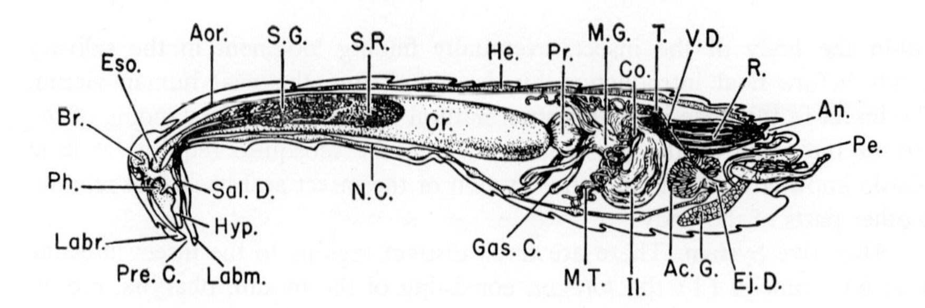

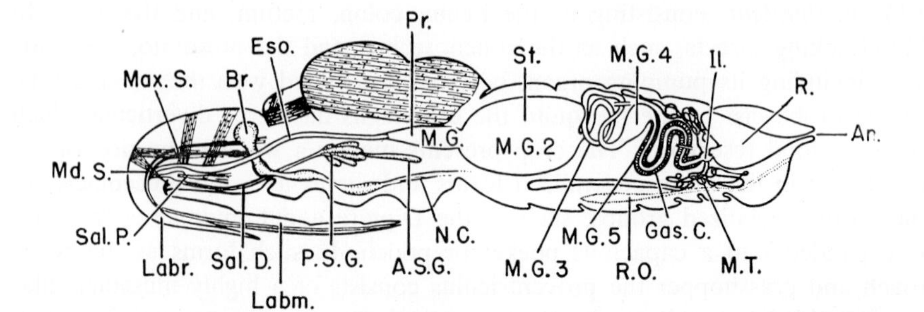

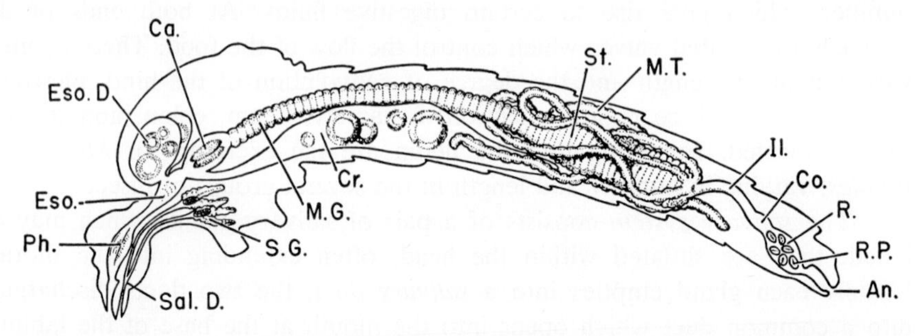

Fig. 6. Showing digestive tract of the cockroach, Order Blattaria (*top*); of assassin bug, Order Hemiptera (*middle*); and of anopheline mosquito, Order Diptera (*bottom*). Explanation of abbreviations: *Ac.G.*, accessory gland; *An.*, anus; *Aor.*, aorta; *A.S.G.*, accessory salivary gland; *Br.*, brain; *Ca.*, cardia; *Co.*, colon; *Cr.*, crop; *Ej.D.*, ejaculatory duct; *Eso.*, esophagus; *Eso.D.*, esophageal diverticula; *Gas.C.*, gastric caeca; *He.*, heart; *Hyp.*, hypopharynx; *Il.*, ilium; *Labm.*, labium; *Labr.*, labrum; *Max.S.*, maxillary stylet; *Md.S.*, mandibular stylet; *M.G.*, midgut; *M.T.*, Malpighian tubules; N.C., nerve cord; *Pe.*, penis; *Ph.*, pharynx; *Pr.*, proventriculus; *Pre.C.*, preoral cavity; *P.S.G.*, principal salivary gland; *R.*, rectum; *R.O.*, reproductive organ; *R.P.*, rectal papilla; *Sal.D.*, salivary duct; *S.G.*, salivary gland; *Sal.P.*, salivary pump; *S.R.*, salivary reservoir; *St.*, stomach; *T.*, testis; *V.D.*, vas deferens. (Top figure adapted from Miall; middle figure adapted after Elson; and lower figure, Herms.)

mosquitoes, etc.) are characteristically legless and frequently have an undeveloped or poorly developed head, the variations within the order are considerable. *Maggots* of muscoid flies, for example, are usually smooth, with the body tapering to the apparently headless anterior end, which bears hooklike mouth parts; while the larvae (*wrigglers*) of mosquitoes have a well-sclerotized, freely moving, conspicuous head with faceted eyes, and both the head and body bear many hairs and setae. The larvae of fleas (Siphonaptera) are also legless; the well-sclerotized head is well developed; and each of the thoracic and abdominal segments is well armed with a band of bristles. The larvae of beetles (order Coleoptera) commonly have three pairs of legs on the thorax only; the head is well developed; the body may be hairy, spiny, or naked. The larvae of moths and butterflies (order Lepidoptera) have three pairs of thoracic legs and two to five pairs of abdominal prolegs; the head is prominent, and the mouth parts are usually well developed and mandibulate; they are called *caterpillars* and are hairy, spiny, or naked. The larvae of bees, ants, and wasps (order Hymenoptera) are without legs (apodous); the head is more or less well developed; the body is usually fairly smooth and gourd-shaped.

Insect Classification. The medical entomologist must be able to place the insect at hand correctly in at least its proper order and family; in the case of insects of importance in medical entomology he should be able to run most specimens down to species with the aid of keys, illustrations, and descriptions. To determine the order to which an insect belongs one need usually know only the venation and structure of the wings, if present, the type of mouth parts, the type of metamorphosis, and sometimes one or two other structural characters. Unfortunately, the parasitic forms have undergone many modifications, such as reduction or loss of wings and great alteration in form, but generally the mouth parts, coupled with a salient character or two, will serve as a ready means of crude identification. Before passing to a list of the orders of insects of medical importance, the usual bases for classification may be tabulated, viz.:

1. Wings: (a) presence or absence; (b) form; (c) structure; (d) venation.
2. Mouth parts: (a) biting (mandibulate); (b) sucking (haustellate) (which may be of several subtypes).
3. Metamorphosis: (a) primitive (lacking); (b) simple (incomplete); (c) complex (complete).
4. Special characteristics, such as the modification of the ovipositor in the Hymenoptera.

The Orders of Insects. The student may be confused by the fact that different authorities recognize different numbers of insect orders and that, consequently, the assignment of an insect to a particular order may vary with the authority, e.g., some workers consider the cockroaches as constituting a separate order, the Blattaria, whereas others consider them a part of the Orthoptera. The following list includes only those insects that are of some known medical importance. For a more complete listing of insect orders and a key to separate them, the student is referred to any good textbook of general entomology or to Brues, Melander, and Carpenter's *Classification of Insects*.[1]

1. Order Collembola (Col-lem'bo-la) (*colla,* glue, *embolos,* wedge or peg): springtails, snowfleas. Biting mouth parts, withdrawn into the head; primitive metamorphosis; wingless. These animals have a number of peculiarities: the abdomen is only six-segmented, without external genitalia; and appendages of a peculiar nature are present on the first, third, and fourth abdominal segments in the form of a collophore, a catch, and a spring, respectively. There is a strong tendency to consider the Collembola a class of Arthropoda separate from the insects.

2. Order Blattaria (Blat-tar'ia) (*blatta,* insect that shuns the light): cockroaches. Fore wings modified into tegmina, often shortened; biting mouth parts; simple metamorphosis. The body is rather flattened dorsoventrally, and the pronotum extends forward over the head, usually concealing it from the dorsal view; the legs are fitted for running, the hind femora not being thickened as they are in the jumping Orthoptera.

3. Order Dermaptera (Der-map'ter-a) (*derma,* skin; *ptera,* wings): earwigs. Fore wings modified into tegmina, often shortened; biting mouth parts; simple metamorphosis. The abdomen terminates in a pair of pincerlike cerci. Earwigs may be included among insects of sanitary importance because of their nuisance value.

4. Order Mallophaga (Mal-loph'a-ga) (*mallos,* a lock of wool; *phagein,* to eat): bird lice, biting lice. Wingless; biting mouth parts; simple metamorphosis.

5. Order Ephemeroptera (Eph-em'er-op'ter-a) (*ephemeros,* living but a day; *ptera,* wings): mayflies, dayflies. Two, sometimes one, pair of triangularly shaped, net-veined, membranous wings; vestigial mouth parts; metamorphosis simple, but involving a preadult, fully-winged form (subimago) found only in insects of this order.

6. Order Thysanoptera (Thy'san-op'ter-a) (*thysanos,* fringe; *ptera,* wings): thrips. Wingless or with very narrow, elongated wings, fringed posteriorly with long hairs, and almost without veins; rasping-sucking mouth parts; simple metamorphosis.

7. Order Anoplura (An'o-plu'ra) (*anoplos,* unarmed; *oura,* tail): true lice, sucking lice. Wingless; piercing-sucking mouth parts; simple metamorphosis.

8. Order Hemiptera (He-mip'ter-a) (*hemi,* half; *ptera,* wings): bugs, cicadas, treehoppers, leafhoppers, aphids, scale insects, etc. Wings two pairs (rarely one) or none, either both membranous (Homoptera) or the fore pair thickened only on the basal half (Heteroptera); piercing-sucking mouth parts; simple metamorphosis.

9. Order Trichoptera (Tri-chop'ter-a) (*thrix,* hair; *ptera,* wings): caddisflies. Two pairs of mothlike wings, clothed with hairs (not with scales, as in the moths); biting, though often vestigial, mouth parts; complex metamorphosis.

10. Order Coleoptera (Col'e-op'ter-a) (*coleos,* sheath; *ptera,* wings): beetles, weevils. Fore wings thickened into elytra and concealing the hind wings when at rest; biting mouth parts; complex metamorphosis.

11. Order Diptera (Dip'ter-a) (*dis,* two; *ptera,* wings): flies, gnats, mosquitoes. One pair of wings, the hind pair being replaced by knoblike structures known as halteres; sucking mouth parts; complex metamorphosis.

12. Order Hymenoptera (Hy'men-op'ter-a) (*hymen,* a membrane; *ptera* wings): bees, wasps, ants, sawflies, horntails, etc. Two pairs of membranous wings (sometimes lacking), the anterior pair the larger; chewing or lapping-sucking mouth parts; complex metamorphosis.

13. Order Siphonaptera (Si'phon-ap'ter-a) (*siphon,* a tube; *aptera,* wingless): fleas. Wingless; piercing-sucking mouth parts; complex metamorphosis. Body flattened laterally; hind legs enlarged, fitted for jumping.

14. Order Lepidoptera (Lep'-i-dop'ter-a) (*lepidos,* scale; *ptera,* wings): moths, butterflies. Two pairs of wings (rarely absent), clothed with scales; sucking (siphoning) mouth parts; complex metamorphosis.

THE ARACHNIDA

The Arachnida. The class Arachnida includes the ticks, mites, spiders, scorpions, and related forms. Among the species of arachnids are some of the most important parasites and vectors of disease of man and beast, such as the ticks which carry spotted fever and relapsing fever of man, and Texas cattle fever and bovine anaplasmosis. Parasitic mites cause acariasis, often serious, such as mange, scabies, and various forms of itch, and may, like the ticks, serve as vectors of disease, particularly scrub typhus.

The more important arachnids lack distinct segmentation of the body, e.g., ticks, mites, and spiders; while scorpions, pseudoscorpions, and a few others are clearly segmented. The body is divided into two parts (Fig. 7): first the *cephalothorax* (prosoma) composed of combined head and thorax, and second the *abdomen* (opisthosoma). In the ticks and mites there is a strong fusion of the cephalothorax and the abdomen so that the body becomes saclike in form.

Adult arachnids with few exceptions (such as the eriophyid mites, in which only the first two pairs of legs are developed) have four pairs of legs, though the larvae of ticks and most mites have but three pairs. In spiders there is a pair of *pedipalpi* which may resemble an additional pair of legs; in the scorpions, whipscorpions, and pseudoscorpions these are chelate (that is, the terminal segment of the limb is opposed to the pre-

or absence of the *pedicle;* presence or absence of *telson; chelicerae,* large or small; *pedipalpi,* chelate or unchelate; location and form of *spiracles.*

KEY TO THE TERRESTRIAL ORDERS OF THE CLASS ARACHNIDA

1. Abdomen distinctly segmented 2
   Abdomen with segmentation obscured 7
2. Abdomen with taillike prolongation 3
   Abdomen without taillike prolongation 4
3. Tail stoutly armed with a sting at end .... *Scorpionida* (scorpions)
   Tail slender, without sting .... *Pedipalpida* (whipscorpions)
4. Pedipalpi chelate .... *Chelonethida* (pseudoscorpions)
   Pedipalpi not chelate 5
5. Abdomen constricted at base and narrowly joined to the cephalothorax.... .... *Phrynichida* (tail-less whipscorpions)
   Abdomen not constricted at base and broadly joined to cephalothorax 6
6. Legs very long and slender, body hairless, whole body fused together.... .... *Phalangida* (harvestmen)
   Legs moderate, body hairy, appearing to be in three divisions......... .... *Solpugida* (sunspiders)
7. Abdomen constricted at base and joined to cephalothorax by a narrow stalk (pedicel) .... *Araneida* (spiders)
   Abdomen fused with cephalothorax .... *Acarina* (ticks and mites)

REFERENCES

1. Brues, Charles T.; Melander, A. L.; and Carpenter, Frank M.; 1954. *Classification of Inects.* Cambridge, Massachuetts: Museum of Comparative Zoology, in Bull., vol. 108. 917 pp.

2. Cloudsley-Thompson, J. L., 1958. *Spiders, Scorpions, Centipedes and Mites.* New York: Pergamon Press. xiv + 228 pp.

3. Savory, Theodore H., 1935. *The Arachnida.* London: Edward Arnold & Co. 218 pp.

4. Snodgrass, R. E., 1935. *Principles of Insect Morphology.* New York: McGraw-Hill Book Co., Inc. 667 pp.

Chapter 5

INSECT AND ARACHNID MOUTH PARTS

Importance of Mouth Parts. No doubt all insects possessing mouth parts capable of piercing the skin of man and beast may be regarded with some suspicion by the medical entomologist as being potential vectors of blood-inhabiting microparasites, even though the bloodsucking habit may not normally prevail. The nonpiercing insects manifestly cannot be responsible for infections introduced directly into the circulation, but they can be so involved through the natural orifices of the body or through previously injured surfaces. Thus the house fly, although possessing nonpiercing mouth parts, is recognized as one of the vectors of *Trypanosoma hippicum* Darling, a blood-inhabiting parasite and the causal organism of murrina of horses and mules. It carries the parasites on its proboscis, which becomes contaminated while it is feeding from bleeding wounds caused by stable flies (*Stomoxys*) or other means and conveys the organisms thence to open wounds on healthy animals.

The student of arthropods in relation to disease must have a thorough knowledge of their mouth parts and feeding habits for at least two reasons: first, that he may know how the pathogenic organisms are acquired as well as transmitted and, secondly, that he may know, if occasion requires, what control measures may be best employed. The medical entomologist will soon find that a knowledge of the feeding habits of the adult insect alone is inadequate and that he must be familiar with the feeding habits of the insect in all stages of its life cycle. The larvae of many of the sucking insects have mandibulate (biting-chewing) mouth parts. The biting mouth parts of the wormlike flea larva enable it to ingest particles of excrement or other matter in which eggs of the double-pored dog tapeworm occur, and it may thus become an intermediate host of this worm, passing the infection on to the adult flea which, if ingested by a suitable host, becomes the agent of infection. Insects with complete metamorphosis frequently change from chewing mouth parts in the larval stage to the sucking type in the adult. Most insects with simple metamorphosis, like the cockroaches and bugs, have the same general type of mouth parts in all active stages of development, although in the aquatic groups, the mouth parts may change considerably from the larval type (dragonflies and damselflies), or become vestigial in the adult (mayflies). Snodgrass[2] describes in great detail the feeding apparatus of biting and sucking insects affecting man and animals.

Classification of Mouth Parts. All adult insect mouth parts, however highly specialized, may be traced to the simple primitive type still existing with some modification in the cockroach. Insect mouth parts are commonly divided into two general classes: (1) mandibulate, i.e., biting and chewing, as in the cockroaches, grasshoppers, and beetles; and (2) haustellate, i.e., sucking, as in the bugs, flies, butterflies, and moths. This classification is far from satisfactory for use in the field of medical entomology. For example, the house fly, *Musca domestica* Linnaeus, and the stable fly, *Stomoxys calcitrans* (Linnaeus), both possess haustellate mouth parts and belong to the same family of insects, Muscidae; hence, they are systematically closely related, yet are quite unrelated in their manner of disease transmission. By virtue of its efficient piercing proboscis the stable fly has the power to pierce the skin and suck blood, thus enabling it to become a direct infector; whereas the house fly, because of the structure of its proboscis and its inability to suck blood by piercing the skin, is only indirectly responsible for infection, i.e., it is more particularly a food contaminator.

Obviously insects could be grouped on the basis of mouth parts and feeding habits, into two simple divisions: (1) piercing, as in mosquitoes, and (2) nonpiercing, as in cockroaches. This, however, leaves much to be desired in the light of medical entomology; hence, the following grouping is suggested.

1. *Orthopteron type:* generalized mouth parts consisting of opposable jaws used in biting and chewing; upper and lower lips easily recognized. Orders Orthoptera, Blattaria, Dermaptera, Coleoptera, Isoptera, Odonata, Plecoptera, Mallophaga, Neuroptera, Trichoptera, Collembola, and others.

2. *Thysanopteron type:* mouth parts representing a transitional type, minute in size; approaching the biting form, more particularly rasping, but functioning as suctorial organs; the right mandible is greatly reduced or possibly even absent, causing a peculiar asymmetry shown in the drawing (Fig. 10). Order Thysanoptera.

3. *Hemipteron type:* mouth parts consisting of piercing-sucking organs, comprising four stylets closely ensheathed within the elongated labium, forming a three- or four-segmented proboscis. Order Hemiptera.

4. *Anopluran type:* mouth parts piercing-sucking, in a sac concealed within the head but evertible when functioning. Three stylets, i.e., one consisting of the pair of united maxillae, the other two consisting of the hypopharynx and labium; mandibles vestigial. Order Anoplura.

5. *Dipteron type:* suctorial organs, piercing in some, nonpiercing in others; no single representative is available to illustrate the entire group of Diptera, hence the following subtypes may be recognized.
   a. First subtype: mouth parts consisting of six stylets, loosely ensheathed within the labium; as in the mosquito.
   b. Second subtype: mouth parts consisting of six short bladelike structures used for piercing and cutting, all loosely ensheathed within the labium as in the horse fly.

c. Third subtype: piercing stylets reduced to two in number, closely ensheathed within the labium; as in the stable fly.
d. Fourth subtype: mouth parts consisting of a muscular proboscis, not suited for piercing; stylets rudimentary; as in the house fly.
e. Fifth subtype: mouth parts closely related to those of the third subtype, but the haustellum is fitted for piercing the skin; as in the louse fly.

6. *Siphonapteron type:* piercing-sucking, fully exposed mouth parts consisting of a pair of broad maxillary lobes bearing long palpi; two (paired) stylets, a pair of broad maxillary lacinae (lacinial blades), chief cutting organs commonly regarded as "mandibles"; a slender labium with parallel palpi, and a median unpaired stylet, the "epipharynx," the labrum is difficult to interpret (Snodgrass). Order Siphonaptera.
7. *Hymenopteron type:* mouth parts consisting of suctorial, lapping organs, mandibles specialized for portage, combat, and other nonfeeding purposes. Order Hymenoptera in part; bees, wasps, and ants.
8. *Lepidopteron type:* mouth parts consisting of a suctorial coiled tube. Order Lepidoptera.

MORPHOLOGY OF MOUTH PARTS

Orthopteron Type. To illustrate the orthopteron type of mouth structure either the grasshopper or the cockroach may be used. This type, the mandibulate or biting-chewing, is the generalized or primitive form and will serve as a basis for later comparisons and derivations. It is not directly of importance in medical entomology except as it furnishes a basis for a better understanding of the haustellate or sucking types.

If the head of a cockroach (Fig. 9) is viewed from the side and again from the front, the relative position of the separate parts will be better understood. Separating the individual parts, the following structures will be observed. In front, low down on the head, hangs the *labrum* or lip, easily lifted as one would raise a hinged lid, the hinge line being at the lower edge of the sclerite or plate, known as the *clypeus.*

The labrum functions as does the upper lip in higher animals, i.e., it draws the food toward the mandibles. In this the labrum is greatly aided by a rough structure called the *epipharynx,* which forms the inner lining of the labrum and clypeus. Because of the close association of these two structures, they are often referred to as a double organ, the *labrum-epipharynx.* Removing the labrum, a pair of heavy, opposable jaws, the *mandibles,* is exposed. These are biting structures par excellence. They are toothed and movable laterally. Dislodging the mandibles brings into view the pair of maxillae, or accessory jaws. These organs are known as *first maxillae.* They are composite structures separable into *cardo, stipes, lacinia, galea,* and *palpus,* which should be carefully observed, inasmuch as they undergo great

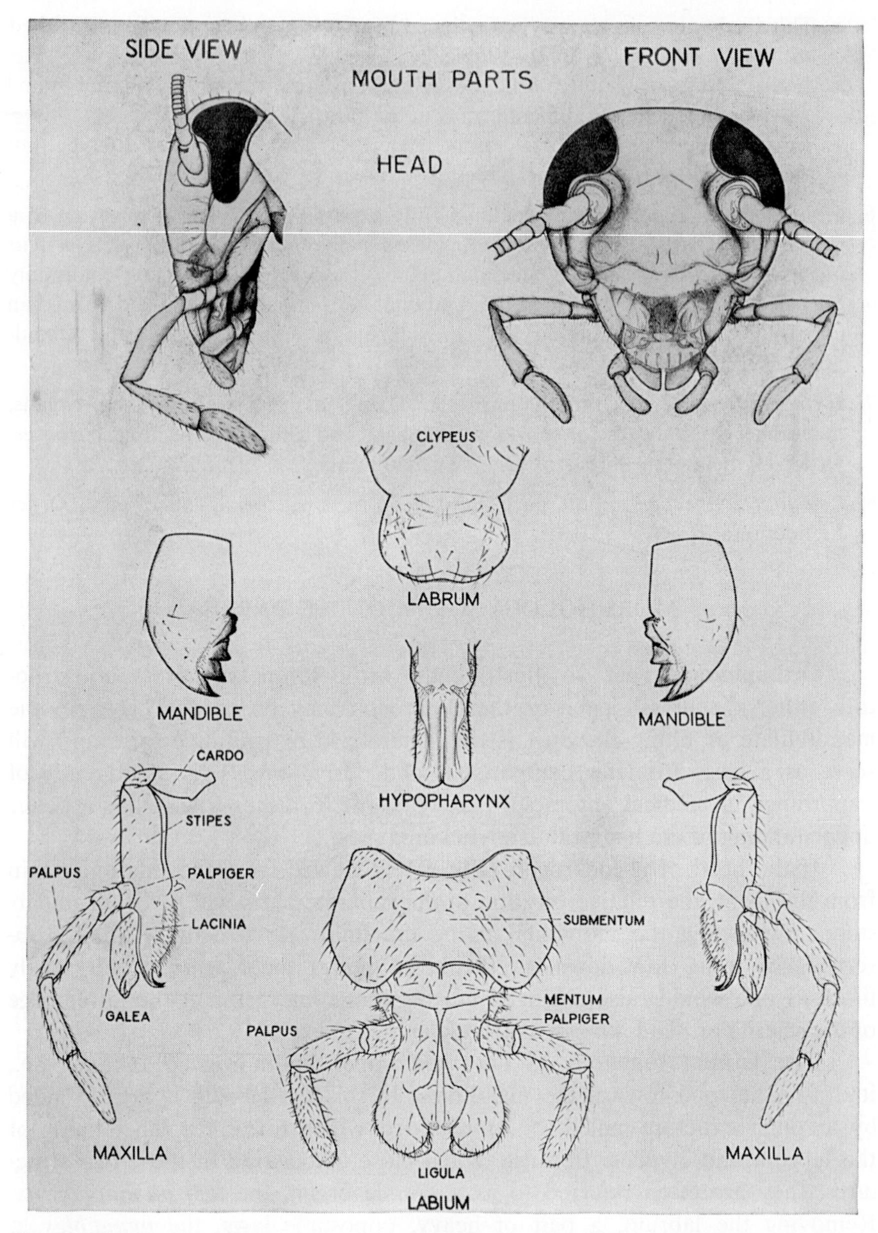

Fig. 9. Head and mouth parts of a cockroach. Orthopteron (mandibulate) type of mouth parts.

modification in the remaining types of mouth parts. The two supporting sclerites of the maxillae are *cardo* (basal) and *stipes* (the second), while the distal lobes are: (1) the *maxillary palpus* (a jointed structure); (2) the *galea* (median and fleshy); (3) the *lacinia* (inner and toothed), capable of aiding in comminuting food.

Underneath the maxillae and forming the floor of the mouth lies the lower lip or *labium,* a double structure frequently called the *second maxilla.* On the same plan as the maxillae, the labium consists of a basal sclerite, the *submentum,* followed by the *mentum,* upon which rest the *labial palpi* (a pair of outer, jointed structures to the right and left), and the *ligula* (a pair of straplike plates which together correspond to the upper lip). The labium is also subject to much modification in insects.

The fleshy organ still remaining in the mouth cavity after the parts just described have been removed is the tongue or *hypopharynx,* an organ of taste, comparable in a measure to the tongue of higher animals.

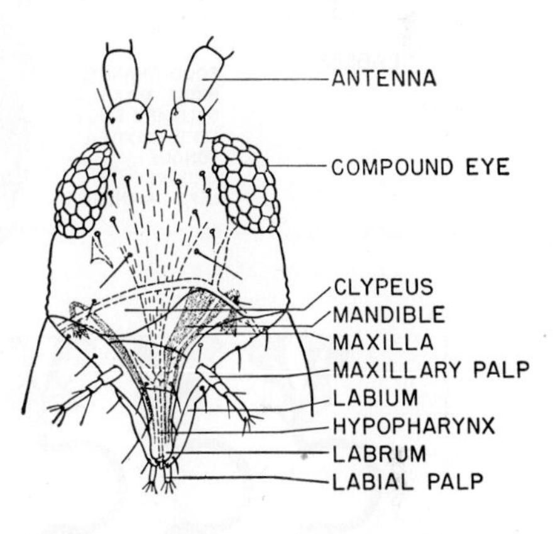

Fig. 10. Head and mouth parts of a thrips. Thysanopteron type. (Redrawn after Borden.)

The mandibles are most useful landmarks since they are almost universally present in insects, although in various degrees of development, from the strong mandibles of certain beetles (Lucanidae) to the vestigial structures of fleas (Siphonaptera). In the Hymenoptera, even though the order is largely haustellate, the mandibles are nevertheless important structures, serving, however, in the honey bee as wax implements and organs of defense, and in the ants as organs of portage and combat. In Hemiptera and many Diptera the mandibles are converted into piercing organs, while the maxillae are also greatly changed in form.

Thysanopteron Type. This type (Fig. 10) is interesting phylogenetically as a connecting link between the biting-chewing and piercing-sucking mouth parts. It is in the very minute thrips, order Thysanoptera, that we find this transitional type of mouth parts, biting in general structure, but sucking in function. Authors disagree as to the identity of the parts; some believe that the right mandible is reduced, while others consider it to be entirely wanting,

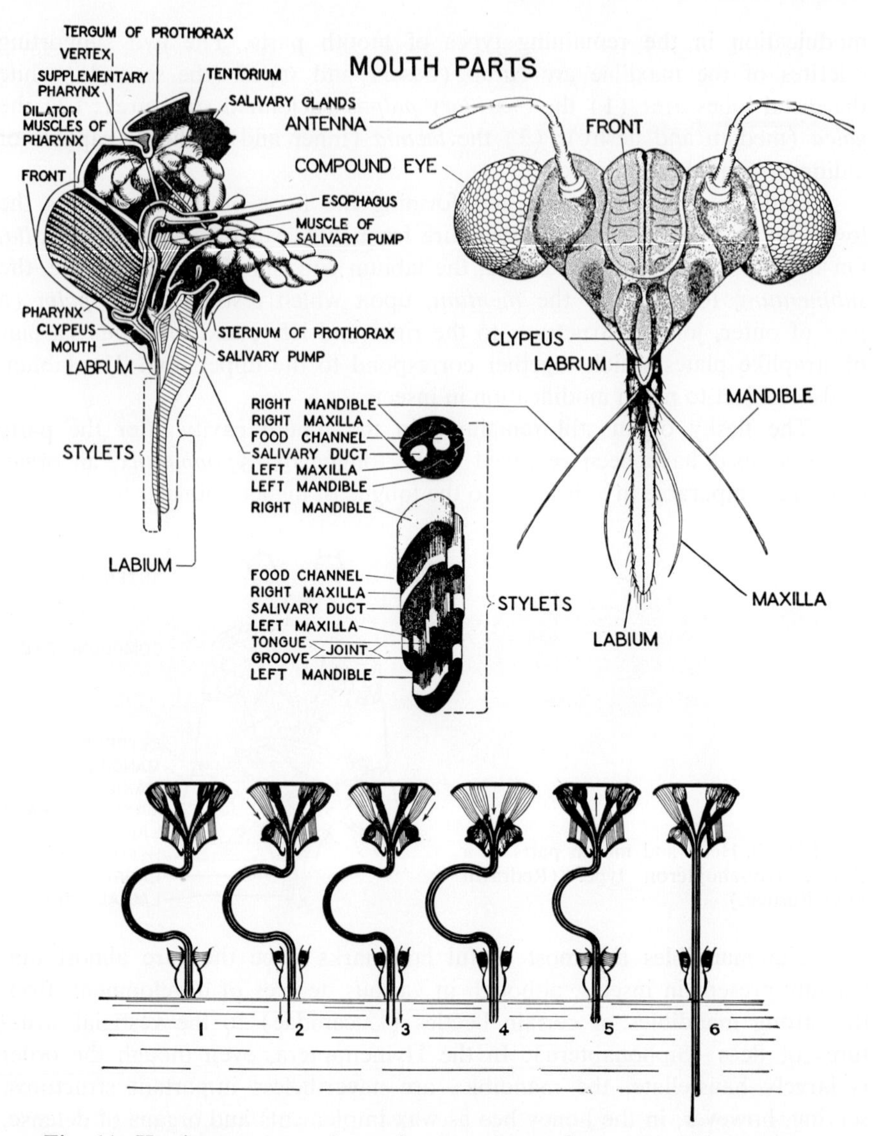

Fig. 11. Hemipteron type of mouth parts. (*Top*) Structure of bug mouth parts, with the piercing stylets (mandibles and maxillae) enclosed in a segmented sheath (mostly labium); (*bottom*) how the stylets are inserted into the tissues on which the bug is feeding. (Adapted after various authors.)

making the head and mouth parts asymmetrical. The left mandible, maxillae, and hypopharynx are elongate, suggesting the stylet of the piercing type, and adapted to move in and out through a circular opening at the apex of the head. No food channel is formed, but the sap from plants is lapped up as it exudes from the abraded surface.

Hemipteron Type. A very different sort of organ from those above described is found in the order Hemiptera (Fig. 11). Here the cylindrical labium forms a prominent beaklike proboscis which is usually three- or four- (rarely one- or two-)segmented and telescopic. It is devoid of palpi. The proboscis encloses a pair of *mandibles,* often terminal barbs, and a pair of *maxillae;* all four are styletlike and efficient piercing organs, the maxillae operating as a unit and the mandibles functioning separately. The maxillae are closely apposed, forming the food and salivary tubes, with the mandibles aiding in rigidity. The *labrum* is quite short and inconspicuous. The *hypopharynx* consists of a small complicated lobe at the base of the other mouth parts.

Anopluron Type. The mouth parts of the Anoplura (sucking lice) are distinctly piercing-sucking in function but lie in a sac concealed within the head (Fig. 12). The prestomal opening is situated at the extreme anterior portion of the tiny snoutlike proboscis and is encircled with a crown of minute sclerotized recurved retractile hooklets which serve as anchorage when everted. The eversible proboscis is said to be formed of the *labrum,* which is armed internally with the small recurved teeth just mentioned. The piercing apparatus (three stylets) lies within a long sac and consists of the united maxillae situated dorsally; the *hypopharynx* and the *labium,* both styletlike are attached posteriorly to the walls of the enclosing sac. The mandibles are vestigial. The apposed maxillae form the food duct, and the hypopharynx forms the salivary channel. In the act of biting, these parts are pushed forward into the skin by intricate muscular action when firm attachment has been made by means of the circlet of oral evertible teeth. Salivary secretion which acts as an anticoagulin is poured into the wound, and the cibarial and pharyngeal pumps draw blood into the pharynx and into the intestine of the louse.

Dipteron Type. This type is divided into five subtypes: (1) mosquito; (2) horse fly; (3) stable fly; (4) house fly; and (5) louse fly.

First Subtype, the Mosquito. A generalized type of dipteron mouth parts is found in the mosquito (Fig. 13); hence, the maximum number of stylets is present, loosely ensheathed within the elongated *labium,* the whole forming a prominent beak or proboscis. The identity of the six stylets is well established, and it is generally accepted that they represent the two *mandibles,* the two *maxillae* (distinctly serrated distally), the *hypopharynx,* and the *labrum-epipharynx.* The palpi are conspicuous structures in all mosquitoes. These represent the maxillary palpi of the cockroach, while the pair of flattened lobelike organs forming the distal portion of the proboscis are said to represent the *labial palpi* and are called the *labella.*

The mouth parts of the male mosquito are subject to considerable modification; reduction in size and strength of the mandibles and maxillae is pronounced. These differences often occur in other Diptera.

(*Text continued on p. 62.*)

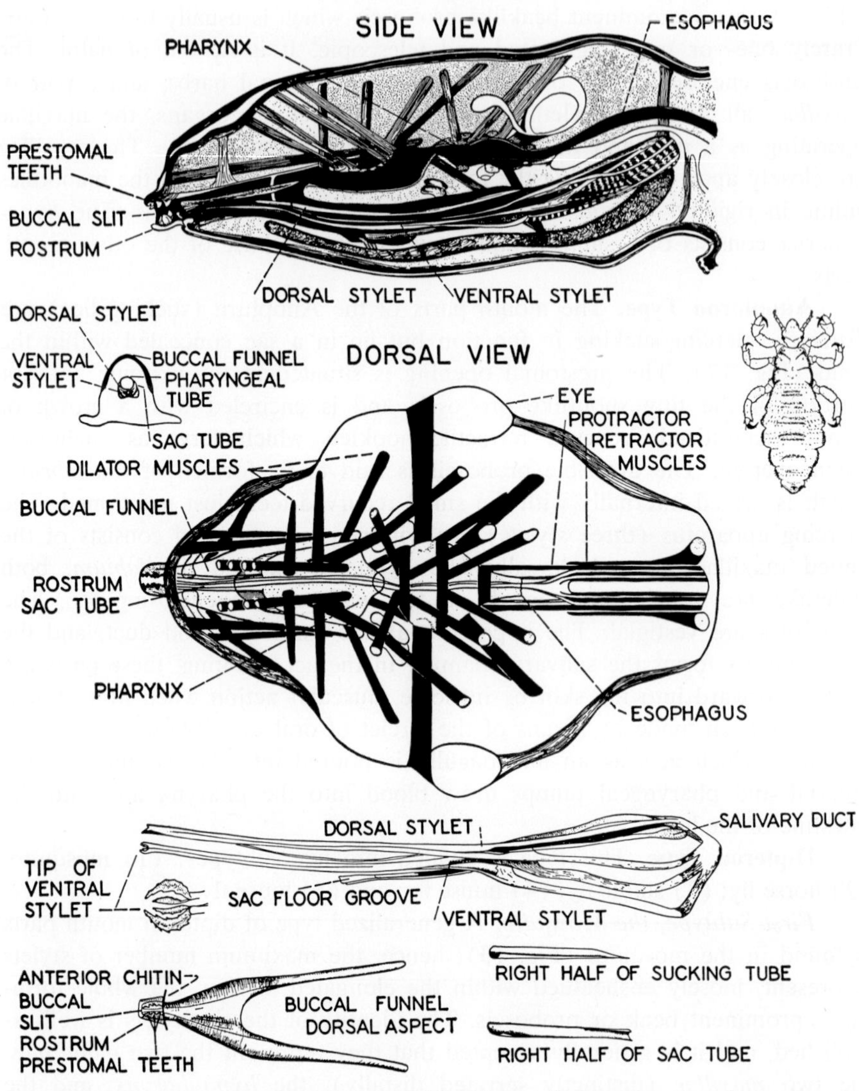

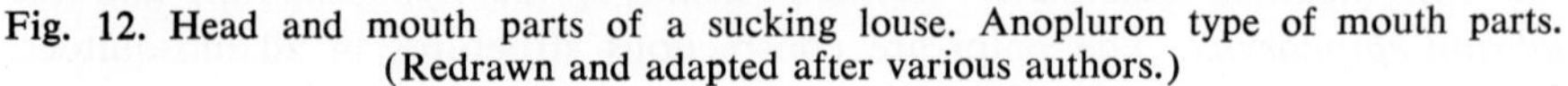

Fig. 12. Head and mouth parts of a sucking louse. Anopluron type of mouth parts. (Redrawn and adapted after various authors.)

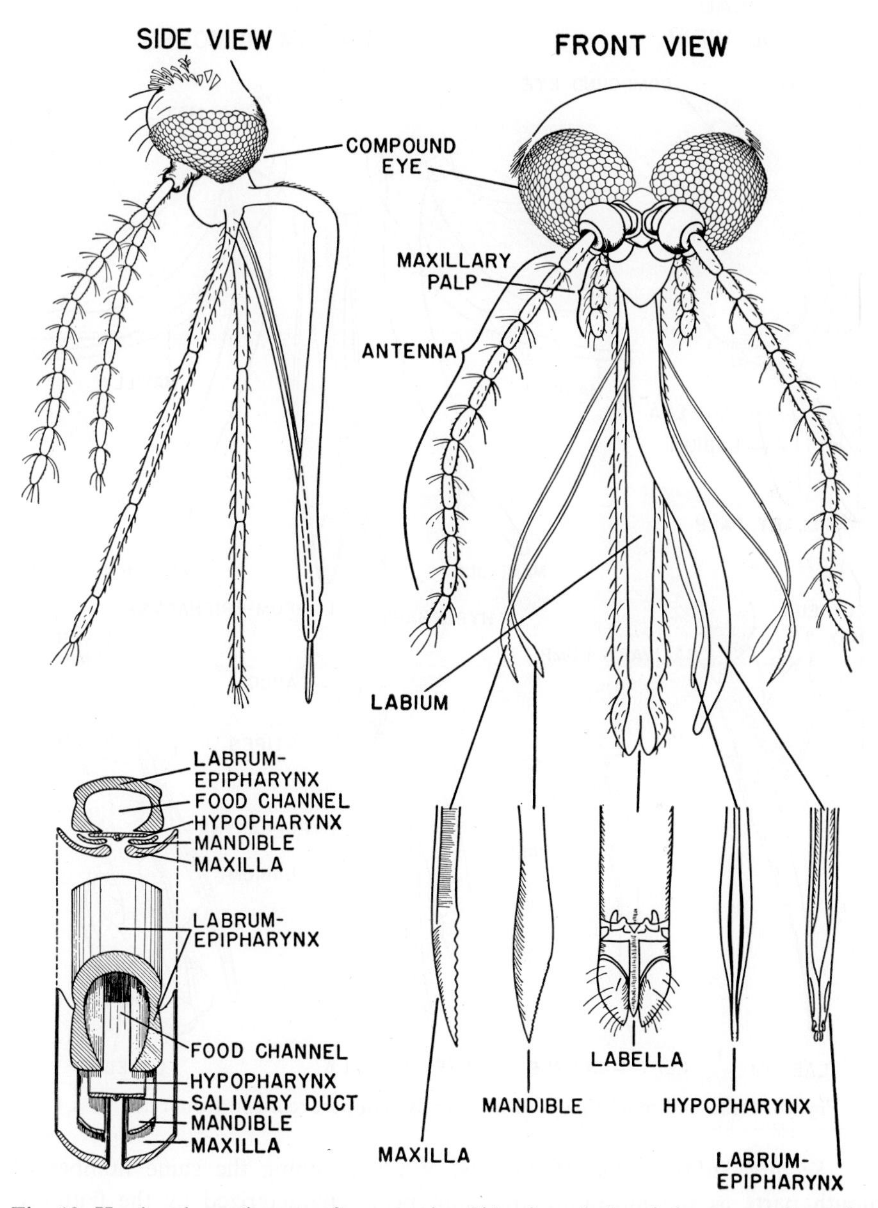

Fig. 13. Head and mouth parts of a mosquito. Side view of *Anopheles* sp. and front view of *Culex* sp., with piercing stylets exposed. (Redrawn and adapted from various authors.)

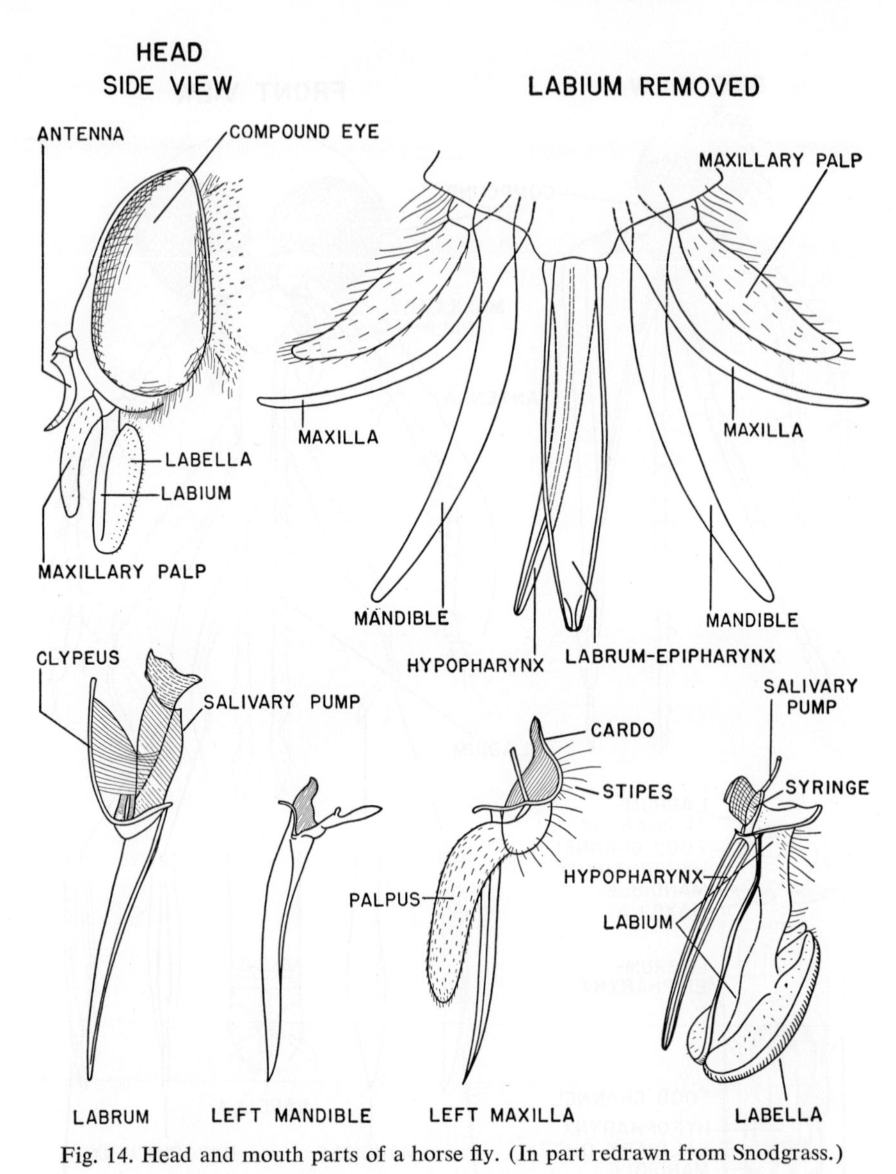

Fig. 14. Head and mouth parts of a horse fly. (In part redrawn from Snodgrass.)

Second Subtype, the Horse Fly. While retaining the same number of mouth parts as the mosquito, this subtype is characterized by the flattened bladelike condition of the stylets (Fig. 14). That these stylets serve as cutting organs is evidenced by the quantity of blood usually drawn by the "bite" of a horse fly, especially one of the larger species, such as the black horse fly, *Tabanus atratus* Fabricius. The *labium* is the conspicuous median portion loosely ensheathing the blades and terminating in a pair of large lobes, the *labella.* The mandibles, movable transversely, are distinctly flattened and saberlike, while the *maxillae* are narrower and provided with conspicuous *palpi.* The *hypopharynx* and *labrum-epipharynx* are both lancetlike. In the males these piercing parts are very weakly developed.

Third Subtype, the Stable Fly. This subtype (Fig. 15) is represented by a group of flies in which the mouth parts are distinctly specialized for piercing and show, together with the next subtype, to what extent these structures may become modified within the same family of insects.

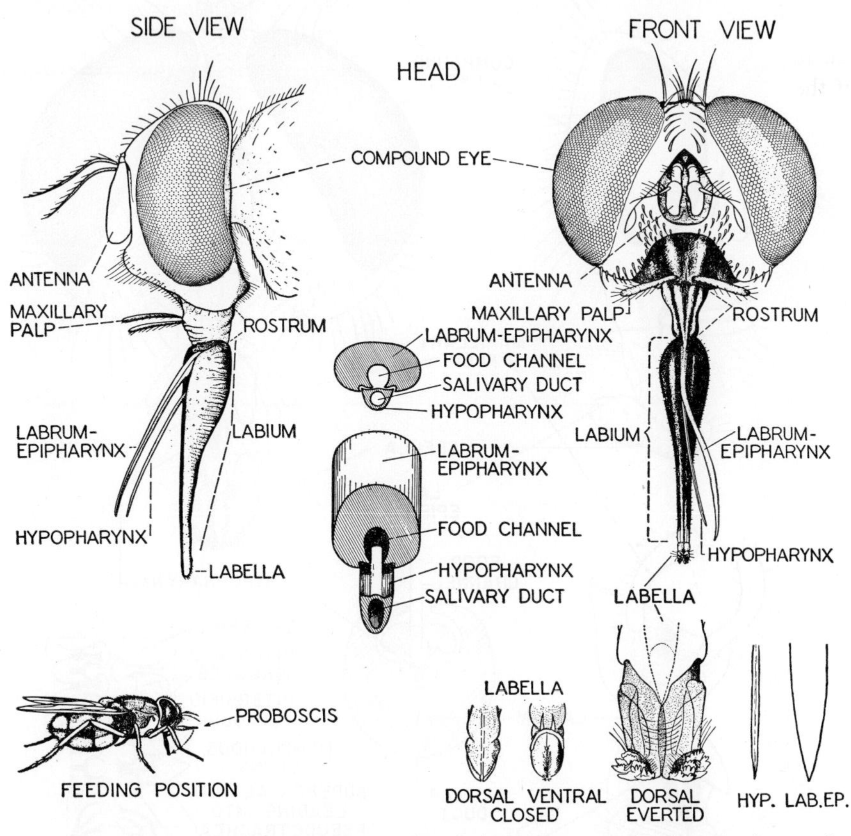

Fig. 15. Head and mouth parts of a stable fly. (Redrawn and adapted after various authors.)

The proboscis at rest is carried at the position of a bayonet at charge and is therefore provided with a prominent muscular elbow or knee. This conspicuous organ (the proboscis) is the *labium* terminating in the *labella,* which are provided with a complex series of rasping denticles. It is forced into the flesh of the victim by a strong thrust of the head and body. Within the folds of the labium, and easily removable through the upper groove, lie two stylets: the *labrum,* the uppermost and heavier, and the *hypopharynx,* a lower and weaker one, the two forming a sucking tube supported within the folds of the labium. The maxillary palpi are located at the proximal end of the proboscis.

Fourth Subtype, the House Fly. Here (Fig. 16) the prominent fleshy proboscis consists mainly of the *labium,* which terminates in a pair of corru-

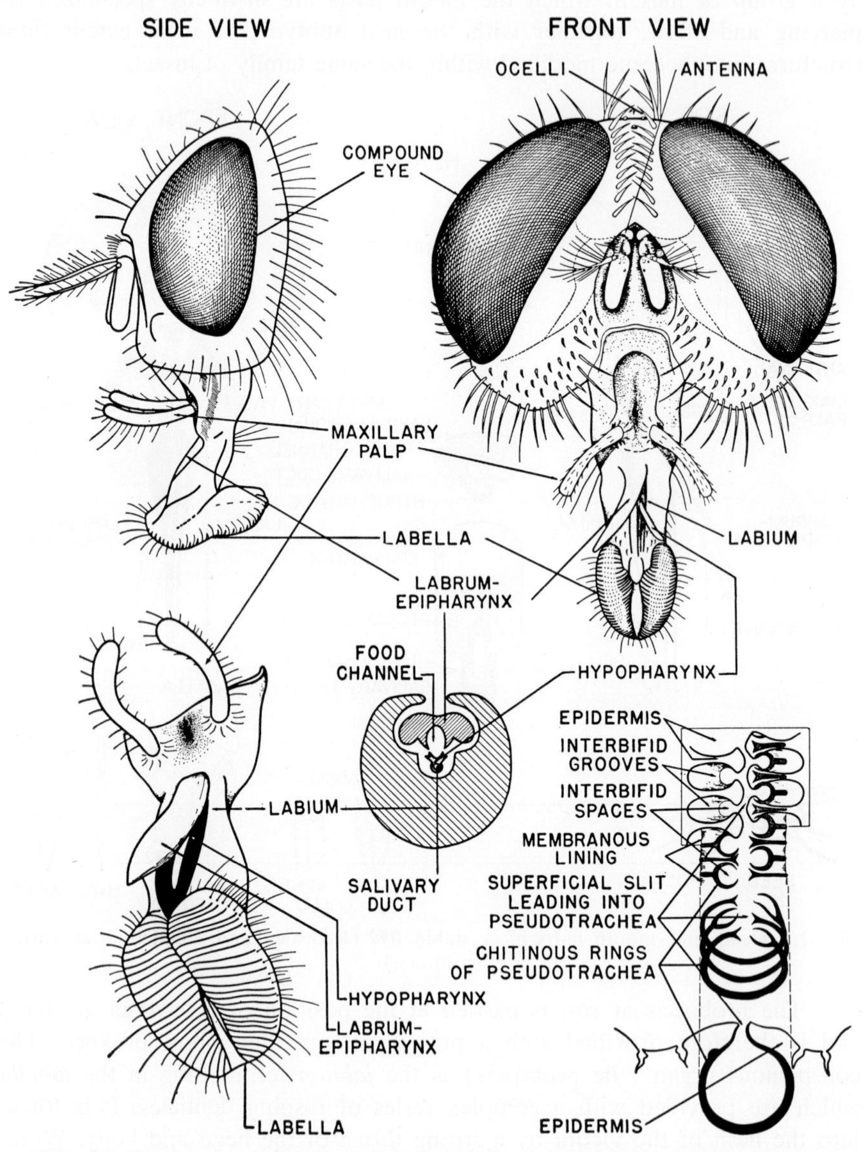

Fig. 16. Head and mouth parts of the house fly. Lower right hand figure shows detailed cross section of a pseudotrachea in the labella. (Redrawn and adapted after various authors.)

gated rasping organs, the *labella,* and is attached in elbowlike form to the elongated head. The entire structure is highly muscular, and may be either protruded in feeding or partially withdrawn while at rest. Lying on top of the grooved labium is the inconspicuous spadelike *labrum,* which forms, with the hypopharynx, a sucking tube, supported by the labium, which also encloses the salivary canal. By an examination of the labrum it will be seen that this forms a sort of convex covering to the concaved hypopharynx, thus giving rise to a food tube. The maxillae have evidently become fused with

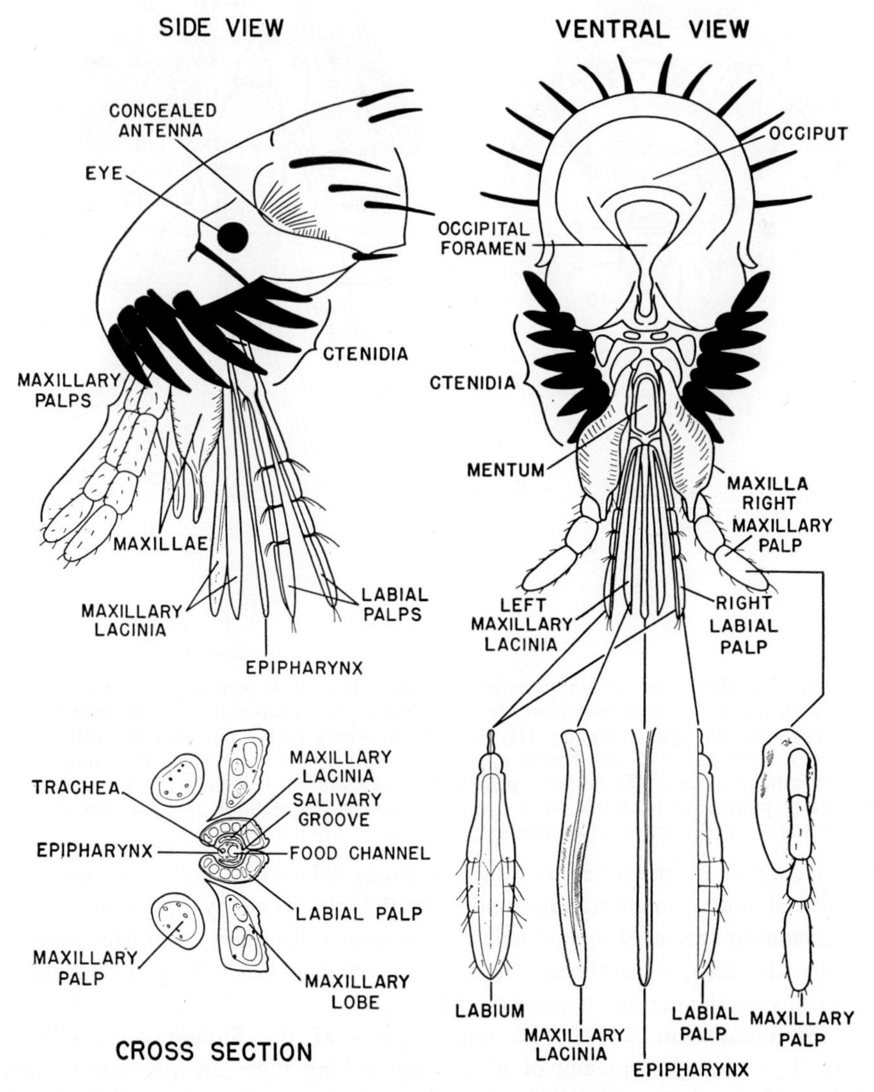

Fig. 17. Head and mouth parts of a flea. (Redrawn and adapted after various authors.)

the fleshy elbow of the proboscis, and only the prominent *maxillary palpi* remain.

Fifth Subtype, the Louse Fly. The louse flies, members of the family Hippoboscidae, have mouth parts closely related to those of the third subtype, the stable fly; the characteristic tubular or cylindrical haustellum is adapted for penetration into the skin of the host. The *labrum-epipharynx* is

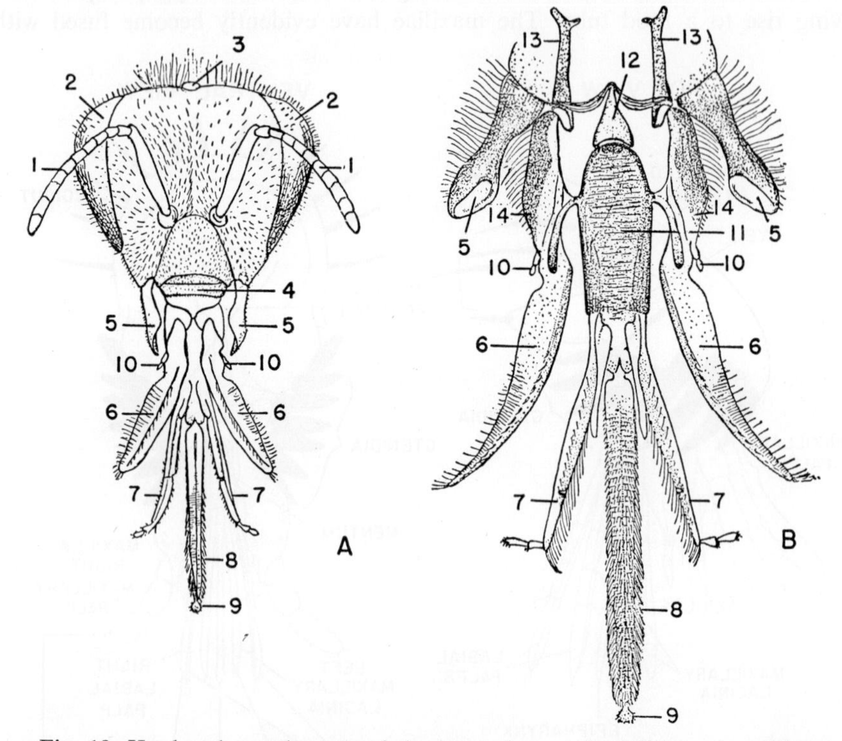

Fig. 18. Head and mouth parts of the honey bee, *Apis mellifera.* A sucking type of mouth parts is developed, but the mandibles are functional as such, being used chiefly for portage and modeling. (Hymenopteron type.) (*A*) Front view of head showing: (1) antennae; (2) compound eyes; (3) simple eye; (4) labrum; (5) mandibles; (6) maxillae (galea); (7) labium (palpi only); (8) labium (glossa); (9) bouton; (10) maxillary palpus. (*B*) Mouth parts in detail, showing in addition to structures already labeled: (11) prementum; (12) mentum; (13) cardo; (14) stipes.

stylet-shaped; its proximal portion is strongly sclerotized and rigid, whereas the distal end is membranous and very flexible.[1] The hypopharynx in the two common species, *Pseudolynchia canariensis* (Macquart) and *Melophagus ovinus* Linnaeus, is nearly as long as the combined haustellum and labellum and is a very slender and hyaline mouth part.

Siphonapteron Type. The mouth parts of the Siphonaptera (fleas) (Fig. 17), though typically of a piercing-sucking type, are peculiar to this order of insects. The broad *maxillary lobes* bearing long palpi are conspicuous landmarks; the other organ (slender) bearing long parallel palpi is the *labium.* The principal bladelike piercing organs are a pair of independently movable structures commonly referred to as mandibles, but are said to be maxillary laciniae by Snodgrass and others. The mandibles are believed to be rudimentary in fleas. The median stylet (unpaired) is said to be the *epipharynx,* not the labrum of many authors, the labrum being difficult to demonstrate. The epipharynx is said to be closely embraced by the lacinial blades. The three stylets (a pair of maxillary laciniae and the epipharynx) are held in the channel by the labium. The labium is rudimentary, and the existence of a hypopharynx is not demonstrable. The wound is made by the protraction and retraction of the maxillary laciniae. As soon as the blood begins to flow, it is drawn up into the pharynx by the action of both the cibarial and the pharyngeal pumps.

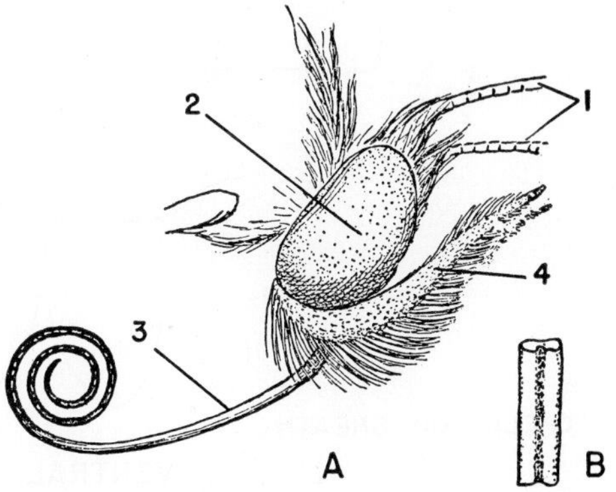

Fig. 19. Head and mouth parts of a butterfly (*Vanessa* sp.). (*A*) Side view: suctorial coiled tube, Lepidopteron type. (1) Antennae; (2) compound eye; (3) proboscis consisting only of galeae; (4) labial palpus. (*B*) Section of proboscis showing double nature.

Hymenopteron Type. In this type the two general classes of mouth structures, the *mandibulate* and *haustellate,* find full development in the same species, though the mandibles are not involved in the feeding process. The honey bee (Fig. 18) serves as a representative species. The *labrum* is narrow and quite simple; the *mandibles* are easily distinguishable and are useful wax implements. In ants the mandibles are highly efficient organs of portage and weapons of defense. The *maxillae* form the lateral conspicuous wings of the suctorial parts; the *lacinia* and *galea* are fused, and the *maxillary palpi* are minute. The *labium* is represented by the long structures to the right and left of the middle tube, which is probably the *hypopharynx.* The hypopharynx terminates in the spoonlike *labellum* or bouton which completes the lapping character of the subtype.

Lepidopteron Type. This type, represented by the commoner butterflies and moths, is typically a coiled, sucking tube capable of great elongation. It functions as a siphoning type. Taking the cabbage butterfly, *Pieris rapae* (Linnaeus), as an example (Fig. 19), the *labrum* is seen to be greatly reduced, and the mandibles are absent. (These may be weakly present in the lower Lepidoptera). The maxillae are apparently represented only by the galeae, which by close approximation of their inner grooved surfaces form the long, coiled proboscis. The double structure of the proboscis can be easily demonstrated by manipulation. The labium is represented by the *labial palpi*.

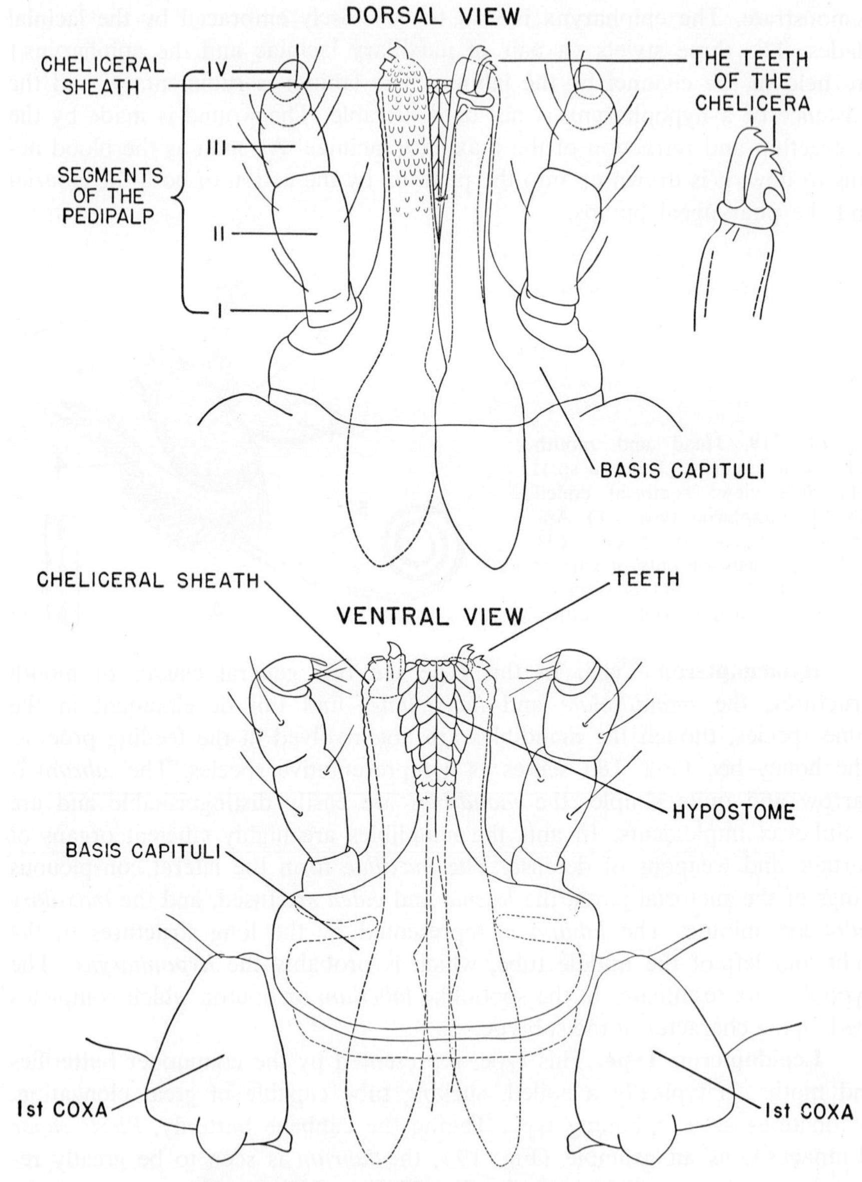

Fig. 20. Tick, capitulum; showing mouth parts.

Arachnid Mouth Parts. In his excellent study of the feeding organs of Arachnida, Snodgrass[3] points out that arachnids come from an ancestral line that never acquired organs for mastication, and even today have no true jaws, hence are forced to subsist on liquids. A liquid diet requires an ingestion pump, and with all arachnids a highly developed sucking apparatus constitutes the essential part of the feeding mechanism. The *chelicerae* (a pair) are the first postoral appendages of the arachnid (see Chapter 19), and while functioning more or less as "jaws" they are not homologous with the mandibles of insects; they are used for grasping, holding, tearing, crushing, or piercing. The leglike *pedipalps* are the second postoral appendages of the Arachnida and are the homologs of the mandibles of mandibulate arthropods (Snodgrass). These organs are modified in various ways, functioning as organs of prehension, protection, and, in male spiders, as sperm-carrying organs. In the scorpions the pedipalps are chelate and serve for catching, holding, and crushing the prey.

According to Snodgrass the only features of the acarine (tick and mite) mouth parts that can not be homologized with structures generally present in other Arachnida are the variously developed appendicular lobes or processes often associated with the distal part of the hypostome (Fig. 20). Also among the trombidiform mites the chelicerae become progressively adapted for piercing by a transformation of the movable digits into hooks or stylets.

REFERENCES

1. Jobling, B., 1926. "A comparative study of the structure of the head and mouth parts in the Hippoboscidae (Diptera Pupipara)," *Parasitology,* **18:**319–49.

2. Snodgrass, R. E., 1944. *The Feeding Apparatus of Biting and Sucking Insects Affecting Man and Animals.* Smithsonian Misc. Coll., vol. 4, no. 7 (Publ. no. 3773). Washington, D. C.: Smithsonian Inst. 113 pp.

3. Snodgrass, R. E., 1948. *The Feeding Organs of Arachnida, Including Mites and Ticks.* Smithsonian Misc. Coll., vol. 110, no. 10. Washington, D. C.: Smithsonian Inst. (Publ. no. 3944). 93 pp. (29 figs.).

Chapter 6

COCKROACHES AND BEETLES

COCKROACHES

Order Blattaria

Modern cockroaches have changed but little in general structure since upper Carboniferous times, some 250,000,000 years ago, when, as indicated by the coal beds of that period, they occurred abundantly in swamps. Cockroaches are usually flattened dorsoventrally with smooth (sometimes pilose) tough integument, varying in color from chestnut-brown to black in the more pestiferous house-invading species, but frequently green, or orange, and other colors in tropical species. The head is decidedly flexed backward and downward when at rest. The prominent antennae are filiform and many segmented. There are two pairs of wings in most species; in some the wings are vestigial; in others, e.g., *Blatta orientalis* Linnaeus, they are well developed in the males and short in the females. The outer pair of wings (tegmina) is narrow, thick and leathery, while the inner pair is membranous and folds fanlike. While most cockroaches possess the power of flight, they are typically runners (cursorial) and can move swiftly by means of their long well-developed legs. They are highly gregarious and primarily nocturnal, but most cockroaches may be seen occasionally during the day. Metamorphosis is simple.

The name cockroach, supposedly derived from the Spanish name for the insect (*cucaracha*), is preferable to the commonly used "roach," which properly should be applied to certain species of cyprinid fishes.

Feeding Habits. The mouth parts of cockroaches are of the generalized biting-chewing type (orthopteron). These insects are omnivorous, feeding on a great variety of foods, with preferences for starchy and sugary materials. They will sip milk, nibble at cheese, meats, pastry, grain products, sugar, sweet chocolate—in fact, practically no edible material available for human consumption is exempt from attack by these vile insects which feed just as freely on book bindings, the sized inner lining of soles, dead insects, their own cast-off skins, and dead and crippled kin, fresh and dried blood, excrement, sputum, and the finger and toe nails of sleeping or comatose human beings. They feed principally at night; hence, many people live in ignorance of their disgusting and dangerous feeding habits.

Furthermore, cockroaches habitually disgorge portions of their partly digested food at intervals and drop their feces wherever they go. They also discharge a nauseous secretion both from the mouth and from glands opening on the body, imparting a persistent and typical "cockroach" odor to food and dishes with which they come in contact.

Identification of Cockroaches. The scope of this work requires only that the student have a means of identifying the common pest species of cockroaches; the vast number of nondomestic forms does not concern us. Rehn[13] has presented a key to the North American genera which, together with the study of Hebard,[5] will form a basis for a more serious study of the Nearctic forms. The following key is designed to separate the species that occur as pests, actual or potential, or as possible vectors of disease in temperate North America. Since pest cockroaches tend to become cosmopolitan, this key should serve to a limited extent for many other parts of the world, especially the temperate regions.

KEY TO THE COMMON PEST SPECIES OF COCKROACHES*

1. Middle and hind femora both with numerous strong spines along the ventral margins 2
   Middle and hind femora without strong spines along the ventral margins, except for a few distal spines 11
2. Front femur, on its ventral anterior margin, with a row of strong spines on its basal half or more and with two or three similar ones near the apex, the intervening ones being suddenly and distinctly much shorter and weaker, closely set, and dentate rather than spinelike.......... 3
   Front femur, on its ventral anterior margin, with a row of strong spines which are either of the same length and strength throughout or (except for a few near the apex) gradually decrease in length toward the apex 4
3. Ventroanterior margin of front femur with three long apical spines (the basal one much the shortest of the three); body length at least 11 mm, often much more; tegmina fully developed or lobate. *Parcoblatta spp.*
   Ventroanterior margin of front femur with two long apical spines; body length about 9 mm or less; tegmina fully developed, not lobate, but sometimes not covering all of abdomen (tegmina with numerous small spots on the veins) ....*Ectobius pallidus* (Olivier)
4. Comparatively large species, 18 mm or more in length; subgenital plate of female divided longitudinally, valvular 6
   Species smaller, less than 18 mm long; subgenital plate of female simple. 5
5. Pronotum with two conspicuous longitudinal dark bars on a pale background ....*Blattella germanica* (Linnaeus)
   Pronotum with disc dark brown, that color extending to both anterior and posterior margins, the lateral margins contrastingly pale; closed tegmina of both sexes appearing to have two transverse brown bars, some pale specimens showing the bars poorly.......... ....*Supella supellectilium* (Serville)

* This key has been prepared for this work with the aid of Dr. Ashley B. Gurney.

6. Tegmina of both sexes short, transversely truncate, touching or but narrowly separated (deep southeastern states) .... *Eurycotis floridana* (Walker)

   Tegmina fully developed or, if not, subtriangular, widely separated 7

7. Tegmina shortened, subtriangular and basal only in female, usually exposing about three to five abdominal segments in male; length normally not exceeding 27 mm; general color rather uniform, ranging from rich chestnut brown to blackish; arolium between claws very small (male) to vestigial (female) .... *Blatta orientalis* (Linnaeus)

   Tegmina fully developed, covering abdomen in both sexes; length usually exceeding 27 mm; color variable, either uniform or in a distinctive pattern; arolium well developed 8

8. Tegmen with a rather broad, long yellow vitta along the anterior margin at its base; pronotum with a complete yellow ring sharply contrasting in color with the dark central part and equally dark margin .... *Periplaneta australasiae* (Fabricius)

   Anterior margin of base of tegmen without a pale vitta and pronotum not so colored, its color pattern less definite 9

9. Pronotum and tegmina a deep mahogany brown, the pronotum darker than the tegmina and without pale markings; posterior margin of supra-anal plate of the male almost transverse, with a slight indentation at the middle .... *Periplaneta fuliginosa* (Serville)

   Pronotum and tegmina reddish brown, the former with pale (though sometimes indefinitely limited) markings 10

10. Last segment of cercus twice as long as wide; supra-anal plate of male with a deep, narrow, acute median emargination .... *Periplaneta americana* (Linnaeus)

    Last segment of cercus not twice as long as wide; supra-anal plate convex in male .... *Periplaneta brunnea* Burmeister

11. Very large cockroaches, usually 50 mm or more in length; arolia absent; pronotum subelliptical. Several species that are commonly introduced into the eastern United States; a common pest species of Cuba which also occurs in southern Florida is .... *Blaberus craniifer* Burmeister

    Medium-sized to large species: arolia present; pronotum more nearly transverse posteriorly or produced angularly in the middle of its posterior margin, not subelliptical 12

12. Large species, about 40 mm or more in length .... *Leucophaea maderae* (Fabricius)

    Medium sized species, less than 30 mm in length 13

13. Pronotum uniformly blackish except for narrow yellow band along anterior and lateral margins (which may be indistinctly interrupted anteriorly) .... *Pycnoscelus surinamensis* (Linnaeus)

    Pronotum pale with a narrow dark longitudinal submarginal band on each side and irregular brown blotches on the disc .... *Nauphoeta cinerea* (Olivier)

Species of Sanitary Importance. There are about 3500 species of cockroaches, constituting the family Blattidae (in the broad sense) of the order Orthoptera or, according to the interpretation of some specialists in the group, a separate order, the Blattaria. Cockroaches occur throughout the world but are largely tropical. World-wide distribution of certain species has been effected by maritime trading; holds of vessels, the galleys, and crew's sleeping quarters are often overrun with cockroaches. Only a very few (less

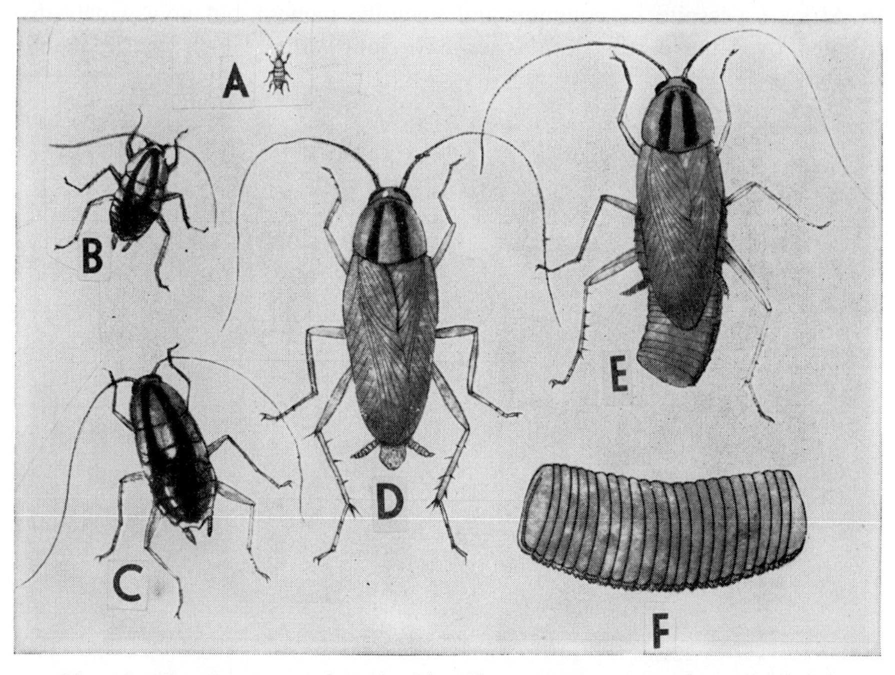

Fig. 21. The German cockroach, *Blattella germanica.* (*A*) First nymphal instar; (*B*) third instar; (*C*) fourth instar; (*D*) adult female; (*E*) female with egg case; (*F*) egg case. Egg case, × 3; others, × 4. (U.S.D.A. photograph.)

than 1 per cent of the known species) are troublesome to man. Among the better-known species invading the household, restaurants, hotel kitchens, grocery stores, etc., are the following.

Blattella germanica (Linnaeus), the German cockroach (also known as the "water bug" or "croton bug") (Fig. 21), is the best known and probably the most widely distributed species. It is a small species, native to Europe, measuring from 12 to 16 mm in length, and is pale yellowish-brown in color with two dark brown longitudinal stripes on the pronotum. Both sexes are fully winged. The female carries the egg capsule partly protruding from the tip of the abdomen until hatching time.

Blatta orientalis Linnaeus, the Oriental cockroach (also known as the "black beetle") (Fig. 22), is very much darker than the German cockroach. It is dark brown to black in color and is about 22 to 27 mm in length; the wings of the female are rudimentary, and those of the male do not quite reach the tip of the abdomen. Enormous colonies of the Oriental cockroach are often found in damp basements where food is available.

Periplaneta americana (Linnaeus), the American cockroach (Fig. 23), is a very large (30–40 mm in length) chestnut-brown species, native probably to Africa[12] (despite its common and scientific names) but now widely distributed over the earth. Both sexes have long wings which are frequently

Fig. 22. The Oriental cockroach, *Blatta orientalis,* female. × 1.3.
Fig. 23. The American cockroach, *Periplaneta americana.* × 1.3.

used in flying short distances. A related household pest in the eastern and southeastern states is *Periplaneta fuliginosa* (Serville), the smoky-brown cockroach. This species is smaller than *americana* and is dark brown to mahogany black in color.

Periplaneta australasiae (Fabricius), the Australian cockroach, is, despite its common name, probably not indigenous to Australia; like *americana* it is a cosmopolitan species. It is reddish brown in color, resembling *americana,* but has a strong straw-colored streak extending about one-third of the way down the outer margin of the wing covers (tegmina), as well as a yellow area around the margin of the pronotum, forming a double dark area on the dorsum. The wings are well developed in both sexes.

Supella supellectilium (Serville), the brown-banded (or tropical) cockroach (Fig. 24), resembles the German cockroach in appearance but is smaller (10–14 mm) and has two brown cross bands, one at the base of the wings and the other about $\frac{1}{16}$ of an inch farther back. The tegmina do not quite reach the tip of the abdomen in the female; the male has longer tegmina and is more slender. This difference in the appearance of the two sexes may delude the housewife into thinking that two species may be involved. Adults fly readily when disturbed. The species is decidedly a gregarious one. Unlike the German cockroach, which confines its activities to the kitchen or around water or heat pipes, the brown-banded cockroach hides in cupboards and pantries, invades all rooms of the house, and fre-

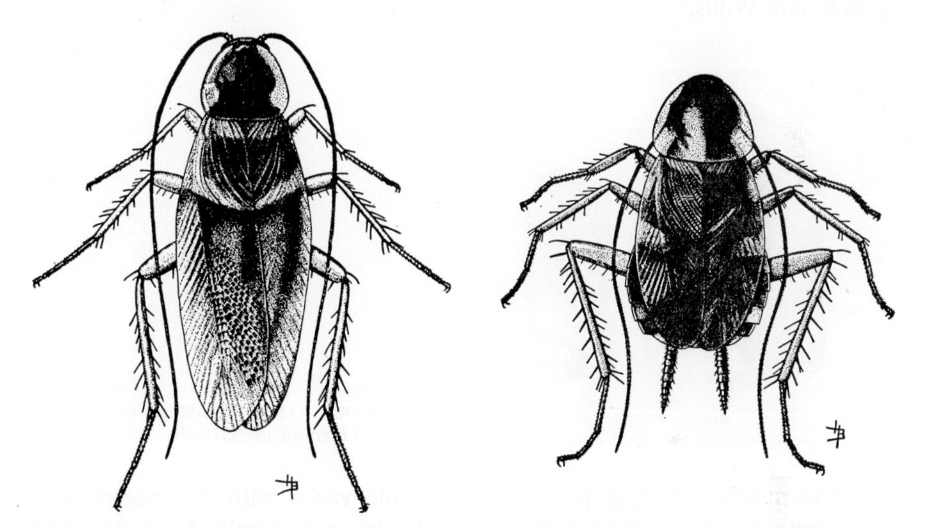

Fig. 24. The brown-banded cockroach, *Supella supellectilium*. (*Left*) Male; (*right*) female. (After Back, 1937.)

quently occurs in high locations such as on shelves in closets or behind pictures and picture molding. The egg capsule is fairly regularly stuck with an adhesive to surfaces, often in furniture, such as radio cabinets; consequently, the insect is sometimes called the "TV roach" or "the furniture cockroach." The insect therefore is carried around easily and is rapidly becoming cosmopolitan.

Pycnoscelus surinamensis (Linnaeus), the Surinam cockroach, is a dark brown to black circumtropical species measuring from 18 to 24 mm in length. It is a burrowing species, burrowing under piles of debris, leaves, etc. It has become established in parts of the southeastern United States.

Other pest species and potentially dangerous cockroaches, particularly with reference to North America, have been discussed by Gould and Deay,[3] Gurney,[4] and Roth and Willis.[16] Among the harmless species that attract attention, *Panchlora nivea* (Linnaeus) is the green Cuban cockroach which is frequently brought to the ports of many lands in bunches of bananas.

Life History. The eggs of cockroaches are lined up vertically, two by two, in the vestibule or oothecal chamber (Fig. 25), and the leathery, bean-shaped ootheca is then extruded to the outside. Some species, such as *Blattella germanica,* may carry the ootheca for several weeks, but most cockroaches will drop or deposit it within a day or two. In the so-called ovoviviparous species this structure is retracted into the uterus or blood sac for incubation until the young are born. In some species facultative parthenogenesis may occur. A valuable account of the reproduction of cockroaches[15] and an analysis of oviparity and viviparity in this group[17] have been given by Roth and Willis.

Fig. 25. Egg cases (oothecae) of cockroaches: (*left*) Oriental cockroach, (right) German cockroach.

The number of eggs within each capsule varies with the species. For *Periplaneta americana* the number is usually 16, occasionally 18 to 24.[3] The normal number for *Blatta orientalis* is also 16, while that for *Blattella germanica* varies between 30 and 40 with a maximum number of 48; for *Supella supellectilium* the average is 18. Many egg capsules are produced during the lifetime of the female cockroach, e.g., as many as 90 by the American cockroach, 18 by the Oriental, and but 4 to 6 by the German.

The length of the incubation period varies with temperature and humidity. At a constant temperature of about 86° F and a relative humidity of about 70 per cent, Gould and Deay[3] found the incubation period for the American cockroach to be 31.8 days; at room temperature it averaged 52.9 days. For the Oriental cockroach the same authors found the incubation period at room temperatures to vary from 42 to 81 days; for the German cockroach under similar conditions (room temperature averaging 76° F), it was 28.4 days. The eggs of the latter species hatched in 16 days at a temperature of 88° F or higher. The brown-banded cockroach required 90 days to hatch at room temperature of 73° F, and 49 days at 82° F.

On hatching, the young cockroaches are almost all white and quite wingless; the skin is cast on emergence, with a second molt in 3 or 4 weeks, followed by other molts at intervals of several weeks until maturity is reached. The American cockroach may have as many as 13 molts, with wing pads appearing in the third or fourth molt, maturity being attained in from 285 to 642 days; however, Gould and Deay report as high as 971 days under similar conditions for one individual. Rau[11] reports the developmental period for the Oriental cockroach as one year. For the smaller species, such as the German cockroach, the developmental period is much shorter, an average of about 2 months (50 to 60 days according to Seamans and Woodruff,[18] and 90 to 95 days at room temperature according to Gould and Deay). There are normally six molts, but there may be seven under adverse conditions. This permits the development of two or more generations a year for the German cockroach.

The longevity of the American cockroach is reported by Gould and Deay to range from 102 to 588 days under room conditions, and the *complete* life span of three females of this species is reported to have been 783, 793, and 913, respectively. The mean length of life of female German cockroaches is reported by these authors to be 200 days, with a maximum of 303 days.

Cockroaches as Vectors. To date, cockroaches have never been positively incriminated in the natural transmission of pathogenic organisms to man. However, that they potentially and, under proper circumstances, actually act in this capacity is virtually undeniable, in the light of recent studies by Roth and Willis.[16] The evidence, though circumstantial, is as strong as much of that which is generally accepted in other instances of mechanical transmission. A particularly convincing bit of such evidence is cited by Roth and Willis. In a pediatric hospital in Brussels, Belgium, an epidemic of *Salmonella typhimurium* persisted in spite of quick isolation of patients, the absence of healthy carriers, and the suppression of direct or indirect contact, other than through cockroaches, between the babies. It was discovered, however, that the cockroaches were running over the clothing, covers, and bodies of the babies by night, and the bacterium was isolated in considerable numbers from the bodies of the insects. The epidemic ceased immediately after the nursery was disinfected with DDT.

Herms and Nelson,[7] by means of a simple bacteriological experiment, showed that cockroaches (*Blattella germanica*) can acquire specific bacteria by crawling over cultures and then depositing the bacteria on food, e.g., by crawling over sugar. They found a minimum of 13,470 bacteria per cockroach. According to Roth and Willis,[16] the parts of the insect that normally come in contact with the substrate are the euplantulae and terminal structures of the tarsi and the tip of the abdomen. It is, consequently, these structures that would be most apt to pick up the pathogens and, by the same token, to deposit them on food.

Roth and Willis list 18 species of domiciliary cockroaches, including most of the common pest species, which have been incriminated by experimental evidence or by the recovery from their bodies of organisms pathogenic to man, or which have been known to bite man. A major consideration relating to the actual role of cockroaches in the transmission of disease concerns the likelihood of those insects passing from contaminated areas and media to homes. Some pertinent facts are the following. Though largely confined to buildings in cooler climates, domestic cockroaches may freely leave such structures under tropical and warm temperate conditions; they may frequently migrate to buildings from sewers, cesspools, septic tanks, privies, and dumps. Most domesticated species readily feed both on human feces and human food. It is well established that cockroaches may nibble at the skin or toenails of sleeping or sick persons, helpless babies, or corpses. The abundance of cockroaches in some areas where poor hygienic conditions prevail is beyond the imagination of persons who live in civilized, highly sanitary areas. The true nature of the problem of cockroaches in relationship to vectorship of disease can not be judged, therefore, from the average community in the United States but, rather, from those areas where these insects afford the greatest threat to human health.

Natural isolations from wild-caught cockroaches include four strains of poliomyelitis virus, about forty species of pathogenic bacteria, largely Enterobacteriaceae but including also what is probably the leprosy bacterium, two pathogenic fungi (*Aspergillus*), and the protozoon *Entamoeba histolytica* Schaudinn. Other pathogenic organisms which cockroaches have been shown to harbor under experimental conditions include the Coxsackie, mouse encephalitis, and yellow fever viruses; the bacterial agents of Asiatic cholera, cerebrospinal fever, pneumonia, diphtheria, undulant fever, anthrax, tetanus, tuberculosis, and others; and the Protozoa *Trichomonas hominis* (Davaine), *Giardia intestinalis* (Lambl), and *Balantidium coli* (Malmsen), all suspected or proven agents of diarrhea or dysentery.

Cockroaches as Intermediate Hosts of Nematode Parasites. It was very early known that cockroaches may become infected with *Spirura gastrophila* Muller of the rat by feeding on rat feces, and that other rats may become infected in turn by feeding on infected cockroaches. Galeb[2] reports that he discovered numerous parasites in the adipose tissue of the cockroach, *Blatta orientalis,* which were identical with nematodes found in the rat, *Rattus r. norvegicus*. He also observed hair of the rat in the alimentary canal of the cockroach. On feeding rats (*Rattus r. rattus*) on infected cockroaches and examining them after the expiration of eight days, he found the parasites in the folds of the mucous membrane of the rats' stomachs. Several nematodes (three females and one male) had already developed sexual organs.

Fibiger[1] presented evidence to support the theory that the nematode

Gongylonema neoplasticum (Fibiger and Ditlevsen), a parasite of the rat, produced malignant tumors in the rat. At least four species of cockroaches serve as intermediate hosts of this parasite. Fibiger's argument was convincing enough that he was awarded the Nobel Prize in 1926 for these discoveries; but Hitchcock and Bell,[8] in a series of carefully controlled experiments, failed to substantiate his findings and produced the same results with a diet deficient in vitamin A. The present evidence indicates that cancer must join beriberi, pellagra, scurvy, and several other diseases wrongly attributed to the vectorship of cockroaches.

Roth and Willis[16] summarize the association of cockroaches with helminths as follows:

> The eggs of 7 species of pathogenic helminths have been found naturally in cockroaches 11 times. The eggs of 4 of these species and of 5 additional species have been fed experimentally to cockroaches 19 times. Cockroaches have been found to serve naturally as the intermediate hosts of 12 species of helminths in about 43 observations. Cockroaches were used successfully as intermediate hosts for 11 of these species and also for 11 other species in about 44 experiments.

Cockroach Control. Cockroach infestations are generally an indication of a breakdown in good housekeeping practices, whether in the home, a restaurant, a hotel, or a grocery store. There are many ways in which these insects (in any stage of development) may be brought in to start an infestation, e.g., in boxes of groceries, in sacks of produce from warehouses, in freight shipments. They may come under their own power at night from neighboring foci; they may follow water pipes, sewers, etc. Many homes, restaurants, grocery stores, etc., have a few cockroaches now and then, so the housekeeper should not feel sensitive about these accidental introductions; there is no reason, however, why infestations should be allowed to develop. Kill the individual intruders at once in any convenient way; do not let them gain a foothold by providing them with food, because of poor garbage disposal or other poor housekeeping practices. See to it that there are no convenient hiding places in cracks in walls, etc. Dark, moist, cluttered-up situations favor cockroaches; open, clean, and neatly kept spaces, permitting plenty of daylight, are not inviting to these darkness-loving pests.

The abatement of infestations generally calls for the application of an appropriate insecticide. Chlordane used as a 2 per cent kerosene solution or emulsion or as a 5 per cent dust is recommended. When larger areas are to be treated, the liquid form is usually applied by means of a pressure sprayer or power equipment. In living quarters, application should be limited to places where cockroaches usually hide, and *care should be taken to safeguard food, dishes, and cooking utensils from contamination.* In some places, such as shelving and the lower surfaces of tables, the liquid may be applied with a paint brush; this adds an element of safety against contamination through the air. Dust is preferable to the liquid in some places; for example, around closely packed stored objects or where there is danger of ignition of the oil from open flames or fuse boxes. Addition of pyrethrum to chlordane will increase its "knock down" power.

DDT, as a 5 per cent spray or a 10 per cent dust, may be used, but it is not as effective as chlordane. The same methods of application are employed. A combination spray containing 2 per cent chlordane and 5 per cent DDT is sometimes used on the assumption that it will give greater immediate, and at the same time longer lasting, control than either chemical used separately. Some resistance to chlordane and DDT has been encountered; lindane or pyrethrum plus a synergist (such as piperonyl butoxide) may be substituted to combat these resistant strains.

Sodium fluoride is still used on occasions for control of cockroaches of all species. This chemical is very toxic to man and animals; hence, it must be used with great caution. As an insecticide it is usually given a bluish- or greenish-gray color so that it will not be confused with flour, soda, etc. *Do not store this insecticide in the kitchen or pantry, and do not dust sodium fluoride in cupboards or where food can be contaminated with it. The container should be labeled "Poison."* For use against cockroaches a mixture is made of sodium fluoride (25 per cent by volume) and pyrethrum (75 per cent). This mixture is applied by means of a dust gun to all cracks and crevices where cockroaches may be in hiding or where they congregate. Applying the powder in the evening is advised, and the application should be repeated in a week or two. The insects come in contact with the dust when running over the treated surface, and afterward they clean themselves and swallow the particles adhering to their feet and bodies; thus the sodium fluoride acts as a stomach poison.

A dramatic new method of control has been proposed by Tarshis.[19] Two sorptive dusts, a silica gel and a silica aerogel, were found to kill the insects by removing the outer waterproof layer or cuticle through a continual adsorption of the lipid elements or through abrasion of the cuticle. The cockroaches died of desiccation. These sorptive dusts are nontoxic to man, but one should wear a mask when applying large quantities of them in order to avoid undue drying of the nose and throat tissues. Since the action of the dusts is physical rather than chemical, there seems to be little likelihood of insects becoming resistant to them.

BEETLES

Order Coleoptera

The order Coleoptera consists of over 270,000 described species of insects. Very few of the families of beetles concern the medical entomologist, but, because of their abundance and successful invasion of all sorts of environments, it is certain that contact will be made with members of this order of insects sooner or later. Familiarity with the order is important.

Characteristics. Beetles are readily distinguishable from all other insects. Their integument is leathery; their mouth parts are strongly mandibulate, i.e., biting-chewing. Although wings are absent in some species, usually at least the fore pair, the elytra, is present; these are not used in flight, are horny, and when at rest they meet in a straight line down the dorsum; the hind wings are membranous and functional, often folded both horizontally and vertically. Metamorphosis is complete (egg, larva, pupa, imago). The larvae are of various forms. Most of them have three pairs of well-developed legs, although those of the weevils and of some other groups are legless.

Scavenger Beetles. All scavenger beetles, of which there are several families, are potentially of some public health importance since their habits of feeding as larvae or adults on dead animals, hides, or other animal matter may accidentally bring them in contact with pathogenic organisms. They may carry infection in at least two ways, either mechanically on their legs, mouth parts, or body, or in their excreta after feeding on infectious material. Destruction of carcasses by incineration is used.

Nuttall[10] reports that, as early as 1894,

> Proust in examining goatskins taken from anthracic animals, found quantities of living *Dermestes vulpinus* Fabr. [= *D. maculatus* De Geer] upon them. He found virulent anthrax bacilli in their excrements, as also in the eggs and in the larvae. It is evident from this that these insects which feed on the skins permit the anthrax spores to pass uninjured through the alimentary tract. Heim (1894) also had occasion to examine some skins which were suspected of having caused anthrax in three persons engaged in handling the leather. He found larvae of *Attagenus pellio* Linn., *Anthrenus museorum* Linn. (both Dermestidae), and *Ptinus;* also fully developed insects of the latter species on the skins. All these insects had virulent anthrax bacilli (spores) on their surface and in their excreta, from which Heim concludes they might spread disease. He says the excreta are very light and easily scattered by the slightest current of air. Heim does not believe the bacilli multiply in the bodies of these insects, but that the latter may be dangerous through their scattering the spores about.

Among the families of scavenger beetles are the following:

1. *Family Staphylinidae,* commonly known as rove beetles, includes many species that feed on carrion, dung, and decaying animal matter; they are characterized by the abbreviated condition of the elytra, which leaves much of the abdomen exposed and gives these beetles a larval appearance; the abdomen is flexible and is often curled up and thrown forward dorsally; the long functional wings are folded up or concealed beneath the short wing covers when not in use. The scavenger species are commonly seen when one turns carrion, hides, heaps of bones, etc. (Fig. 26).

2. *Family Silphidae,* commonly known as carrion beetles, burying beetles, or sexton beetles, is as a rule attracted to dead animals which they undermine and, in the case of small ones, may even bury. They deposit their eggs on the dead animals, and the larvae feed on the decomposing flesh (Fig. 27).

26 27

Fig. 26. Rove beetles (Staphylinidae). × 1.5.
Fig. 27. Sexton beetles (Silphidae). × 1.5.

3. *Family Dermestidae,* which includes hide beetles, larder beetles, museum pests, dermestids, are small oval or elongated beetles, often mottled, grayish or brownish in color. The hairy larvae as well as the adults feed on dead animals, museum specimens, wool, cured meats, cheese, and many other animal as well as vegetable products (cereals). *Dermestes lardarius* Linnaeus is known as the larder beetle; *Dermestes maculatus* De Geer (= *vulpinus* Fabricius) is commonly used to clean dried flesh from bones for museum use; *Anthrenus scrophulariae* (Linnaeus) is a carpet beetle and a museum pest. Larvae of the carpet beetle may enter the ears of persons and cause much discomfort (Fig. 28).

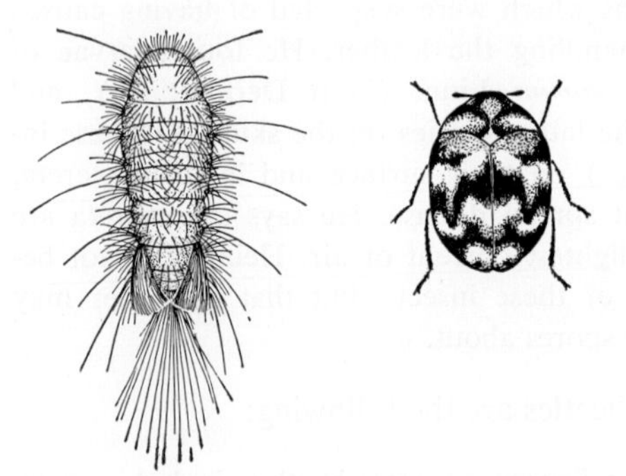

Fig. 28. The varied carpet beetle, *Anthrenus verbasci,* larva (*left*) and adult (*right*).

Beetles as Intermediate Hosts of Helminths. Many species of beetles serve as intermediate hosts of helminthic parasites of man and of wild and domesticated animals. The common relationship is no doubt due to the variety of feeding habits of beetles which enables them to ingest fecal matter in which eggs of intestinal parasites of animals commonly occur; thus, many cereal and omnivorous feeders, as well as coprophagous beetles, may readily lend themselves as intermediate hosts. The infective stage of nematode worms of the genus *Gongylonema* commonly occur in dung beetles belonging to the family Scarabaeidae, such as members of the genus *Aphodius;* also in meal worms belonging to the family Tenebrionidae such as *Tenebrio molitor* Linnaeus. *Gongylonema pulchrum* Molin parasitizes many species of mammals, such as goats, swine, and occasionally man. It invades tissues of the oral cavity and esophagus, causing *gongylonemiasis.*

May beetles or cockchafers (family Scarabaeidae) are known to be intermediate hosts both in the larval and adult stages of the thorn-headed worm, *Macracanthorhynchus hirudinaceus* (Pallas) (= *Gigantorhynchus gigas* [Bloch]), a parasite of swine said also to occur in man in rare instances. This nematode worm in its adult stage measures 200 to 300 mm in length and about 3 to 5 mm in thickness and inhabits the small intestine of the host. The eggs pass out with the feces which may be ingested by the larvae of cockchafers. These are often extremely abundant among the rootlets of grass in heavily sodded pastures, and swine with free range are fond of these grubs, in search of which they diligently root up the soil with their snouts. Thus every opportunity is given for the grubs, and in turn the swine, to become infected. In Europe the intermediate host is commonly *Melolontha melolontha* (Linnaeus) or *Cetonia aurata* (Linnaeus). May beetles of the genus *Phyllophaga* (according to Stiles, *Phyllophaga fervida* [Fabricius] [= *Lachnosterna arcuata* Smith] and others) are probably all more or less concerned. In districts infested with thorn-headed worms a systematic crusade against cockchafers would be the logical means of control, together with treatment of swine.

Numerous species of beetles have been proved to be intermediate hosts of the fowl tapeworm, *Raillietina cesticillus* (Molin). The species listed by Reid, Ackert, and Case[14] belong to the following families: Scarabaeidae, two species; Tenebrionidae, one species; Carabidae, subfamily Harpalinae, 26 species, to which they added 12 not previously reported, giving a total of 38 species in this family. The beetles belonging to the genus *Amara* proved to be particularly favorable hosts, although the largest number of cysticercoids were produced by a species of *Pterostichus,* a total of 626 by one beetle which had been fed on four proglottids.

Canthariasis is a term used to designate the rare accidental beetle (larva or adult) infestations of organs of the body, e.g., infestations of the alimentary canal by larvae of the churchyard beetle, *Blaps mortisaga* Linnaeus, as the result of superstitiously drinking foul graveyard water in which these beetles may occur. The ingestion of meal- and flour-infesting insects such as the meal worm, *Tenebrio molitor* Linnaeus, has also been known to occur.

Vesicating Beetles. Many beetles possess a vesicating substance in their body tissues which produces blisters when coming in contact with the skin. The family Meloidae, commonly referred to as the blister beetles, contain the species which are the most important source of cantharidin used medicinally. Among the species are the Spanish fly, *Lytta vesicatoria* (Linnaeus), the telini fly, *Mylabris cichorii* (Linnaeus) and *Epicauta hirticornis* (Haag-Rutenberg) of India. At least two species of the family Oedemeridae, *Sessinia collaris* (Sharp) and *S. decolor* Fairmaire, known as coconut beetles by the Gilbertese, cause severe blistering if the skin is contacted.

Rose Chafers Poisonous to Poultry. The rose chafer, *Macrodactylus subspinosus* (Fabricius), family Scarabaeidae, was found by Lamson[9] to be poisonous to chickens, ducklings, goslings, and young turkeys. Fatal cases of poisoning terminate in death within twenty-four hours.

Sundry Annoying Beetles. Aside from any economic or other injury for which the beetles may be responsible, the sheer abundance of certain species at times causes annoyance. For example, while trying to do microscope work or write reports in the tropics, Herms,[6] stripped to the waist during the warm evenings, was greatly disturbed by the presence of hordes of the copra "bug" (red-legged ham beetle), *Necrobia rufipes* De Geer, family Corynetidae. These small greenish-blue beetles, 3–5 mm long, originated in vast numbers in copra stored in neighboring sheds. The larvae of this species may also enter the ears of persons.

Tiny (3-mm long) saw-toothed grain beetles, *Oryzaephilus surinamensis* (Linnaeus), belonging to the family Cucujidae, may invade bed chambers in great numbers, crawl over the bodies of occupants, and nibble the skin. An infestation of this kind was traced to the bathroom and thence out of the house through the yard and into an old barn where, under the stalls, grain from the manger had collected, affording a breeding ground for the beetles. Extreme dryness had apparently driven the insects to the bathroom for moisture, and the attack on occupants of the adjoining bedchamber was merely accidental.

Minute species of Staphylinidae (such as *Atheta occidentalis* Bernhaeur), a blackish species 3-mm long, are often encountered on the wing in the late autumn, and may accidentally enter the eyes, causing a severe burning sensation and temporarily blinding the victim. Such a mishap to a person driving a motor car might lead to a serious accident. These minute species breed in cow dung and decomposing plant refuse.

The so-called tule beetle or stink beetle, *Agonum maculicolle* (Dejean), of California, is normally a beneficial predator, but when its natural habitat in the marshes becomes dry in summer it commonly leaves in search of moisture and may invade homes in the neighborhood. Heavy early winter rains and cold weather may likewise cause invasions. The nauseous odor of this beetle is almost intolerable. It belongs to the family Carabidae, which contains many other species possessing vile odors.

Beetles as Parasites. Belonging to the family Platypsyllidae, indeed the only representative of this family, is the coleopterous parasite of the beaver, *Platypsyllus castoris* Ritsema. This is a permanent, obligate parasite in all its stages. The eggs are deposited on the skin of the beaver among dense hairs. If occurs in both Europe and North America.

Another family of Coleoptera, the Leptinidae, includes beetles which are parasitic on beavers and certain other rodents. The three known species are *Leptinus testaceus* Muller, parasitic on mice and shrews in Europe and North America; *Leptinillus validus* (Horn), found on North American beavers; and *Leptinilus aplodontiae* Ferris, taken on *Aplodontia,* the mountain beaver of the Pacific coast states.

KEY TO THE FAMILIES OF COLEOPTERA REFERRED TO IN THIS CHAPTER*

1. Antennae variable in structure but never lamellate 2
   Antennae with a club composed of from three to seven leaflike segments (lamellate); legs usually fossorial; tarsi five-segmented (May beetles, June beetles, cockchafers) ....Scarabaeidae
2. Anterior and intermediate tarsi five-segmented; posterior tarsi four-segmented 3
   All of the tarsi either three-, four-, or five-segmented 4
3. Head as wide as prothorax; anterior coxal cavities open behind; body not heavily sclerotized (blister beetles) ....Meloidae
   Head narrower than prothorax; anterior coxal cavities closed behind; body usually heavily sclerotized (darkling ground beetles) ....Tenebrionidae
4. Elytra long, covering most of abdomen; abdominal tergites mostly membranous 5
   Elytra short, exposing most of abdomen; abdominal tergites mostly sclerotized 8
5. Fourth segment of tarsus distinct, free; antennae clavate, capitate or moniliform 6
   Fourth segment of tarsus very small, fused with fifth segment; antennae usually filiform; body often brightly colored (leaf beetles) ..Chrysomelidae
6. Abdomen with five visible sternites 7
   Abdomen with six visible sternites; tibial spurs large; antennae gradually thickened or clavate (carrion beetles, burying beetles) ....Silphidae
7. Anterior coxae conical, prominent; antennae moniliform; flat, nonscaly beetles (flat beetles, grain beetles) ....Cucujidae
   Anterior coxae globular, not prominent; antennae capitate or clavate; convex, scaly beetles (leather beetles, skin beetles) ....Dermestidae
8. Wingless; eyes wanting or abortive 9
   Winged; the wings folded under the short elytra; eyes usually well developed; tarsi from three- to five-segmented (rove beetles) ...Staphylinidae
9. Anterior coxae globular (beaver beetles) ....Platypsyllidae
   Anterior coxae flat (rodent beetles) ....Leptinidae

REFERENCES

1. Fibiger, Johannes, 1913. "Ueber eine durch Nematoden (Spiroptera sp. n.) hervorgerufene papillomatöse und carcinomatöse Geschwulstbildung im Magen der Ratte," *Berl. klin. Wchnschr.,* **50:**289–98.

* Prepared by Dr. E. Gorton Linsley.

2. Galeb, Osman, 1878. "Observations et expériences sur les migrations du *Filaria rytipleurites,* parasite des blattes et des rats," *Compt. rend. Acad. d. sc.,* **87:**75–77.

3. Gould, George E., and Deay, H. O., 1940. *The Biology of Six Species of Cockroaches Which Inhabit Buildings.* Lafayette: Purdue Univ., in Agric. Exper. Sta. Bull. no. 451, 31 pp.

4. Gurney, Ashley B., 1953. "Distribution, general bionomics, and recognition characters of two cockroaches recently established in the United States," *Proc. U. S. Nat. Museum,* **103:**39–56.

5. Hebard, Morgan, 1917. *The Blattidae of North America North of the Mexican Boundary.* Philadelphia: Mem. Amer. Entomol. Soc., no. 2, 284 pp. (10 plates).

6. Herms, William B., 1926. "Diocalandra taitensis (Guerin) and other coconut pests of Fanning and Washington Islands," *Philippine J. Sc.,* **30:**243–71.

7. Herms, William B., and Nelson, Y., 1913. "The croton bug (*Ectobia germanica*) as a factor in bacterial dissemination," *Am. J. Pub. Health,* **3:**929–34.

8. Hitchcock, C. R., and Bell, E. T., 1952. "Studies on the nematode parasite, *Gongylonema neoplasticum* (*Spiroptera neoplasticum*) and avitaminosis A in the forestomach of rats: Comparison of Fibiger's results," *J. Nat. Cancer Inst.,* **12:**1345–87.

9. Lamson, G. H., Jr., 1922. *The Rose Chafer as a Cause of Death of Chickens.* Storrs: Univ. Conn., in Agric. Exper. Sta. Bull. no. 110, pp. 117–34.

10. Nuttall, G. H. F., 1899. "On the role of insects, arachnids, and myriapods as carriers in the spread of bacterial and parasitic disease of man and animals. A critical and historical study," *Johns Hopkins Hospital Reports,* **8:**1–154.

11. Rau, P., 1924. "Biology of the roach," *Tr. Acad. Sc. St. Louis,* **25:**57–79.

12. Rehn, James A. G., 1945. "Man's uninvited fellow traveler—the cockroach," *Sc. Monthly,* **61:**265–76.

13. Rehn, John W. H., 1950. "A key to the genera of North American Blattaria, including established adventives," *Entomol. News,* **61:**64–67.

14. Reid, W. M.; Ackert, J. E.; and Case, A. A.; 1938. "Studies on the life history and biology of the fowl tapeworm, *Raillietina cesticillus* (Molin)," *Tr. Am. Micr. Soc.,* **57:**65–76.

15. Roth, Louis M., and Willis, Edwin R., 1954. *The Reproduction of Cockroaches.* Washington, D. C.: Smithsonian Misc. Coll., vol. 122, no. 12. 49 pp. (12 plates).

16. Roth, Louis M., and Willis, Edwin R., 1957. *The Medical and Veterinary Importance of Cockroaches.* Washington, D. C.: Smithsonian Misc. Coll., vol. 134, no. 10. 147 pp. (7 plates).

17. Roth, Louis M., and Willis, Edwin R., 1958. "An analysis of oviparity and viviparity in the Blattaria," *Trans. Amer. Entomol. Soc.,* **83:**221–38 (7 plates).

18. Seamans, Lois, and Woodruff, Laurence C., 1939. "Some factors influencing the number of molts of the German roach," *J. Kansas Entomolog. Soc.,* **12:**73–76.

19. Tarshis, I. Barry, 1959. "Sorptive dusts on cockroaches," *Calif. Agriculture,* **13** (2):3–5.

Chapter 7

THE BUGS
Bed Bugs, Conenoses, and Other Bugs

Order Hemiptera

Order Hemiptera. This order contains about 55,000 described species and is divided into two suborders: (1) Heteroptera, in which the fore wing (hemelytron) is usually divided into a coriaceous or leathery basal and a membranous apical portion, the latter overlapping the membranous part of the opposite fore wing; and (2) Homoptera, in which the fore wing is usually of the same texture throughout.

The suborder Homoptera includes such important phytophagous families as the Aphidae (plant lice), Cicadidae (cicadas or harvest flies), Cicadellidae (leafhoppers, sharpshooters), Membracidae (treehoppers), and many others of great agricultural importance, particularly many vectors of plant diseases. These families include plant-feeding insects with piercing mouth parts, such as leafhoppers and treehoppers, many of which have been reported as biting or sucking blood from human beings. Usinger[20] attributes this uncommon phenomenon of bloodsucking in the normally phytophagous groups of the Hemiptera to three influences, namely, the "stimulus of artificial light or other unusual conditions of the environment, the attractive qualities of exposed liquids, mainly perspiration, and hunger." He remarks further that this change

> . . . from plant feeding to bloodsucking, is not such a profound one as would at first be supposed. This is evidenced by a comparison of the composition of plant juices and blood and by the various plant-feeding groups, some members of which have adapted themselves to a predaceous habit or have shown their ability occasionally to suck the blood of mammals.

The Heteroptera are the true bugs and are characterized by a segmented suctorial proboscis attached anteriorly, which, when not in use, is flexed under the head. The true bugs are separated into two divisions: (1) the **Gymnocerata,** in which the antennae are conspicuous and capable of being moved freely in front of the head, e.g., *Cimex lectularius* Linnaeus, the bed bug, *Anasa tristis* (De Geer), the squash bug, and *Triatoma protracta* (Uhler), a conenose; and (2) the **Cryptocerata,** in which the antennae are concealed in small concavities (foveae) and are closely pressed to the under side of the head, e.g., *Lethocerus americanus* (Leidy), the giant water bug. Metamorphosis is simple.

THE BED BUGS

Family Cimicidae

Family Cimicidae. The family Cimicidae, which includes the bed bugs, swallow bugs, and the poultry bug, is characterized by a very short, broad head, broadly attached to the prothorax, an oval body, well-developed compound eyes, absence of ocelli, four-segmented conspicuous antennae, a three-segmented proboscis lying in a groove beneath the head and thorax, and very short padlike hemelytra. The bodies are broad and flat, enabling the bugs to creep into narrow crevices. A nasty pungent odor is attached to the group as a whole with few exceptions. They are night-prowling and bloodsucking in habit, some feeding on birds and bats, and others, on human beings. Peculiar to these bugs is the organ of Ribaga located in the fourth and fifth abdominal segments. The presence or absence of this organ and its particular location when present provide a character useful in identification of species.

Three genera of North American Cimicidae contain representatives of importance sufficient to be mentioned here. These are: (1) *Cimex,* e.g., *C. lectularius* Linnaeus, the cosmopolitan bed bug; *C. hemipterus* (Fabricius), tropical and subtropical, also known as the Indian bed bug; *C. boueti* Joyeux,[7] the tropical bed bug of Africa and South America, all of which resemble one another very closely, as do the following: *C. columbarius* Jenyns, parasitic on pigeons in Europe, *C. pipistrelli* Jenyns, parasitic on bats in Europe, and *C. pilosellus* (Horvath), parasitic on bats in North America; (2) *Oeciacus,* in which the body is clothed with long silky hairs, the filiform third and fourth segments of the antennae are only a little thinner than the first and second, *e.g., O. hirundinis* (Jenyns), the European barn-swallow bug and *O. vicarius* Horvath, the corresponding American species; (3) *Haematosiphon,* in which the rostrum is long, reaching to the posterior coxae, of which *H. inodorus* (Duges) is the only known species. This species infests poultry in the southwestern United States and in Mexico, and it has been reported on occasions to invade human habitations and to cause serious annoyance to their occupants. Its bionomics have been studied by Lee.[10] Its native hosts are the California condor and the great horned owl.[22]

Other North American genera include *Hesperocimex,* represented by two species parasitic on martins (Ryckman[19] has studied the bionomics of *H. sonorensis* Ryckman and is continuing taxonomic studies on the group); *Synxenoderus,* represented by one species on swifts in California and Nebraska; *Cimexopsis,* containing a small species distributed widely in the eastern United States in nests of the chimney swift; and finally *Primicimex,* which contains the largest of the species of Cimicidae. The latter has been found in bat caves in Texas and Guatemala.

The Bed Bug. The adult of the bed bug, *Cimex lectularius* Linnaeus (Fig. 29) measures 4 to 5 mm in length and 3 mm in breadth; it is obovate and much flattened. The adult is reddish brown in color, whereas the young are yellowish white. Among the local names applied to bed bugs are "chinches," "chintzes," "red coats," "mahogany flats," "wall louse," "common bed bugs," or simply "bugs."

Bed bugs, like lice, have been the constant companions of man for centuries; the earliest writings on natural history (Pliny and Aristotle) mention them. Bed bugs occasionally gain a foothold among laboratory animals, such as white rats and guinea pigs, upon which they feed readily. They are nocturnal in their feeding habits, hiding in crevices during the day. At night they are very active, crawling out of their hiding places, often traveling considerable distances to attack their victims. This is especially true where iron bedsteads are used, as these do not provide convenient hiding places for the

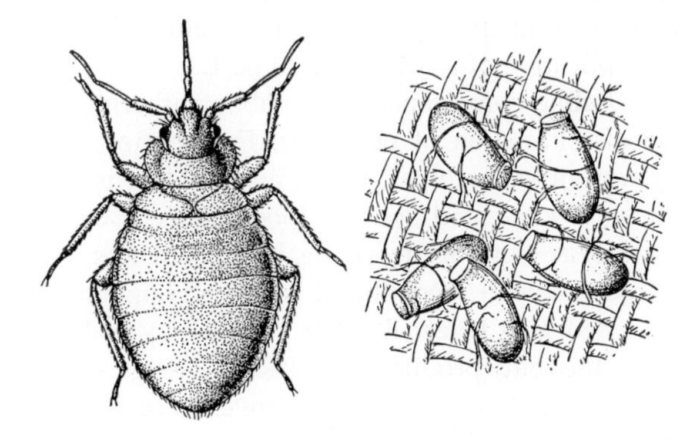

Fig. 29. The bed bug, *Cimex lectularius.* Eggs shown at right.

bugs. Ordinarily, where wooden bedsteads are used, the bugs stay closer to their point of attack. Mattresses in any case may afford harborage. Bed bugs are gregarious; hence, great assemblages often may be found in some convenient crevice or beneath some nearby loose wallpaper, where the eggs are deposited and the tarry-black excrement collects.

The females deposit eggs in batches of from 10 to 50, totaling from 200 to 500, spread out in a yellowish patch. The eggs are large and yellowish white in color. Oviposition occurs at intervals during a period of from two to three months, apparently limited to the spring and summer months, notwithstanding the fact that the insects are commonly favored by warm rooms during the winter. The young hatch in from 7 to 30 days (usually about 10 days), according to temperature, which also affects their later growth. The time required for development from egg to maturity is given as from 45 days to 11 months, although the time is greatly influenced by temperature; there may be three or more generations a year under average conditions. Ordinarily they require 6 to 8 weeks to reach maturity. Bed bugs are evidently sensitive to high temperatures; even a temperature of 100° F with fairly high humidity will kill many of them. Activity ceases below about 60° F. At

60° to 65° F bed bugs have lived 136 days without food. Normally fed individuals may survive from 54 to 316 days under ordinary room-temperature conditions. The presence or absence of food influences longevity; without food adults may survive from 17 to 42 days.[11] Bed bugs molt five times, and the minute wing pads characteristic of the adult insect make their appearance with the last molt. Ordinarily but one meal is taken between each molt and one before egg deposition; an average period of 8 days is required between moltings.

Method of Distribution. Bed bugs, lice, or other organisms cannot originate spontaneously in filth as some uninformed persons still believe; infestations are traceable to introduced eggs, young, or adults. Thus, the introduction of one impregnated female might furnish the nucleus for a well-developed colony in a few months. Hence, the best-regulated household is not exempt from invasion, though cleanliness is the best preventive against the multiplication of any household pest.

Public conveyances and public gathering places are common avenues for the dissemination of bed bugs. Furthermore, migration from house to house by way of water pipes, walls, and the like is not at all unlikely when infested houses are vacated and the food supply is cut off. The insects are also easily carried in clothing, traveling bags, suitcases, laundry, etc., and they may be introduced with secondhand beds, bedding, and furniture.

Bed Bug Bites. Persons "bitten" by bed bugs are affected differently; in some the bite produces marked swellings and considerable irritation, while in others not the slightest inconvenience is caused. (This is also true in the case of flea and mosquito bites.) The bite, so-called, of the bed bug is produced by piercing organs of the hemipteron type already described. It is probable that puncture by these stylets, unattended by contamination or specific poisons, would produce little pain. The welts and local inflammation are unquestionably caused by an anticoagulant enzyme secreted by the salivary glands of the insect and introduced in the act of feeding. The bed bug is able to engorge itself completely with blood in from three to five minutes. Although persons are usually bitten at night while in bed because of the nocturnal habits of the bed bugs, the insects will bite freely in subdued light by day.

Disease Transmission. The fact that bed bugs are obliged to feed at least five times, either upon the same or a different host, in order to reach maturity has placed these insects under grave suspicion as potential vectors of disease. In consequence of statements made by earlier authors that bed bugs are capable of transmitting plague and other septicemic infections, Nuttall, in 1899, and several subsequent workers have attempted to prove or disprove this claim experimentally. Virtually all evidence has been negative or inconclusive. The bed bug would, therefore, appear to be relatively unimportant as a disease vector. In spite of the fact that it can experimentally transmit the pathogens of plague, relapsing fever, leprosy, kala-azar, and Chagas' disease, and, questionably, tularemia (the experiments in support of this transmission being defective), there is no convincing evidence that it is a vector of these or any other diseases at present known. It is of course possible, as shown in laboratory tests, that occasional transmission may be effected.

Bed Bug Control. A bed bug infestation in dwellings, barracks, etc., can usually be successfully eradicated by the application of a 5 per cent DDT spray applied to beds, mattresses, wall crevices, and other infested situations. A single correct treatment will "bug proof" for six months or longer. A 5 per cent kerosene solution or emulsion is recommended; it is applied as a spray until misty-wet to all parts of mattresses (standing on edge), bedsprings, or bedsteads. In heavy infestations the walls around the beds, particularly cracks along baseboards, surfaces back of loose wall paper, and all other harborages must also be sprayed. Chicken coops infested with the chicken bed bug can also be freed of these pests by using DDT spray. Not only should food be protected against the spray, but *spraying must not be done near an open flame*. Where there is danger from the latter source, a dust may be used effectively.

DDT-resistant strains of *Cimex lectularius* and *C. hemipterus* have been reported from various parts of the world. When such resistance is encountered, a synergized pyrethrum spray, e.g., one containing 0.2 per cent of pyrethrins and 1 per cent of piperonyl butoxide, is effective.

KEY TO NORTH AMERICAN CIMICIDAE*

1. Head longer than broad, clypeus narrowed anteriorly. Labrum much longer than broad. Legs very long, the femora extending beyond sides of body for a distance greater than width of pronotum. Organ of Ribaga absent .... *Primicimex cavernis* Barber

   Head broader than long, clypeus broadened anteriorly. Labrum short, about as broad as long. Legs relatively short; the femora not much longer than width of pronotum and only briefly projecting beyond sides of body. Organ of Ribaga absent 2

2. Middle and hind coxae subcontiguous, the metasternum compressed. Large bristles of body dentate only at their tips. Organ of Ribaga dorsal 3

   Middle and hind coxae rather widely separated, the metasternum broad and platelike, widening posteriorly. Large bristles of body dentate on convex side. Organ of Ribaga ventral 7

3. Rostrum long, reaching hind margin of mesosternum. Posterior abdominal tergites in female strongly sinuate, organ of Ribaga located at middle of fifth segment. New Mexico, Texas, Oklahoma, California, Mexico. Hosts: California condor, great horned owl, domestic chicken .... *Haematosiphon inodorus* Duges

   Rostrum shorter, not reaching mesosternum. Posterior abdominal sutures only feebly sinuate 4

* Slightly modified from a key prepared by Dr. Robert L. Usinger.

4. Pronotum strongly narrowed posteriorly. Posteroventral portion of head and adjoining prosternum strongly convex. California, Nebraska. Host: white-throated swift .... *Synxenoderus comosus* List
   Pronotum not strongly narrowed posteriorly. Head beneath and prosternum not strongly convex 5
5. Body clothed with long bristles, sides of abdomen with some bristles twice as long as width of an eye 6
   Body with very short, inconspicuous bristles, those of sides of abdominal segments much shorter than width of an eye. Eastern and central United States. Host: chimney swift .... *Cimexopsis nyctalis* List
6. Color yellowish brown above; all of external genital structures straight. Colorado, Mexico. Hosts: gray-breasted martin and other swallows.. .... *Hesperocimex coloradensis* List
   Color dark brown above; terminal portion of external genitalia strongly curved. Arizona, Mexico. Host: purple martin.................... .... *Hesperocimex sonorensis* Ryckman
7. Pubescence long and sericeous. Last two antennal segments subequal in length.................................. *Oeciacus vicarius* Horvath
   Pubescence short, stiff. Third antennal segment longer than fourth. Genus *Cimex* Linnaeus 8
8. Sides of pronotum not widely dilated and not reflexed, fringed with sparse, nearly straight hairs. Hemelytra with apical margins distinctly rounded. Tropicopolitan. Host: man ...... *Cimex hemipterus* (Fabricius)
   Sides of pronotum widely dilated, broader than width of an eye, and densely fringed with backward-curved hairs. Apical margins of hemelytra nearly straight, rounded toward inner angles 9
9. Length of contiguous portions of hemelytra shorter than scutellum. Second antennal segment slightly longer than third. Fringing hairs of pronotal margin shorter than width of an eye. Widely distributed in temperate regions. Host: man .... *Cimex lectularius* Linnaeus
   Length of contiguous portions of hemelytra longer than scutellum. Second and third antennal segments equal in length. Fringing hairs of pronotum longer than width of an eye 10
10. Marginal hairs relatively long. Tergum strigate. Eastern North America. Host: bats .... *Cimex adjunuctus* Barber
    Marginal hairs relatively short. Tergum not transversely strigate. Western North America. Host: bats .... *Cimex pilosellus* Horvath

THE ASSASSIN BUGS

Family Reduviidae

Family Reduviidae. The Reduviidae are typical examples of the Heteroptera. As a family they are commonly known as the assassin bugs. There are more than 2500 species divided among 15 subfamilies, of which the Harpactocorinae is the largest, containing more than a third of all the species, and next in size is the subfamily Reduviinae. A very large percentage of the reduviids are predaceous and feed on insects, many of which are harmful; hence the family is in the main beneficial. A number of the species when handled carelessly defend themselves by biting, and a few have developed a definite habit of sucking mammalian blood. The subfamily Triatominae, commonly known as conenoses in the United States and called *vinchucas* in South America, comprises those members of the family which feed exclusively on blood of vertebrates. The subfamily is predominantly American. Comprehensive taxonomic treatments of it have been published by Neiva and Lent,[13] by Usinger[21] for North and Central America, and by Abalos and Wygodzinsky[1] for Argentina. A catalog of the Triatominae is currently being prepared by R. I. Sailer.

In the Tratominae, the head is more or less elongated or cone-shaped, giving rise to the name conenose; the head has remarkably free movement; the ocelli are located behind the compound eyes; the sturdy, three-segmented proboscis can be thrust forward, but in repose lies beneath the head; the piercing stylets can be extended far beyond the tip of the proboscis; the long, slender, four- or five-segmented antennae are situated in front of the eyes or on the border of the head; the prothorax is strongly developed; most of the species are able to fly well.

Life History. The rather large, more or less barrel-shaped eggs of reduviids (often with stellate or fringed caps) are generally deposited in situations where the adults occur, i.e., the ground-inhabiting forms deposit their eggs on the ground; arboreal forms lay their eggs on leaves and stems; and house-inhabiting forms oviposit in dusty corners. Much information has been given by Miller,[12] mostly in the form of illustrations, on the eggs, and Readio[14] has illustrated the eggs of many species and has published an excellent account of the bionomics of the family.[15]

The eggs are commonly deposited singly, but sometimes in small clusters, the total number per female varying considerably from a few dozen to upward of 600. The incubation period varies from 8 or 10 days to nearly a month, depending upon the species and temperature. The newly hatched nymphs are wingless. The usual number of nymphal instars is five, although Readio states that *Melanolestes picipes* (Herrich-Schaeffer) passes through only four. Some species overwinter in the egg stage, others as adults, and still others as nymphs. In most cases there appears to be but one generation a year. The length of the life cycle of *Triatoma rubrofasciata* (De Geer) was found by Neiva to cover 210 days, and for *Panstrongylus megistus* (Burmeister) it was 260 days. Usinger[21] reports a two-year life cycle for *Triatoma recurva* Stål (= *longipes* Barber).

Assassin Bug Bites. Many of the species of assassin bugs inflict a painful bite when handled carelessly. Most notorious of all is the "kissing bug," *Reduvius personatus* (Linnaeus), a widely distributed species (belonging to the subfamily Reduviinae) particularly active in the middle western and eastern United States. As early as 1899 Howard,[6] quoting LeConte, wrote as follows:

This species is remarkable for the intense pain caused by its bite. I do not know whether it ever willingly plunges its rostrum into any person, but when caught or unskillfully handled it always stings (pierces). In this case the pain is almost equal to that of the bite of a snake, and the swelling and irritation which result from it will sometimes last for a week. In very weak and irritable constitutions it may even prove fatal.

The wheel bug, *Arilus cristatus* (Linnaeus), belonging to the subfamily Harpactocorinae, also has a bad reputation as a biter. Reporting on the bite of this species, Hall[4] states:

The finger became reddened and felt hot to the touch. In the course of a few days, growths resembling papillomas developed at the sites of the punctures, the largest of these projecting as a small hornlike structure. Both of these growths persisted for months, the largest slowly disappearing between six and nine months after the infliction of the bite. The injured finger remained warmer than the other fingers during this period, and, according to the patient's statement, still feels warmer than the other fingers, a year later. The development of pronounced cutaneous growths after a bite appears indicative of the action of some toxin as a stimulant irritant.

The feeding bites of *Triatoma* and *Panstrongylus* are in themselves benign; they are hardly, if at all, felt by their hosts. If this were not so, xenodiagnosis (see p. 96) would be impractical. The painless bite is an adaptation to the habitual bloodsucking habit in contrast to the painful bite of the occasional bloodsucker.[21] On the other hand, the thrust produced in self-defense (but not the feeding bite) of *Triatoma rubrofasciata* (De Geer) in Hawaii is sharp and painful and is accompanied by the emission of an offensive musk.[27]

In some individuals, however, serious complications may result from anaphylactic reactions. Examples of such reactions resulting from the bite of *Triatoma protracta* (Uhler) (Figs. 30A, 31A), a widely distributed Pacific coast species commonly known as the China bed bug or cross bug and normally occurring in nests of wood rats, *Neotoma* spp., were observed and described by a reporting physician as follows: "In a few minutes after a bite the patient develops nausea, flushed face, palpitation of the heart, rapid breathing, rapid pulse, followed by profuse urticaria all over the body. The symptoms vary with individuals in their intensity." A blood examination made on a man about four hours after he was bitten on the left arm showed a leucocyte count of 11,000 (polymorphonuclears, 66 per cent; lymphocytes, 28 per cent; monocytes, 3 per cent; eosinophils, 3 per cent). This man's symptoms a few minutes after the bite were large hivelike swellings in the regions of the glands, intense itching and redness, especially in the hands; pulse rate, normally 60, increased to 140.

The bite of the bloodsucking conenose or "Mexican bed bug," *Triatoma sanguisuga* (LeConte), is said to result, in sensitive individuals, in "a burning

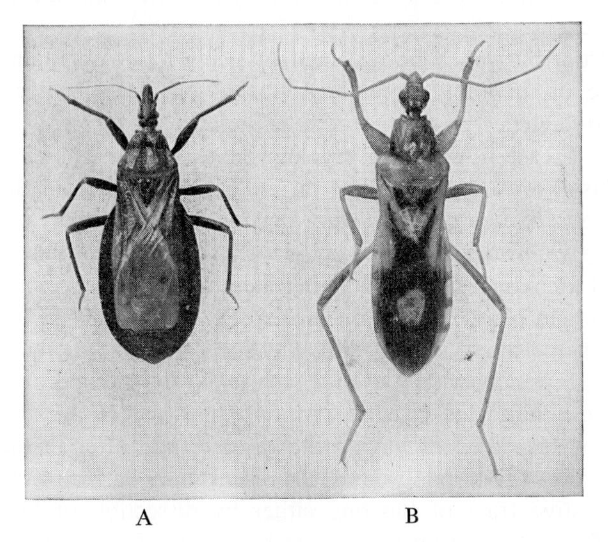

Fig. 30. Members of the family Reduviidae. (*A*) *Triatoma protracta;* (*B*) *Rasahus thoracicus.*

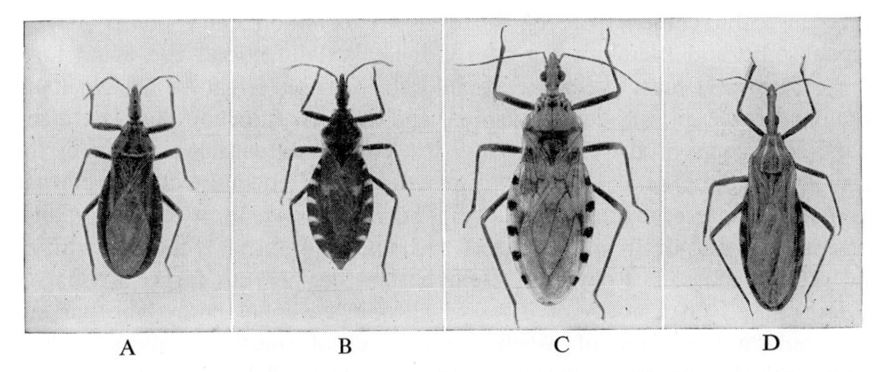

Fig. 31. Examples of Reduviidae: (*A*) *Triatoma protracta;* (*B*) *Triatoma sanguisuga;* (*C*) *Panstrongylus geniculatus;* and (*D*) *Rhodnius pallescens.*

pain, intense itching and much swelling . . . with red blotches and welts all over the body and limbs." The effect of the bite may last for months; however, it usually disappears within a few days. In Hawaii *Triatoma rubrofasciata* produces similar symptoms, the feeding bites resulting in intensely itching welts that may become swollen and painful.

The "two spotted corsairs," *Rasahus biguttatus* (Say) and *R. thoracicus* Stål (Fig. 30B), belong to the subfamily Piratinae, the former common in the southern United States, Cuba, and South America, and giving way to the latter in the Northwest and California. Bites of these species are the cause of many complaints; in southern California they are often mistakenly considered as "spider bites."

Relief from bites may be obtained by using lotions containing 0.25 per cent or more of menthol; 1 per cent phenol or 2 per cent camphor may give temporary relief.[8]

Chagas' disease (American trypanosomiasis, also known as Brazilian trypanosomiasis) was first described in 1909 by Chagas from Brazil. Chagas named the causative organism *Schizotrypanum cruzi* (now more generally known as *Trypanosoma cruzi*), a spindle-shaped trypanosome with a single flagellum and a characteristic undulating membrane. The trypanosome occurs sparsely in human blood; hence, diagnosis of the infection by recovery of the organism from the blood is very difficult. The diagnostic method of Brumpt[3] (xenodiagnosis) is now widely used. Essentially, this method involves the use of appropriate noninfected (clean) *Triatoma* bugs, which are allowed to feed upon a person suspected of having the disease, and after incubation in the body of the insect the trypanosomes, if present, may be recovered very easily from the digestive tract of the bug either by dissection or by microscopic sampling of feces taken from the rectum by means of a slender pipette.

The most apparent symptom of Chagas' disease in most cases is the unilateral swelling of the eyelid and face known as the sign of Romaña. This is because the conjunctivae of the eyes are common entry points for the trypanosome and therefore the site of the initial infection. The acute form of the disease is most prevalent in children in whom it causes a high, long-continued fever, facial edema, adenitis, and anemia. Infection may last many years. Symptoms of the chronic stage are commonly cardiac because of the cardiotropism of the causal organisms; death is frequently due to chronic myocarditis and is commonly sudden. The *Leishmania* form of the trypanosome invades and destroys endothelial and other cells, notably those of cardiac and skeletal muscles. Romaña[16] re-emphasizes the nervous forms of Chagas' disease, based on a study of cases of chronic encephalopathy; the patients presented "a syndrome of psychic states and of spastic paralysis," which agrees with the classical descriptions of Chagas and Villela. The disease occurs in man throughout most of South and Central America from Argentina to Mexico. It has been recorded in Texas,[26] and it has probably occurred, though unreported or not diagnosed, in areas of the Southwest near the Mexican border. In reservoir animals the infection occurs rather widely in the southern United States, particularly in the Southwest.

Transmission of the Infection. Chagas reported successful transmission of the infection through the agency of *Panstrongylus megistus,* but believed it was effected through the bite of the insect. Brumpt,[2] using *Rhodnius prolixus* Stål, disproved the salivary theory of transmission by demonstrating that the infectious stage of the life cycle of the trypanosome is completed in the hindgut of the insect and that infection reaches the victim in the feces of the bug, which almost invariably defecates on the skin of its victim while in the act of sucking blood. From the soiled skin trypanosomes are readily transferred by fingers or otherwise to the highly receptive conjunctiva of the eye or the mucosa of the mouth or nose, where entry of the infectious agent takes place. Inoculation may also be effected by *rubbing in* the organisms through the excoriated skin, e.g., by scratching. The incubation period in man is said to be from 10 to 12 days.

Although bugs may receive infection from man, it is no doubt usually received from reservoir animals. Bugs may become infected through so-called "cannibalism," or the feeding of nymphs on engorged nymphs, apparently without any detriment to the latter.[17] The percentage of *Triatoma* found infected in nature is startling; thus, studies of this nature by various workers in widely separated areas cited by Usinger[21] showed that 43 per cent of 4181 bugs were infected. Aside from transmission associated with the bite of triatomines, the possibility of congenital transmission of Chagas' disease must be considered; three such cases were recorded by Howard et al.[5]

Panstrongylus megistus (Burmeister), a bug with distinctly domestic habits, is the chief vector of the disease in Brazil. This is a rather large bug, 21 to 34 mm in length, blackish in color, with four reddish spots on the pronotum and a series of six reddish spots on each side of the abdomen. In the south of Brazil and in Uruguay, Paraguay, Argentina, Chile, and southern Bolivia, this species is replaced in importance by *Triatoma infestans* (Klug), also a highly domestic species. *Triatoma infestans* is a little smaller, its head is longer, and the red spots on the pronotum are lacking. At least eleven additional Triatominae in Argentina,[1] and an equal number in Brazil, have been found naturally infected with *Trypanosoma cruzi*.

Among the conenose bugs which have been found naturally infected in the area extending from northern South America into the United States are the following: *Rhodnius prolixus* Stål in Mexico and Venezuela; *Panstrongylus geniculatus* (Latreille) in Brazil and Panama; *Nesotriatoma flavida* (Neiva) in Cuba; *Triatoma dimidiata* (Latreille) in Mexico, Panama, Guatemala, and San Salvador; *Triatoma rubida* (Uhler), *T. hegneri* Mazzotti, *T. barberi* Usinger, and *T. phyllosoma* (Burmeister), all in Mexico; *T. sanguisuga* (LeConte), *T. sanguisuga ambigua* Neiva, *T. gerstaeckeri* (Stål), and *T. protracta woodi* Usinger in Texas; *T. recurva* Stål, *T. protracta* Uhler, and *T. rubida uhleri* Neiva in Arizona. In California S. F. Wood[25] found a high natural infection in *Triatoma protracta* (Uhler), namely, 25 per cent of 816 bugs examined.

The infection occurs in natural reservoirs such as armadillos, opossums, house mice, rats (Norway), bats (several species), cats, dogs, squirrels (*Sciurus*), and wood rats.

Kofoid and Donat[9] reported on the occurrence of the infection in the wood rat, *Neotoma fuscipes macrotis* Thomas, in San Diego County, California, with *Triatoma protracta* as the vector. Fae Donat Wood,[24] reporting more fully, states that the bloodsucking bug, *T. protracta,* and the wood rat, *Neotoma fuscipes macrotis,* are natural carriers of *Trypanosoma cruzi* in southern California. She was able experimentally to infect the following animals with the trypanosome: albino rats, albino mice, rhesus monkeys, a puppy, an opossum, the dusky-footed wood rat, and five species of white-footed mice. Ryckman[18] succeeded in obtaining fatal infections in the lizard, *Gerrhonotus multicarinatus webbi* Baird, a common co-inhabitant of *Neotoma* lodges, both by injection of *Triatoma* feces and by feeding *Triatoma* to the lizards.

Several species of bed bugs are capable of transmitting the infection experimentally, as well as many species of ticks, among these *Amblyomma cajennense* (Fabricius), *Rhipicephalus sanguineus* (Latreille), *Ornithodorus moubata* (Murray), and *O. savignyi* (Audouin). *Ornithodorus turicata* (Duges) has been proven to be an experimental vector of the Brazilian strain by Wheeler.[23]

Control. The medical and social importance of Chagas' disease is being widely recognized with the growing knowledge of the disease and particularly with the advance in the knowledge of its vectors. Although the use of certain antibiotics and antimalarial drugs shows promise in its chemotherapy, measures to prevent the spread of the infection should still be aimed at the suppression of the insect vectors and limitation of reservoir animals. The widespread distribution and common occurrence of both vectors and reservoirs add tremendously to the difficulty of the problem. Educational measures that will reach the general public in all infested areas are of paramount importance.

The triatomines which serve as important vectors of Chagas' disease have domestic habits; they hide in cracks in floors and walls and in and under furniture in poorly constructed rural dwellings. The reservoir animals may live in burrows around and under the same building. It is generally agreed that one of the major approaches to the problem is improvement in housing conditions in endemic areas to reduce and exclude reservoir animals (both wild and domestic) and to prevent entrance and multiplication of the responsible insects.

Disinfection of sleeping quarters, dwellings, and outhouses by the use of benzene hexachloride is recommended. Extensive campaigns have been carried on, with the use of this insecticide, in Brazil, Argentina, Chile, and other parts of South America, and, to date, development of resistance has not been recorded. DDT has proven ineffective against *Triatoma infestans* and *Panstrongylus megistus.*

KEY TO SOME PREDACEOUS NORTH AMERICAN REDUVIIDAE LIKELY TO BE OF MEDICAL IMPORTANCE*

1. Hemelytra with a quadrangular or discoidal cell at the base of the membrane. Subfamily Harpactocorinae.......................... 2
   Hemelytra without a quadrangular or discoidal cell at the base of the membrane.. 4
2. Sides of mesosternum without a tubercle or fold in front. Basal segment of beak about as long as front portion of head. Tribe Zelini........
   ....*Zelus socius* Uhler
   ....*Zelus exsanguis* (Stål)
   Sides of mesosternum with a tubercle or fold in front of the hind angles of the prosternum. First segment of the beak longer than front portion of head. Tribe Harpactocorini.................................. 3
3. Front femora but little, if at all, thickened, unarmed, a little granulated. Pronotum produced posteriorly over scutellum and with a high median tuberculate ridge. Form robust..............*Arilus cristatus* (Linnaeus)
   Front femora thickened, spinose, densely granulated. Pronotum not produced or elevated as above. Form slender. Genus *Sinea;* several species, for example.............................*Sinea diadema* (Fabricius)
4. Pronotum constricted behind the middle. Front coxae with outer sides flat or concave. Subfamily Piratinae........................... 5
   Pronotum constricted at or before the middle. Front coxae not flattened, their outer sides concave... 6
5. Apical portion of anterior tibia angularly dilated beneath, the spongy fossa being preceded by a small prominence. Hemelytra entirely black........................*Melanolestes picipes* (Herrich-Schaeffer)
   Tibia not dilated, the spongy fossa elongate. Corium and membrane of hemelytra each marked with a yellow spot.....*Rasahus biguttatus* (Say)†
6. Antennae inserted on top of head between margins close to eyes. Antenniferous tubercles not projecting from sides of head. Beak stout, distinctly curved. Front of head turned downward. Subfamily Reduviinae.......
   ....*Reduvius personatus* (Linnaeus)
   Antennae inserted in lateral or dorsolateral margins of head. Antenniferous tubercles projecting slightly from sides of head. Beak slender and relatively straight. Head strongly produced anteriorly. Subfamily Triatominae 7
7. Head very long and slender with antennae inserted near the apex. Clypeus widened apically. Tribe Rhodniini...............*Rhodnius prolixus* Stål
   Head moderately long with the antennae inserted at or behind anteocular region. Clypeus narrowed apically. Tribe Triatomini................ 8
8. Size large, over 24 mm in length................................ 9
   Size smaller, 24 mm or less in length........................... 11

* Prepared originally by Dr. Robert L. Usinger for purposes of this book, and expanded by Dr. Reece I. Sailer.

† Also, *R. thoracicus* Stål, considered by some a synonym of *R. biguttatus.*

9. Second antennal segment with erect bristles as long as or longer than thickness of segments.................... *Triatoma dimidiata* (Latreille)
   Second antennal segment with shorter decumbent hairs.............. 10
10. First antennal segment short, not reaching apex of clypeus. Upper body surface almost naked, hairs short appressed.. *Triatoma gerstaeckeri* (Stål)
   First antennal segment reaching or exceeding apex of clypeus. Upper surface of body clothed with distinct curved black hairs.............
   .... *Triatoma phyllosoma* (Burmeister)
11. Upper surface of body hairy, the hairs rather short, stiff, dense.........
   .... *Triatoma lectularius* (Stål)
   Upper surface of body entirely naked or with very sparse, inconspicuous, very short appressed hairs.................................... 12
12. Eyes relatively large, about half or more as wide as interocular space. Posterior prolongation of scutellum long, cylindrical, not turned down at apex................................ *Triatoma sanguisuga* Leconte
   Eyes small, always distinctly less than half the width of the interocular space. Posterior prolongation of scutellum short, tapering throughout and turned down at apex.................. *Triatoma protracta* (Uhler)

SOME OTHER BUGS

Some aquatic hemiptera may leave the water at night and fly toward artificial lights. Among these are the Belostomatidae or giant water bugs, which include the largest living Hemiptera, some of which attain a length of 3 inches. The adults, sometimes known as "electric light bugs," have been known to attack a person during their nightly flights and to bite severely. Matheson has recorded an instance of a flicker being attacked and killed, the proboscis of the bug having penetrated the bird's brain.

The back swimmers, family Notonectidae, another aquatic group, bite viciously when handled roughly. The Germans sometimes refer to these insects as *Wasserbienen,* or water bees. Several groups of terrestrial predators may at times bite man. Minute bugs of the family Anthocoridae may suck blood and cause very irritating bites, particularly on warm sunny days. In the United States, *Orius tristicolor* (White) and *O. insidiosus* (Say) have been known to act in this capacity. Some normally phytophagous hemiptera, such as Tingidae, the lace bugs, have been known to bite man.

KEY TO THE PRINCIPAL FAMILIES OF HEMIPTERA-HETEROPTERA OF NORTH AMERICA WHICH CONTAIN PREDACEOUS SPECIES*

1. Antennae at least as long as the head; either free or, in the Phymatidae, fitting in a groove beneath the lateral margins of the pronotum. Suborder Gymnocerata.. 6

* Prepared by Dr. Robert L. Usinger for purposes of this book; with slight modifications.

Antennae shorter than the head and nearly or quite concealed in a cavity beneath the eyes. Suborder Cryptocerata 2

2. Ocelli present. Shore-frequenting insects (toad bugs) .... Gelastocoridae
   Ocelli absent. Aquatic forms 3
3. Hind tarsi with indistinct, setiform claws (except in the minute, 3 mm or less, Pleinae). Swim with ventral side upward (back swimmers) .... Notonectidae
   Hind tarsi with distinct claws 4
4. Membrane of the hemelytra without veins. Abdomen without caudal appendages (water creepers) .... Naucoridae
   Membrane of the hemelytra with distinct veins. Abdomen with caudal appendages 5
5. Caudal appendages of abdomen long and slender. Tarsi one-segmented (water scorpions) .... Nepidae
   Caudal appendages of abdomen short, flat, and retractile. Tarsi two-segmented (giant water bugs) .... Belostomatidae
6. Apex of last tarsal segment more or less split. Claws of at least the front tarsi inserted before the apex. Superfamily Gerroidea 7
   Last segment of hind tarsi entire, with claws of all the legs inserted at apex 8
7. Hind femora much surpassing apex of abdomen. Middle and hind coxae approximate, distant from front ones (water striders) .... Gerridae
   Hind femora scarcely surpassing tip of abdomen. Middle coxae (except in *Rhagovelia*) equally distant from front and hind ones (broad-shouldered water striders) .... Veliidae
8. Head very long, at least as long as the three thoracic segments combined. Body linear. Legs and antennae very long and slender (marsh-treaders) .... Hydrometridae
   Head shorter than pronotum and scutellum together 9
9. Antennae five-segmented. (Only members of the subfamily Asopinae are predaceous. These have nonraptorial front legs, three-segmented tarsi, and the first segment of the beak short, thick, and free) (stink bugs) .... Pentatomidae
   Antennae four-segmented (except in one genus of the Hebridae and the genus *Pagasa* of the Nabidae, where they are five-segmented, and in the ectrichodine genus *Rhiginia* of the Reduviidae, where they are eight-segmented. These exceptions do not have the combination of characters listed under Asopinae) 10
10. Beak three-segmented 11
    Beak four-segmented 16
11. Front legs more or less raptorial. Head cylindrical. Prosternum with a median longitudinal stridulatory groove which receives the tip of the beak 12
    Front legs not raptorial. Head rarely cylindrical. Prosternum without a median longitudinal stridulatory groove between the front coxae 13
12. Front legs with greatly thickened femora (ambush bugs) .... Phymatidae
    Front legs somewhat thickened but much less than half as wide as long (assassin bugs) .... Reduviidae

13. Hemelytra with a cuneus (i.e., apical triangular region of corium separated by a fracture) (flower bugs) . . . . Anthocoridae
Hemelytra without a cuneus 14
14. Ocelli absent. Hemelytra reduced to small pads, without any trace of a membrane. Body oval in form (bed bugs, bat bugs, etc.) . . . . . Cimicidae
Ocelli present 15
15. Membrane, when present, without veins. Clavus of same texture as membrane. Body linear (water treaders) . . . . Mesoveliidae
Membrane with distinct, looped veins. Clavus and corium alike in texture. Body suboval (shore bugs) . . . . Saldidae
16. Hemelytra lacelike, the body and wings with reticulate sculpturing. Small bugs, usually under 5 mm in length (lace bugs) . . . . Tingidae
Hemelytra not lacelike, the body and wings not reticulate 17
17. Hemelytra with a cuneus (as defined in couplet 13) (leaf bugs) . . . . Miridae
Hemelytra without a cuneus 18
18. Body densely clothed with a very short, velvety pile. Membrane without veins (velvet water bugs) . . . . Hebridae
Body not clothed with a velvet pile 19
19. Hemelytra reduced to small pads. Ctenidia (combs of thick flat spines) present at least on under side of head and often on antennae, head, pronotum, and elsewhere (bat bugs) . . . . Polyctenidae
Hemelytra usually well developed. Without ctenidia 20
20. Front legs raptorial. Beak with basal segment stout and very short 21
Front legs not raptorial. Beak long and slender, the first segment long, held between the bucculae at rest 22
21. Hemelytra entirely membranous (gnat bugs) . . . . Enicocephalidae
Hemelytra with basal portions thickened to form a corium distinct from the apical membrane (damsel bugs) . . . . Nabidae
22. Membrane with numerous veins which more or less run together (squash bug, etc.) . . . . Coreidae
Membrane with only four or five simple veins usually arising from the base (chinch bug, etc.) . . . . Lygaeidae

REFERENCES

1. Abalos, J. W., and Wygodzinsky, P., 1951. *Las Triatominae Argentinas (Reduviidae, Hemiptera)*. Tucumán: Univ. Nac., Inst. de Med. Regional, Pub. 601, Mon. 2. 179 pp.

2. Brumpt, E., 1912. "La *Trypanosoma cruzi* evolue chez *Conorhinus megistus, Cimex lectularius, Cimex boueti* et *Ornithodorus moubata,* cycle evolutiv de ce parasite," *Bull. Soc. path. exot.,* **5:**360.

3. Brumpt, E., 1914. "Le xénodiagnostic application au diagnostic de quelques infections parasitaires et en particulier à la Trypanosome de Chagas," *Bull. Soc. path. exot.,* **7:**706–10.

4. Hall, Maurice C., 1924. "Lesions due to the bite of the wheel-bug, *Arilus cristatus* (Hemiptera; Reduviidae)," *Arch. Int. Med.,* **33:**513–15.

5. Howard, Jorge E.; Rios, Carlos; Ebensperger, Ines; and Olivos, Patricio; 1957. "Enfermedad de Chagas congénita," *Bol. Chileno de Parasitol.,* **12:**42–45.

6. Howard, L. O., 1899. *The Insects to Which the Name "Kissing Bugs" Became Applied during the Summer of 1899.* Washington, D. C.: Dept. Agric., in Div. Entomol. Bull., no. 22.

7. Joyeux, Charles, 1913. "Biologie de *Cimex boueti,*" *Arch. de parasit.,* **16:**140–46.

8. Keh, Benjamin, 1956. "Cone-nosed bugs of California," *Calif. Vector Views,* **3:**47–50.

9. Kofoid, Charles A., and Donat, Fae, 1933. "South American trypanosomiasis of the human type—occurrence in mammals in the United States," *Calif. & West. Med.,* **38:**245–49.

10. Lee, Robert D., 1955. "The biology of the Mexican chicken bug, *Haematosiphon inodorus* (Duges)," *Pan-Pacific Entomol.,* **31:**47–61.

11. Marlatt, C. L., 1946. "Bedbugs and their control," *Pest Control and Sanitation,* **1:**8–11.

12. Miller, N. C. E., 1956. *The Biology of the Heteroptera.* London: Leonard Hill (books) Ltd. 162 pp.

13. Neiva, A., and Lent, H., 1941. "Sinopse dos triatomideos," *Rev. de Entomol.,* **12:**61–92.

14. Readio, P. A., 1926. "Studies on the eggs of some Reduviidae (Heteroptera)," Lawrence: Univ. Kansas, in *Sc. Bull.,* **16:**157–79.

15. Readio, P. A., 1927. "Studies on the biology of the Reduviidae of America north of Mexico," Lawrence: Univ. Kansas, in *Sc. Bull.,* **17:**1–289.

16. Romaña, C., 1947. "Miocarditis cronica equizo trepanosica," *An. d. Inst. med. regional,* Univ. Nacional de Tucumán, Argentina, **2:**1–39.

17. Ryckman, Raymond E., 1951. "Recent observations of cannibalism in *Triatoma* (Hemiptera: Reduviidae)," *J. Parasitol.,* **37:**433–34.

18. Ryckman, Raymond E., 1954. "Lizards: a laboratory host for Triatominae and *Trypanosoma cruzi* Chagas," *Trans. Am. Microscop. Soc.,* **73:**215–18.

19. Ryckman, Raymond E., 1958. "Description and biology of *Hesperocimex sonorensis,* new species, an ectoparasite of the purple martin (Hemiptera: Cimicidae)," *Ann. Entomol. Soc. Amer.,* **51:**33–47.

20. Usinger, Robert L., 1934. "Bloodsucking among phytophagous Hemiptera," *Canad. Entomol.,* **66:**97–100.

21. Usinger, Robert L., 1944. *The Triatominae of North and Central America and the West Indies and Their Public Health Significance.* Washington, D. C.: Govt. Print. Office, in Public Health Bull., no. 288. iv + 83 pp.

22. Usinger, Robert L., 1947. "Native hosts of the Mexican chicken bug, *Haematosiphon inodora* (Duges)," *Pan-Pacific Entomol.,* 23:140.

23. Wheeler, Charles M., 1938. "Experimental infection of *Ornithodorus turicata* (Duges) with a Brazilian strain of *Trypanosoma cruzi* Chagas," *Proc. Soc. Exper. Biol. & Med.,* **38:**191–93.

24. Wood, Fae Donat, 1934. "Natural and experimental infection of *Triatoma protracta* (Uhler) and mammals in California with American human trypanosomiasis," *Am. J. Trop. Med.,* **14:**497–517.

25. Wood, S. F., 1942. "Observations on vectors of Chagas' disease in the United States. I. California," *Bull. Calif. Acad. Sc.*, **41** (pt. 2):61–69.

26. Woody, N. C., and Woody, H. B., 1955. "American trypanosomiasis (Chagas' disease), first indigenous case in the United States," *J.A.M.A.*, **159**:676–77.

27. Zimmerman, Elwood C., 1948. *Insects of Hawaii. Vol. 3, Heteroptera.* Honolulu: Univ. of Hawaii Press. 255 pp.

Chapter 8

THE LICE
The Sucking Lice*

Order Anoplura

General Characteristics. The sucking lice comprise the order Anoplura. Some believe them so closely related to the biting lice that both groups are placed in the same order, viz., Anoplura, with the Mallophaga (biting lice) reduced to a suborder, and the sucking lice placed in the suborder Siphunculata. Morphological evidence, according to Ferris,[7] does not support this view. For the purposes of this work the lice are classified as members of two orders, Anoplura (sucking) and Mallophaga (biting), resembling each other in many respects, but differing radically in their feeding habits, the former being bloodsuckers while the latter feed on scales, secretions, and detritus of the skin. Wings are absent in both groups, and metamorphosis is simple. The body is flattened; the legs are in part adapted for clinging to hairs and feathers. The Anoplura have a protrusible proboscis at the tip of the head. The biting lice are, as a rule, much more active than the sucking lice.

The Anoplura parasitize mammals, while the Mallophaga are parasites of both mammals and birds and in all cases are normally host-specific, permanent ectoparasites, very rarely, except accidentally or experimentally, transferable to a different species. The human body louse can be reared successfully on selected rabbits. The entire life cycle, egg to egg, is normally spent on one host.

Classification of Anoplura. Students technically concerned with the sucking lice will need to consult the classical works of Ferris, particularly his monograph of the species of the world.[7] The order comprises about 225 species arranged in six families, three of which include species of medical or veterinary importance: (1) the *Haematopinidae,* in which eyes are lacking and the abdominal segments bear strongly sclerotized paratergal plates (dorsolateral lobes), consist in the restricted sense of two genera, the common *Haematopinus* and the peculiar pecary parasite *Pecaroecus.* (2) The *Linognathidae,* often considered a part of the Haematopinidae, lack paratergal plates and all external evidence of eyes, except for one species that parasitizes camels; this family includes two genera of veterinary importance, namely, *Linognathus* and *Solenopotes.* (3) The *Pediculidae,* the only family that contains human parasites, have distinctly developed eyes; *Pediculus* and

* For extensive list of references (961) see "Bibliography on Lice and Man, with particular reference to wartime conditions," by Mary E. Grinnell, and Ina L. Hawes, U. S. Dept. Agric. Washington, D. C. *Bibliographical Bull.* no. 1, July, 1943.

Phthirus are referred to this family, although some authorities place the latter genus in a separate family. The genus *Pedicinus,* considered by most authorities to belong to the Pediculidae, is transferred on morphological grounds to another family (the Hoplopeuridae) by Ferris; members of this genus parasitize Old World monkeys of the superfamily Cercopithecoidae. The Haematomyzidae, included by some authors in the Anoplura and considered by others as a link between this order and the Mallophaga, has been placed by Ferris[6] in the Mallophagan suborder, Rhynchopthirina; this family includes but the single species *Haematomyzus elephantis* Piaget of the elephant.

The genus *Pediculus,* according to Ferris, includes only three or four species: (1) *Pediculus humanus* Linnaeus, the head louse and body louse of man; (2) *Pediculus mjöbergi* Ferris of *Ateles* apes; (3) *Pediculus shäffi*

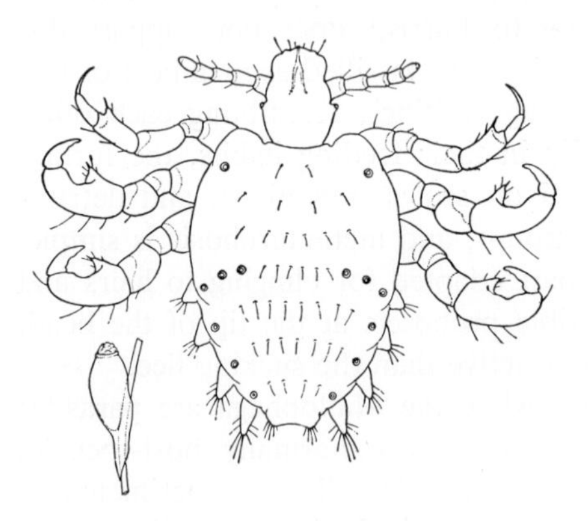

Fig. 32. The pubic louse, *Phthirus pubis.* Egg attached to hair, lower left.

Fahrenholz, of the chimpanzee; and (4) possibly *Pediculus pseudohumanus* Ewing, described from a monkey (*Pithecia monachus*), and subsequently recorded by Ewing from aboriginal man in tropical America and Polynesia. The nomenclature affecting the species considered here as *Pediculus humanus* has been confused in the literature. Ferris has discussed this subject in detail. The names adopted here, in accordance with the usage of Ferris and of the Entomological Society of America, are *Pediculus humanus humanus* Linnaeus for the body louse (= *P. humanus corporis* and *P. vestimenti* of much of the literature) and *Pediculus humanus capitis* De Geer (= *P. capitis*) for the head louse.

The genus *Phthirus* (also spelled *Phthirius*) includes the crab lice, *Phthirus pubis* (Linnaeus) of man, and *Phthirus gorillae* Ewing, of the gorilla.

The crab louse, *Phthirus pubis* (Linnaeus), also called pubic louse (Fig. 32), is easily recognized by its crablike appearance. It is 1.5 to 2 mm long, nearly as broad as long, and grayish white. Its middle and hind legs are much stouter than those of the head louse and the body louse. It infests the pubic regions particularly but also the armpits and more rarely other parts of the body, such as the mustache, beard, eyelashes, and eyebrows. The writer (Herms) has seen soldiers infested with this louse from the ankles to the eyebrows. These lice are remarkably stationary in their habits, often remaining attached for days at one point with mouth parts inserted into the skin. The pruritus caused by the bites of these parasites is very intense, and a discoloration of the skin usually results if the infestation continues for some time. The term *phthiriasis* may be employed to designate infestations of pubic lice, although the term *pubic pediculosis* is also used.

The female louse deposits its eggs on the coarser hairs of the body where the parasites occur. The number of eggs deposited per female is apparently quite small, although Nuttall[18] states that he would not be surprised to learn that 50 or more eggs may be laid. The incubation period seems to

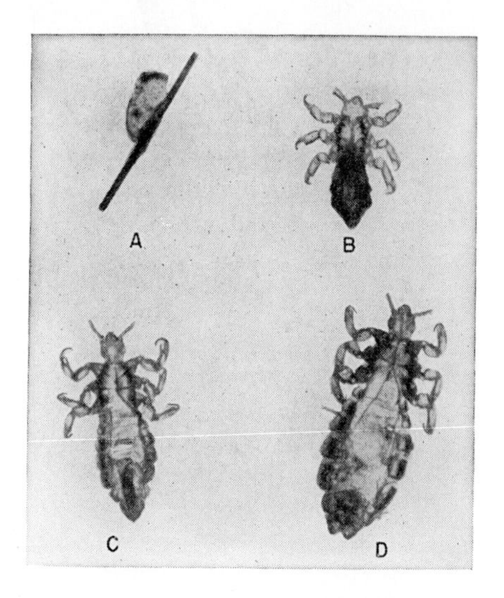

Fig. 33. Life cycle of the head louse, *Pediculus humanus capitis.* (*A*) Egg attached to hair; (*B*) nymph; (*C*) adult male; (*D*) adult female.

be 6 to 8 days. After three molts the adult stage was reached in Nuttall's experiments in from 15 to 17 days, and the egg-to-egg period was 22 to 27 days. Pubic louse infestations are very common among adults. Spread is usually by physical contact with infested individuals or use of infested toilet seats, blankets, etc.

The head louse, *Pediculus humanus capitis* De Geer (Fig 33), is gray in color, but is said to vary according to the color of the hair and color of the host (Murray[13]). The male averages 2 mm in length and the female 3 mm. This species occurs on the head, about the ears and occiput, but from reliable statements made by a number of observers in heavy infestations it may establish itself on other hairy parts of the body. In severe infestations the hair may become literally matted with eggs (nits), parasites, and exudate from the pustules which originate from the louse bite. The term *plica palonica* is applied (Stiles) to the fetid mass, forming a sort of carapace (*trichoma*), in which fungus may develop, and beneath which myriads of lice may be found.

The number of eggs deposited by the female ranges from 50 to 150. These are glued to the hair and hatch in from 5 to 10 days, an average of 7 days. Development is very rapid (incomplete metamorphosis with three molts), three weeks usually covering the entire cycle from egg to egg. Lice are easily disseminated by physical contact, stray hairs, etc., hence, slight infestations may occur under the best of sanitary conditions, particularly among school children. However, the continued presence of lice on head or body

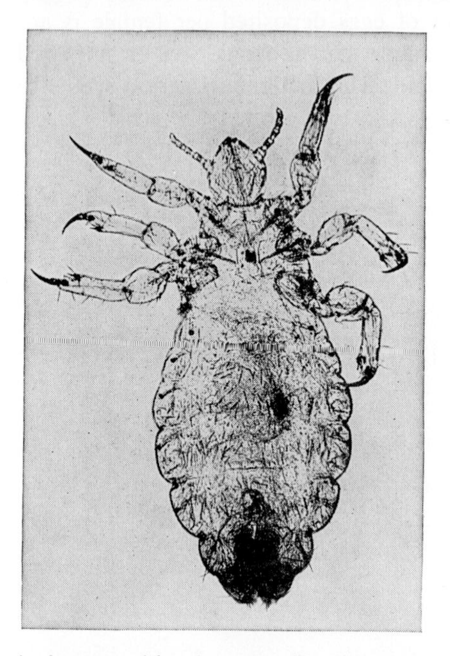

Fig. 34. Human body louse, *Pediculus humanus humanus*. × 15.

is inexcusable since eradication is simple if the proper lousicides are used. The mere use of soap and water in washing the head and hair is ineffective in destroying lice present in the hair.

The body louse, *Pediculus humanus humanus* Linnaeus (Fig. 34), is the common clothing louse which during World War I became known as the "cootie," also called the "gray-back." During World War II it became known as "mechanized dandruff."

Body lice infest the clothing where it comes in close contact with the body rather continuously, e.g., the fork of the trousers, the armpits, the waistline, neck, and shoulders. In his inspection of troops at delousing stations during World War I, the author (Herms) usually found lice on the underclothing, but the nits were generally found in the seams of the breeches at the crotch, if present at all. After all clothing was removed, lice were occasionally found on the body. Eggs are undoubtedly by preference deposited on fibers in the seams of clothing as already mentioned. Nuttall and others have satisfactorily proved that the body louse may at times attach its eggs to the coarser hairs of the body.

Nuttall[16] states that a female body louse may lay from 275 to 300 eggs, the average number laid per day being about 10 for 20 to 30 days. The shortest incubation period varies from 5 to 7 days when eggs are kept near the body at between 35° and 38° C. Hatching, according to Leeson[10] does not occur when the temperature reaches 23° C or below, nor at 38° C or higher. At 24° C the incubation period is 17 to 21 days; at 29° C it is from 9 to 11 days; at 35° C it is 5 to 7 days; at 38° C the eggs will not hatch. The effective zone for the egg stage is apparently from about 23° to 38° C.

After hatching, the young lice begin sucking blood at once and throughout their development feed frequently both day and night, particularly when the host is quiet. Maturity is reached in 16 to 18 days after oviposition. There are three molts. Females begin laying eggs a day or two after reaching maturity. The egg-to-egg cycle averages about 3 weeks. Unfed lice soon die; probably 10 days would cover the longest period of survival without food. However, if fed, lice may live from 30 to 40 days. Moist fecal matter in masses or spiral threads is extruded as the louse feeds; the feces dry quickly in the air. Death may lurk in the excrement of a louse.

Dissemination of Body Lice. Lice live normally on the surface of the body or in clothing being worn. Lice do not voluntarily leave unless the body grows cold in death or becomes hot with high fever. Even then they cannot travel far but are easily dislodged and may fall to the ground; they will quickly invade a new host if there is one close enough. Proof that lice are uncommon in blankets used by heavily infested troops was obtained by Peacock[19] who reports 0.8 per blanket and 31.4 per man including clothing. Louse infestation is mainly the result of contact with lousy persons or their infested clothing. As many as 10,428 lice and 10,253 nits have been reported on one shirt; in heavily infested populations one may readily collect 400 to 500 lice from one person.

Pediculosis. The presence of lice on any part of the body may be referred to as *pediculosis.* That louse bites may produce certain systemic disturbances seems to be indicated in a report made by Moore:[12]

> I started feeding about 700 to 800 twice a day. Almost immediately a general tired feeling was noticed in the calf of the legs and along the shin bones, while on the soles of the feet and underneath the toes this tired feeling was so intense as often to prevent sleep until late in the night. An irritable and pessimistic state of mind developed. An illness resulted with symptoms very similar to grip and a rash similar to German measles was present, particularly over the shoulders and abdomen.

The skin of persons who continuously harbor lice becomes hardened and deeply pigmented, a condition designated as *vagabond's disease* or *morbus errorum.* To relieve itching due to pediculosis a lotion made of 1 per cent spirits of thymol may be used, or a mixture of 5 per cent benzocaine, 2 per cent methyl salicylate, and 0.5 per cent salicylic acid made up with 70 per cent alcohol.

Epidemic relapsing fever has occurred in many parts of the world and was probably once cosmopolitan. Widespread epidemics no longer occur. Great epidemics did occur, however, during World War I, notably in Rumania and later in North Africa in 1921 and after World War II, in 1945–1946. There were frequent epidemics of this disease in Europe during the eighteenth and nineteenth centuries, and it was in the 1868 epidemic in Berlin that Obermeier observed "myriads of living and actively motile spirilla in the blood of relapsing fever patients during the febrile attacks." In 1873 during another epidemic Obermeier applied Ehrenberg's nomenclature and called these organisms "*Spirochaeta.*" To honor the discoverer of the organism in the blood of relapsing fever patients, Cohn gave the name *Spirochaeta obermeieri.* The name currently accepted by microbiologists is *Borellia recurrentis* (Lebert), although the combination *Spirochaeta recurrentis* (Lebert) has been widely used in the literature.

Although lice had long previously been under suspicion, it was not until 1907 that Mackie[11] in India secured evidence that relapsing fever is in part a louse-borne disease. He noted that the spirochetes multiplied within the gut of the lice and that they could be found in the ovary, testis, and the Malpighian tubules of the insect. Mackie believed that infection might result from the insect's regurgitating the contents of its gut into the wound in the act of feeding. Later (1912) Nicolle, Blaizot, and Conseil[14] failed to transmit the spirochetes through the bites of infected lice and found that the only reliable successful experiments involved the injection or subcutaneous inoculation of an extract of infected lice. On the basis of experiments in which men and monkeys were exposed to hundreds of bites, they concluded that infection results from spirochetes which collect under the fingernails and on the finger tips of an individual after he has crushed lice on his skin, and which, in scratching, he inoculates into the excoriated skin.

Nicolle and his colleagues also found that the spirochetes disappear from and later reappear in the louse. Only a few remain in the insect's intestine up to 5 or 6 hours after infection, and none after 24 hours; but they reappear in the insect in from 8 to 12 days and are then present in the general body cavity, none being found in the alimentary canal. The authors believe that the spirochetes were transmitted to the offspring of infected lice. Chung and Feng[3] (1936) have shown that transovarian transmission of *Borrelia recurrentis* does not occur in lice. They also state that the salivary glands and Malpighian tubules of infected lice do not contain the spirochetes, and that the feces of infected lice are not infectious. The gastric juice of lice is detrimental to the *Borrelia;* only about 1 to 5 per cent or less of the ingested spirochetes gain access to the tissue and coelomic cavity where multiplication takes place, multiplication being by transverse division.

Man is the reservoir of the louse-borne infection (man-to-louse-to-man). There must be a human carrier in a louse population. In tick-borne or endemic relapsing fever, endemicity is maintained in reservoir animals (rodents, etc.). Nuttall has reported that a single infective louse crushed upon the excoriated skin has produced relapsing fever. The incubation period in the human is from 6 to 10 days. The onset of the disease is sudden, with headache, chills and fever, and generalized pains. The fever remains high for 4 to 6 days and subsides abruptly, with an afebrile period of 4 to 8 days followed by one or more relapses. Mortality is usually low but may vary from 2 to 50 per cent, or even higher in crowded poverty-stricken and louse-infested populations. Microscopic (darkfield) examination of blood smears taken during febrile periods will readily reveal *Borrelia.* Mouse inoculation with the patient's blood will produce the organisms in the blood of the mouse in from 24 to 48 hours. (For tick-borne or endemic relapsing fever consult Chapter 19.)

European Typhus, Typhus Fever. Classical or epidemic typhus fever, known also by such names as tabardillo (Mexico), Brill's disease (United States), jail fever, or war fever, is a disease of ancient origin and wide distribution, chiefly in Europe, north Africa, Asia, and higher altitudes of Mexico and Central and South America. The causal organism is *Rickettsia prowazekii* Da Rocha-Lima. Whenever human beings are concentrated in close quarters, especially in times of war and famine, this disease may become rampant. It is chiefly a disease of winter and spring, with mortality from 15 to 75 per cent. The disease is characterized by a high fever continuing about two weeks, backache, intense headache, bronchial disturbances, mental confusion, stupor, a congested face (designated also as a "besotted expression"), and on the fifth or sixth day by a brick-red macular eruption on chest and abdomen, which later spreads to other parts of the body, even to hands, feet, and face. This mottling led to the belief that tabardillo of Mexico was identical with spotted fever of Montana, a supposition that was proven erroneous by Ricketts and Wilder.[21] Ricketts contracted typhus fever during the course of this investigation and died of the disease.

Prior to 1870, louse-borne typhus was widespread and endemic, or in some cases prevalent, throughout much of Europe, but since that date, except during times of national emergencies, there has been a gradual decline to the point that no lives were sacrificed to the disease during most of the period between World War I and World War II. During World War I, severe epidemics occurred in Russia, Poland, and the Balkan states. According to the *Statistical Bulletin* of the Metropolitan Life Insurance Company issued in November, 1941, Russia alone is said to have lost 2,500,000 to 3,000,000 of her people. Typhus fever was again threatening in the early years of World War II. During 1942 there were some 3000 cases in Egypt and about 80,000 in the rest of North Africa. When Allied forces landed in Italy in September, 1943, a typhus epidemic was threatening Naples, a city of nearly a million persons, where there was congestion, unsanitary living conditions, food scarcity, undernourishment, and confusion. The bombproof shelters were converted into "human warrens," in which bodies of dead and living were piled together with lice crawling over the bedclothes. In the course of the epidemic as high as 81 per cent of the victims died, and the city would have been virtually wiped out, except for the effectiveness of the delousing campaign that followed the Allied invasion. An excellent account of the Naples epidemic and its control has been given by Cushing.[5] A similar epidemic threatened in Cologne, Germany, but prompt action arrested it.

Transmission by Lice. That the louse, *Pediculus humanus,* is probably the sole agent in the transmission of typhus fever from man to man was shown by Nicolle *et al.*[15] (1909, working in Tunis) and Ricketts and Wilder[22] (1910, working in Mexico). The latter found that the monkey *Pithecus* (*Macaca*) *rhesus* (Desmarest) can be infected with tabardillo (Mexican typhus) invariably by the injection of virulent blood from man taken on the eighth to tenth day of fever, that the monkey may pass through an attack of typhus so mild that it cannot be recognized clinically and that immunity results. Typhus was transmitted to the monkey through the feeding of the louse in two experiments, the lice in one instance deriving their infection from man, and in another from the monkey. Another monkey was infected through the introduction of the feces and abdominal contents of infected lice into small incisions. There is a tendency to disregard the head louse, *P. humanus capitis,* as a vector of typhus; however, it must be remembered that Goldberger and Anderson[9] did succeed in transmitting typhus to a monkey by cutaneous injection of a saline suspension of crushed head lice.

Nuttall[17] points out that if lice (*Pediculus humanus humanus*) are crushed 9 or 10 days or if their feces are collected 3 to 6 days after they have fed on infective blood, the crushed lice or the feces are capable of producing infection if placed upon excoriated skin. The usual channel of infection is through fecal contamination, though it may be brought about also through the crushed body contents of the louse. The rickettsiae may remain alive and virulent in louse feces kept dry at room temperature for more than 60 days; thus, infection may be acquired through the respiratory passages by inhalation of minute particles of louse excrement. It is generally believed that the normal channel is through scratches and through contact with the conjunctivae or mucous membranes by fingers contaminated with louse feces.

The typhus fever patient is infectious for the louse, generally speaking, from early in the disease to about the tenth day, though later infections are possible. The rickettsiae multiply enormously in the midgut of the louse, the epithelial cells become so distended after a few days that they rupture, and enormous numbers of rickettsiae appear in the insect's feces. It appears that infected lice may die in a week or 10 days because of the enormous multiplication of these organisms. Few lice become infected while feeding on a typhus fever patient, probably less than half. If a louse survives the infection, it remains infective for the rest of its life.

Murine (flea-borne) typhus fever is a much milder disease, maintained in nature in rats and transmitted to man by rat fleas. The use of the terms "endemic" and "epidemic" to distinguish the "flea-borne" from the "louse-borne" strain of typhus is open to criticism, since both must have an endemicity to survive and both may be epidemic at times. (The relation of fleas to murine typhus is discussed in Chapter 18.)

Trench fever, also known as five-day fever, Wolhynian fever, shank fever, and, His-Wernerische Krankheit, is a nonfatal disease characterized by sudden onset of fever, headache, dizziness, pains in the muscles and bones, particularly in the legs, with especial tenderness of the shins, and lasting 24 to 48 hours or longer, followed at intervals of about 5 days by other attacks of fever of less and less severity. This disease was first noticed during World War I when, under conditions of trench warfare, it became of considerable importance, involving at least 1,000,000 men. It reappeared in Yugoslavia and the Ukraine during World War II.

The causal organism of trench fever is believed to be *Rickettsia quintana* Schminke. This organism is found in the stomach lumen of the louse, while *Rickettsia prowazekii* of typhus invades the epithelial cells. As in the case of endemic typhus, infection is acquired, not by the bite of the louse, but through louse feces or crushed bodies coming in contact with the broken skin.

Tularemia. Though there is no evidence of louse transmission in nature, Price[20] has shown that *P. humanus humanus* can be infected experimentally with *Pasteurella tularensis* and that the bacterium will multiply extensively in some of the lice. Lice infected as first-stage nymphs were capable of retaining the infection to the adult stage, and tularemia organisms retained for 35 days showed no significant reduction of virulence for white mice.

Delousing methods practiced over a long period of years prior to and including the early part of World War II were cumbersome and usually expensive. The results were as a rule not wholly satisfactory in that the recently deloused individual was immediately subject to reinfestation if exposed to lousy persons. The method usually consisted of proper bathing plus treatment of clothing by laundering, ironing or the application of dry heat, steam sterilization, or a louse powder consisting chiefly of naphthalene. Dry storage of garments for three weeks or more was assumed to be sufficient to kill lice by starvation. Methyl bromide, a fumigant which would destroy all stages of the louse but which was dangerous to use, was developed in the intervals between the two World Wars.

Lousicides. Great credit is due to the group of workers stationed at the

Orlando, Florida, laboratory of the United States Bureau of Entomology and Plant Quarantine who developed the MYL insecticide powder. This mixture is composed of pyrethrins with or without allethrin, a synergist (*N*-isobutylundecylenamide or, in more recent formulations, sulfoxide), an ovicide (2,4-dinitroanisole), and an antioxidant (Phenol S), in pyrophyllite. It has a very rapid effect against all species of human lice and not only repels them but also kills them and their eggs. The powder is dusted lightly into the seams of the underclothing or on the infested parts of the body at weekly intervals.

The standard lousicide, except in areas where resistance is encountered, is 10 per cent DDT in pyrophyllite. DDT has an advantage over MYL powder in its residual action, but it is slow to take effect, and it is not an ovicide. A single application can eradicate an infestation, however, since the eggs normally hatch in less than two weeks and the young nymphs will be killed by the residual insecticide. The use of DDT was largely responsible for the success of the Naples campaign, although MYL powder was used in its earlier stages. A serious blow to the louse control program occurred in Korea during the winter of 1950–51 when it was found that DDT would no longer kill these pests. Resistance has subsequently been demonstrated in Japan, Egypt, and other parts of the world. One per cent lindane in pyrophyllite may be used where DDT-resistant strains are encountered, although resistance to this insecticide is also becoming widespread. Lindane does not have as lasting a residual action, so a second application within 7 to 10 days is recommended. Synergized pyrethrins (pyrethrins plus sulfoxide or piperonyl butoxide) are also effective substitutes for DDT, and it now appears as though malathion powders may be added to this list.[4]

Procedure. During the Naples epidemic in World War II, the number of dustings for lice was reported as 3,265,786. Wheeler[23] described the procedure as follows:

> It consisted essentially of forcefully blowing powder, by hand dusters or power dusters between the layers of clothing worn by the individual and between the innermost layer of clothing and the skin of the body. This was accomplished by a uniform technique, inserting the nozzle of the duster up the sleeves, down the neck (both front and back), around the waistline and into the crotch area of clothing. Hair and any cap or hat were dusted thoroughly. An infested person properly dusted is no longer a menace to others and will remain so for a period of at least two weeks, at the end of which he should be redusted. Approximately 1 to 1 1/2 oz of powder per person is sufficient to insure the thorough dusting of all clothing worn.

In the use of *louse powders under military conditions,* dusting with powder dust guns should follow a certain routine to avoid missing some parts of the clothing being worn. Also, in spite of the fact that few lice occur in blankets, bedding, extra clothing, and mattresses, these must be dusted to prevent reinfestation. If the treatment is done by the individual himself with a "sifter can," it is necessary to remove all clothing from the body. From 1 1/2 to 2 oz of the powder are needed on an average per person; however, under field conditions as much as 4 oz may be needed. Lice are usually killed in 24 hours, but the eggs are not killed; however, because of the lasting qualities of DDT all the young lice will be killed eventually on hatching. Where troops are working in intimate contact with infested populations, semimonthly dusting is recommended to prevent reinfestation.

More lasting results can be obtained through the use of DDT-impregnated clothing. Impregnation of clothing may be feasible particularly under military conditions and may be accomplished by dipping garments in a cleaning solvent or in water containing the desired amount of DDT. The method is described more fully in United States Department of Agriculture Circular No. 977, 1955. Two suits of properly impregnated underwear should keep an individual free from lice during a winter. For treatment of clothing, a dosage of DDT equivalent to about 2 per cent of the dry weight is generally recommended. A garment properly treated should remain effective through 6 to 8 launderings.

Classical typhus has been the scourge of armies throughout recorded history. During World War I military hospitals in the Balkan countries were crowded with typhus patients, thousands being admitted daily during 1915. In striking contrast, there were only 64 cases of louse-borne typhus in the American Army during all of World War II (Philip).

Treatment for Head Lice. Among the many and various methods employed in the eradication of head lice, from the primitive use of fingers, still a practice among natives as many of us have observed, and the use of a fine-toothed comb dipped in kerosene, which some of us have experienced, to the most modern use of DDT louse powder, only two can be recommended today:

1. Dusting the hair and scalp with DDT or MYL louse powder previously described, rubbing the powder in with the hands; an additional treatment is suggested in a week to 10 days later; the head should not be washed for at least 24 hours after each treatment. For a heavy infestation, or against DDT-resistant strains, the MYL powder should be used. MYL stops the activity of lice very quickly, whereas with DDT the lice become abnormally active and may cause intense irritation of the skin before they die.

2. NBIN formula, recommended by the United States Bureau of Entomology and Plant Quarantine:* benzyl benzoate 68 parts by weight, DDT 6 parts, benzocaine (or ethyl *p*-aminobenzoate) 12 parts, and Tween 80 (sorbitan monooleate, polyoxyethylene derivative) 14 parts; dilute in 5 volumes of water and apply to scalp and hair; one treatment will kill all lice and nits.

Treatment for Crab Lice. Usually the treatments effective against head lice can also be used against crab lice, *Phthirus pubis.* The liquid or powder

* Publication 606 on DDT.

must be applied to the pubic and anal regions of the body, under the arms and wherever the body is hairy; in particularly hairy persons the lousicide must be applied from neck to foot, perhaps also to the eyebrows and beard. Whatever material is used, it must be well distributed and must reach the skin. DDT, MYL, and NBIN (already described), as well as 5 per cent rotenone in 10 parts of petrolatum, are all effective if used as directed.

Anoplura Affecting Domesticated Mammals. The important sucking lice of domesticated ungulate mammals belong to three genera, *Haematopinus,* in the family Haematopinidae, and *Linognathus* and *Solenopotes,* in the family Linognathidae. *Swine* have one species of louse, *Haematopinus suis* (Linnaeus) (= *adventicius* Neumann) (Figs. 35, 36). This is the largest

35 36

Fig. 35. Hog louse, *Haematopinus suis.* × 7.
Fig. 36. Nits (eggs) of the hog louse attached to the hairs of the host. One of the eggs has hatched. × 10.

species of the entire group, measuring as much as 5 to 6 mm in length; it is cosmopolitan in distribution. According to Florence[8] hog lice feed readily on man but will not feed on guinea pigs.

Cattle lice belonging to the Anoplura number four species, namely: (1) *Linognathus vituli* (Linnaeus), commonly known as the long-nosed ox louse or "blue louse," measuring about 2 mm in length and distinguished from the next species by its long nose and slender body; cosmopolitan in distribution; (2) *Haematopinus eurysternus* (Nitzsch), the cosmopolitan short-nosed ox louse, somewhat larger (3.5 to 4.75 mm in length) than the former and much broader in proportion; (3) *Haematopinus tuberculatus* (Burmeister), the buffalo louse, infests cattle in parts of Australia; common on cattle and carabao in India; absent in North America; measures from 3.5 to 5.5 mm; resembles *H. eurysternus* closely but differs in that the number of setae at the margin of the abdominal segments caudal of the paratergal plates is usually eight or more (may be five or six); (4) *Solenopotes capillatus* Enderlein has been redescribed by Bishopp[1] and shown to have a wide distribution in the United States as well as in many other parts of the world. It is known as the little blue cattle louse. It measures from 1.2 to 1.5 in length and in general appearance resembles the short-nosed ox louse.

Horses, mules, and *asses* are frequently infested with one species of sucking louse, *Haematopinus asini* (Linnaeus), which measures from 2.5 to 3.5 mm in length. It resembles the hog louse except that the head is relatively longer and more robust. *Sheep* in some parts of the United States are affected by the so-called foot louse, *Linognathus pedalis* (Osborn). *Dogs* are commonly heavily infested with *Linognathus piliferus* (Burmeister), and *rabbits* harbor *Haemodipsus ventricosus* (Denny).

THE BITING LICE

Order Mallophaga

The biting lice (Mallophaga), of which there are about 2700 described species in the world, are much more numerous than the Anoplura but are of little medical importance. Most of them attack birds but some, particularly members of the family Trichodectidae, are ectoparasites of mammals. The injury done by them is largely restricted to poultry, although some trouble may result when mammals are badly infested. Man is attacked only by accident, if at all. Poultry suffer from irritation or itching caused by the creeping insect and their incessant gnawing at the skin. Some species, such as the chicken body louse, *Menacanthus stramineus,* frequently obtain blood by gnawing through the skin or by rupturing the quills of pinfeathers. Parts of feathers, particularly the barbs and barbules, constitute a major part of the food of this and certain other species. The irritation from the feeding of the louse causes the host to become exceedingly restless, thereby affecting its feeding habits and proper digestion; egg production in fowls is greatly reduced and development retarded. Losses are most evident in young birds. A lousy flock of poultry is not a good investment. When lice are abundant, uncleanliness and overcrowded conditions usually exist.

Lice Infesting Domestic Fowls. More than 40 species of lice are said to occur on domestic fowls. The commoner lice of chickens are: (1) the chicken body louse, *Menacanthus stramineus* (Nitzsch), a rapidly running species occurring on all parts of the fowl; and (2) the shaft louse, *Menopon gallinae* (Linnaeus) (Fig. 37), which resembles the body louse very closely but is smaller in size, and occurs mainly on the shafts of the feathers. The shaft louse may infest turkeys, ducks, and guinea fowl, especially when they are housed with chickens, and it sometimes attacks horses that are stabled nearby. *Pigeons* are often abundantly infested with the slender pigeon louse, *Columbicola columbae* (Linnaeus) (= *Lipeurus baculus* Nitzsch), a very slender species measuring about 2 mm in length, and with the small pigeon louse, *Campanulotes bidentatus* (Scopoli), about 1 mm in length, whitish in color with the head rounded in front. A number of additional species infest domestic birds, but these are of lesser importance.

Biting Lice of Domesticated Mammals. The biting lice of domesticated mammals are for the most part rather easily identified by their presence on a given host, since commonly not more than one species of Mallophaga is found on each species of mammalian host. *Cattle* are often heavily infested on the withers, root of tail, neck, and shoulders with the biting cattle louse, *Bovicola bovis* (Linnaeus) (Fig. 38), a little red louse about 1 1/2 mm in length, definitely marked with transverse bars (ladderlike) on the abdominal segments. *Horses, mules,* and *asses,* but horses more particularly, when poorly or irregularly groomed may suffer from two species, the horse

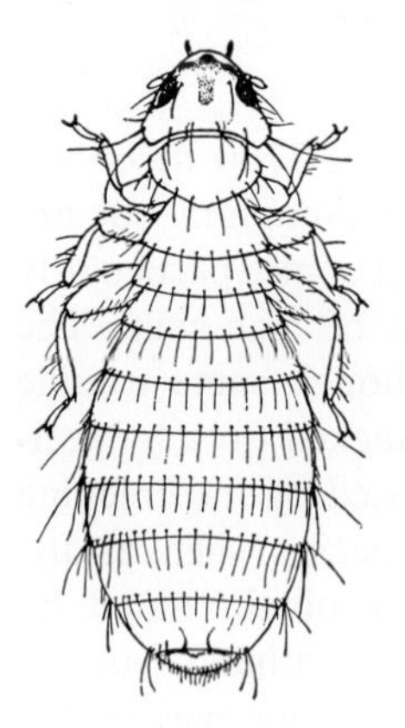

Fig. 37. The common shaft louse of poultry, *Menopon gallinae.*

biting louse, *Bovicola equi* (Linnaeus), and the European horse biting louse, *Trichodectes pilosus* Geibel. *Sheep* may at times show severe infestation of the sheep biting louse, *Bovicola ovis* (Linnaeus). *Goats* are very commonly enormously infested with biting lice. Several species from goats have been described, about which there is still some confusion, but the common species is *Bovicola caprae* (Gurlt). *Dogs,* particularly puppies, may suffer much irritation from the dog biting louse, *Trichodectes canis* De Geer, a broad short species, measuring about 1 mm in length. *Cats* may become heavily infested with the cat louse, *Felicola subrostratus* (Nitzsch). *Trichodectes tibialis* Piaget is very abundant on California deer.

Lice and Taeniasis. *Dipylidium caninum* (Linnaeus), the double-pored dog tapeworm, is a common parasite of the dog and is occasionally found in humans, especially children. It measures from 10 to 14 inches in length, has long seedlike proglottids and an armored scolex; as its larval host it has the biting dog louse, *Trichodectes canis* De Geer (Fig. 39), the dog flea, *Ctenocephalides canis* (Curtis), or the human flea, *Pulex irritans* Linnaeus. The cysticercoid stage has been experimentally produced in the louse by placing ripe crushed proglottids of the tapeworm on the skin of a dog infested with lice.

As has already been explained, the biting lice subsist on epidermal scales, skin exudations, and other matter on the skin of the animals. This habit makes it comparatively easy for the louse to become infected by swallowing egg capsules. The dog, on the other hand, readily infects itself by devouring the lice (or fleas) which irritate its skin.

Persons, particularly children, while fondling louse-infested (or flea-infested) dogs may easily become infected by accidentally swallowing lice (or fleas) which contain bladder worms (larval tapeworms). This is more readily accomplished if the person is eating while fondling dogs.

38 39

Fig. 38. The biting ox louse, *Bovicola bovis*. × 26.
Fig. 39. The biting dog louse, *Trichodectes canis*. × 35.

REFERENCES

1. Bishopp, F. C., 1921. "*Solenopotes capillatus,* a sucking louse of cattle not heretofore known in the United States," *J. Agric. Research,* **21:**797–801.

2. Buxton, P. A., 1939. *The Louse.* London: Edward Arnold & Co. viii + 164 pp.

3. Chung, Huei-Lan, and Feng, Lan-Chou, 1936. "Studies on the development of *Spirochaeta recurrentis* in body louse," *Chinese M. J.,* **50:**1181–84.

4. Cole, M. M.; Clark, P. H.; and Weidhaas, D. E.; 1958. "Sleeve tests with malathion powders against DDT-resistant body lice," *J. Econ. Entomol.,* **51:**741–42.

5. Cushing, Emory C., 1957. *History of Entomology in World War II.* Washington, D. C.: Smithsonian Inst., Pub. 4294. 117 pp.

6. Ferris, G. F., 1934. "A summary of the sucking lice (Anoplura)," *Entomol. News* **45:**70–74, 85–88.

7. Ferris, G. F., 1951. *The Suckling Lice.* San Francisco: Pacific Coast Entomol. Soc., Mem. 1. 320 pp.

8. Florence, Laura, 1921. *The Hog Louse, Haematopinus suis Linné: Its Biology, Anatomy, and Histology.* Ithaca: Cornell Univ. in Agric. Exper. Sta. Memoir, No. 51, pp. 641–743.

9. Goldberger, J., and Anderson, J. F., 1912. "The transmission of typhus fever, with special reference to transmission by the head louse (*Pediculus capitis*)." U. S. Public Health Service, *Pub. Health Rep.,* **27:**297–307.

10. Leeson, H. S., 1941. "The effect of temperature upon the hatching of the eggs of *Pediculus humanus corporis* DeGeer," *Parasitology,* **33:**243.

11. Mackie, F. P., 1907. "The part played by *Pediculus corporis* in the transmission of relapsing fever," *Brit. M. J.* **2:**1706–09.

12. Moore, W., 1918. "An interesting reaction to louse bites," *J.A.M.A.,* **71:**1481–82.

13. Murray, Andrew, 1860. "On the pediculi infesting the different races of man," *Tr. Roy. Soc. Edinburgh,* **22:**567. (Cited by Osborn.)

14. Nicolle, C. N.; Blaizot, L.; and Conseil, E.; 1913. "Etiologie de la fièvre récurrente. Son mode de transmission par les poux," *Ann. Inst. Pasteur,* **27:** 204–25.

15. Nicolle, Charles; Conte, C.; and Conseil, E.; 1909. "Transmission expérimentale du typhus exanthématique par le pou du corps," *Compt. rend. Acad. d. sc.,* **149:**486–89.

16. Nuttall, G. H. F., 1917. "The biology of *Pediculus humanus,*" *Parasitology,* **10:**80–185.

17. Nuttall, G. H. F., 1917. "Lice and disease," *Parasitology,* **10:**43–79.

18. Nuttall, G. H. F., 1918. "The biology of *Phthirus pubis,*" *Parasitology,* **10:**383–405.

19. Peacock, A. D., 1916. "Structure of the mouth parts and mechanism of feeding in *Pediculus humanus,*" *Parasitology,* **11:**98–117 (1 plate).

20. Price, Roger D., 1956. "The multiplication of *Pasteurella tularensis* in human body lice," *Am. J. Hyg.,* **63:**186–97.

21. Ricketts, H. T., and Wilder, R. M., 1910. "Further investigations regarding the etiology of tabardillo, Mexican typhus fever," *J.A.M.A.,* **55:**309–11.

22. Ricketts, H. T., and Wilder, R. M., 1910. "The transmission of the typhus fever of Mexico (tabardillo) by means of the louse (*Pediculus vestimenti*)," *J.A.M.A.,* **54:**1304–07.

23. Wheeler, Charles M., 1946. "Control of typhus in Italy 1943–1944 by use of DDT," *Am. J. Pub. Health,* **36:**119–29.

Chapter 9

GNATS
Simuliid Gnats, Phlebotomus Flies, and Others

(FAMILIES SIMULIIDAE, PSYCHODIDAE, CERATOPOGONIDAE ETC.)

Order Diptera

Order Diptera. The several families of gnats discussed in this chapter, as well as those insects discussed in the following eight chapters, are members of the Order Diptera, the "flies," which comprise some 75,000 described species belonging to some 140 families (see Curran[9]). Many species of insects belonging to this order are involved in the transmission of important diseases of man and animals; hence, the medical entomologist must be extensively familiar with the Diptera.

As the name implies, all winged members of the order have only one pair of wings; the posterior pair is represented in nearly all species by a pair of short (often minute) knobbed organs known as halteres. In certain families, e.g., muscoid flies, there are membranous structures at the juncture of the wings with the body; these are known as squamae, calypters, or alulae. The squamae are two pairs in number, one, the thoracic, being more closely associated with the thorax, and the other, the alar, being close to the wing. The latter should not be confused with the anal lobe of the wing. Conspicuous compound eyes are present, and most species possess three simple eyes (ocelli). The metamorphosis is complete, consisting of four stages—egg, larva, pupa, and adult (imago). Some species are viviparous, notably the tsetse flies. The mouth parts, as previously described, are subject to great variation although all are suctorial; many species are provided with very effective piercing stylets which enable them to "bite" fiercely and to suck blood.

Much attention must be given to the larval stages because the larvae frequently invade the tissues and organs of the body of man and animals, causing myiasis (see Chapter 14); also a wider knowledge of aquatic larvae (of which there are many species) is important in pursuing work with mosquitoes and other gnats, as well as in the study of the biology of water supplies (see Johannsen[23]).

The Diptera have a wide range of breeding habits. There are few habitats suitable for animal life which have not been invaded by flies. The petroleum fly, *Psilopa petrolei* Coquillett, as the name implies, actually passes its larval life in crude oil, and several species of the same family

(Ephydridae) inhabit the Great Salt Lake. The extent to which Diptera can withstand adversity is illustrated by the fact that blow fly larvae frequently remain alive after being immersed in 70 per cent alcohol for 24 hours.

Classification of the Diptera. In the classification of the Diptera, knowledge of wing venation is important (Fig. 40). The great diversity of antennal structure provides a useful series of characters (Fig. 41), as does the ar-

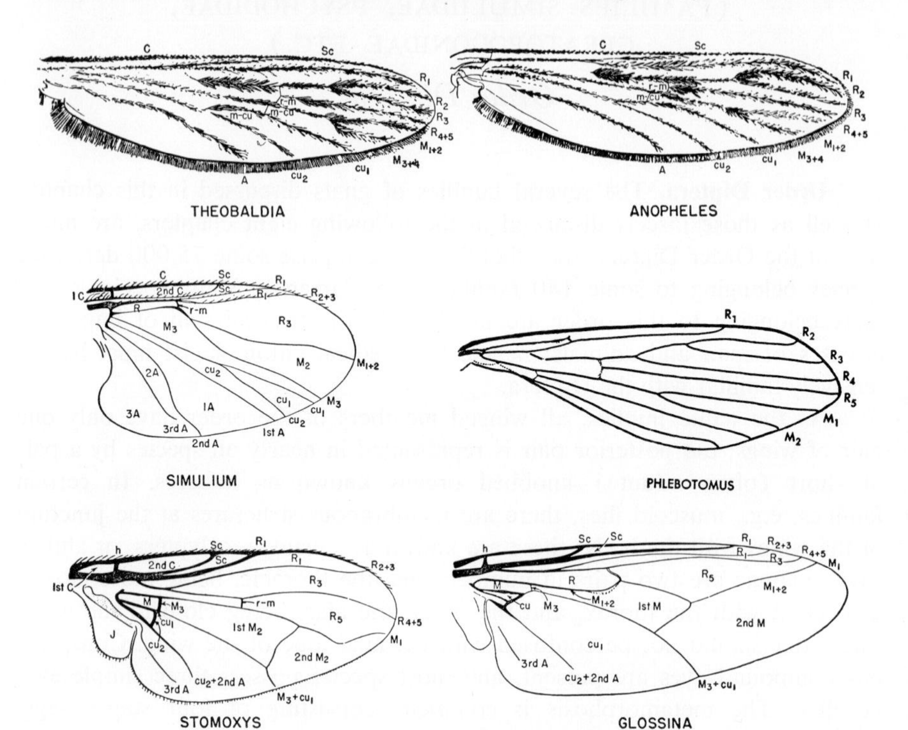

Fig. 40. Wings of Diptera. For explanation of venation, see Figure 2.

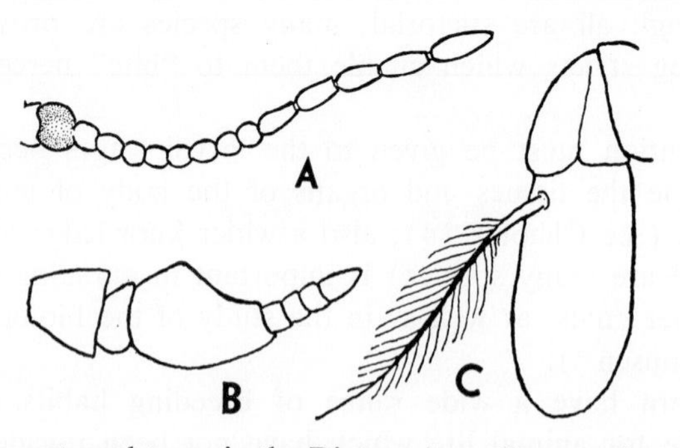

Fig. 41. Three antennal types in the Diptera; in outline, setation and hairs omitted. (*A*) The many-segmented type, *Culicoides* (after Irving Fox); (*B*) the stylate type, *Tabanus;* (*C*) the aristate type, *Sarcophaga.*

rangement of bristles (chaetotaxy) on the body of certain species such as the blow flies (see Chapter 14). The terminalia are important taxonomic structures in many Diptera. Structures of special importance in the various groups will be discussed under the individual group involved.

In respect to suborders, several classifications of the Diptera are in common use, but the one to which many students of the Diptera are inclining is the following: (1) **Nematocera,** in which the antennae are filiform and many-segmented, as in mosquitoes; (2) **Brachycera,** in which the antennae are short, not filamentous, generally three-segmented, often with a style or arista, as in horse flies; (3) **Cyclorrhapha,** in which the insect escapes from the puparium through a circular opening by pushing off the anterior end by means of a bladderlike structure known as the ptilinum and in which the antenna is three-segmented and usually of the aristate type, as in house flies and blow flies. The Nematocera and Brachycera, as here defined, are sometimes united into the Orthorrhapha; in these flies the adult escapes from the pupal case through a T- or Y-shaped anterodorsal slit.

SUBORDER I. NEMATOCERA

Larvae with well-developed, exserted head and horizontally biting mandibles; pupae free. Antenna of adult many-segmented, often longer than the head and thorax combined, but sometimes much shorter, composed of eight or more segments, the majority of those beyond the second usually alike; no differentiation of the antennal segments into a style or arista. Palpi usually four- or five-segmented, pendulous (with notable exceptions, as in the mosquitoes). Anal (second anal) cell when present widely open.

SUBORDER II. BRACHYCERA

Larvae with incomplete head, usually retractile, and with vertically biting mandibles; pupae usually free. Antenna of adult shorter than thorax, reduced to three apparent segments, the last of which is actually a complex and may be annulated, variously differentiated, or with a style or arista; arista, when present, terminal or nearly so. Palpi two- or three-segmented, porrect. Anal cell contracted before the apex or closed.

SUBORDER III. CYCLORRHAPHA

Larvae with vestigial heads and with mouth hooks which operate side by side vertically, or with only one such hook; pupa coarctate (enclosed in a puparium). Antenna of adult three-segmented, the third "segment" without evidence of its composite nature except for the arista, which is dorsal in position (rarely, a style, instead of the arista, is present in some forms of no medical importance). Palpi one-segmented, porrect. Anal cell contracted or closed.

KEY TO THE FAMILIES OF NEMATOCERA THAT CONTAIN FORMS OF MEDICAL IMPORTANCE

1. Mesonotum with an entire V-shaped suture. Of no medical importance but likely to be confused with mosquitoes.............Family Tipulidae
   Mesonotal suture transverse or wanting, not V-shaped.............. 2
2. Costa continuing around margin of wing, though weaker beyond the apex 3
   Costa ending at or near the apex of the wing...................... 6
3. Wing short and broad, folded rooflike over the body when at rest, usually pointed; small, hairy, mothlike flies................Family Psychodidae
   Wings long, or if broad the apex is very broadly rounded, always lying flat over the back when at rest................................ 4
4. Apical wing veins strongly arched, without scales. Of no medical importance, but likely to be confused with mosquitoes......Family Dixidae
   Wing veins straight or nearly so, with scales, or at least scales on the wing margin.. 5
5. Proboscis not elongated, extruding but little beyond the clypeus; wings with scales confined mostly to the fringe...........Family Chaoboridae
   Proboscis elongated, extending far beyond the clypeus; wings with scales on the margin and on the veins....................Family Culicidae
6. Wing very broad, the posterior veins weak and poorly developed; antenna shorter than thorax, never plumose.................Family Simuliidae
   Wing narrow and long, the posterior veins not noticeably weakened; antenna usually longer than the thorax, often plumose............. 7
7. Mesonotum and metanotum without a median longitudinal groove; wings lying flat over the body when at rest; femora sometimes swollen; mouth parts fitted for sucking blood (Heleidae)........Family Ceratopogonidae
   Mesonotum anteriorly and metanotum with a median longitudinal groove; mouth parts not fitted for sucking blood. Of no medical importance except as a source of annoyance, but likely to be confused with mosquitoes (Tendipedidae)...........................Family Chironomidae

FAMILY SIMULIIDAE

(Buffalo Gnats—Black Flies)

Characteristics. The family Simuliidae, consisting of over 600 species,[38,50] includes insects commonly known as buffalo gnats, black flies, and turkey gnats. They are small (1 to 5 mm long) bloodsucking flies, with mouth parts bladelike and piercing in the female but more or less rudimentary in the male. They are stout-bodied and variable in color; the term "black fly" is somewhat of a misnomer since certain species may be gray or even predominantly yellow. The thorax presents a strong development of the scutum and reduction of the prescutum resulting in a prominent hump (Fig. 42). The antennae are usually eleven-, sometimes nine- or ten-, segmented; the eyes of the female are distinctly separated (in the male they are usually close together and prominent, i.e., holoptic); ocelli are absent; the palpi are five-segmented; the wings are broad and irridescent, with distinct alulae, the venation being characterized by a strong development of the anterior veins (Fig. 40). Buffalo gnats often occur in enormous swarms during late spring and early summer in hilly sections where swiftly flowing streams provide well-aerated water for larval development. They are particularly abundant in the north temperate and subarctic zones.

Larvae are found in running water, shallow mountain creeks being favored breeding places. Some species, including certain notable pests, breed in

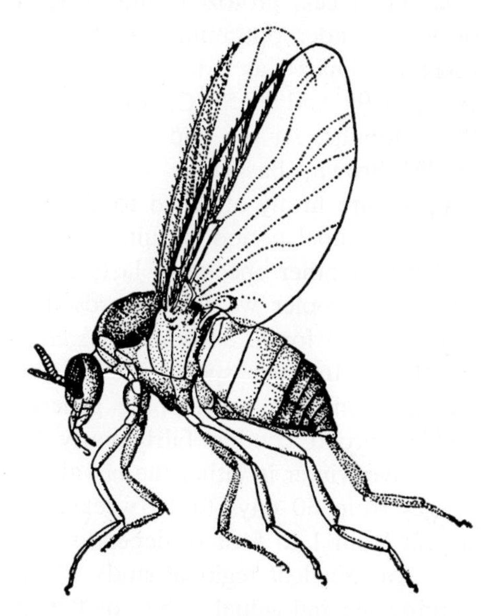

Fig. 42. A buffalo gnat, *Cnephia pecuarum*. (Redrawn after Garman.)

larger rivers; others live in temporary or semipermanent streams. Larvae attach themselves to rocks and other solid objects in the stream; sometimes they cling to aquatic vegetation. The sides and concrete drop structures in irrigation canals may produce large number of larvae. Adults may migrate 7 to 10 miles from their breeding sites,[10] and they may be carried much farther by the wind, *Simulium arcticum* traveling as far as 90 miles in this way.

Life History. Eggs to the number of 150 to 500 per female are deposited in masses at the water surface of aquatic plants, logs, and water-splashed rocks. Comstock says he has often watched the gnats hovering over the brink of a fall where there was a thin sheet of swiftly flowing water, and has seen them dart into the water and out again. At such times he has always found the surface of the rock more or less thickly coated with eggs, and he has no doubt that an egg is fastened to the rock each time a fly darts into the water. The shiny eggs are at first creamy white, changing to almost black.

The time required for hatching is from 5 to 30 days, depending on temperature and motion of the water. In running water at a temperature of 20° to 22° C the incubation period is 4 to 5 days.[52] The newly emerged larva attaches itself by means of a caudal sucker to any submerged object, such as a stone or log, and is kept from being washed away by a silken thread. Movement from place to place is achieved by shifting anchorage. In some favorable locations, such as riffles on the downstream side of an old log partially damming a stream, there may be thousands of these tiny, black, spindle-shaped larvae. The larvae, as well as the pupae, are provided with gill filaments, and usually remain submerged or partly so. The food of the larvae consists of small crustacea, protozoa, and algae. The larval period may require 12 days or fewer under optimum conditions; that for *Simulium ornatum* Meigen is given by Smart[39] as 7 to 10 weeks when temperatures in the stream ranged between 9° and 15.5° C. Some species overwinter as larvae. There are six larval moults. At the end of the larval period, the organism spins a rough reddish-brown, basketlike cocoon in which pupation takes place. These cocoons are firmly attached to shallowly covered objects such as rocks.

The pupal period is quite short in some species, requiring not over 2 to 6 days; in other species it lasts 3 to 4 weeks. Temperature influences this stage, i.e., cooler weather retards the emergence of adults. Smart gives the pupal period for *S. ornatum* Meigen as 3.75 days at a constant temperature of 21° C. In some species there is continual breeding from early spring to late autumn with overlapping generations; in others there is evidently one sudden brood coming fairly early in the spring with stragglers following. They overwinter in either the larval or egg stage. The life history, egg to adult, ranges from 60 days to 15 weeks and over, and the number of generations a year from 1 to 5 or 6, depending on species and climatic conditions.

An excellent regional study which contains a wealth of information concerning the individual habits of the species involved is that of Sommerman, Sailer, and Esselbaugh[41] on the biology of the black flies of Alaska.

Larvae. The light brown-to-black larvae are cylindrical, twelve-segmented, slightly thinner in the mid-region, and when fully grown from 10 to 15 mm in length (Fig. 43). The posterior end of the body is provided with a toothed disklike sucker, composed of two modified parapodia. The anterior pseudopod is also modified into a prehensile toothed disk. By means of these organs the larvae move from place to place with a looping motion. They attach themselves to rocks or other supports in the water by means of the posterior sucker, the hooks of which they insert into the network of silken threads produced by secretions from the salivary glands with which they cover the substratum. The larvae may hang from threads produced in similar fashion or travel along their length.

Although the larvae are provided with a well-developed tracheal system, and nine pairs of spiracles may be observed, these are not *open,* and respiration is carried on by means of gills, recognized as branched retractile structures located dorsally on the last abdominal segment. The fan-shaped filamentous structures located on the head are for the purpose of creating a current by means of which food is drawn into the mouth.

Pupae. When the larva is ready to pupate, it spins a crude pocketlike cocoon which is open at the upper end. The pupa is provided with respiratory filaments attached anteriorly to the dorsal portion of the thorax. The filaments are often quite numerous and because of their constancy in number in a given species may be of diagnostic value (Fig. 43).

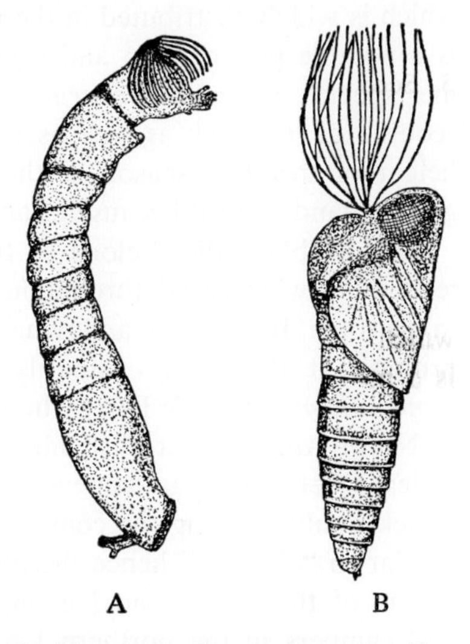

Fig. 43. (*A*) Larva and (*B*) pupa of Simulium; latter removed from cone-shaped cocoon. (Redrawn after Lugger from Washburn.)

Classification. The family Simuliidae is divided into six genera according to Smart,[38] namely *Parasimulium, Prosimulium, Cnephia, Simulium, Gigantodax,* and *Austrosimulium.* The first four of these, together with *Gymnopais* Stone[43] and *Twinnia* Stone and Jamnback,[44] which have been described since the publication of Smart's paper, occur in temperature North America. The following key, adapted from several sources, will separate the Nearctic genera.

KEY TO THE NEARCTIC GENERA OF SIMULIIDAE (ADULTS)

1. A bulla present behind the eye laterally; middle of mesonotum with stout erect hairs but no fine recumbent hairs . . . . *Gymnopais*
   No bulla behind the eye; middle of mesonotum usually with fine recumbent hairs but never with stout erect ones 2
2. Macrotrichia of anterior wing veins hairlike, not intermingled with spinelike ones; radial sector forked 3
   Macrotrichia of anterior wing veins mixed hairlike and spinelike; radial sector not forked (except in some *Cnephia*) 5

3. Vein R_1 joining the costa at about the middle of the wing. . . . . *Parasimulium*
   Vein R_1 joining the costa well beyond the middle of the wing. 4
4. Antenna nine-segmented; ovipositor short, not extending beneath the anal lobes . . . . *Twinnia*
   Antenna eleven-segmented; ovipositor longer, extending beneath anal lobes . . . . *Prosimulium*
5. Second segment of hind tarsus with a distinct notch (pedisulcus) dorsally near the base; basal cell absent. . . . . *Simulium*
   Second segment of hind tarsus without a pedisulcus; basal cell usually distinguishable . . . . *Cnephia*

Common Species. *Prosimulium hirtipes* (Fries), a holarctic species which is widely distributed in the northern United States, Canada, and Alaska, is a notable pest of man and domestic animals. It is a spring and early summer species. *Cnephia pecuarum* (Riley), the southern buffalo gnat, is a great scourge of livestock as well as of man in the Mississippi Valley. During the height of the gnat season in the early spring, work on plantations is often greatly handicapped because of annoyance to work animals.

Most black flies belong to the genus *Simulium. Simulium vittatum* Zetterstedt is widespread throughout North America and is a common species in Europe. It may be annoying because of its crawling over the skin and probing; it does not ordinarily bite man, but it attacks livestock freely. *Simulium meridionale* Riley, the turkey gnat, is also common and widespread in North America but particularly in the Mississippi Valley and the southern states, where the gnats appear in late spring following the buffalo gnat. They attack poultry, biting the combs and wattles, and are said to cause symptoms similar to "cholera," hence the name "cholera" gnat. *Simulium venustum* Say is one of the most annoying and widespread species. It torments fishermen and campers in the northern United States, Canada, and Alaska. The gnats occur in the greatest numbers during June and July but may persist throughout the summer. *Simulium arcticum* Malloch is a plague of livestock in western Canada where vast numbers of this gnat frequently attack and kill livestock. In 1944, 1945, and 1946, 800 domestic animals, 80 per cent of which were cattle, were killed by this fly in Saskatchewan.

Simulium colombaschense Fabricius is the infamous goloubatz fly of middle and southern Europe. In 1923 two immense swarms of this fly invaded southwest Roumania in May, June, and July, causing the death of 16,474 domestic animals, including cattle, horses, pigs, sheep, and goats. Large numbers of deer, foxes, and hares, as well as other wild animals, were reported to have been killed at the same time.

The Bite. There is perhaps no other insect of equal size that can inflict so painful a bite as can the buffalo gnat. It is a daytime biter and is rarely found indoors. The mouth parts are of the dipteron type (similar to those of the horse fly), consisting of six bladelike lancets.

Human beings as well as domesticated animals are viciously attacked. The eyes, ears, nostrils, wrists, and all exposed parts of the body of man are subject to attack. The extreme pain, intense itching, and the resultant local swellings, together with occasional severe complications, indicate the presence of an active toxin. In some individuals the face, arms, and other exposed parts may be greatly swollen as a result of the bites; in others, effects other than blood loss may scarcely be noticeable. Losses due to the bite of this fly are considerable. Death seems in most cases to be the consequence of a toxemia caused by the bites or the result of an anaphylactic shock, although debility resulting from blood loss and suffocation brought about by inhalation of the flies is apparently a contributing cause. Myriads of these gnats appear after the spring floods of the Mississippi River and its tributaries. Horses, mules, and cattle are often killed in a few hours by the venomous bites and loss of blood. This sudden appearance of the gnats in the Mississippi Valley is usually explained by the large accumulation of eggs that may have been washed into the area during floods. These eggs do not hatch until the next flood causes movement of the water, for it is in flowing and well-aerated water that the larvae hatch and develop rapidly.

Relation to Disease. Owing to the vicious intermittent bloodsucking habits of the buffalo gnats, it has long been suspected that they might play a role in the transmission of disease.

With the startling report of Sambon[32] in 1910 ascribing the transmission of pellagra to a buffalo gnat, the study of the Simuliidae gained new impetus. The gnats, however, were shown to have no relation to this disease. Pellagra is neither infectious nor contagious but is essentially of dietary origin, and the disease does not develop in those who consume a mixed, well-balanced, and varied diet. The most important disease transmitted by simuliid flies is *onchocerciasis* (onchocercosis), a disease of natives of certain parts of Africa, Mexico, and South and Central America. It is caused by a filarial worm, *Onchocerca volvulus* (Leuckart) (*O. caecutiens* Brumpt), which requires black gnats as intermediate hosts. The female worm measures from 350 to 700 mm in length, the male 20 to 40 mm. These worms occur in conspicuous subcutaneous nodular tumors located primarily on the trunk, shoulders, and head of infected persons. Several adult worms and numerous larvae (produced viviparously) usually occur in each tumor. Serious involvements of the eye occur, often resulting in complete blindness due to migration of the larvae. Strong[45] points out that from a clinical standpoint the association of ocular disturbances (such as photophobia) with the disease is emphasized by the high percentage of failing vision and blindness in a locality where at least 95 per cent of the population is infected with the parasite and has demonstrable nodules. The student should particularly consult a treatise on ocular onchocerciasis by Hisette.[20]

Blacklock,[3] working in Sierra Leone, has shown that when the microfilariae are taken up with the bite of *Simulium* flies, they migrate from the fly's stomach, finding lodgment in the thoracic muscles, where further development takes place, and then travel to the head and finally to the labial structures of the fly, where escape is made when the fly bites, and the infection of the human being is accomplished; development in the gnat requires about 10 to 14 days. The time required for development in the human from inoculation by the bite to maturity of the worm in the skin nodule has not been definitely determined, but it is probably about 6 months. The species of fly observed in Blacklock's experiments was *Simulium damnosum* Theobald, a widely distributed black gnat of tropical Africa. Bequaert[2] points out that of 57 species of Simuliidae described from the Ethiopian region, only 5 are definitely reported as biting people, but all must be looked upon with suspicion as possible carriers of onchocerciasis, although *S. damnosum* and *S. neavei* Roubaud are the only ones positively incriminated.

Onchocerciasis and its vectors in Guatemala have been studied in detail by several workers, particularly by Dalmat whose monograph on the subject[10] contains a wealth of information. About 35 per cent of the population in the disease zones of that nation is infected; ocular involvement is manifest in more than half the persons infected; and blindness occurs in about 5 per cent. The most important vector in the light of host preference, feeding habits, and epidemiologic information, seems to be *Simulium ochraceum* Walker, but *S. metallicum* Bellardi and *S. callidum* Dyar and Shannon readily bite man and occupy the highly endemic sections of the disease zone. Three additional species in Guatemala attack man readily and should be placed on the list of potential vectors; these are *S. haematopotum* Malloch, *S. exiguum* Roubaud, and *S. veracruzanum* Vargas, Martinez, and Diaz.

Bovine Onchocerciasis. It has been pointed out by Steward[42] that bovine onchocerciasis is of considerable economic importance in Australia, that the "worm nodules" due to *Onchocerca gibsoni* Cleland and Johnston cause losses to the state of Queensland estimated at £500,000 per annum. The work done by Steward in England with *Onchocerca gutturosa* Neumann proved that this parasite is transmitted by *Simulium ornatum* Meigen.

Leucocytozoon Infections of Poultry. The name Leucocytozoon was given to certain sporozoa found in the blood of birds by Danilewsky in 1890, and in 1895 Theobald Smith discovered a *Leucocytozoon* in the blood of turkeys; this parasite was named *Leucocytozoon smithi* by Volkmar. In 1932 Skidmore[37] working in Nebraska, reported the successful transmission of this parasite by *Simulium occidentale* Townsend. In 1938 Johnson *et al.*[24] reported transmission through the agency of *Simulium jenningsi* malloch (= *nigroparvum* Twinn). When the organism is taken into the stomach of the fly gametes are formed, macrogametes being clearly observable as well as the zygote. An important infection of both domestic and wild ducks, caused by the protozoon parasite *Leucocytozoon simondi* Mathis and Leger (= *anatis* Wickware), occurs in the northern United States and Canada. *Simulium venustum* Say has been accepted as the chief vector, but Shewell[34] has shown that the true vector is probably *S. rugglesi* Nicholson and Mickel, a recently (1950) described form which can quite easily be mistaken for *S. venustum.*

Black Fly Control. Stream sanitation is important in black fly control, particularly when those insects are found adhering to vegetation rather than to rocks and other solid substrata. In the vicinity of communities, streams in which these insects are breeding should be kept as free as possible from debris, including submerged roots and dipping branches of overhanging trees.

Effective control of black fly larvae dates back to the work of Fairchild and Barreda[12] in Guatemala. These men found that DDT applied to a stream at the rate of 0.1 pounds per minute (p.p.m.) for 1 hour controlled larvae downstream for a distance of 10 kilometers. Subsequent tests were made in Guatemala, Saskatchewan, Alaska, New York,[22] and elsewhere, with very satisfactory results. DDT has been applied by air, by hand equipment, by means of a drip from a container adjusted to empty in the desired period of time, and by other methods. Concentrations of 0.1 to 0.3 p.p.m. are usually sufficient to control black fly larvae when applied to flowing water, and dosages of 0.1 to 0.2 pound per acre, estimated on a swath-acre basis, are effective when applied by aerial methods. At these rates, there is no harmful effect on fish, although insects other than black flies may be affected for a limited period of time. The length of time required for stream application varies with the stream to be treated; Lea and Dalmat[26] found 3 minutes at 0.1 p.p.m. of DDT emulsion sufficient for short rivulets. More commonly, 10 to 15 minutes will be required. The insecticide is, of course, effective in killing and dislodging only those larvae which are present at the time that it is applied. Larval mortality is probably due as much to the destruction of dislodged larvae by predators and by the mechanical action of the currents as to the action of the insecticide itself.

R. D. Glasgow, New York State entomologist, reports economical and successful control of black fly adults by applying DDT aerosol fog by means of a helicopter. About 1 quart of a 15 per cent solution of DDT in a petroleum solvent was used per acre. Sprays and aerosols directed against adults are often disappointing in their effects, however; moreover, reinfestation by migration from other areas may soon nullify the results.

For an excellent study of black fly control in New York state, the student should consult the paper of Jamnback and Collins.[22] For repellents, see the discussion in Chapter 3.

FAMILY PSYCHODIDAE

(Moth Flies—Phlebotomus Flies)

Family Psychodidae. The family consists of several hundred species and includes the tiny gnats known as owl midges, moth flies, and phlebotomine sand flies. The ovate, usually pointed wings, and the body are densely covered with hairs, whence the name, moth flies. In the *Psychoda* flies the wings when held at rest lie rooflike over the abdomen. Only the longitudinal wing veins are prominent, the cross veins, if present, being restricted to the base of the wing. The antennae are usually fairly long and usually twelve- to sixteen-segmented. The Nearctic species have been monographed by Quate.[30]

For the purposes of this work, the family may be divided into two subfamilies: (1) the Psychodinae, the moth flies or owl midges, whose females are not bloodsucking, whose wings are held rooflike over the body, and whose larvae are commonly aquatic; and (2) the Phlebotominae, whose females are bloodsuckers, whose wings are not held rooflike over the body, and whose larvae are never aquatic. Two other subfamilies may be recognized, but these are uncommon and of no medical importance.

Psychoda Flies. Several species of *Psychoda* and *Telmatoscopus* are commonly found in great numbers around sewage disposal plants, cesspools, and washbasins in bathrooms where the larvae may develop in sink drains in spite of hot water and soap. Although the flies of these genera are not bloodsuckers, they may breed in such numbers in the filter beds of sewage disposal plants as to constitute a real annoyance to neighboring households. *Psychoda alternata* Say, a widespread species occurring in most of the United States, is known as the "trickling filter fly." These gnats may become annoying in the house, where they originate in the surface of the gelatinous material in sink and bathroom drain traps. Their life cycle is short, ranging from 21 to 27 days at room temperature at Berkeley, California, according to Quate.

The adult gnats may be controlled by spraying their resting places with a 5 per cent DDT emulsion or suspension at the rate of 1 qt to 250 sq ft of area. Caution must be exercised in the use of DDT emulsions for the control of the larvae because of damage of filter growth by the solvent. Simpson[36] states that suspensions with a wetting agent eliminate adverse effects. He recommends addition of a quantity of DDT at one time equal to 1 p.p.m., based on the daily flow, and retarding filter operation 1/2 to 1 hour for contact time and repeating the operation every two weeks.

Phlebotomus (= Flebotomus) Flies. The genus *Phlebotomus* (*Flebotomus*) of the family Psychodidae comprises many species of small-sized hairy gnats or midges measuring from 1.5 to about 4 mm in length. They are commonly known as sand flies. They differ from *Psychoda* and *Telmatoscopus* in that the wings are held upward and outward so that the costal margins form angles of about 60° with each other and with the body. The body is less hairy than in the Psychodinae. The venation is peculiar; the radial sector branches in a pectinate fashion with the result that the apparent second vein (actually the true second vein, R_{2+3}, plus the anterior branch of the third, R_4) is three branched (Fig. 40). The females alone have piercing mouth parts and are bloodsuckers; some species feed on cold-blooded animals such as lizards and snakes; others feed on a variety of warm-blooded animals, including man. There is evidence that some females take plant juices[1]; this is important, since the capacity of one known species to transmit *Leishmania donovani* is enhanced by feeding on raisins. The males suck moisture from any available source and are said even to suck up sweat from humans. These gnats are active only at night when there is little or no wind, seeking protection by day in shelters both out of doors in crevices, caves, and among vegetation, and within buildings where they hide in dark corners. Their noiseless flight, which is commonly described as weak, is usually in short so-called "hops" when they are disturbed; however, in longer flights their progress is slow and steady and can be followed with the eye. Townsend[49] points out that "deep canyons, free from wind and dimly lighted, are especially adapted to them."

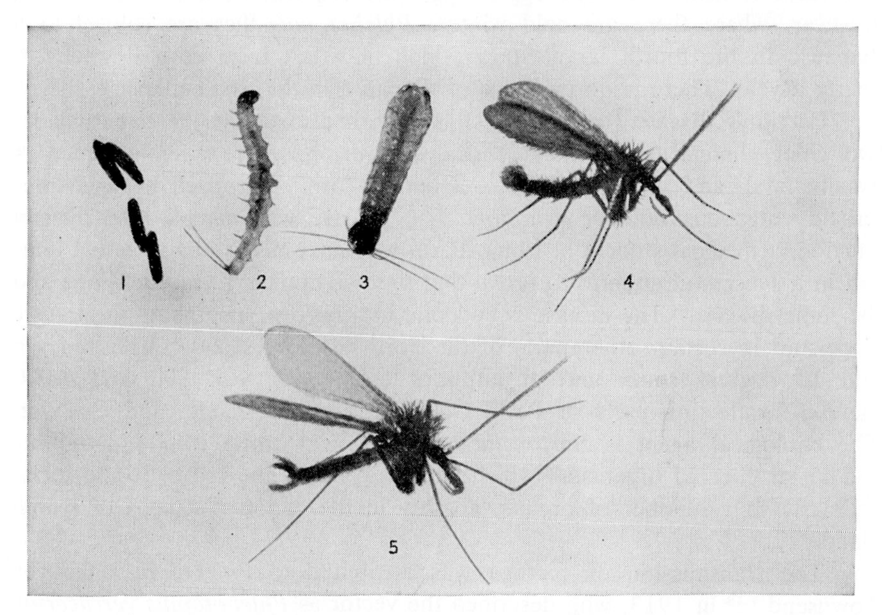

Fig. 44. Life cycle of *Phlebotomus verrucarum*. (1) Eggs; (2) larva; (3) pupa (*P. noguchii*); (4) adult female; (5) adult male. (Adapted from Hertig.)

Life History of Sand Flies. Hertig[18] who has had wide experience with *Phlebotomus* flies, points out that the breeding-places of sand flies are "typically under stones, in masonry cracks, in stables, poultry houses, etc., in situations combining darkness, humidity, and a supply of organic matter which serves as food for the larvae. In no case is the breeding-place aquatic." To situations mentioned above may be added hollow trees and animal burrows. Rodent burrows, which fulfill very well the three requirements stipulated by Hertig, have been shown to be an extensive habitat for these larvae in various parts of the Old World.[1] This habitat has some epidemiologic significance since certain species of rodents are reservoirs of *Leishmania tropica* which is propogated among them by flies living in their burrows.

The eggs are deposited in small batches (Fig. 44). The incubation period is from 6 to 17 days. The minute whitish larvae have long anal spines; the mouth parts are strongly mandibulate. The larvae feed on organic debris, such as moist excrement of lizards and mammals and decaying plant material. There are four instars; the duration of the larval stage is usually 4 to 6 weeks, with extremes ranging from about 2 to 10 weeks.[6] The pupa, which is naked, requires about 10 days for development. The female usually lays eggs in 5 to 7 days under microclimatic conditions of virtually 100 per cent relative humidity. Refeeding habits of females in relation to oviposition vary greatly with the different species, and this fact has considerable significance in respect to disease transmission. The egg-to-egg cycle requires from 7 to 10 weeks; however, where there are cold winters *Phlebotomus* flies are subject to a diapause in the fourth larval stage which may last from several weeks to nearly a year. There is no evidence of diapause in the tropical species.

Carrión's disease (bartonellosis) is known also under the names of its two chief clinical forms, namely *Oroya fever,* a severe anemia which is usually fatal, and *verruga peruana,* a benign form recognized by a characteristic cutaneous nodular eruption. The disease was named after Daniel Carrión, a medical student at Lima, Peru, who gave his life by infecting himself in a successful attempt to prove that the two clinical forms were one and the same disease. "The disease is endemic in a narrow strip along the Pacific slope and in certain other parts of the Peruvian Andes between latitudes 6 and 13 degrees south and at altitudes usually between 800 and 3,000 meters,"[19] affecting parts of Peru, Colombia, Bolivia, Chile, and Ecuador. The etiological agent is *Bartonella bacilliformis* (Strong *et al.*), a minute rodlike or coccoid organism "which occurs in or on the red cells and intracellularly in a number of organs, notably in the endothelial cells of lymph glands."

The transmission of verruga was attributed to *Phlebotomus* flies by Townsend[47,48] in 1913, who described the vector as *Phlebotomus verrucarum* and attributed a human infection to this species. Based on careful field studies in the "Verruga zone," Noguchi *et al.*[29] substantially confirmed Townsend's contention that *Phlebotomus verrucarum* is a vector of verruga and added another species, *P. noguchii* Shannon, as a probable vector. Hertig indicates some of the taxonomic difficulties encountered in these investigations and cites the experimental work of Battistini 1927–1931, in which positive transmission to a monkey (positive in 18 days) was made through the agency (by bites) of wild sand flies of a mixed lot of *P. verrucarum* and *P. noguchii.* In 1939 Hertig[18] discovered a clue to the mechanism of infection in that the verruga organism was recovered in pure culture from the extreme tip of the proboscis, the piercing stylets themselves being thoroughly infected. The developmental cycle of the etiological agent in the sand fly has not been thoroughly determined; therefore, the means by which the stylets have become contaminated must remain hypothetical.

Subsequent work has substantiated the case against *P. verrucarum* as the chief, and perhaps the sole, vector of Carrión's disease in its area.[1] *Phlebotomus noguchii* restricts its feeding to field mice, and consequently must be eliminated so far as transmission to man is concerned. In epidemic areas of Colombia, where *P. verrucarum* is not known to occur, the vector is probably the closely related *P. columbianus* Ristorcelli and Van Ty.

Sand fly fever, also known as pappataci fever, three-day fever, and Phlebotomus fever, is a seasonal (May to October) febrile *virus* disease of short duration occurring in the *Phlebotomus*-infested regions of the Mediterranean, South China, parts of India, Ceylon, the Near East, and parts of Central Asia. It is a nonfatal infection. Commonly a large percentage of a ship's company on shore leave, even for only one night during the proper season, may be stricken with sand fly fever within 2 or 3 days after leaving port. The incubation period in the insect is from 7 to 10 days. Epidemiologic evidence strongly indicates that the infection may be transmitted transovarially, hence the insect itself is probably the reservoir. *Phlebotomus papatasii* Scopoli in the Mediterranean region becomes infective 6 to 8 days after an infecting blood meal; the virus is present in man's blood for 24 hours prior to onset and for the first 24 hours of the disease, hence the infective period for the sand fly is limited to that length of time. After a person has been bitten by an infected fly the incubation period is usually 3 or 4 days, but this period may range from 2.5 to 9 days. *Phlebotomus papatasii* Scopoli is the only proven vector, and the geographic distribution of the disease corresponds, with some exceptions, with that of the vector. *Phlebotomus perniciosus* Newstead has been suggested as a vector, but the case against it is quite inconclusive. Other species may serve as vectors in China, where *P. papatasii* is not known to occur.

Leishmaniasis is caused by various species of parasitic protozoa belonging to the genus *Leishmania,* round or oval intracellular bodies, which develop flagellate leptomonal stages in the gut of insects. Several types of human leishmaniasis are transmitted by *Phlebotomus.* For successful transmission, a vector must fulfill certain requirements which may be rigid; but in general, as pointed out by Adler and Theodor,[1] it must have a sterile alimentary tract, since human leishmanias do not tolerate bacterial contamination. In some instances, a definite dependence upon plant juices as a partial diet is also essential.

Kala-azar, dumdum fever, or tropical splenomegaly is a visceral leishmaniasis traceable to *Leishmania donovani* (Laveran and Mesnil) which localizes in the reticuloendothelial cells. It is a widespread disease, occurring in all countries on the shores of the Mediterranean, south Russia, India,

China, Manchuria, northern (Mediterranean) and equatorial Africa, Brazil, and other parts of South America. In man there is progressive enlargement of the spleen and later of the liver. As the disease progresses, the skin becomes grayish in color, whence the name "black disease." In untreated cases it is usually fatal, death resulting within a few weeks in acute infections and in from two to three years in chronic cases.

Visceral leishmaniasis exists in three epidemiologic types: (1) In India it occurs in both endemic and epidemic forms; all age groups, but mostly young adults, are attacked. No animal reservoir is known, but the epidemiologic picture can be explained by assuming that man himself constitutes the chief reservoir.[1] (2) In the Sudan, and probably other parts of tropical Africa, cases are sporadic, but epidemics occur in which cases may be unevenly distributed. No animal reservoir is known, but there may be such. It is in this area that studies of the bionomics of wild *Phlebotomus* may be most important. (3) In the Mediterranean and some other areas within its range, this disease attacks to a high degree children under the age of 5 years. Here dogs are highly susceptible, in fact, the incidence among dogs usually far surpasses that among human beings. A separate pathogen, *Leishmania infantum* (Nicolle), has been considered responsible for this form of the disease, though *infantum* is now considered a synonym of *donovani*. This form of the disease is more widespread than has previously been suspected in tropical America, especially Brazil, where the wild dog, *Lycalopex vetulus* (Lund) seems to form the chief reservoir.

Various species of bloodsucking arthropods have been suspected as being vectors. The low susceptibility of laboratory animals made progress difficult, but with the discovery that hamsters were highly susceptible to the infection rapid progress was made. Shortt and his co-workers in India recorded, in 1926, a massive infection of the pharynx and buccal cavity of *Phlebotomus argentipes* Annandale and Brunetti, and subsequently, in 1931,[35] reported successful transmission by the bite of the fly. The vectorship of *P. argentipes* was not proven, however, until 1952, when Swaminath, Shortt and Anderson[46] succeeded in transmitting the disease to 5 out of 6 volunteers, but only after the infected *Phlebotomus* had previously been fed on raisins. In the case of P. *argentipes,* there seems to be a necessary relationship between the intake of plant juices and the ability to infect the mammalian host. Some have considered this relationship one of blocking the digestive tract, analogous to that of the blocked flea, but Adler and Theodor believe that the ingestion of fruit juices stimulates a descent of the flagellates to the tip of the proboscis where they can readily enter the wound.

In China, where dogs form the reservoir of the disease, *P. chinensis* Newstead is the incriminated vector. *Phlebotomus perniciosus* is the chief vector in the Mediterranean region, although *P. major* Annandale is a local, and *P. longicuspis* Nitzulescu a probable vector. In Brazil, *P. longipalpis*

Lutz and Neiva has been found naturally infected and has been used to produce experimental infections.

Oriental Sore. Oriental sore, also known as Baghdad or Delhi boil, is a cutaneous leishmaniasis caused by *Leishmania tropica* (Wright); it has a wide distribution in Mediterranean areas, Palestine, Arabia, Asia Minor, Iraq, India, French Congo, and other parts of the world. It is not necessarily coextensive with kala-azar. In oriental sore the leishmanias inhabit the skin and do not invade the viscera. Adler and Theodor succeeded in incriminating *P. papatasii* to the extent that *L. tropica* was passed successfully from a naturally infected sand fly to the human host and back to the sand fly, but attempts to obtain infection by the bite of the insect were unsuccessful until saline was added to the infective material. These workers found that the developmental cycle of the *Leishmania* in the fly required 8 to 21 days. They report that in India *P. sergenti* Parrott is the most effective vector. The infection is apparently perpetuated by sand flies inhabiting the burrows of various species of gerbils, and this explains outbreaks among groups of human beings passing through uninhabited regions. Dogs also become naturally infected.

American mucocutaneous leishmaniasis (naso-oral), also known as espundia or uta, is widely distributed in South and Central America. The causal agent is *Leishmania brasiliensis* Vianna. The horrible disfiguring effects of this infection are shown by Goldman,[16] who points out that it is the mucosal involvement which is so characteristic of American cutaneous leishmaniasis. Once the infection gets into the mucocutaneous junction, it destroys all types of tissue including cartilage and bone. Goldman states that:

> . . . prevention of cutaneous leishmaniasis in the endemic areas appears to be a well-nigh hopeless affair. It is likely the incidence could be reduced considerably by definite knowledge of vectors, animal reservoir, and transmission. If the foreigner in the endemic area wishes some simple practical advice, the use of modern repellents, insecticides, adequate fine-mesh screening, and the other measures for the maintenance of careful hygiene of the skin in the tropics, and early attention to indolent lesions on exposed parts of the body may be suggested.

Various species of *Phlebotomus* flies are looked upon with suspicion based on experimental evidence; among these are *P. intermedius* Lutz and Neiva, *P. pessoai* Coutinho, and *P. longipalpus* Lutz and Neiva.

American Species of Phlebotomus. According to Quate,[30] there are six species of sand flies in the United States, none of which have received much attention, namely: (1) *Phlebotomus vexator* Coquillett, and (2) *P. shannoni* Dyar, both widely distributed in the southern states; (3) *P. diabolicus* Hall from Texas, reported to feed on humans and experimentally on Syrian hamsters; (4) *P. texanus* Dampf, also from Texas; (5) *P. stewarti* Mangabeira and Galindo, from California, collected in wild rodent burrows in arid fields;

and (6) *P. anthophorus* Addis, another Texas species, but found also in Mexico, which apparently feeds on rabbits but not on man.

Investigators concerned with the numerous species of South American *Phlebotomus* flies will need to consult the many excellent contributions of Mangabeira, particularly his 1942 contribution,[27] which contains a valuable bibliography, and those of Barretto.[4,5,6] The latter author, in his catalog of the American *Phlebotomus,*[7] lists 155 species for the New World.

Phlebotomus Control. Marett[28] suggests, as means of controlling *Phlebotomus,* the facing of rock walls, removal of heaps of stones, blocking of holes affording shelter for the gnats, encouragement of gardening (cultivation of ground), planting of embankments with native aromatic plants, etc. As sand flies are highly susceptible to pyrethrum sprays, painting screens lightly each evening with a mixture of 1 part pyrethrum extract concentrate (20 to 1) and 20 parts of light lubricating oil has been recommended. Because of the minute size of these gnats ordinary mesh screens do not exclude them; therefore, a 0.0334-inch mesh is recommended. Repellents such as diethyltoluamide, ethyl hexanediol, and dimethyl phthalate applied to skin and clothing give quite a bit of protection.

Hertig[19] states that the habits and life history of sand flies render them peculiarly vulnerable to DDT. They make short flights with relatively long pauses on entering or leaving any shelter, breeding place, or structure—a process repeated nearly every night of their adult lives. Any surface capable of retaining residual DDT, and on which sand flies must alight, may become a lethal barrier. House spraying gives virtually complete protection indoors. Hertig states that, in Peru, house spraying, combined with treatment of outdoor shelters such as stone walls, reduced the local sand fly population to negligible numbers, an effect which persisted up to a year-and-a-half. The short flight range limits infiltration, and the long life cycle delays recovery of a depleted sand fly population.

FAMILY CERATOPOGONIDAE (HELEIDAE)

(*Biting Midges—Punkies*)

Characteristics. The Ceratopogonidae are very small (0.6–5.0 mm in length), slender, bloodsucking gnats (males do not bite) resembling the nonbiting midges belonging to the family Chironomidae, to which family they have sometimes been referred in the past. In their biting habits they resemble the black flies (Simuliidae) and are frequently mistaken for them. Among the 50 or more genera comprising the family, three will serve the purpose of this section, namely *Culicoides* (Fig. 45), *Lasiohelea,* and *Leptoconops,* commonly known as "punkies," "no-see-ums," or "sand flies" (not to be confused with the phlebotomine sand flies). The wings, which are narrow, with few veins and usually with no scales, may be clear or hairy, and are folded flat over the abdomen when at rest; the alulae are slender. The larvae (Fig. 46) are aquatic or semiaquatic, and are found in fresh, brackish, or salt water; they may live in moist earth or in tree holes. R. E. Ryckman (personal communication) reports that he reared ceratopogonids, including

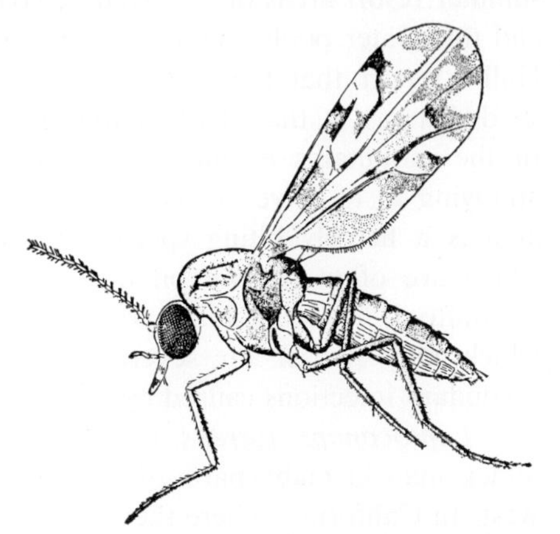

Fig. 45. *Culicoides* sp., female. (After Dampf.)

four species of *Culicoides,* in considerable numbers from decaying cactus (*Opuntia, Cereus,* and *Pachycereus*) in California, Arizona, and Baja California. A catalog of the bloodsucking midges of the Americas, with keys to the Nearctic species, has been published by Fox,[15] and a monograph of the Neotropical *Culicoides* has been presented by Forattini.[14] A study by Foote and Pratt[13] of the species of the "Eastern United States" covers a broader

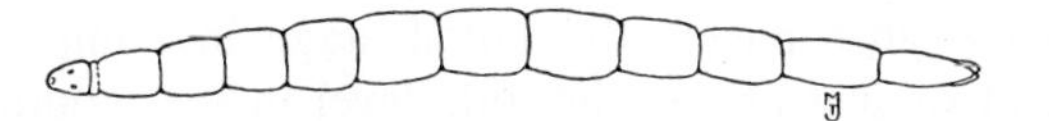

Fig. 46. *Culicoides variipennis,* larva. (Drawing by James in Edmondson, W. T., 1959. Ward and Whipple's *Fresh Water Biology*. New York: John Wiley & Sons, Inc. Fig. 41.14, p. 1068.)

scope than its title would suggest and is noteworthy for its wealth of well-executed illustrations. A very useful regional study of the Ceratopogonidae is that of Wirth[51] for California. The following key will serve to separate adults of the genera that attack man.

1. Radiomedial cross vein absent; anterior branch of media not forked; antenna of female with 12 to 14 segments.................. *Leptoconops*
   Radiomedial cross vein present; anterior branch of media forked into M_1 and M_2; antenna of female with 15 segments..................... 2

2. Empodium (padlike structure between tarsal claws) well developed; wings hairy but not pictured; humeral pits not developed............*Lasiohelea*
   Empodium not developed; wings usually pictured, sometimes clear; humeral pits conspicuous..*Culicoides*

Culicoides canithorax Hoffman, *C. melleus* (Coquillett), and *C. furens* (Poey) (= *C. dovei* Hall) constitute a serious economic problem in the summer resort areas of the Atlantic coast, particularly about fresh-water inlets and tide-water pools where these midges are most numerous. Dove, Hall, and Hull[11] report that the larvae are found in decaying humus of the densely shaded areas at the edges of the grass marshes of the upper Atlantic coast. In the mountains of the West, *Culicoides obsoletus* (Meigen) may be so annoying as to drive out campers and fishermen. *Culicoides diabolicus* Hoffman is a fiercely biting species in Mexico. The bites of these minute flies, which are often blamed on the larger and more conspicuous black flies or mosquitoes, cause itching and, in sensitive individuals, welts and lesions which may persist for several days. They are sometimes complicated by secondary infections caused by scratching to relieve the itch.

Leptoconops torrens (Townsend) and *L. kertèszi* (Kieffer) severely attack man in many parts of the United States, particularly in the south and west. In California, where they constitute a major pest, the former is known as the "valley black gnat" and the latter as the "Bodega black gnat." Both species bite viciously, feeding on man, domestic animals, and birds. The bite usually produces a transient swelling which may become vesicular, rupture, and produce an open lesion which may exude moisture for weeks. Itching resulting from the bite is intense. The following account of the two species is from a publication by Smith and Lowe.[40] The valley black gnat passes the larval stage in clay or clay-adobe soils situated along the western side of the Sacramento Valley and in isolated deposits in the San Joaquin Valley. The Bodega black gnat passes the larval stage in damp sand with some organic matter, at or just above high-tide level in the mouths of fresh-water streams which enter Bodega and Tomales bays (California).

Adults of the Bodega black gnat occur from mid-April until early October, in a continuous flow from the soil. Females may feed as many as four times. Males form large swarms, dancing in the lee of windbreaks. Eggs are laid on the surface of damp sand where the salt concentration is about 640 p.p.m. The larval stage lasts for 8 to 10 months. Pupation occurs in the sand; pupae wriggle to the surface, orienting themselves vertically, before the adult emerges. The pupal period is 8 days. Adult females captured in the field lived a maximum of 11 days, with blood meals.

Adults of the valley black gnat occur for 4 to 6 weeks, beginning usually in the middle of May. Females feed only once. Unfed gnats lived only 6 hours in captivity; with a blood meal, females lived a maximum of 5 days.

The larvae occur in clay-adobe soils at a depth of 15 to 30 inches. Egress and entrance is dependent upon the drying and cracking of the soil. The larval period is at least 2 years in length. Larvae spend the summers in immobile estivation. If the soil does not crack on schedule, the mature larvae enter a diapause. Some evidence is given to indicate that larvae may diapause for at least three years. Larvae are found in summer in soil with a moisture content of 17 to 20 per cent, a salt concentration of 400 p.p.m. a *p*H of 9.6, and a temperature of 65° to 68°F. Methods of identifying breeding grounds consist of trapping adults as they emerge from the soil, and washing larvae from the soil.

The known role of bloodsucking ceratopogonids in the transmission of human and animal diseases is small, yet it is of some importance. The night-biting *Culicoides austeni* Carter, Ingram, and Macfie was reported by Sharp,[33] and later confirmed by Hopkins and Nicholas,[21] as an intermediate host of the filarial worm *Acanthocheilonema perstans* (Manson). The embryos of this worm are found in the peripheral circulation both by day and by night. Sharp has observed that diurnal periodicity is the more common. In the vast majority of cases it is said to be nonpathogenic. It is primarily equatorial and African in distribution, although it occurs also in British Guiana and in New Guinea. Sharp has shown that the microfilariae undergo metamorphosis in the body of *Culicoides austeni,* increasing to three times their original length before they appear in the proboscis of the insect. The cycle in the fly requires 7 to 9 days. *Culicoides grahami* Austen also seems to be a natural carrier. Buckley[8] found that *Culicoides furens* (Poey), a widely distributed species along the Atlantic and Gulf coasts in the West Indies and Central America, transmits the filarial worm *Mansonella ozzardi* (Manson). Several filarial and viral diseases of domestic animals are known or suspected to be transmitted by species of *Culicoides.* In the southwestern United States blue tongue disease of sheep appears to have *Culicoides variipennis* (Coquillett) as its vector. The viruses of eastern equine encephalomyelitis in Georgia and of Venezuelan equine encephalomyelitis in Ecuador have been isolated from undetermined species of *Culicoides.*[25]

Control. Because of the variety of breeding places involved, it becomes necessary first of all to determine these for the species giving trouble. Some species breed in salt marshes, in which case dikes, tide gates, and other salt-marsh control devices may be employed. Other species breed in mud and plant debris along the margins of fresh-water streams or ponds; for the control of these removal of vegetation and channelization are suggested, or filling in low ground may be helpful. Still other species breed in holes in shade trees; in that case holes should be treated with DDT or creosote, or otherwise made unfavorable for breeding.

Punkies may be excluded from the house by painting window screens and screen doors with a 5 per cent DDT solution to which 10 to 20 per cent of lubricating oil can be added. The same can be done for bed netting, but the heavy oil should be omitted from the spray. Aerial and ground sprays and fogs may be applied under certain circumstances, but their effectiveness is limited.

Rees and Smith[31] obtained effective control of *Leptoconops kerteszi* by treating the ground in which these gnats were breeding with DDT at the rate of 1 pound in 28 gallons of water per acre. Adult gnats were killed by a DDT residual spray and by a DDT thermal smoke aerosol.

FAMILY CHIRONOMIDAE (TENDIPEDIDAE)

(*Midges*)

Although the midges are commonly mistaken for mosquitoes they bear little resemblance to them on closer examination. In the midges the proboscis is short and not adapted for piercing, the palpi are three- or four-segmented, and the wings are bare or haired. The antennae are plumose in the males and sparsely haired in the females (Fig. 47). Midges are widely distributed and may often be extremely abundant in the vicinity of standing water, since the larvae (Fig. 48) of most species are aquatic. Occasionally great swarms of

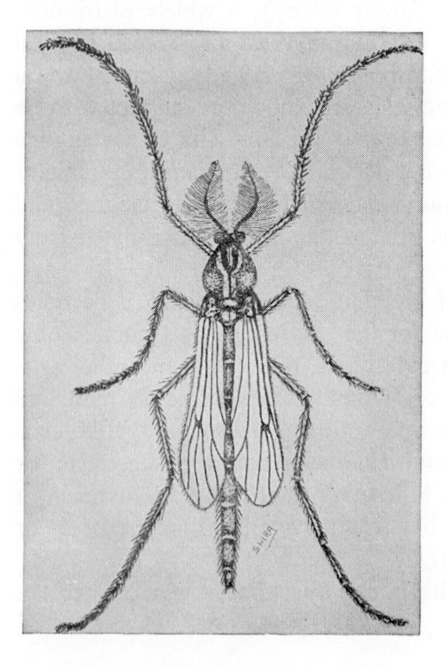

Fig. 47. A male midge (Chironomidae), commonly mistaken for a mosquito. × 12. (After Osborn.)

these insects hover in the air toward evening and produce a distinct humming sound. They are attracted to light in great numbers. The family is a very large one, comprising about 2000 species. Aside from the fact that adults may cause annoyance by swarming into homes and around lights, the family has no medical importance.

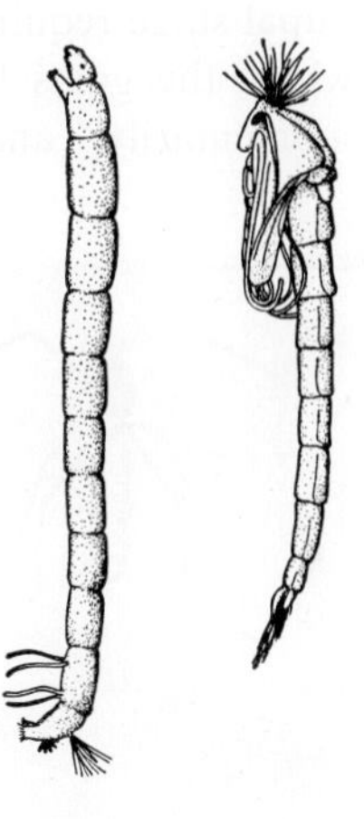

Fig. 48. Larva (*left*) and pupa (*right*) of a chironomid gnat (midge). (Larva redrawn after Needham, and pupa redrawn after Grünberg.)

FAMILY DIXIDAE

(*Dixa Midges*)

Dixa midges, sometimes considered a subfamily (Dixinae) of mosquitoes, have a characteristically different venation and have the wings almost devoid of hairs and scales; the proboscis, although somewhat projecting, is not fitted for piercing. The family is mentioned here particularly because the larvae are frequently mistaken for those of *Anopheles,* being commonly found in similar situations, and also because the adults resemble and are related to the true mosquitoes. Dixa larvae are usually seen at the surface of water among vegetation and debris, moving in a horizontal U-shaped position.

FAMILY CHAOBORIDAE

(*Chaoborid Gnats*)

The Chaoboridae, sometimes considered a subfamily (Chaoborinae) of mosquitoes, constitute a group of nonbloodsucking flies which have some importance as predators of mosquitoes; on the other hand, they may at times be nuisances. Their gill-breathing larvae, which live in deep water, are almost transparent and are seen with some difficulty, except when in motion, even in fairly clear water; hence they are called "phantom larvae." The tiny lead-colored, cigar-shaped eggs are deposited in great numbers on the surface of still water, such as ponds, lagoons, lakes, etc. The eggs soon sink to the bottom. The incubation period is less than 24 hours. The larvae grow slowly during the summer, reaching approximately full growth by winter, remaining thus through the winter, and pupating in the early spring. The pupal stage requires about two weeks. The pupae quickly come to the surface, where the gnats literally "pop" out of the pupal skins, balance on the water momentarily, and then fly shoreward. *Chaoborus astictopus* Dyar and

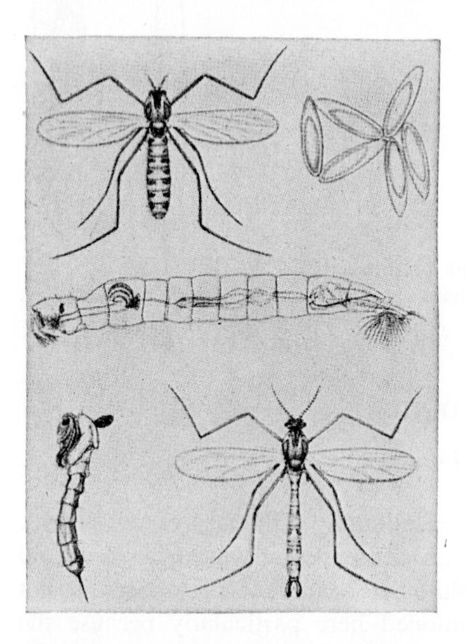

Fig. 49. A chaoborid, the Clear Lake gnat, *Chaoborus astictopus,* showing life cycle. (*Top left*) female gnat; (*top right*) eggs; (*lower left*) pupa; (*lower right*) male gnat; (*middle figure*) larva.

Shannon (= *C. lacustris* Freeborn), the Clear Lake gnat (Fig. 49) on which the foregoing life history is based, is a distinct nuisance along the shores of Clear Lake, California.[17] Adequate control has been obtained by the use of TDE (dichlorodiphenyl dichloroethane) which is less toxic to fish than DDT, an important consideration in the control of aquatic insects in large bodies of water. A dosage of about 1 part of active ingredient to 45–50 million parts of water will suffice.

REFERENCES

1. Adler, S., and Theodor, O., 1957. "Transmission of disease agents by phlebotomine and flies," *Annual Rev. Entomol.,* **2:**203–26.

2. Bequaert, J. C., 1938. "The black-flies, or Simuliidae, of the Belgian Congo," *Amer. J. Trop. Med.,* **18** (Supp.):116–36.

3. Blacklock, D. B., 1926. "The development of *Onchocerca volvulus* in *Simulium damnosum*," *Ann. Trop. Med. & Parasitol.*, **20:**1–48 (4 plates).

4. Barretto, Mauro Pereira, 1941. "Morfologia dos ovos, larvas e pupas de alguns flebótomos de São Paulo," Univ. São Paulo, *An. Fac. Med.*, **17:**357–427 (52 plates).

5. Barretto, Mauro Pereira, 1942. *Contribuição para o Estudo da Biologia dos Flebótomos em Condições Experimentais.* São Paulo: Fac. Med. Univ. São Paulo, Tese de Doutoramento. 162 pp.

6. Barretto, Mauro Pereira, 1943. *Observações sobre a Biologia, em Condições Naturais, dos Flebótomos do Estado de São Paulo.* São Paulo: Fac. Med. Univ. São Paulo, Tese de Concurso à Docencia-Livre de Cadeira de Parasitologia. 162 pp.

7. Barretto, Mauro Pereira, 1947. "Catálogo dos flebótomos americanos," *Arq. de Zool. do Estado de São Paulo,* **5:**177–242.

8. Buckley, J. J. C., 1933. "A note on the development of *Filaria ozzardi* in *Culicoides furens* Poey," *J. Helminthol.*, **11:**257–58.

9. Curran, C. H., 1934. *The Families and Genera of North American Diptera.* New York: The Ballou Press. 512 pp.

10. Dalmat, Herbert T., 1955. *The Black Flies (Diptera, Simuliidae) of Guatemala and their Role as Vectors of Onchocerciasis.* Washington: Smithsonian Misc. Coll. 125, no. 1, 425 pp. (44 + 1 colored plate).

11. Dove, W. E.; Hall, D. G.; and Hull, J. B.; 1932. "The salt marsh sand fly problem," *Ann. Entomol. Soc. Amer.*, **25:**505–22 (3 plates).

12. Fairchild, G. B., and Barreda, E. A., 1946. "DDT as a larvicide against *Simulium*," *J. Econ. Entomol.*, **38:**694–99.

13. Foote, Richard H., and Pratt, Harry D., 1954. *The Culicoides of the Eastern United States (Diptera, Heleidae).* U. S. Public Health Service: Pub. Health Mon. 18. 53 pp.

14. Forattini, Oswaldo Paulo, 1957. "Culicoides da região neotropical," *Univ. São Paulo, Arq. Fac. Hig. e Sal. Pub.*, **11:**161–526.

15. Fox, Irving, 1955. "A catalogue of the bloodsucking midges of the Americas (*Culicoides, Leptoconops,* and *Lasiohelea*) with keys to the subgenera and nearctic species, a geographical index, and bibliography," *Univ. Puerto Rico J. Agric.*, **39:**214–85.

16. Goldman, Leon, 1947. "Types of American cutaneous leishmaniasis—Dermatological aspects," *Amer. J. Trop. Med.*, **27:**561–84.

17. Herms, W. B., 1937. *The Clear Lake Gnat.* Berkeley: Univ. Calif., in *Agric. Exper. Sta. Bull.*, no. 607, 22 pp.

18. Hertig, Marshall, 1942. "Phlebotomus and Carrión's disease," *Amer. J. Trop. Med.*, **22** (Supp.):1–81.

19. Hertig, Marshall, 1948. "Sand flies of the genus *Phlebotomus*—a review of their habits, disease relationships and control," *Proc. 4th. Internat. Cong. Trop. Med. & Malaria (Abstracts)*, Washington, D. C.

20. Hisette, Jean, 1938. "Ocular onchoceriasis," *Amer. J. Trop. Med.*, **18** (Supp.):58–90.

21. Hopkins, C. A., and Nicholas, W. L., 1952. "*Culicoides austeni,* the vector of *Acanthocheilonema perstans*," *Ann. Trop. Med. & Parasitol.*, **46:**276–83.

22. Jamnback, Hugo, and Collins, D. L., 1955. *The Control of Blackflies (Diptera: Simuliidae) in New York.* Albany: New York State Mus. Bull. 350. 113 pp.

23. Johannsen, O. A., 1933–37. *Aquatic Diptera,* parts 1–3. Ithaca: Cornell Univ., in Agric. Exper. Sta. Memoirs, nos. 164, 177, and 205.

24. Johnson, E. P.; Underhill, G. W.; Cox, J. A.; and Threlkeld, W. L.; 1938. "A blood protozoon of turkeys transmitted by *Simulium nigroparvum (Twinn),*" *Am. J. Hyg.,* **27:**649–65 (3 plates).

25. Karstad, L. H.; Fletcher, O. K.; Spalatin, J.; Roberts, R.; and Hanson, R. P.; 1957. "Eastern equine encephalomyelitis virus isolated from three species of Diptera from Georgia," *Science,* **125:**395–96.

26. Lea, Arden O., Jr., and Dalmat, Herbert T., 1955. "Field studies in larval control of black flies in Guatemala," *J. Econ. Entomol.,* **48:**274–78.

27. Mangabeira, O., Filho, 1942. "Contribuição ao estudo dos flebotomos: Descriçao dos machos de 24 novas espécies," *Mem. Inst. Oswaldo Cruz,* **37:**111–218 (148 figures).

28. Marett, P. J., 1913. "The Phlebotomus flies of the Maltese Islands," *Roy. Army Med. Corps J.,* **20:**162–71. (Abstracts in *Rev. Applied Entomol.,* **1** [ser. B]:27–29.)

29. Noguchi, H.; Shannon, R. C.; Tilden, E. B.; and Tyler, J. R.; 1929. "Etiology of Oroyo fever: The insect vectors of Carrion's disease," *J. Exper. Med.,* **49:**993–1008 (3 plates).

30. Quate, Larry W., 1955. "A revision of the Psychodidae (Diptera) in America north of Mexico," *Univ. Calif. Pub. Entomol.,* **10:**103–273.

31. Rees, Don M., and Smith, James V., 1950. "Effective control measures used on biting gnats in Utah during 1949," *Mosq. News,* **10:**9–15.

32. Sambon, L. W., 1910. "Progress report of investigations of pellagra," *J. Trop. Med.,* **13:**271–87 and 305–19.

33. Sharp, N. A. D., 1928. "Filaria perstans: Its development in *Culicoides austeni,*" *Tr. Roy. Soc. Med. & Hyg.,* **21:**371–96.

34. Shewell, G. E., 1955. "Identity of the black fly that attacks ducklings and goslings in Canada (Diptera: Simuliidae)," *Canad. Entomologist,* **87:**345–49.

35. Shortt, H. E.; Smith, R. O. A.; Swaminath, C. S.; and Kishman, K. V.; 1931. "Transmission of Indian kala-azar by the bite of *Phlebotomus argentipes,*" *Indian J. Med. Research,* **18:**373–75.

36. Simpson, R. W., 1948. "DDT emulsion may damage filter growths," *Sewage Works Engineering,* **19:**23–24.

37. Skidmore, L. V., 1932. "*Leucocytozoon smithi* infection in turkeys and its transmission by *Simulium occidentale* Townsend," *Zentralbl. f. Bakt.,* **125:**329–35.

38. Smart, John, 1945. "The classification of the Simuliidae (Diptera)," *Tr. Roy. Entomol. Soc.,* London, **95:**217–38.

39. Smart, John, 1934. "On the biology of the black fly, *Simulium ornatum* Mg. (Diptera, Simuliidae)," *Proc. Roy. Physical Soc.,* **22:**217–38.

40. Smith, Leslie M., and Lowe, Homer, 1948. "The black gnats of California," *Hilgardia* (Calif. Agric. Exper. Sta.), **18:**157–83.

41. Sommerman, K. M.; Sailer, R. I.; and Esselbaugh, C. O.; 1955. "Biology of Alaskan black flies (Simuliidae, Diptera)," *Ecol. Monographs,* **25:**345–85.

42. Steward, J. S., 1937. "The occurrence of *Onchocerca gutturosa* Neumann in cattle in England, with an account of its life history and development in *Simulium ornatum* Meig.," *Parasitology,* **29:**212–18 (1 plate).

43. Stone, Alan, 1949. "A new genus of Simuliidae from Alaska," *Proc. Entomol. Soc. Washington,* **51:**260–67.

44. Stone, Alan, and Jamnback, Hugo A., 1955. *The Black Flies of New York State.* Albany: New York State Mus. Bull. 349. 144 pp. (23 plates).

45. Strong, R. P., 1938. "Onchocerciasis in Africa and Central America," *Am. J. Trop. Med,* **18**(Supp.):1–57.

46. Swaminath, C. S.; Shortt, H. E.; and Anderson, L. A. P.; 1942. "Transmission of Indian kala-azar to man by the bites of *Phlebotomus argentipes,* Ann. and Brun.," *Indian J. Med. Research,* **30:**473–77.

47. Townsend, Charles H. T., 1913. "The transmission of verruga by *Phlebotomus,*" *J.A.M.A.,* **61:**1717–18.

48. Townsend, Charles H. T., 1913. "Human case of verruga directly traceable to *Phlebotomus verrucarum,*" *Entomol. News,* **25:**40.

49. Townsend, Charles H. T., 1913. "A Phlebotomus, the practically certain carrier of verruga," *Science,* **38:**194–95.

50. Vargas, L.; Palacios, A. Martinez; and Najera, A. Diaz; 1946. "Simulidos de Mexico; Datos sobre sistematica y morfologia. Descripcion de nuevos subgeneros y especies," *Rev. d. Inst. Salub. y Enferm. Trop.* (Mexico), **7:**101–92 (25 plates).

51. Wirth, Willis W., 1952. "The Heleidae of California," *Univ. Calif. Pub. Entomol.,* **9:**95–266.

52. Wu, Yi Fang, 1931. "A contribution to the biology of *Simulium* (Diptera)," *Papers of Michigan Acad. Sc., Arts & Letters,* **13:**543–99.

Chapter 10

MOSQUITOES
Order Diptera, Family Culicidae

CLASSIFICATION AND BIOLOGY

Importance. Among the numerous species of bloodsucking arthropods that annoy man and other warm-blooded animals, both wild and domestic, mosquitoes stand out most prominently. Their number is legion, and they are an almost constant annoyance; there are some that bite by night and others that bite by day. Great swarms may be produced even in small quantities of water. They breed in practically all sorts of water, fresh and salt, foul or potable; water in tin cans, broken gourds, hoofprints, tree holes, reservoirs of impounded water; and vast stretches of salt marsh. Great areas of seacoast are at times made uninhabitable by salt-marsh mosquitoes, and agriculture may be retarded. Potential recreational areas may be made unsuitable for that use, and normal outdoors living around the home, and even within the home, may be interfered with. Real estate values suffer where the mosquito pest prevails, and losses resulting from lowered industrial efficiency are frequently considerable because of mosquito annoyance. Economic losses due to mosquitoes would alone, no doubt, amply justify the great sums now spent on mosquito abatement, yet these losses are minor compared with the prodigious damage done to the public health by mosquitoes as vectors of disease.

Mosquitoes are the sole vectors of the malarias, yellow fever, and dengue, and they participate very importantly in the transmission of filariasis and the encephalitides. It is reported that in an ordinary year in India alone, before the nation-wide antimalaria campaign went into effect, at least a hundred million persons suffered from, and a million succumbed to, the direct ravages of malaria. The indirect effect in lowered vitality and susceptibility to other diseases accounted for another million deaths.

Family Culicidae. Although some authors, Edwards[12] and others, include the dixa midges and the chaoborid gnats (see Chapter 9) as well as the true mosquitoes in the family Culicidae, only the latter are so classified for the purpose of this book. Excepting the huge sturdily built American gallinippers, *Psorophora ciliata* (Fabricius) (body length 9 mm and the wingspread 13 mm), and a few other species, mosquitoes are small and fragile, ranging in body length from 3 to 6 mm. Abundant scales are present on the wing veins and fringing the margins; the body, head, and legs are scaly.

Mosquitoes are distinguished by their characteristic wing venation (Fig. 40) as follows: subcosta (Sc) long, reaching the costa; radius (R) four-branched; R_{2+3} forked; R_{4+5} simple; no cross-vein connections of R_1 and R_2; media (M) two-branched; cross veins r-m and m-cu both present; cubitus (Cu) forked; anal vein (A) long and reaching wing margin; characteristic scale clothing the wings, and more or less abundant on the head and body (often scant or wanting); characteristics of the thorax, such as the absence of a definite suture between the prescutum and scutum, completely divided pronotum. The true mosquitoes have elongate mouth parts formed for piercing, and for bloodsucking in the females, though not all mosquitoes are bloodsuckers, and males are normally not bloodsuckers. The

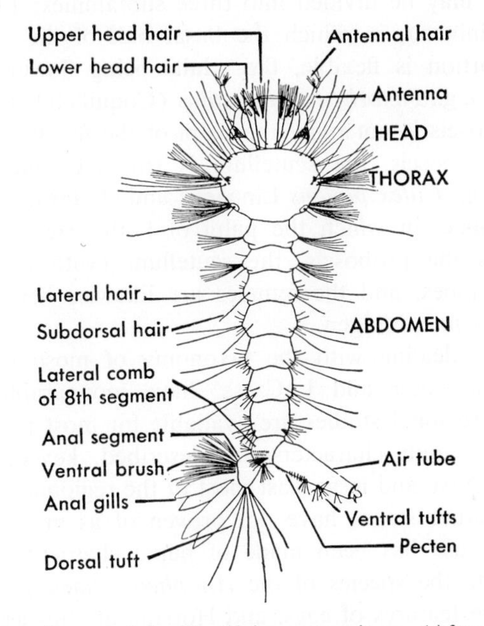

Fig. 50. Larval characters used in identifying mosquitoes. (After Stage, Gjullin, and Yates; U.S.D.A. photograph.)

antennae are long and filamentous with 14 or 15 segments, hairs in whorls, plumose in the males of most species; males of *Opifex* and *Deinocerites* do not have plumose antennae.

The larvae of mosquitoes are without exception aquatic and are distinguished from all other dipterous larvae by the possession of a complete head capsule and the presence of only one pair of functional spiracles, situated dorsally on the eighth abdominal segment. The anatomic structures of the mosquito larva that are most used in taxonomy are shown in Figure 50. It may be important to collect larvae of mosquitoes for several reasons: (1) in survey work, the capture of larvae may give a positive record in the absence of adult specimens; (2) larvae, in some cases, may be identified more positively than adults; (3) determination of larvae may serve as an aid to or a check on the determination of adults; (4) perfect adult specimens of both sexes may often be obtained through rearing, whereas those taken as adults may be damaged and difficult to identify; (5) when infection-free stock is desired, it is best obtained from reared sources.

There are about 2400 described species of mosquitoes in the world; about 120 occur in temperate North America.[35,48] These ubiquitous insects occur at elevations of 14,000 feet in Kashmir and as low as 3760 feet below sea level in gold mines of South India;[45] they are abundant in species in the tropics, and almost unbelievably large swarms of them occur in Arctic regions. Mosquitoes may be divided into three subfamilies: (1) **Toxorhynchitinae** (= Megarhininae), in which the basal half of the proboscis is rigid and the distal portion is flexible, the adults being flower-feeding and the larvae predaceous, e.g., *Toxorhynchites rutilus* (Coquillett); (2) the **Culicinae,** in which the proboscis is not rigid, the palpi of the female are less than half as long as the proboscis, the scutellum is trilobed, and the females are hematophagous, e.g., *Culex pipiens* Linnaeus and *Aedes aegypti* (Linnaeus); (3) the **Anophelinae,** in which the palpi of both sexes are as long as or nearly as long as the proboscis, the scutellum (with few exceptions) is rounded, without lobes, and the females are likewise hematophagous, e.g., *Anopheles maculipennis* Meigen.

The literature dealing with the taxonomy of mosquitoes has become very extensive. Carpenter and LaCasse[5] have monographed the Nearctic species; state and regional studies are available for most parts of the United States. Larval and adult characters are described, keyed, and figured by Carpenter and LaCasse and in at least most of the regional works. Characters of the other immature stages have not proven of as much value in identification, but some use has been made of pupal characters. Falleroni[14] was able to differentiate the species of the *Anopheles maculipennis* complex on the basis of surface features of eggs, and Horsfall and his associates[29,30] have shown that the eggs of some *Psorophora* and *Aedes* can similarly be differentiated.

Male Terminalia. The most critical differences used in the identification of adult mosquitoes are to be found in the male terminalia[15] (Fig. 51). It is of importance to know that the terminal portion of the abdomen of the adult male begins to rotate on its axis within a few hours after emergence from the pupa, and a rotation of 180° is completed in from 12 to 24 hours; this portion of the abdomen remains upside down for the rest of the mosquito's life. The terminalia may be prepared for microscopic study by first clipping off the tip of the abdomen with fine scissors and then dropping it into 70 per cent alcohol for a few moments, after which it is transferred to hot 10 per cent KOH for about 3 minutes, or until the specimen can be seen under the dissecting microscope to have attained its normal shape. It is then transferred to 95 per cent alcohol for a minute or two for dehydration and to

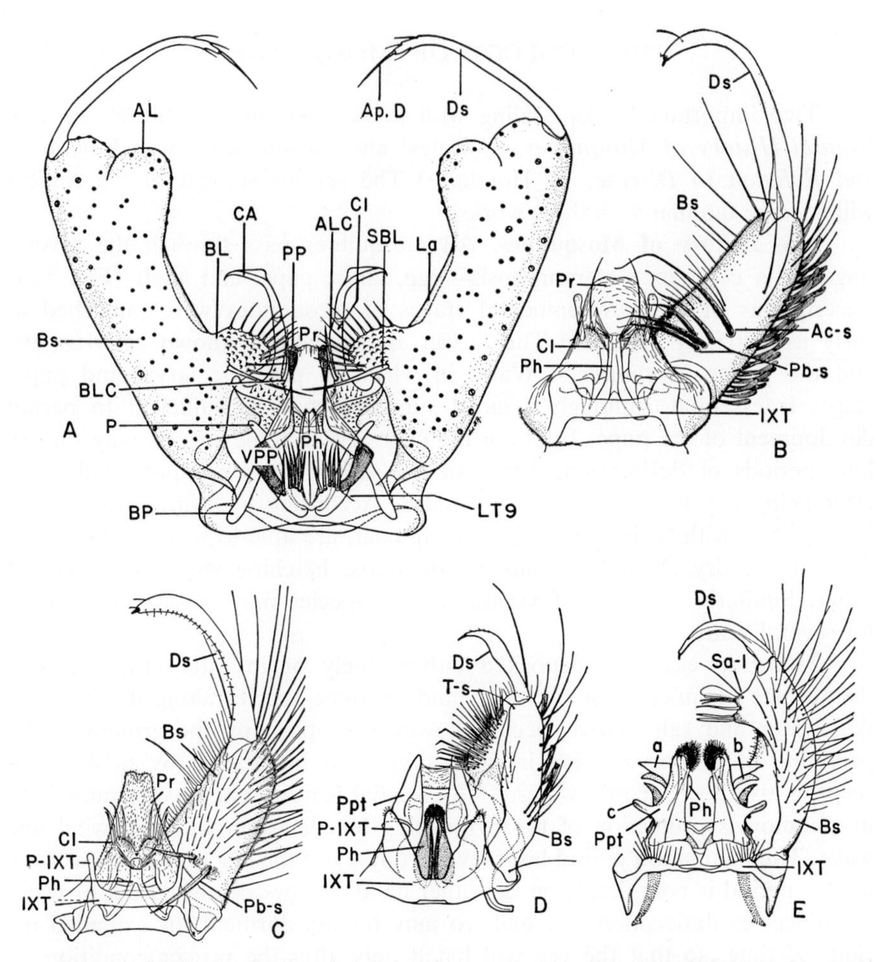

Fig. 51. Male terminalia of (*A*) *Aedes squamiger,* (*B*) *Anopheles gambiae,* (*C*) *Anopheles freeborni,* (*D*) *Aedes aegypti,* and (*E*) *Culex pipiens quinquefasciatus. AL,* apical lobe; *ALC,* apical lobe of claspette; *Ap.D,* appendage of dististyle; *Bs,* basistyle; *BL,* basal lobe; *BLC,* basal lobe of claspette; *BP,* basal plate; *Cl,* claspette; *CA,* claspette appendage; *Ds,* dististyle; *La,* lacuna; *LT9* (= P—IXT), lobe of 9th tergite (= process of 9th tergite); *P,* paramere; *Ph,* phallosome; *Ppt,* paraproct; *Pr,* proctiger; *SBL,* spine of basal lobe; *VPP,* ventral arm of paraproct; *IXT,* 9th tergite. (B to E after Ross and Roberts.)

beechwood creosote for a minute or two for clearing; it may then be mounted in thin balsam on a clean slide and covered with a cover slip which should be supported by whatever pieces of broken cover slip may be needed. Microscopic identification is made by comparison with drawings of the terminalia of various species in such publications as the *Mosquito Atlas* by Ross and Roberts.[41] A description of the technique for dissecting male terminalia of moquitoes is given by Komp.[34]

THE ECOLOGY OF MOSQUITOES

Two important books dealing with the ecology of mosquitoes are *The Natural History of Mosquitoes,* by Bates[1] and *Mosquitoes, Their Bionomics and Relation to Disease,* by Horsfall.[28] The serious student of the subject will need be familiar with these works.

Life History of Mosquitoes. All mosquitoes pass through the several stages of a complex metamorphosis—egg, larva, pupa, and adult (Fig. 52). Descriptions of the developmental stages of mosquitoes were published as early as 1665 by Hooke.[45] The larvae are commonly known as *wrigglers,* and the pupae as *tumblers.* Water in which to pass the larval and pupal stages is essential, although a moist substrate may be sufficient to permit development of the pupa. Eggs, on the contrary, in some species may survive long periods of desiccation. Those of the yellow fever mosquito will hatch after being dry for a period of 6 months. According to Dyar,[11] the eggs of *Psorophora,* with their spinose protecting coat, are able to withstand desiccation on the dry ground for months or years, hatching with the advent of water. Similarly the eggs of various *Aedes* species may survive desiccation for several years.

Mosquito eggs are deposited either singly or in rafts (Fig. 52) on the surface of quiet pools of water, and by some species along the margins; floodwater and salt marsh species, however, oviposit on the ground in depressions or among rubbish in sites subject to inundation by tidal water, seepage, overflow, or rain water. One essential feature that all sites must have in common is protection of the ovipositing female from action of wind and wave. The incubation period lasts several days, and the egg may hatch as soon as this period is completed; on the other hand, in eggs deposited out of water or subject to desiccation, the embryo may remain dormant for extended periods of time, so that the egg will hatch only after the proper conditioning. The exact nature of this conditioning is not fully understood and varies from one group of mosquitoes to another. In the case of the snow mosquitoes, eggs laid during the summer and autumn remain buried under the snow through the winter and hatch with the melting snow in spring; thus one brood is produced annually. Eggs of floodwater mosquitoes do not all hatch at one time; most of the eggs of one laying will hatch after the first flooding, but a certain percentage of them will remain for the second and subsequent floodings.

The larvae of the various many-brooded species, most commonly observed in rain barrels, watering troughs, and similar situations, hang suspended diagonally from the surface by means of a prominent breathing siphon with head downward, as in the Culicinae. The larvae of the Anophelinae lie horizontally just beneath the surface of the water, suspended particularly by means of palmate hairs (Fig. 52). The larvae of most species secure their food by browsing on microorganisms, both plants and animals.

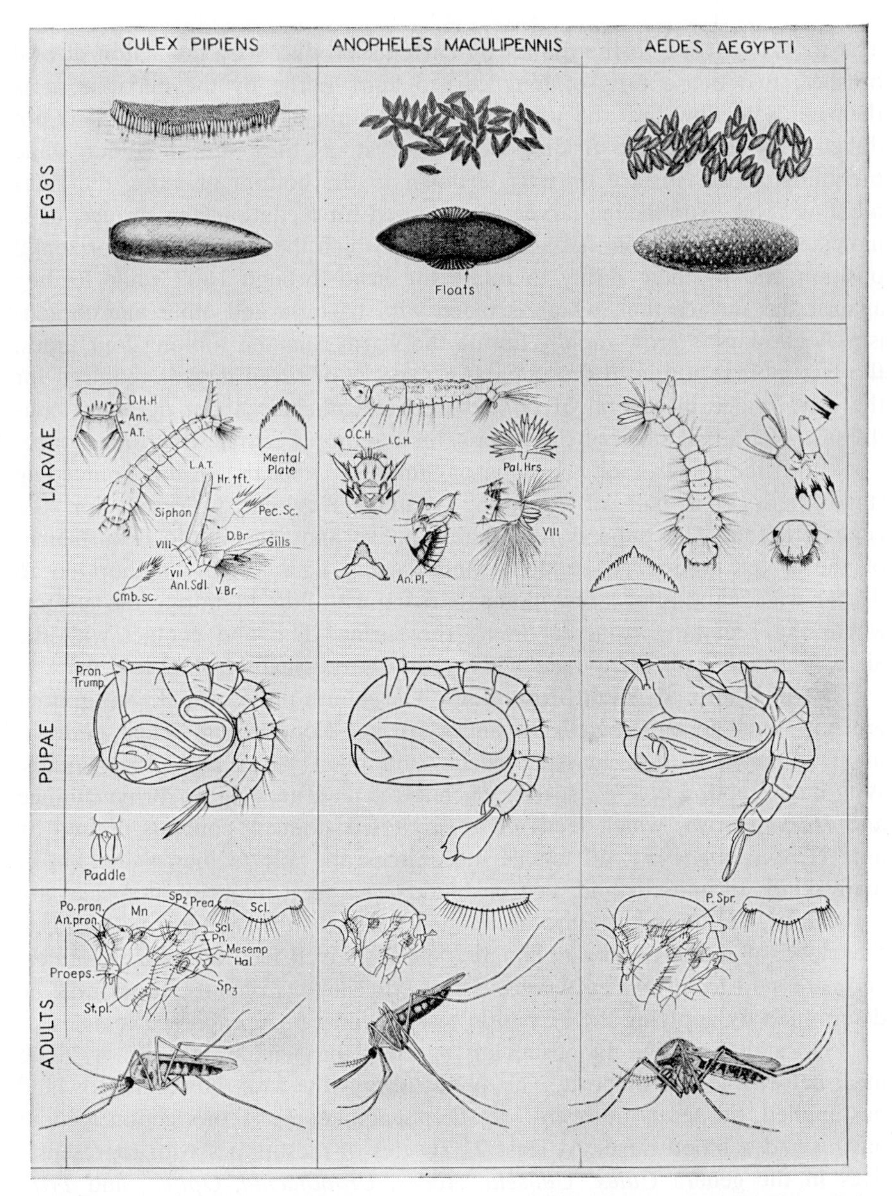

Fig. 52. Anatomic details and life history of three genera of mosquitoes, *Culex, Anopheles,* and *Aedes.* Explanation of abbreviations: *An.Pl.,* anal plate; *An.pron.,* anterior pronotal setae; *Anl.Sdl.,* anal saddle (dorsal plate); *Ant.,* antenna; *A.T.,* antennal tuft; *Cmb.Sc.,* comb scale; *D.Br.,* dorsal brush; *D.H.H.,* dorsal head hair; *Hal.,* halter; *Hr.tft.,* siphon hair tuft; *I.C.H.,* inner clypeal hair; *L.A.T.,* lateral abdominal tuft; *Mesemp,* mesepimeral setae; *Mn.,* mesonotum ($tergum_2$); *O.C.H.,* outer clypeal hairs; *Pal.Hrs.,* palmate or float hairs (tuft); *Pec.Sc.,* pecten scale; *Pn.,* postnotum; *Po.pron.,* posterior pronotal setae; *Prea.,* prealar setae; *Pron.Trump.,* pronotal trumpet; *Proeps.,* proepisternal setae; *P. Spr.,* postspiracular setae; *Scl.,* scutellum; *Sp.,* spiracle; *St.pl.,* sternopleural setae; *V.Br.,* ventral brush. (Adapted after various authors.)

The food is carried to the mouth by currents produced by the action of oral brushes, two dense tufts of long curved hairs borne by the maxillae; it is then made to flow into the water through suction of the pharynx.[28] It is not difficult to observe the feeding of the larvae as they squirm about while breathing at the surface or wriggle down to the bottom or along the sides nibbling food. Anopheline larvae are adapted for feeding at the surface, as is indicated by the palmate hairs by means of which they maintain a horizontal position and by their ability to rotate the head through 180° while feeding against the surface film, which is laden with bacteria and other microorganisms.[9] The larvae grow rapidly during the warm summer, molting four times, the last molt resulting in the pupa. An average of seven days is required for the larval stage in several of our commoner Culicinae under optimum conditions. The larval stage of the Anophelinae requires a somewhat longer time.

With the fourth molt the pupa or "tumbler" appears. In this nonfeeding stage there is a pair of breathing "trumpets" situated dorsally on the cephalothorax. The pupa is remarkably active and sensitive to disturbances of the water, letting go suddenly and darting with a tumbling motion to deeper water, and after a few moments rising with little motion to the surface, where the breathing trumpets break the surface film and contact with the air is re-established. The pupa stage is quite short, usually from 2 to 3 days.

Food Habits of Adult Mosquitoes. The mouth parts of male mosquitoes are not suited to piercing; hence males are not bloodsuckers. Their nourishment is normally derived from nectar and plant juices and other liquids. With the exception of a few species, such as the plant-feeding Toxorhynchitinae and *Harpagomyia,* which feeds on regurgitated stomach contents offered by ants (*Cremastogaster*), all female mosquitoes are able to pierce the skin of many kinds of animals and feed on blood. The great majority of species are *zoophilous,* i.e., feed in nature on animals other than man; some will feed on the blood of reptiles and amphibians. Species which feed on man by preference are said to be *anthrophilous.* The feeding habits of mosquitoes may be determined by applying the precipitin test to wild-caught engorged females.

Normally, in the bloodsucking species, the female requires a blood meal before she can oviposit. This is not always the case, however. Rowland has applied, the term "autogeny" to the phenomenon of reproduction without having had a blood meal. At least 21 species of mosquitoes with representatives in the genera *Culex, Culiseta, Aedes, Uranotaenia, Opifex,* and *Tripteroides* are known to have autogenous strains.

Flight Habits of Mosquitoes. Most domestic species of mosquitoes remain fairly close to their point of origin, i.e., within a distance of a few city blocks to half a mile. Dispersal takes the form of either creeping movements or migrations.[29] Creeping flights may be directed toward the following sites: (1) diurnal; (2) oviposition; (3) feeding; (4) hibernation; or (5) swarming.

Some species are notable for their migrations. Salt-marsh mosquitoes are often a source of great annoyance far from their breeding places, and a knowledge of their migratory habits is important in mosquito control. *Aedes sollicitans* (Walker), an important salt-marsh species of the Atlantic seaboard, is known to migrate at least 40 miles. The migrations of *Aedes squamiger* (Coquillett) have been traced on the Pacific coast for a distance of 50 to 75 miles.[19] Males are seldom found far from their point of origin, although the males of *Mansonia perturbans* (Walker) are said to accompany the migrating females.

The flight range of *Aedes vexans* (Meigen) and *A. sticticus* (Meigen) (as *aldrichi* Dyar and Knab) has been studied by Stage, Gjullin, and Yates[47] by using a stain applied with a compressed-air hand sprayer to newly emerged adult mosquitoes resting on vegetation near their breeding places. Mosquitoes were collected in this area at regular intervals until no more could be found. The following results are recorded: (1) Both species and both sexes were dispersed in all directions, with and against general wind currents, for a distance of about two miles. (2) Males moved away from the breeding areas more slowly than females. (3) Females of both species traveled one-half mile across part of the Columbia River (Oregon) within 24 hours after being stained. (4) One *Aedes vexans* female was recovered 46 days after being stained, 3 miles distant and across the Columbia River. (5) One *Aedes* sp. male was taken at a point 5 miles distant 24 days after being stained. This was the greatest distance for any positive flight record obtained. (6) The pests were abundant to a distance of 15 miles from the breeding grounds then diminished rapidly, until at about 30 miles only one female was taken during a 10-minute search.

Using the fluorescent dye, Rhodamine B, to mark the mosquitoes, Reeves[39] and associates released over 20,000 *Culex tarsalis* Coquillett; the maximum range of recovery was 2.5 miles for females and 1.1 miles for males. The majority of recoveries were made within 1 mile. On the basis of these studies it is recommended that control measures for *Culex tarsalis* be carried out in a zone not less than 1 1/2 miles beyond the human or animal hosts to be protected.

In conducting control operations for many years involving *Anopheles quadrimaculatus* Say, it has been assumed that the usual maximum flight of this species is about 1 mile, and this procedure is in the main sound; however, Eyles, Sabrosky, and Russell[13] recaptured marked individuals 2.0 to 2.7 miles from the point of release and a single individual at 3.63 miles. It is pointed out, however, that there were no domestic blood supply sources between the flooded swamp and the station of recapture. The flight range of *Anopheles freeborni* Aitken during dispersal and hibernation flight is, of course, much greater, being as much as 25 miles.

Longevity of Mosquitoes. Male mosquitoes usually remain alive for but 6 or 7 days, although *Anopheles pseudopunctipennis franciscanus* Mc-

Craken males have been kept alive for over a month, and *A. punctipennis* (Say) for 89 days.[37] Females with ample food may live for 4 or 5 months, particularly under hibernating conditions. During their period of greatest activity it is likely that the average lifetime of the females is not far from 30 days. Where summers are hot, this figure may be closer to two weeks.

The staining experiment by Stage *et al.*[47] produced important data relative to longevity. Thus, six *Aedes stricticus* females were taken 52 days after staining, one female of the same species 85 days after staining, one *Aedes vexans* female after 55 days; also, under especially favorable conditions, one 94-day A. *sticticus* male was taken, and females of both *Aedes stricticus* and *A. vexans* were collected from 104 to 113 days after staining. The latter species appears to have the greater maximum longevity by approximately 15 to 20 days.

Freeborn[17] has found that increased humidity has a protective influence on the longevity of *Anopheles freeborni* Aitken kept at constant temperature; but at a constant of 80° F no amount of relative humidity can protect them for the full life span of a month. A relative humidity of 55 per cent ensures the normal life span at 70° F. Freeborn points out that 55 per cent humidity involves a saturation deficiency of 3.6 grains per cubic foot, by which can be expressed the drying power of the air in the absence of wind currents. A deficiency of 3.8 grains at 76° F was tolerated for only 3 weeks instead of more than 4 weeks. It is pointed out that the lethal effect may be caused by either a fatal temperature or by desiccation of the insect's body. With an increase of temperature or a decrease in relative humidity, the saturation deficiency increases and the demand on the insect's moisture content becomes greater. The ability of a particular species to retain adsorbed water in the presence of existing saturation deficiencies undoubtedly explains the variability of resistance of the different species to desiccation, according to Freeborn. The length of life of *A. freeborni* as well as other vectors of malaria has important bearing on their ability to transmit the infection, i.e., if the mosquito dies before the malaria parasite is fully developed, the latter must also perish. Also, length of life is related to the multiple-bite potential so important in transmission of any mosquito-borne disease.

Internal Anatomy of Mosquitoes. To be prepared to study the relation of mosquitoes to such diseases as malaria and filariasis, the student must be familiar with their internal anatomy. The student is referred to Figure 6 (p. 46) and the accompanying discussion.

SUBFAMILY TOXORHYNCHITINAE

Characteristics. The members of the subfamily Toxorhynchitinae occur in tropical as well as temperate climates and are usually highly colored;

they are day fliers; both sexes are flower-feeders and do not suck blood. The basal half of the proboscis is stout and rigid, while the distal portion is flexible, which accounts for the curious hooklike position of the proboscis when at rest. The palpi vary in length from one-fourth the length of the proboscis to nearly the same length. The huge larvae are predaceous and cannibalistic. Their appetites are prodigious; one larva during its last stage was reported by Garnham *et al.*[18] to have devoured 195 mature larvae of *Aedes aegypti* during 12 days. On the other hand, they are resistant to starvation for considerable periods of time.

The eggs are deposited singly. The larvae breed in small confined collections of water, such as may occur in bamboo stems, tree holes, pitcher plants, and the like.

Stone *et al.*[48] list 59 species of the "tropicopolitan" genus *Toxorhinchites* (*Megarhinus*), the only one in the tribe. One species represented by two subspecies occurs in the United States. *Toxorhinchites rutilus rutilus* (Coquillett), the typical form, occurs only in the extreme southwest, but *T. rutilus septentrionalis* (Dyar and Knab) is much more widely distributed. The giant species *T. inornatus* (Walker) was introduced from New Britain into the Hawaiian Islands[50] for purposes of mosquito control, without practical result, although two other species, *T. brevipalpis* Theobald and *T. splendens* (Wiedemann), appear to have become established there more recently.

SUBFAMILY CULICINAE

Characters. All members of the subfamily Culicinae have the scutellum trilobed with each lobe bearing bristles, but with areas between lobes without bristles. The abdomen is completely clothed with broad scales, which nearly always lie flat; the larvae have a prominent siphon with usually a well-developed pecten (Fig. 50), and one to several hair tufts on the siphon. The eggs are deposited in tight raftlike masses on the surface of the water, singly on the surface of the water, on mud, or on the ground; they lack the floats characteristic of the anopheline eggs.

The subfamily Culicinae includes about 1500 species distributed among more than 20 genera; roughly two-thirds of the described species belong to the genera *Culex* and *Aedes*.

The Culex Pipiens Complex. The northern house mosquito, or rain-barrel mosquito *Culex pipiens pipiens* Linnaeus, and the southern house mosquito, *Culex pipiens quinquefasciatus* Say (*fatigans* Wiedemann) are best considered subspecies of the same polytypic species.[36] Barr[2] has shown that, in North America, *C. p. pipiens* occurs only north of the 36th parallel and *C. p. quinquefasciatus* (except in coastal California) only south of the 39th; in the area of overlap, identification is rendered difficult because of the frequent occurrence of intergrades and hybrid swarms. The two subspecies can be separated definitely only on the basis of male genitalia. Both these mosquitoes occur widely in the Old World. A third form occurs in North America, *C. p. molestus* Forskål. Unlike *C. p. pipiens* and *C. p. quinquefasciatus,* this form is autogenous, that is, it may deposit eggs without previously having had a blood meal. Barr gives evidence to support his belief that "*Culex molestus*" represents merely local populations of *C. p. pipiens* that have developed autogeny. The thorax, abdomen, and proboscis of *Culex pipiens* are brown; the latter is darker toward the tip. The basal white bands on the abdomen join lateral basal triangular patches. This mosquito, a domestic species, lays its eggs in rafts on water, in rain barrels, tanks, cisterns, catch basins, and other small collections of water. Where breeding places are favorable, it may occur in enormous numbers. It invades houses freely. Because of its vicious bites (particularly of *molestus*) and high-pitched, tantalizing hum continued late into the night, it may be a terrific pest. Although greatly influenced by temperature,[28] the life history requires but about 10 to 14 days under warm summer conditions, egg stage 24 to 36 hours, larva about 7 to 10 days, and the pupa about 2 days.

Woke[52] fed 38 *Culex pipiens* on man, and these mosquitoes deposited 29 egg masses, totaling 2118 eggs, or an average of 73.0 eggs per mass. At the same time 39 females fed on a canary deposited 22 egg masses, totaling 4473 eggs, or an average of 203.3 eggs per mass. Over twice as many eggs per mass or per milligram of blood ingested were produced by mosquitoes fed on canary blood as were produced by mosquitoes fed on the blood of man.

Culex p. pipiens and *C. p. quinquefasiatus* may serve as intermediate hosts of *Wuchereria bancrofti.* They may also be involved in the transmission of bird malaria, heartworm of dogs (*Dirofilaria immitis*), and fowl pox. The viruses of western and St. Louis encephalitis have been isolated from wild-caught individuals of *C. p. pipiens.*

Culex tarsalis Coquillett (Fig. 53) is an abundant and widespread species of the semiarid regions of North America; however, it occurs throughout the southern United States as far northeast as Indiana. It has been taken at elevations of 9000 feet. It is an important vector of the virus of western equine and St. Louis encephalitis. It is a fairly large and robust species; generally dark brown to black in color; the black abdomen has broad, segmented, basal bands of yellowish-white scales; each segment of the venter with V-shaped markings of black scales, the apex of the V anteriorly; femora are black with a dotted white line along both sides, knees white; tibiae black, also with white line, bases and apices white; tarsi black; hind tarsi with apical and basal white bands on all segments, last tarsal segment white; proboscis black, with a sharply outlined white ring just before the middle. It breeds in all sorts of ground pools, roadside ditches, pools in and around corrals, artificial containers, etc. It hibernates, in northern climates, as gravid females. Autogenous strains are known to occur in this species,[7] as in *C pipiens*. Domestic and wild birds are the preferred hosts, although this mosquito readily bites man, horses, and cattle. The mosquito bites chiefly at night.

The genus Culiseta (= *Theobaldia*) includes nine North American species. The postspiracular bristles (Fig. 52) are absent, and in the females of most species the anterior and posterior cross vein tend to lie in one line. In *Culiseta incidens* (Thomson), a western species (west of the Rocky Mountains), the wings are spotted. It breeds throughout the year, where temperature permits, in all sorts of permanent pools and is a common domestic

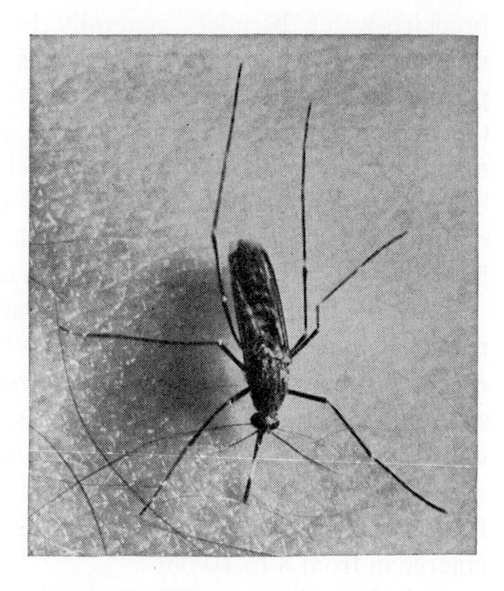

Fig. 53. *Culex tarsalis,* an important vector of the virus of western equine encephalitis. (Photograph by R. Craig.)

species. It lends itself particularly well to laboratory experimentation. *Culiseta inornata* (Williston) is found thoughout the United States and southern Canada. Its wings are broad and clear, the cross veins are scaled, and the very short black palpi have white scales at the tip. Precipitin tests indicate that it feeds chiefly on large mammals, such as horses and cattle. Both *C. incidens* and *C. inornata* may have some importance in relation to transmission of the encephalitides.

The Genus Aedes. Nearly half of all the species of mosquitoes in North America belong to the genus *Aedes*. In most of the species, the claws are toothed in the female, postspiracular bristles are present, the pulvilli are absent or hairlike, and the female abdomen tends to be more pointed and the cerci longer than in other groups. The larvae have short siphons bearing one pair of posteroventral hair tufts, and nearly always a distinct pecten (Fig. 50). The eggs are deposited singly on the surface of the water, on mud, or even in situations where there may be little moisture but where submergence may follow. The females of all species bite, many of them viciously. Many species are diurnal in biting habits, most of them biting toward evening.

Salt-marsh Mosquitoes. *Aedes dorsalis* (Meigen), a fierce day biter, is widely distributed throughout the northern half of the United States, Canada, Europe, and Asia. In general the body is straw colored (tan), varying from almost white to dark brown; the thorax has three longitudinal bright brown stripes; the hind tarsi have white bands at bases and apices of all segments, the last one wholly white. Although the species breeds freely and abundantly in fresh water, such as flood water, rice fields, and drainage from irrigation, it is nevertheless the commonest salt-marsh mosquito of the Pacific coast north of Monterey, California. It is here a distinctly brackish-water breeder, generally breeding in pools reached only by the monthly "rip" tides. There are thus several monthly broods, the first appearing as early as March. The eggs are deposited singly, most of them in the mud along the edge of receding pools; they may remain unhatched for many months in situations from which water is excluded. Development after hatching is rapid, and emergence of the adult mosquitoes may be within 8 or 9 days. *Aedes squamiger* (Coquillett), the California salt-marsh mosquito biter, occurs only along the California coast.

Aedes taeniorhynchus (Wiedemann) is a typical salt-marsh breeder distributed along the coastal area of the United States northward to Connecticut on the East Coast and to Santa Barbara on the West Coast. It is the brown salt-marsh mosquito; its proboscis is distinctly white-banded. It is a fierce day biter, and its egg-laying habits are similar to those of *A. dorsalis* and *A. squamiger*. There are monthly broods throughout the summer. Development is exceedingly rapid; the larval stage may require but 4 days, the adults emerge in from 8 to 10 days.

Aedes sollicitans (Walker), the pestiferous salt-marsh mosquito of the Atlantic coast, breeds from Maine to Florida and thence west along the Gulf of Mexico to Texas. There are many broods and in its southern range breeding may be continuous.

The numbers of larvae appearing in certain pools is almost unbelievable. Smith[46] states:

> I have found pools so crowded that an estimate of 100 wrigglers in an area of one square inch was scarcely equal to the fact. Half that number is a common occurrence. This means over 7,000 in an area of one square foot, and it needs an area of less than 150 square feet—a pool roughly ten by fifteen feet—to produce 1,000,000 mosquitoes at one hatching. If these figures seem incredible they can be easily verified anywhere along shore by anyone who will put on a pair of gum boots and will hunt out a few breeding places.

Flood-water Aedes. *Aedes vexans* (Meigen) is a typical flood-water mosquito having practically a holarctic distribution. It is one of the fiercest day biters and exceedingly abundant; it is truly a vexatious mosquito. It breeds in greatest numbers along the edges of rivers subject to overflow and like other *Aedes* species lays its eggs along the muddy edges of receding pools, where they may hatch the same season when water due to intermittent flooding or freshets reaches them, or they carry over. There may thus be several broods where flooding occurs as a result of melting mountain snows or thunderstorms, or there may be only one brood where there is a single spring flood. The species is a rapid breeder and migrates many miles. It varies in color from brown to gray; the tarsi are basally narrowly banded; the wings are uniformly brown.

Fig. 54. Tree hole where *Aedes* larvae are found. (After Stage, Gjullin, and Yates; U.S.D.A. photograph.)

Aedes dorsalis (Meigen), already referred to as a salt-marsh breeder, is also a prolific breeder in open flood-water pools, particularly in irrigated pastures after flooding and in drainage pools due to excess water. It is often found in association with *A. vexans*.

Aedes nigromaculis (Ludlow) is becoming of increasing importance as an irrigated pasture mosquito in the western United States. Development is extremely rapid; adults may appear as early as 4 days after the eggs have been wetted by irrigation. Swarms of these annoyers may bring normal activity of livestock virtually to a standstill.

Tree-hole Mosquitoes. Although the habit of breeding in water-holding tree holes (Fig. 54) occurs in various species belonging to other genera, e.g.,

Anopheles barberi Coquillett, there are a number of typical tree-hole breeders in *Aedes,* notably *A. sierrensis* Ludlow, a Pacific Coast species; *A. triseriatus* (Say) of the eastern United States; *A. luteocephalus* Newstead, Ethiopian; *A. simpsoni* Theobald, Ethiopian; *A. seoulensis* Yamaca, Chinese; and others.

Aedes sierrensis (Ludlow) (= *varipalpus* [Coquillett]) has bright white markings on the legs at both bases and apices of the tarsal segments and many white or silvery scales distributed over the body so as to give the vestiture a silver mottled appearance. It is one of our smallest mosquitoes but a fierce biter. This Pacific coast species deposits its eggs on the sides of tree holes, notably holes in live oaks (*Quercus agrifolia*), also California laurel (*Umbellularia californica*) and valley oaks (*Quercus lobata*). Freeborn[16] states that the eggs

> . . . hatch whenever they are wet by the rising waters. There is some evidence that the eggs may drop off after a period of desiccation or, as an alternative method, the larvae may hatch without intervention of actual wetting and fall into the water below. The straw-colored larvae with bright brown heads and enormously developed gills swim about their secluded medium with snake-like movements, but spend most of their time with their heads and thoraces buried in the silty deposit at the bottom of the tree holes. . . . The developmental period is extremely long, lasting from one to seven months. Although there is an intermingling of the broods, there are two pronounced peaks, one in the early summer and another in the fall. The fall adults deposit eggs which produce the larvae that overwinter.

Aedes triseriatus (Say) lacks the white rings on the tarsal segments. It is a widespread treehole breeder east of the Rocky Mountains. Both *A. triseriatus* and *A. sierrensis* may be very annoying pests, and their special larval habitat may be overlooked unless one realizes that they are tree-hole breeders.

Boreal Aedes or Snow Mosquitoes. An interesting group of *Aedes* consists of the so-called snow mosquitoes which appear in the early spring in the high mountains and northern ranges of distribution, breeding in the pools left by the melting snow (Fig. 55). These *Aedes* have but one generation and appear in enormous swarms in the higher elevations and northern ranges much to the dismay of the alpine traveler. Dyar,[10] speaking of the occurrence of Alpine mosquitoes in the Sierra Nevada, says:

> At an altitude of 6,000 feet, pupae were abundant May 25 and by the first week in June the breeding was complete; even the pools that still contained water or had only just thawed out were empty. Adults appeared by the first of June, and by the 15th the woods were filled with them in all directions. . . .
>
> The seasonal appearance of these mosquitoes varies with the altitude in the ratio of about a month in time to 1,000 feet of elevation. At Yosemite, at about 5,000 feet, all the species were about a month earlier than at Lake Tahoe, at 6,000 feet, while at Summit, at 7,000 feet, they were still another month later, larvae and pupae of *tahoensis* and *hexodontus* being taken there on July 2, 1916, about

the same stage that they were taken at Fallen Leaf [vicinity of Lake Tahoe] on June 1, 1916.

At an elevation of about 10,000 feet the author (Herms) encountered a vertible plague of *Aedes ventrovittis* Dyar and *A. communis* (De Geer) along the shores of Young Lakes in the Sierra Nevada Mountains July 22, 1936. Larvae and pupae were still present in small pools of snow water along the shores of the lakes. Apparently only certain pools were infested.

In northern Alaska the spring thaw is followed by a sudden emergence of swarms of mosquitoes. Like other boreal mosquitoes, they overwinter in

Fig. 55. Typical breeding place for snow mosquitoes on floor of Yosemite Valley, California. (Photograph by H. F. Gray.)

the egg stage and hatch as soon as the ice thaws from around the eggs in the spring. There is but one generation a year. Jachowski and Schultz,[31,32] who studied *Aedes punctor* (Kirby), *A. communis* (De Geer), and *A. impiger* (Walker) (= *nearcticus* Dyar), classify the sites from which they collected larvae as grassy sloughs, mossy pools ("tundra pools"), frost ditches, and willow-alder pools. The eggs hatch almost immediately after the spring thaw, and if a freeze occurs after this, the larvae will freeze into the ice and thaw out again when it warms up. The larval period was observed to be about 28 days and the pupal period from 3 to 5 days. During chilly night hours mosquitoes were observed to gather in large numbers about the open doors of heated quarters or hover in the warm draft from chimneys. Blood meals, if necessary, are readily available from herds of caribou, large populations of rodents, and nesting ducks, geese, and other birds.

Mosquitoes of the tundra may occur in almost unbelievably large swarms. In a transition area between tundra and forest in Quebec, Jenkins and Knight[33] sampled, with a few sweeps of the net, a swarm that surrounded them; the sample contained 194 *Aedes,* and the swarm was estimated at 1500 individuals. Grazing animals may be driven into a restless flight by these annoyers. *Aedes nigripes* (Zetterstedt), strictly a species of the tundra, together with *A. impiger* (Walker) (= *nearcticus* Dyar) are the most abundant species of the far north; they are both circumpolar in distribution.[49]

Aedes aegypti (Linnaeus), the yellow fever mosquito, is not only the most important vector of yellow fever but likewise of dengue fever. This is

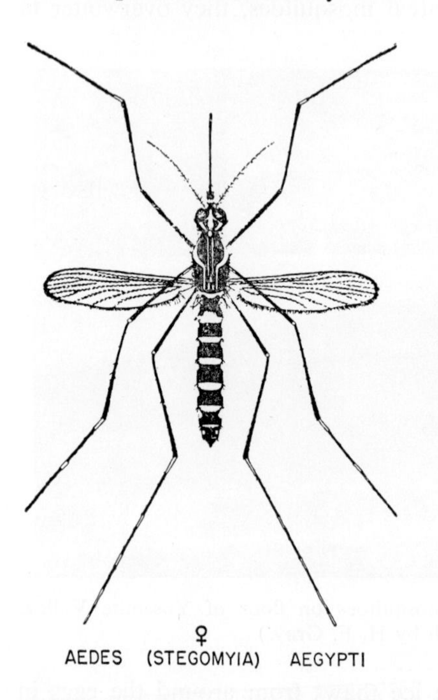

Fig. 56. *Aedes aegypti,* an important vector of the viruses of yellow fever and dengue. (Adapted after Soper, Wilson, *et al.*)

widely distributed within the limits of 40° N and 40° S latitude, but it is highly susceptible to temperature variations. According to Hindle,[26] it soon dies in the open air at a temperature of 7° to 8° C, succumbing in a few seconds to an exposure of 0° C, and 37° C is rapidly fatal. Furthermore, it does not thrive in dry hot climates. The adult insect (Fig. 56) is beautifully marked with silvery-white or yellowish-white bands and stripes on a nearly black background, whence the name "tiger mosquito." It has a "lyrelike" pattern dorsally on its thorax, i.e., two outer curved yellowish-white lines and two median parallel lines. The legs are conspicuously banded, and the last segment of the hind leg is entirely white. The head is covered with broad flat scales with only a single row of upright forked scales.

The yellow fever mosquito is a typical domestic species seldom found far from man's habitations. It is a day-flying and day-feeding species, but older individuals (6 or 7 days after emergence, or, rather, those which have had a blood meal) will extend their feeding period into the night. Younger females bite under artificial light. The male does not bite, but his probing after moisture from sweat may be almost as annoying as biting.

The eggs of the yellow fever mosquito are deposited singly on the surface of the water, usually in containers at or near the waterline; they are dark in color, and each egg is surrounded by air cells (Fig. 52). Comparatively few eggs are deposited at one laying, and while there may be two layings, possibly more, the total number of eggs produced averages about 140 (144 according to Woke) when *A. aegypti* had fed on man. Woke[53] produced greater numbers of eggs when *A. aegypti* had been fed on frog or turtle; also he has shown that *A. aegypti* fed on frog blood and turtle blood produced viable eggs, and that the larvae developed normally and produced normal adults.

The eggs can withstand desiccation to a very marked degree, even up to a year's time. Ordinarily the eggs hatch within 4 days.

The larvae are quite robust, the breathing siphon is comparatively short and heavy and black (Fig. 52), and their position in the water is almost vertical, considerably more so than that of other culicine species. The larval stage is ordinarily passed in about 9 or 10 days under average conditions and in from 4 to 7 days under warmer conditions.

The pupae have broadly triangular breathing trumpets. Normally from 1 to 5 days are spent in the pupal stage.

According to Howard the shortest period of development from egg to imago observed by Reed and Carroll in Cuba was 9 1/2 days, i.e., egg stage, 2 days; larval stage, 6 days; pupal stage, 36 hours. From this very short period, the time ranges from 11 to 18 days according to the same author.

The yellow fever mosquito breeds by preference in artificial containers of rain water. (It is known, however, at times to breed naturally in brackish water.) Rain-water barrels, tanks, cisterns, tin cans, urns, etc., provide suitable breeding places (wooden containers seem to be preferred); water collected among the leaves of certain members of the agave family, also water collected in banana palms, may produce many mosquitoes.

Although *Aedes aegypti* is called the yellow fever mosquito and is undoubtedly the most important vector of this disease under natural conditions because of its domestic breeding habits, there are nevertheless a dozen other species which are able to transmit the disease (see p. 206).

Other Genera. The genus *Psorophora,* which includes only 12 Nearctic species, is distinguished by the presence of both prespiracular and postspiracular bristles and by the second marginal cell of the wing, which is more than half as long as its petiole. The larvae of some species are predaceous, feeding on other mosquito larvae and other small aquatic animals in temporary ground pools.

Psorophora confinnis (Lynch-Arribálzaga) (= *columbiae* [Dyar and Knab]) is widely distributed in the eastern United States, but ranges from parts of South America through Cuba and Mexico to Canada. It is strikingly speckled in appearance and is a fierce biter. It commonly breeds in rice fields. In 1932 this species is reported to have caused great loss of livestock in the Everglades section of Florida. The *United States Insect Pest Survey Bulletin* (vol. 12, no. 10, p. 428) describes the plague:

> . . . by evening of that day the buzzing was as loud as that of a swarm of bees. During the night livestock could be heard running and thrashing in the underbrush, and on the morning of September 6, dead animals were found throughout the section. The recorded mortality was 80 head of cattle, 3 horses, 1 mule, 67 hogs, 20 chickens, and 2 dogs. Post-mortem examinations showed no mosquitoes in the respiratory apparatus, indicating that the animals died either from loss of blood, nervous exhaustion, or the effects of some toxin.

The milk supply was also greatly reduced during the 4 days of the infestation.

The genus *Mansonia* is characterized in large measure by the scales of the wings, which are very broad by comparison with those of other species of mosquitoes. The larvae have the air tube pointed, enabling them to pierce the stem or roots of aquatic plants from which they obtain air and to which they remain attached (submerged) throughout larval development.

Mansonia perturbans (Walker) is a small species (5 mm) which is widely distributed throughout North America. It has severe biting habits and evidently travels some distance from its breeding place. The larvae hibernate in the mud. The biology of this and other species of the genus is fascinating indeed.

The genus *Orthopodomyia* includes only two species from North America. The adults are described by Matheson as "rather gaily ornamented and easily recognized by their coloring." The larvae are found in tree holes, also in broken bamboo and leaf axils of certain plants. *Orthopodomyia signifera* (Coquillett) extends along the eastern seaboard of the United States and westerly from Florida into southern California, thence northerly to near Sacramento.

SUBFAMILY ANOPHELINAE

Characteristics. The following characters are generally employed to characterize the subfamily Anophelinae: palpi of both sexes are usually about as long as the proboscis; (except in *Bironella*); the scutellum (Figs. 52 and 57) is evenly rounded (except in *Chagasia* where a slightly trilobed condition occurs); legs are very long and slender, there are no distinct tibial bristles and no pulvilli; the abdomen is without scales, or at least with the sternites largely bare; the wings usually have distinct markings.

The subfamily Anophelinae has been divided into numerous genera such as *Myzorhynchus, Arribalzagia, Neomyzomyia, Myzomyia,* and more than 30 others. Edwards, as well as other culicidologists, reduced the number of genera to three: *Chagasia,* with the scutellum slightly trilobed; *Bironella,* with scutellum evenly rounded, wing with stem of median (M) fork wavy; and *Anopheles,* with scutellum evenly rounded, wing with stem of median (M) fork straight. There are three species of *Chagasia,* all of tropical America. The genus *Bironella* includes seven species, all of New Guinea and Melanesia. The genus *Anopheles* includes over 300 species and subspecies,[45] of which about 90 occur in the Americas, 14 in North America.

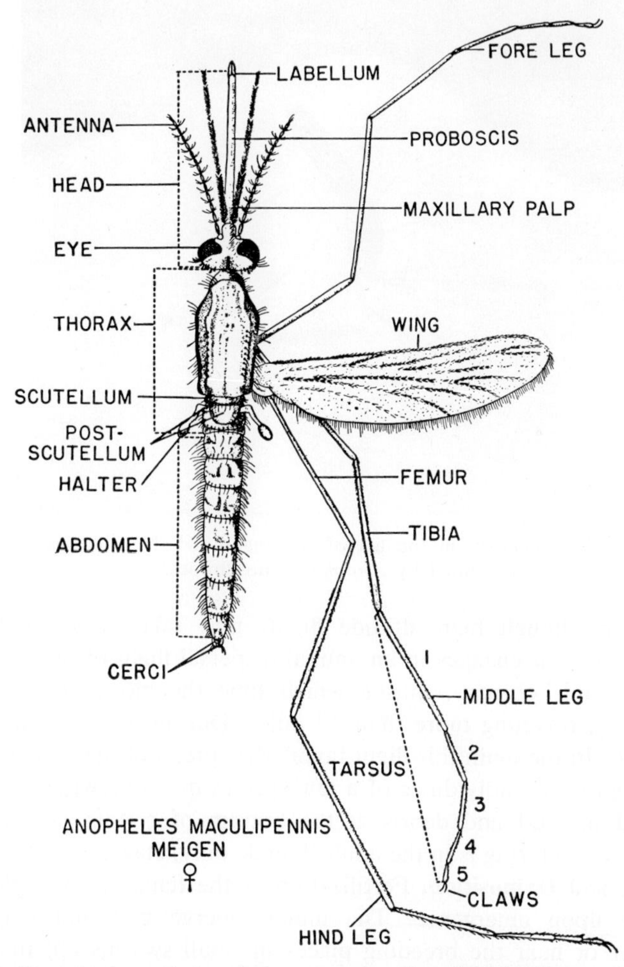

Fig. 57. Dorsal view of *Anopheles* mosquito (female) showing certain structural details useful in classification. (Modified after Essig in *College Entomology,* The Macmillan Company, New York, 1942.)

The common species rest with the proboscis, head, and abdomen nearly in a straight line and when resting have the appearance of a splinter lifted at an angle from a given surface (Fig. 58). In exceptional cases, as in *Anopheles culicifacies* Giles of India, the resting position is *Culex*-like. Hoffman[27] states that *A. grabhamii* Theobald rests with its body almost at a right angle to the vertical surface. *Anopheles hyracanus sinensis* Wiedemann takes a similar position. The hum of anophelines is distinctly low pitched and almost inaudible unless they are close to the ear or in a bottle. Most of our common anophelines are not strong fliers and usually take to cover even in a moderate breeze. Dispersal is usually the result of creeping low movements in

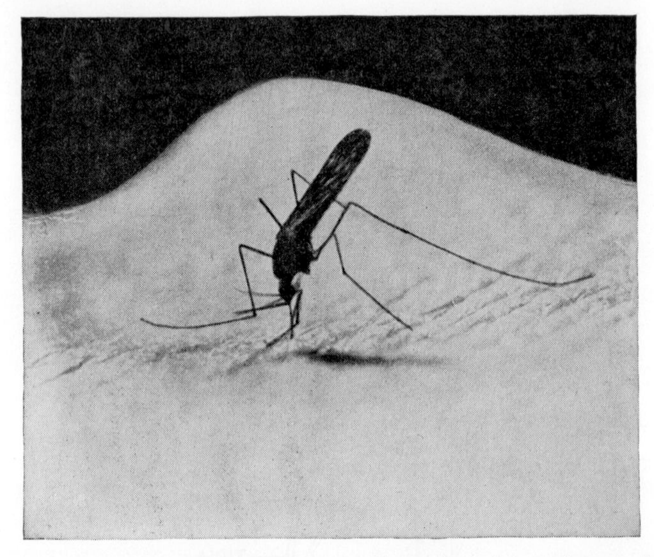

Fig. 58. *Anopheles freeborni* in the act of sucking blood. Note characteristic position assumed by *Anopheles* mosquitoes.

the vegetation, though high altitude flights may take place. In California, *Anopheles freeborni* engages in an annual dispersal flight of overwintering females about mid-February, during which time the mosquitoes may invade much territory, traveling more than 25 miles. During this flight the first eggs are deposited. In the main this flight favors the spread of the species.

Although some individuals of a few species may overwinter in the larval stage buried in mud and debris at the bottom of certain pools, the usual method of overwintering is in the adult (female only) stage.

Mating and Oviposition. Fertilization of the females takes place almost immediately upon emergence. The males emerge first and may be seen dancing over or near the breeding places in small swarms apparently awaiting the appearance of the females; when these dart into the dancing swarm, mating occurs. This type of mating requiring wide spaces is known as *eurygamous,* while those forms, such as *Anopheles sacharovi* Favre, which mate in confinement in a small space are known as *stenogamous.* Overwintering females are fertilized by the last brood of males during autumn, and the eggs are deposited soon after the spring dispersal flight. In certain localities at least, there is a period when the species exists only in the larval stage, all the adults having died after egg deposition. There is probably only a single laying at this time.

Oviposition takes place on the surface of water that is free from wave action, the female either resting on the water or dropping the eggs while hovering a short distance above it. Eggs are laid singly. Herms and his associates[24,25] found the average number of eggs deposited per batch for *A. freeborni, A. punctipennis,* and *A. pseudopunctipennis franciscanus* to be respectively, 200, 203, and 151. At least three batches of eggs may be laid during the lifetime of a female. Total depositions of more than a thousand eggs during the lifetime of a female have been recorded. Herms reports a female of *A. freeborni* as depositing 174 eggs in 19 minutes, an egg every 6 to 7 seconds with intervening periods of rest. During the entire operation the female resting on the surface of the water remained motionless except for the monotonous jerking of the abdomen when the egg was released. The eggs fell in a heap beneath the insect, pearly white in color, toppling over and forming geometrical patterns and becoming deep brownish black in about 45 minutes.

Egg Characters. The characters of anopheline eggs used in classification are: presence or absence of floats, position and length of the float, presence or absence of frill, and pattern (Fig. 59). Christophers and Barraud[8] classify anopheline eggs as of four types:

1. Eggs, probably of primitive type, with full-float surrounding egg.
2. Eggs with terminal frill (*pseudopunctipennis franciscanus* of Herms and Freeborn).
3. Whale-back eggs with floats separated from dorsal surface.
4. Various types of boatlike eggs with floats touching margin of dorsal surface.

The egg of the Californian *A. freeborni* Aitken (Fig. 59) is fusiform, slightly rounded at each end and tapering to the extent that one is slightly broader than the other (Herms and Frost).[25] The upper surface is flattened with a slightly longitudinal concavity, while the lower surface is broadly convex, the convexity becoming more pronounced at the broad end of the egg. The upper surface is granular, bordered by a laterally striated frill 16μ in width, except at the floats, while the lower surface shows, under proper light, a silvery reticulation. Medially placed are two roughly oval lateral floats, each divided in a majority of cases into 12 scalloped compartments. The larger part of the area covered by these floats is on the lateral faces of the egg, but

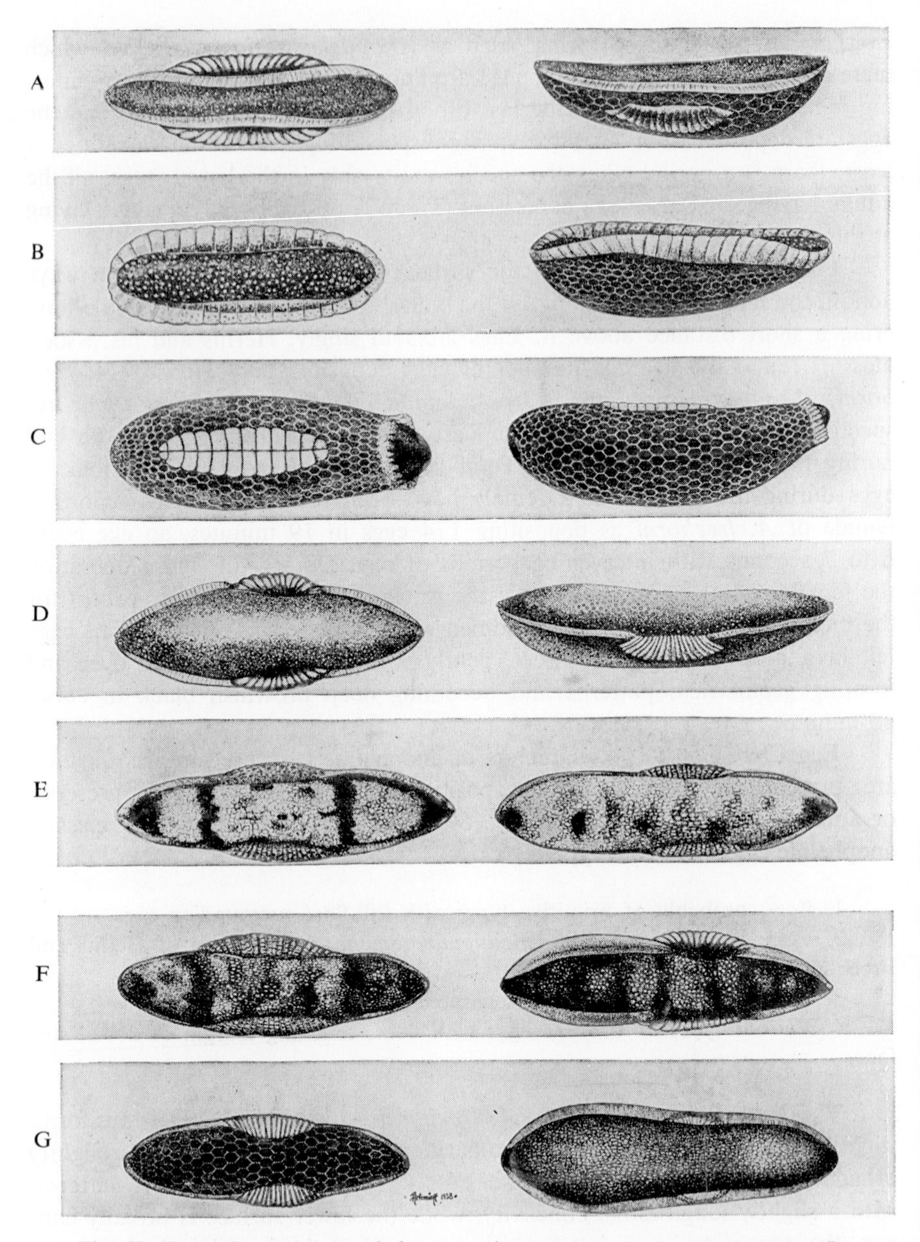

Fig. 59. Eggs of certain *Anopheles* mosquitoes. (*A row*) *A. punctipennis;* (*B row*) *A. pseudopunctipennis franciscanus,* usual form; (*C row*) same, rare form; (*D row*) *A. freeborni;* (*E row*) *A. maculipennis maculipennis,* left, and *A. labranchiae,* right; (*F*) *A. maculipennis messeae,* left, and *A. labranchiae atroparvus,* right; (*G row*) *A. maculipennis melanoon,* left, and *A. sacharovi,* right.

they project dorsally over the margins, which are described as "gunwales" rather aptly by one author who likens the egg to a boat. The eggs range in length from 596 to 656μ. The floats vary in length from 122 to 224μ.

Falleroni, Martini, Hackett, and Missiroli (see Hackett[21] and Hackett and Lewis[22]) have shown that what formerly was called *Anopheles maculipennis* Meigen in Europe actually comprises several distinct forms which can be distinguished only by egg patterns and coloration. These are, according to Stone, Knight, and Starcke[48] as follows: *A. maculipennis* Meigen and its subspecies *messeae* Falleroni and *melanoon* Hackett; *A. labranchiae* Falleroni and its subspecies *atroparvus* Van Thiel; and *A. sacharovi* Favre.

The eggs of *A. punctipennis* (Say) resemble those of the Californian *A. freeborni* Aitken with these exceptions: in the *punctipennis* form the "frill" extends along the margins of the egg without interruption at the site of the floats which are located on the upper portion of the ventral surface, and extending farther along the sides of the egg are a greater number of compartments, ranging from 16 to 22, which do not converge in fanwise as in *freeborni*.

The eggs of *Anopheles pseudopunctipennis franciscanus* McCracken occur in at least two different forms in California. The student can well determine the difference between these by consulting Figure 59.

Rozeboom[43] states that the egg of *A. pseudopunctipennis* Theobald in Panama resembles the eggs of the California species as described by Herms and Freeborn, except that in Panamanian form the floats are large and have many float ridges; the collarlike frill being identical.

Breeding Habits. The breeding habits of anophelines differ considerably for even very closely related species, e.g., the American *Anopheles freeborni* Aitken and *A. quadrimaculatus* Say, both four-spotted anophelines separable with accuracy as adults only on differences in male terminalia, have widely different breeding requirements, the former, at least in California, breeding largely in open sunlit shallow seepage water (Figs. 60 and 61) and the latter in impounded water with floating debris and aquatic vegetation. The European races of *A. maculipennis* Meigen have characteristic larval sites which, within certain limits, differ from one race to another.

The following example illustrates the very great importance of knowing the breeding habits in the conduct of malaria control operations. Williams[51] points out that in the Federated Malay States *Anopheles umbrosus* (Theobald) is the vector of malaria in the coastal plain, breeding in practically stagnant water densely shaded by mangrove. Its production is controlled, as Williams points out, by clearing the swamps and letting in the brilliant sunshine, or by cutting ditches and confining the water to definite channels. The same type of work when practiced on high inland plateaus increases the malaria rate, because here the vector is *Anopheles maculatus* Theobald, which prefers the quiet edges of trickling streams in the open sunshine. *Anopheles minimus*

Fig. 60. Typical breeding place of *Anopheles freeborni* in sunlit weed-grown ditch with slowly moving water.

Fig. 61. Breeding place for *Anopheles freeborni* in overflow from river. Larvae particularly along margins and in hoofprints at edge. (Photograph by L. L. Williams, Jr.)

Theobald, the principal vector of malaria in the Philippines, breeds in small flowing streams in the foothills (Russell[44]). Several species of *Anopheles* (though unimportant as vectors) are tree-hole breeders, viz.: *A. plumbeus* Stephens (European) and *A. barberi* Coquillett (American). *Anopheles bellator* Dyar and Knab, an important Caribbean vector, breeds in collections of water among bromeliads.

An unusual situation is reported for *Anopheles sergentii* (Theobald), a north African and Palestinian species, the larvae of which inhabit small pools and springs among stones at the edge of the lake (Tiberias). The larvae are often under the stones and not easily found (Buxton[4]).

Life History of Anophelines. Although there is much variation in the life histories of the species of *Anopheles* mosquitoes as well as considerable variation within the species due to temperature and other factors, the length of time required for development from egg to adult is generally longer than in other genera, except in genera where the egg stage may be greatly prolonged, as in *Aedes.*

The usual incubation period for *Anopheles* is about 2 days. Apparently, the only stimulus needed for the hatching of the embryo is that the egg be floating in water suitable for the development of the larva. The egg shows very little resistance to desiccation. Some tropical species may survive 2 weeks or even more on a moist surface, but severe drying always kills or injures the embryo or retards its development.[28]

Herms,[23] testing 20,000 eggs of *Anopheles freeborni,* determined the duration of the egg stage at room temperature as 72 hours. Under field conditions, the egg stage lasted 2 to 4 (average, 2.5) days for *A. freeborni* and 2 to 6 (average, 3.2) days for *A. punctipennis.*

The eggs of *A. freeborni* removed from the water and dried at temperatures of 74° F and 65° F remained viable after a period of desiccation not over 72 hours. No hatching was obtained from eggs of *A. punctipennis* after 24 hours' desiccation. Hatching generally took place during the evening and night in the experiments cited.

With yeast as food in distilled water at *p*H of 6.6 to 7.6 the larvae of *A. freeborni* reached the pupal stage in 15 to 16 days. The pupal stage requires about 3 days. Thus the entire life history from egg to adult in *A. freeborni* under experimental conditions requires about 21 to 22 days; the same is true for *A. punctipennis* and *A. pseudopunctipennis franciscanus.* Under field conditions this period may be considerably prolonged. Adult mosquitoes reared in the laboratory did not begin oviposition until 13 to 15 days after receiving a blood meal.

The life cycle of *Anopheles albimanus,* the important vector of malaria of the Panama Canal Zone, has been carefully studied by Rozeboom.[42] With room temperature between 27° and 32° C and water temperature for larvae from 21° to 27° C, and eggs and pupae at 27° to 30° C, the entire cycle (egg to adult) required from 18 to 24 days, an average of 3 weeks. A period of 7 days, or a little over, was necessary for the development of the ovaries, an average of 435 eggs being deposited; the incubation period was 40 to 48 hours; the larval stage required from 6 to 22 days, usually 8 to 13 days in hay infusion water; the pupal stage took 30 to 33 hours; the longest observed adult life of a female was 31 days and of a male, 27 days.

Anopheles quadrimaculatus Say is the chief vector of malaria in the eastern, central, and southern United States. According to Williams:[51]

> It breeds almost wholly in still water that is relatively clean. It requires some sunshine, never being found in dense shade. However, it requires some darkness, never being found in waters which are wholly unshaded, unless they have a type of flotage which casts narrow strips of shade where the mosquito larvae may lie during a portion of the daylight hours. . . . An ideal breeding place for *quadrimaculatus* is in freshly impounded water which floods a basin containing some underbrush and which is sparsely covered with trees. Such a body of water quickly gathers flotage of dead and dying land vegetation, twigs and leaves, among which algae soon appear. Such flotage not only offers the requisite amount of shade, but an abundant food supply. Such an impounding will not acquire a large quantity of natural enemies, such as top minnows and aquatic insects, for a number of years and seldom acquires enough to prevent production of the mosquito.
>
> The normal detritus passing down a narrow stream will clog the interstices of a fallen tree or branch and create a dam. These natural impounded waters are excellent breeding places for *quadrimaculatus*. Swamps covered by a growth of virgin timber, on the other hand, are not good breeding places. Such swamps are almost invariably covered with such a dense timber growth that sunlight can reach the surface of the water only in those small areas where an opening has been made by the fall of a dead tree. Swamps of this description have a small seeding of *quadrimaculatus,* but not enough to propagate malaria. When the lumberman enters, cutting out large trees, leaving the small ones, the branches and the tree tops, he changes a safe water surface into one almost ideal for *quadrimaculatus* production. He has let in the sunshine without removing all of the shade, and he has left behind waste which not only creates fine flotage, but large portions of which tend to clog the channel which traverses the average swamp, thus making a series of ponds.

The brood peaks of this species in southwestern Georgia according to Boyd[3] are from 20 to 30 days apart, and there are from 8 to 10 annual broods, the first appearing from 20 to 30 days after the last frost, and the last brood, the tenth, if there is favorable weather, in December. January and February, he states, are the only months when no broods emerge. An excellent description of the techniques used in large-scale rearing of *Anopheles quadrimaculatus* is given by Greenwald, Cochran, and Scharff.[20]

Biting Habits. In determining the relative importance of various species of mosquitoes as vectors of diseases, a knowledge of their biting habits is essential. They may be preponderantly *zoophilous,* feeding on animals other than man, or preponderantly *anthropophilous,* i.e., feeding on man; they are seldom exclusively either. That a species is a strong vector of any given infection is probably not always due to a larger degree of domesticity. A close and constant contact between the vector of a disease and the human victims is essential to extensive transmission of the disease. There are some species, such as *Anopheles minimus flavirostris* (Ludlow), an important vector of malaria in the Philippine Islands, and *A. albimanus* Wiedemann, a vector in the Caribbean area, which do not remain indoors during the day after feeding indoors at night, an important factor in making malaria surveys.

It is often pointed out that the fact that certain species of mosquitoes predominate indoors or are the sole entrants must be weighed against the production and proximity of these and other species under comparison. Carter, Le Prince, and Griffitts[6] have observed that *Anopheles quadrimaculatus* Say is much more often found in residences than *A. punctipennis* (Say). Mayne (Mitzmain)[38] in a table comparing the collections of *A. punctipennis* (Say) and *A. quadrimaculatus* Say, totaling 1377 specimens, compares the numbers of each species taken inside dwellings, under dwellings, in privies, vacated buildings, cattle sheds, horse and mule sheds, fowl roosts, and wagon and tool sheds. In commenting on his results he states:

> It is indicated that in the three sources of direct human influence, namely, inside dwellings, under dwellings, and in privies, the last produced the greatest number of specimens of *A. punctipennis.* This species comprised less than one-third (30 per cent) of the catch in houses, while under dwellings 62 per cent of the mosquitoes collected proved to be *A. punctipennis.* . . . It has been observed by service officers, conducting malarial surveys, that although *A. punctipennis* rarely bites while inside a dwelling, it is found to attack persons seated on the porch or gallery of the house, after which these mosquitoes seek rest, presumably under the house in preference to the interior.

Studies by Herms indicate that *A. freeborni,* like *A. quadrimaculatus,* readily invade houses, while *A. punctipennis* (Say) is chiefly an outdoor biter, porch biter, etc. *Anopheles pseudopunctipennis franciscanus* McCracken is considered to be a field mosquito in California. The frequency with which *Anopheles* mosquitoes invade houses, and likewise the frequency with which they bite man rather than other animals, takes on a double significance if one considers that a mosquito must bite two human victims, viz., a carrier and a susceptible individual in order to transmit a disease such as malaria. Methods used to study the feeding habits of mosquitoes are well described by Reeves and Hammon.[40] In this study they used the precipitin test in which mosquito blood smears were tested with the antisera of domestic rabbits against the sera of the horse, cow, sheep, dog, man, and chicken. In Mexico, Central America, and southerly, *Anopheles pseudopunctipennis pseudopunctipennis* Theobald invades human habitations and is an important malaria vector.

Some North American Anophelines. *Anopheles freeborni* Aitken, *A. occidentalis* (Dyar and Knab), *A. aztecus* Hoffman, and *A. earlei* Vargas, constitute the American members of the *maculipennis* group; *A. freeborni,* the principal vector of malaria in the western United States, is the brown, unicolorous form of the irrigated western regions, west of the Rocky Mountains, extending northerly into British Columbia and southerly into parts of Arizona and Mexico, the western tip of Texas, and Baja California (Mexico). *Anopheles occidentalis* is the "silver" or "bronze-tipped" melanic form of the cool western seacoast; *A. earlei,* a very similar species but readily distinguishable by the male genitalia and larvae, extends across the continent through southern Canada and the northern areas of the United States to Connecticut. *Anopheles*

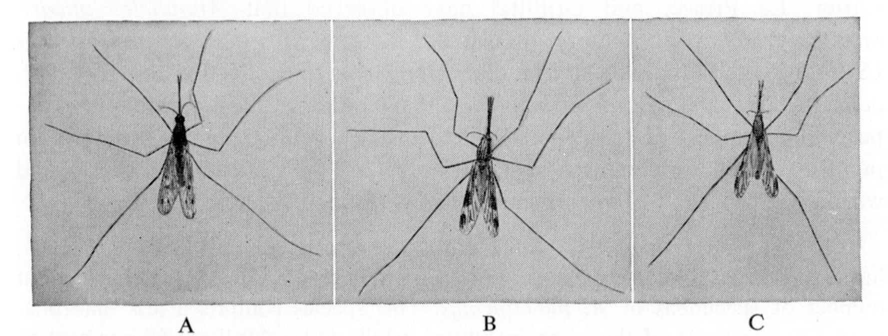

Fig. 62. California *Anopheles:* (*A*) *A. freeborni;* (*B*) *A. punctipennis;* and (*C*) *A. pseudopunctipennis franciscanus.*

aztecus is the large, long-winged, linear scaled species of the Mexican plateau, at elevations of 5000 to 7000 feet and over.

Anopheles quadrimaculatus Say is the common malaria vector of the eastern United States, extending from southern New Hampshire and southern Ontario westerly to Minnesota and south to Vera Cruz, Mexico. It is particularly abundant in the southeastern United States. The wing scales are all dark, some forming four blackish spots; palpi and hind tarsi are black; femora have small white spots at tip, "knee spots."

Anopheles punctipennis (Say) (Fig. 62) is said to be the most widespread anopheline in North America, ranging from southern Canada to the Mexican plateau. The wings have black and yellow scales, the latter forming two spots on the costal margin, one of which is long and situated beyond the middle, the second smaller and near the apex, giving a mottled appearance to the wings. The proboscis is black, and the palpi are unbanded. The general appearance of the body is dark brown. This species breeds in clear, cool, shaded pools. The females seldom enter dwellings but invade unscreened porches and bite in the open.

Anopheles pseudopunctipennis Theobald is a widespread plains and highland species, extending from Argentina along the Andean region of South America, through Central America, Mexico, and the south central United States. It resembles *A. punctipennis* (Say) somewhat, but is easily separated by the white banding of the palpi. The tip of each palpus is white. It breeds primarily in sunlit pools along the courses of receding streams, the larvae being exceedingly abundant in the mats of green algae.

Anopheles pseudopunctipennis franciscanus McCracken (Fig. 62) is very abundant in many parts of California where it was previously recorded as *Anopheles pseudopunctipennis* Theobald; it also occurs in Nevada, Utah, Arizona, New Mexico, western Texas, and California. Its breeding habits resemble those of *pseudopunctipennis.* It differs from the latter in that the tips of the palpi are black. It rarely enters human habitations.

Anopheles crucians Wiedemann, *Anopheles bradleyi* King, and *Anopheles georgianus* King resemble each other very closely and constitute the *"crucians"* complex. The palpi of all three species are banded with white, and the last segment is entirely white. Separation of the species can be made only in the larval stage. *Anopheles crucians* has been found from Massachusetts southwesterly to Kansas, Oklahoma, and Texas. It breeds in ponds, lake margins, swamps, and pools of both intermittent and permanent character; it breeds extensively in acid waters as in the cypress swamps of Florida and Georgia (Matheson). The females bite freely during the day. *Anopheles bradleyi* occurs along the Atlantic and Gulf coasts from Maryland to Vera Cruz, Mexico. It normally breeds in saline waters. *Anopheles georgianus* occurs widely in fresh water in the Gulf states. It can be distinguished from the other two members of the complex with difficulty.

Anopheles barberi Coquillett occurs in the eastern United States from New York southward. It breeds commonly in water collected in tree holes, but occasionally in artificial containers.

Anopheles walkeri Theobald is a widely distributed species in the eastern United States to the Gulf of Mexico and north to Minnesota. The presence of white "knee spots" and usually (but not always) the golden color of the halters distinguish it from *A. atropos.*

Anopheles atropos Dyar and Knab is strictly a salt-water mosquito confined to the shores of the Gulf of Mexico from Florida to Louisiana. It is small and very dark with unspotted wings. It lacks white "knee spots." Within its range it is said to outnumber *A. crucians* three to one and breeds by preference in permanent salt pools or in shallow water on muck or alluvial marshes. It is reported to be a tormenting pest, biting in direct sunlight as well as by night.

Anopheles albimanus Wiedemann is considered to be the most important anopheline species in the Caribbean region. The hind tarsi are conspicuously white-banded; the apical segment of the palpi is entirely white. It develops freely in brackish or salt water. This species has been reported from several points in the extreme southern parts of the United States, e.g., Key West, Florida, and the Rio Grande Valley (Brownsville), Texas.

KEY* TO CULICID SUBFAMILIES AND GENERA OF THE UNITED STATES (ADULTS)

1. Abdomen without scales, or at least with the sternites largely bare. Scutellum never trilobed; crescent-shaped with the marginal setae evenly distributed. Palpi (males and females) as long or almost as long as the proboscis. Subfamily Anophelinae .... *Anopheles*
   Abdomen with both tergites and sternites completely clothed with scales. Scutellum trilobed (except Toxorhynchitinae). Palpi of female much shorter than the proboscis 2
2. Proboscis rigid, outer half more slender and bent backwards. Subfamily Toxorhynchitinae .... *Toxorhynchites*
   Proboscis more flexible, of uniform thickness (unless swollen at tip), outer half not bent backward. Subfamily Culicinae 3
3. Postnotum with a tuft of setae .... *Wyeomyia*
   Postnotum without setae 4
4. Wing membrane without microtrichia. Cell R_2 shorter than its stem; anal vein ending about opposite base of cubital fork .... *Uranotaenia*
   Wing membrane with microtrichia. Cell R_2 longer than its stem; anal vein extending well beyond fork of cubitus 5
5. Postspiracular bristles (Fig. 63) present 6
   Postspiracular bristles absent 8
6. Spiracular bristles (Fig. 63) present (even if few) .... *Psorophora*
   Spiracular bristles absent 7
7. Wing scales mostly narrow, or when broad, setae are present on upper side of base of vein R_1 .... *Aedes*
   Wing scales broad; setae absent on upper side of vein R_1. . *Mansonia* (in part)
8. Spiracular bristles present; lower side of base of vein R_1 distinctly pilose .... *Culiseta*
   Spiracular bristles absent; lower side of base of vein R_1 scaly or bare . . 9
9. Pulvilli present 10
   Pulvilli absent 11
10. Third (second apparent) segment of antenna (first flagellar) very long in both sexes; antenna of male not plumose .... *Deinocerites*
    Third segment of antenna of usual length, no longer than each succeeding segment; antenna of male always plumose .... *Culex*
11. Fourth segment of front tarsus very short in both sexes; first segment of front tarsus longer than the last four together........... *Orthopodomyia*
    Fourth segment of front tarsus not shortened in the female; first segment of front tarsus not longer than the last four together. . *Mansonia* (in part)

* Modified from a key prepared by T. H. G. Aiken after various authors.

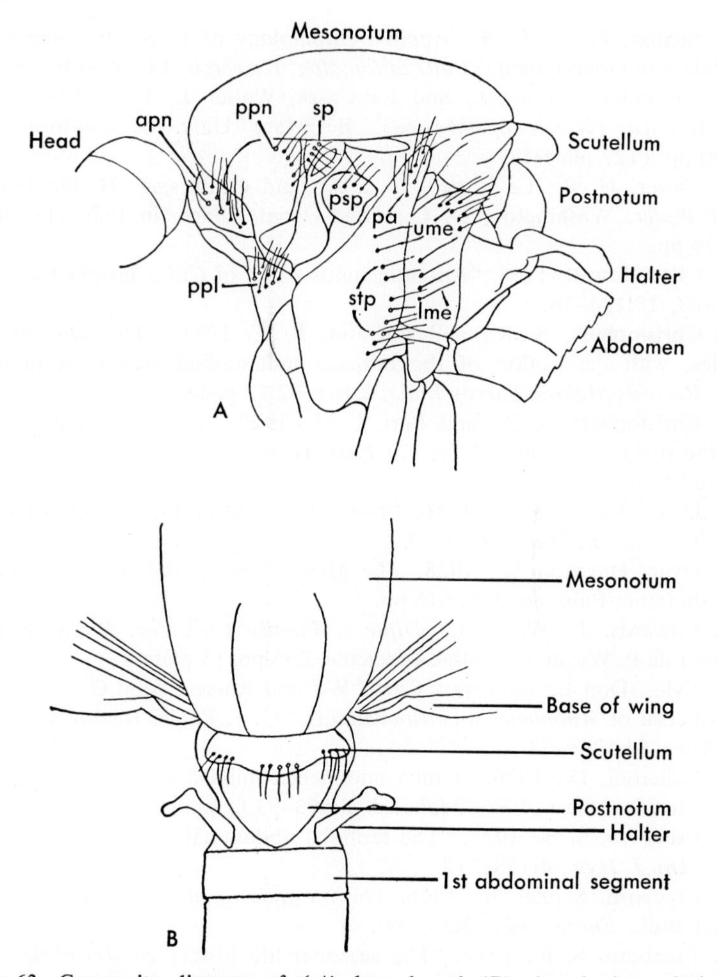

Fig. 63. Composite diagram of (*A*) lateral and (*B*) dorsal view of thorax of adult mosquito showing structures and pleural bristles. Explanation of abbreviations: *apn,* anterior pronotal; *lme,* lower mesepimeral; *pa,* prealar; *ppl,* propleural (prosternal); *ppn,* posterior pronotal (proepimeral); *psp,* postspiracular; *sp,* spiracular; *stp,* sternopleural; *ume,* upper mesepimeral. (After King, Bradley, and McNeel; U.S.D.A. photograph.)

REFERENCES

1. Bates, Marston, 1949. *The Natural History of Mosquitoes.* New York: The Macmillan Company. xv + 379 pp.

2. Barr, A. R., 1957. "The distribution of *Culex p. pipiens* and *C. p. quinquefasciatus* in North America," *Am. J. Trop. Med.,* **6**:153–65.

3. Boyd, Mark F., 1929. "Studies on the bionomics of North American anophelines. I. The number of annual broods of *A. quadrimaculatus,*" *Am. J. Hyg.,* **7**:264–75.

4. Buxton, P. A., 1924. "Applied entomology of Palestine, being a report to the Palestine Government," *Bull. Entomolog. Research,* **14:**289–340 (5 plates).

5. Carpenter, Stanley J., and La Casse, Walter J., 1955. *Mosquitoes of North America (North of Mexico).* Berkeley: Univ. of California Press. vii + 360 pp. (127 plates).

6. Carter, H. R.; Le Prince, J. A. A.; and Griffitts, T. H. D.; 1916. *Impounded Water.* Washington, D. C.: Govt. Print. Office, in Pub. Health Bull., no. 79. 34 pp.

7. Chao, Jowett, 1958. "An autogenous strain of *Culex tarsalis* Coq.," *Mosquito News,* **18:**134–36.

8. Christophers, S. R., and Barraud, P. J., 1931. "The eggs of Indian Anopheles, with description of the hitherto undescribed eggs of a number of species," *Records Malaria Survey India,* **2:**161–92 (5 plates).

9. Christophers, S. R., and Puri, I. M., 1929. "Why do Anopheles larvae feed at the surface, and how?" *Tr. Far East Assoc. Trop. Med.,* Seventh Congress held in India, **2:**736–38.

10. Dyar, Harrison G., 1916. "New Aedes from the mountains of California," *Insec. Inscit. Mens.,* **4:**80–90.

11. Dyar, Harrison G., 1928. *The Mosquitoes of the Americas.* Carnegie Inst. Washington, Publ. no. 387. 616 pp.

12. Edwards, F. W., 1932. *Diptera, Family Culicidae.* Brussels: Genera Insectorum de P. Wytsman, 194me Fascicule. 256 pp. (5 plates).

13. Eyles, Don E.; Sabrosky, Curtis W.; and Russell, John C.; 1945. "Long-range dispersal of *Anopheles quadrimaculatus,*" U. S. Public Health Service, *Pub. Health Rep.,* **60:**1265–73.

14. Falleroni, D., 1926. "Fauna anophelica italiana e suo 'habitat'. Metodo di lotta contro la malaria," *Riv. Malariol.,* **5:**553–93 (1 plate).

15. Freeborn, S. B., 1924. "The terminal abdominal structures of male mosquitoes," *Am. J. Hyg.,* **4:**188–212.

16. Freeborn, Stanley B., 1926. *The mosquitoes of California.* Univ. Calif. Technical Bull., *Entomology,* **3:**333–60.

17. Freeborn, S. B., 1932. "The seasonal life history of *Anopheles maculipennis* with reference to humidity requirements and hibernation," *Am. J. Hyg.,* **16:**215–23.

18. Garnham, P. C. C.; Harper, J. O.; and Highton, R. B.; 1946. "The mosquitoes of the Kaimosi Forest, Kenya Colony, with special reference to yellow fever," *Bull. Entomol. Research,* **36:**473–96 (2 plates).

19. Gray, H. F., 1936. "Control of pest mosquitoes for comfort," *Civil Engineering,* **6:**685–88.

20. Greenwald, Margaret; Cochran, J. H.; and Scharff, Donald K.; 1948. "Large scale rearing of *Anopheles quadrimaculatus* Say at Orlando, Florida," *Mosquito News,* **8:**50–56.

21. Hackett, L. W., 1934. "The present status of our knowledge of the subspecies of *Anopheles maculipennis,*" *Tr. Roy. Soc. Trop. Med. & Hyg.,* **28:**109–28.

22. Hackett, L. W., and Lewis, D. G., 1935. "A new variety of *A. maculipennis* in Southern Europe," *Riv. di Malariol.,* **14:**377–83.

23. Herms, W. B., 1929. "Anopheline mosquito investigations in California," Fourth Internat. Congress of Entomology, Ithaca, August, 1928. **2:**708–21.

24. Herms, W. B., and Freeborn, S. B., 1920. "Egg-laying habits of California anophelines," *J. Parasitol.,* **7:**69–79.

25. Herms, W. B., and Frost, Florence M., 1932. "A comparative study of the eggs of California anophelines," *J. Parasitol.,* **18:**240–44 (3 plates).

26. Hindle, Edward, 1914. *Flies in Relation to Disease: Blood-sucking flies.* London: Cambridge Univ. Press. xv + 398 pp.

27. Hoffman, W. A., 1926. "Resting position of Haitian Anopheles," *Am. J. Trop. Med.,* **6:**377–79.

28. Horsfall, William R., 1955. *Mosquitoes, Their Bionomics and Relation to Disease.* New York: The Ronald Press Company. 723 pp.

29. Horsfall, William R., and Craig, George B., Jr., 1956. "Eggs of floodwater mosquitoes, IV. Species of *Aedes* common in Illinois (Diptera: Culicidae)," *Ann. Entomol. Soc. Amer.,* **49:**368–74.

30. Horsfall, William R.; Miles, R. C.; and Sokatch, J. T.; 1952. "Eggs of floodwater mosquitoes, I. Species of *Psorophora* (Diptera: Culicidae)," *Ann. Entomol. Soc. Amer.,* **45:**618–24.

31. Jachowski, Leo A., Jr., and Schultz, Carlos, 1948. *Notes on the Biology and Control of Mosquitoes at Umiat, Alaska.* Nav. Med. Research Inst., Nav. Med. Center, Bethesda, Md., Project NM 005-017, Rep. no. 1. 17 pp.

32. Jachowski, Leo A., Jr., and Schultz, Carlos, 1948. "Notes on the biology and control of mosquitoes at Umiat, Alaska," *Mosquito News,* **8:**155–65.

33. Jenkins, Dale W., and Knight, Kenneth L., 1950. "Ecological survey of the mosquitoes of Great Whale River, Quebec (Diptera, Culicidae)," *Proc. Entomolog. Soc. Wash.,* **52:**209–23.

34. Komp, W. H. W., 1942. "A technique for staining, dissecting, and mounting the male terminalia of mosquitoes," U. S. Public Health Service, *Pub. Health Rep.,* **57:**1327–33.

35. Matheson, Robert, 1944. *Handbook of the Mosquitoes of North America,* 2nd. ed. Ithaca: Comstock Publ. Co., Inc. viii + 314 pp.

36. Mattingly, P. F.; Rozeboom, L. E.; Knight, K. L.; Laven, H.; Drummond, F. H.; Christophers, S. R.; and Shute, P. G.; 1951. "The *Culex pipiens* complex," *Trans. Roy. Entomol. Soc. London,* **102:**331–82.

37. Mayne, B., 1922. "How long does a mosquito retain malaria parasites?" U. S. Public Health Service, *Pub. Health Rep.,* **37:**1060–63.

38. Mitzmain, M. B., 1917. "Anopheline mosquitoes, their distribution and infection under field conditions," U. S. Public Health Service, *Pub. Health Rep.,* **32:**536–40.

39. Reeves, W. C., 1948. "A final summary of flight range studies on *Culex tarsalis* and notes on wild bird malaria in Kern County," *Proc. and Papers, 16th Ann. Conf. Calif. Mosq. Control Assn.* (Berkeley), pp. 58–59.

40. Reeves, W. C., and Hammon, W. McD., 1943. "Feeding habits of the proven and possible mosquito vectors of western equine and St. Louis encephalitis in the Yakima Valley, Washington," *Am. J. Trop. Med.,* **24:**131–34.

41. Ross, Edward S., and Roberts, H. Radclyffe, 1943. *Mosquito Atlas: Part I. The Nearctic Anopheles, Important Malaria Vectors of the Americas,*

and Aedes aegypti, Culex quinquefasciatus. iv + 44 pp. Part II. *Eighteen Old World Anophelines Important to Malaria.* iv + 44 pp. Philadelphia: Amer. Entomological Soc.

42. Rozeboom, L. E., 1936. "The life cycle of laboratory-bred *Anopheles albimanus* Wiedemann," *Ann. Entomolog. Soc. Amer.*, **29**:480–89.

43. Rozeboom, L. E., 1937. "The eggs of *Anopheles pseudopunctipennis* in Panama," *J. Parasitol.*, **23**:538–39.

44. Russell, P. F., 1932. "The control of *Anopheles minimus* mosquito larvae in the Philippines by stranding and flushing," *Philippine J. Sc.*, **47**:439–45.

45. Russell, Paul F.; Rozeboom, Lloyd E.; and Stone, Alan; 1943. *Keys to the Anopheline Mosquitoes of the World, with Notes on Their Identification, Distribution, Biology, and Relation to Malaria.* Philadelphia: Amer. Entomolog. Soc. 152 pp.

46. Smith, John B., 1902. *The Salt Marsh Mosquito, Culex sollicitans* Wlk. New Jersey Agric. Exper. Sta., Special Bull. T.

47. Stage, H. H.; Gjullin, C. M.; and Yates, W. W.; 1937. "Flight range and longevity of floodwater mosquitoes in the lower Columbia River Valley," *J. Econ. Entomol.*, **30**:940–45.

48. Stone, Alan; Knight, Kenneth L.; and Starcke, Helle; 1959. *A Synoptic Catalog of the Mosquitoes of the World (Diptera, Culicidae)*. Washington, D. C.: Entomological Society of America, Thomas Say Foundation. vol. 6. 358 pp.

49. Vockeroth, J. R., 1954. "Notes on the identities and distribution of *Aedes* species of northern Canada, with a key to the females (Diptera: Culicidae)," *Canad. Entomol.*, **86**:241–55.

50. Williams, F. X., 1931. *The Insects and Other Invertebrates of Hawaiian Sugar Cane Fields.* Exper. Sta. Hawaiian Sugar Planters' Assn. 400 pp. (p. 279).

51. Williams, L. L., Jr., 1937. "Mosquitoes and malaria," *J. Econ. Entomol.*, **30**:20–26.

52. Woke, P. A., 1937. "Comparative effects of the blood of man and of canary on egg production of *Culex pipiens* Linn.," *J. Parasitol.*, **23**:311–13.

53. Woke, P. A., 1937. "Cold-blooded vertebrates as hosts for *Aedes aegypti* Linn.," *J. Parasitol.*, **23**:310–11.

Chapter 11

MOSQUITOES AS VECTORS OF DISEASE

THE MALARIAS

From the standpoint of disease transmission, mosquitoes are of outstanding importance as vectors of three types of organisms pathogenic to man. These are: (1) the plasmodia, causative organisms of the human malarias, belonging to the phylum Protozoa; (2) the viruses of yellow fever, dengue, the encephalitides, and other diseases of man; (3) filarial worms of the genus *Wuchereria,* the causative organisms of Bancroft's and Brug's filariasis.

A valuable reference for students of the subject, which treats not only with the general aspects of the subject but with the regional ones, region by region, on a world-wide basis, is "Mosquitoes of Medical Importance," by Foote and Cook.[26] This work also presents pictorial keys, which include only the medically important species, however, and summaries of the bionomics and relation to disease for each of the species of medical importance.

Human Malaria

Malaria is a widely distributed disease, at one time prevalent to a greater or less degree on every continent and on many islands of the seas. Though the popular mind usually associates malaria with tropical or subtropical climates, such is not the case; Sweden, Finland, and northern Russia have, in the past, been subject to serious epidemics. Whether or not malaria existed in North America prior to the discovery of the continent has not been definitely established; however, this disease was evidently recognized as a factor in colonization on the Massachusetts coast and the Georgia-Carolina coast as early as the middle of the seventeenth century.[7] As recently as the 1930's, there were six to seven million cases annually in the continental United States.[76] For the past 75 years, however, the disease has been declining in many parts of the world. Europe, once widely malarious, is now in large part free from the disease, and South America can entertain hopes of its eradication. In the United States, fewer than 10 proven cases of natural malarial transmission by mosquitoes were reported in 1957. Malaria was considered at one time the most important disease of mankind, but in many previously malarious areas it is now a rarity. Malariologists now talk in terms of area eradication, as well as over-all control.

The presence of endemic malaria is dependent upon a complex of environmental factors favorable to the development of large numbers of vector (anthropophilus) mosquitoes, as well as to the *Plasmodia* causing the disease. Temperature, particularly as it affects the development of the plasmodium in the mosquito, and temperature combined with humidity as it affects the life of the vector, are critical factors; a mean summer isotherm of 15° to 16° C in general limits its geographic distribution fairly well. The distribution of malaria is dependent upon the availability of water for mosquito breeding, not necessarily heavy rainfall; naturally arid regions may be seriously affected because of imperfections in irrigation if this is practiced. Although lowlands are more likely to be affected, this does not hold as a general rule, because if one or more important factors are lacking in a lowland region the area is nonmalarious. The disease may occur at high elevations (9000 feet in Quito, Ecuador) under favorable circumstances. Herms found endemic malaria in California at an elevation of about 5500 feet; it is present in Mexico at an elevation of near 7500 feet.

Few diseases have so large a list of synonyms; among these are ague, chills and fever, jungle fever, paludism, marsh fever, remittent fever, intermittent fever, *Wechselfieber, Kaltesfieber,* etc. The symptoms are commonly characterized by more or less regularly occurring febrile paroxysms. In most cases there are three fairly well-defined stages, viz.: the *cold stage* (the chill) in which the skin becomes pale and has the appearance of "gooseflesh," the patient's teeth may chatter, and he may shiver more or less violently; the next stage is the *hot stage,* or fever, the temperature rising during the chill, the skin is hot and flushed; the third stage is marked by the appearance of a general *perspiration,* the fever falls, and the temperature approaches normal. The entire paroxysm may last but a few hours. In many cases the stages are not well marked, neither do the paroxysms recur at the same intervals. The intervals depend largely on the type of infection. When the paroxysms occur at intervals of 24 hours, as is often true in the early stages of infection or in multiple infections, it is *quotidian;* when the interval is 48 hours or every third day it is *tertian;* and when the interval is 72 hours or every fourth day, it is *quartan.*

The disease is caused by an infection with one or more of several species of blood-inhabiting protozoa (Class Sporozoa) belonging to the genus *Plasmodium.* Under the clinical term "malaria," there are really combined four or more diseases, which, while caused by closely related parasites and having a common means of transmission, nevertheless possess individual characteristics, namely: *vivax* malaria, tertian (benign tertian); *falciparum* malaria; *quartan* malaria, quartan fever; *ovale* malaria, ovale tertian.

The plasmodial parasites attack the red blood corpuscles, destroying them while undergoing asexual reproduction; this asexual reproduction or sporulation occurs at more or less regular intervals, i.e., 48 or 72 hours, depending upon the species of *Plasmodium.* The infection, according to Reed,[62] results in: (1) changes in organs, such as enlargement of the spleen and liver, and heart involvement; in fatal cases of subtertian malaria capillaries in the brain and pia are found congested or blocked by schizonts and sporulating forms of plasmodia, with punctiform hemorrhages in the white matter of the cerebral cortex; (2) leucopenia with increase of mononuclears and varying degrees of anemia as the result of direct destruction of red cells by plasmodia and indirect degeneration of others; (3) malarial pigment (*melanin*) in macrophages in the splenic sinuses is characteristic, as are also the heavy deposits in the cells in the splenic vein and liver; it is the same pigment as that produced in the red cells by the plasmodia and released with the rupture of infected red cells; (4) changes in physiology such as periodic febrile paroxysms; these are quite regular in benign tertian malaria, but because of irregular maturing of plasmodia the periodicity of the paroxysms is often concealed in falciparum (subtertian) malaria; focal symptomatology due to localization in subtertian [*Plasmodium falciparum* (Welch)] arising from the "sticky tendency" of parasitized red cells which causes agglutination and blockage; (5) malaria cachexia, a chronic condition following repeated malarial attacks. Persons concerned technically with malaria should consult: *Practical Malariology* by Russell, West, and Manwell;[78] *Malariology* by Boyd;[8] and *The Epidemiology and Control of Malaria,* by MacDonald.[54]

Historical. Although the name "malaria" was not employed until the middle of the eighteenth century, the disease was known for many centuries, Hippocrates having divided periodic fevers into quotidian, tertian, and quartan. The fable of Hercules and the Hydra is believed to refer to malaria. In 1753 Torti named the disease "malaria," believing it to be air-borne and emanating from the bad air (*mal aria*) rising from swamps and marshes. Credit for the discovery of the causal agent (1880) belongs to Laveran, a French army surgeon who was then stationed in Algeria. Although the mosquito transmission theory is said to have been held for many years by Italian and Tyrolese peasants and the natives of what was formerly German East Africa, the first well-formulated mosquito-malaria theory was advanced by King in 1883.[47] In 1885 and 1886, Golgi[28] discovered that the course of the fevers corresponded to the development of the parasites in the blood corpuscles and particularly to their periodic sporulation. He demonstrated this for both the quartan and tertian parasites.

Manson expressed a strong belief in the malaria-mosquito theory as early as 1884, and it was his sustained guidance and encouragement that carried Ross[72] on to those brilliant discoveries in India in 1897–1898 that definitely incriminated mosquitoes as vectors of malaria, and twice won for him the Nobel prize. Although Ross made important discoveries in the field of human malaria and its anopheline vector, his chief discovery was the complete life cycle of the causal organism of bird malaria in a culicine mosquito; he established the bird-to-mosquito-to-bird cycle.

Credit is due MacCallum[53] for his discovery in 1897 that the flagellated bodies which Ross had found in the intestines of mosquitoes were actually male parasites and that these fertilize the female cells, thus giving the clue to the nature of the pigmented cells in the stomach wall of the mosquitoes. MacCallum actually observed the process of fertilization in blood taken from a patient suffering from estivo-autumnal malaria. During this same period of discovery in the field of malaria, Grassi[30] and associates proved that human malaria is transmitted by a particular genus of mosquito, namely, *Anopheles*.

In 1900 Sambon and Low, at the suggestion of Manson, built a mosquito-proof hut in the Roman Campagna, in which they lived during the most malarial months of that year without contracting malaria, having taken precautions against mosquito bites by promptly retiring within doors at sunset; otherwise they lived as did the natives. At this time these investigators sent infected *Anopheles* mosquitoes from the Roman Campagna to London, where Manson's son, Dr. P. Thurburn Manson, and Mr. George Warren permitted themselves to be bitten by these mosquitoes and

. . . shortly afterwards both of these gentlemen, neither of whom had been abroad or otherwise exposed to malarial influences, developed characteristic malarial fever, and malarial parasites were found in abundance in their blood, both at that time and on the occurrence of the several relapses of malarial fever from which they subsequently suffered. The mosquito-malaria theory has now, therefore, passed from the region of conjecture to that of fact.[55]

Bass and Johns[4] in 1912 were the first to cultivate successfully the malaria parasite *in vitro*.

The Plasmodia. The causal organism of malaria, belonging to the genus *Plasmodium* (class Sporozoa, Phylum Protozoa), are blood-inhabiting microparasites, passing the principal portion of their asexual cycle within the red cells of the host where they produce, with the aid of hemoglobin, a characteristic malarial pigment (melanin).

If parasites are present in the blood, they should be visible, after proper staining, on careful thin-smear microscopic examination, as pigmented intracorpuscular bodies in the form of signet rings, ameboid forms, segmenting forms, or as crescents in estivo-autumnal fever of 10 or more days' duration. An excellent manual by Wilcox[94] is available for the microscopic diagnosis of malaria in man.

Ross[73] states that the parasites:

. . . will not generally be numerous enough to cause illness unless there is at least one parasite to 100,000 haematids; that is, 50 parasites in 1 cmm of blood; or 150,000,000 in a man 64 kilograms (142 pounds) in weight. . . . Such calculations demonstrate the absurdity of supposing that there are no plasmodia present in a person because we fail in finding one after a few minutes' search. As a matter of fact, even if as many as 150,000,000 plasmodia are present in an average man, the chances are that ten to fifteen minutes' search will be required for each plasmodium found; while if we are careless or unfortunate, we may have to look much longer.

The time elapsing from inoculation by the mosquito to appearance of infected erythrocytes (presumably one or more exoerythrocytic cycles) varies with the species of the plasmodium as well as with the strain and other factors. In *falciparum* malaria the incubation period for the Coker strain ranged from 6 to 25 days, while that for the Long strain ranged from 9 to 10 days.

Plasmodium falciparum (Welch 1897) (*Plasmodium praecox* Blanchard 1900) is the causal organsim of *estivo-autumnal* fever (malignant tertian, subtertian) of the tropics and subtropics, the most severe form of malaria, often resulting fatally. Although it is a *tertian* fever, there is considerable irregularity in the occurrence and duration of the febrile stage, owing to a corresponding irregularity in the sporulation of the parasites, schizogony usually requiring about 48 hours, although often less. The infected red corpuscles are usually normal in size, although some may be slightly shrunken, often crenated, and rather dark green (brassy). The intracorpuscular parasite in all its stages is small (not over two-thirds the size of a corpuscle) and fairly ovoid in outline; the pigment is darker than in other forms; the infected cells agglutinate, and "Maurer's dots" appear in the corpuscles in the later stages. The *signet ring* is thin and small, and the chromatin dot is commonly double and out of line with the ring. There may be two and even four signet rings in one red corpuscle.

The segmented state, rarely if ever seen in the peripheral blood, produces from 8 to 25 merozoites. Characteristic crescent-shaped or kidney-shaped bodies appear in the peripheral blood in about 10 days after infection; these are the sexual forms (*gametocytes*) and occur as crescents in this species of *Plasmodium* only. The *macrogametocyte* or female form, measuring from 10 to 15μ shows the chromatin granules well concentrated in the mid-region, while the *microgametocyte* or male form, measuring from 7 to 10μ, has a more hyaline appearance. A remnant of the red blood corpuscle often remains slung from the opposite ends of the crescent and forms the so-called "bib."

Plasmodium vivax (Grassi and Feletti, 1890) is the cause of tertian (benign tertian) fever of temperate climates, which occurs also abundantly in the tropics and subtropics, with regularly recurrent paroxysms every 48 hours. The parasitized corpuscles are distinctly enlarged, quite pale, and usually contain fine pigment granules known as "Schüffner's dots." The signet ring is large and conspicuous, and the dot is in line with the ring and rarely double. The fully grown *merocytes* or *schizonts* are very irregular and bizarre in form.

The number of elements, *merozoites,* in the sporulating or segmented stage commonly seen in the peripheral blood is from 12 to 24 (usually about 16), and their arrangement is irregular. Sporulation occurs regularly every

48 hours. There are no "crescents" in this species; the gametocytes are round or oval in form, filling practically the entire red cell when full grown. The *macrogametocyte* has the chromatin arranged in a compact mass; the *microgametocyte* has the pigment well distributed and presents a more hyaline appearance.

Plasmodium malariae (Laveran 1881) is the cause of the quartan fever, with recurrent paroxysms every 72 hours. This form of malaria is much less common but coincides in distribution with estivo-autumnal fever. The pigment is coarse and generally occurs in marginal streaks. The parasitized corpuscles are usually normal in size, and the parasite is small and more or less oval in shape though, when partly grown, it frequently extends across the equator of the corpuscle in the form of a band. The ring-forms have one vacuole and usually one dot. The gametocytes are rarely seen. The segmenting stage gives rise to the typical "daisy" form, each sporulated body radiating from the center. The number of bodies varies from 6 to 12, usually 8. Sporulation occurs every 72 hours. The gametocytes resemble those of *Plasmodium vivax*.

Rodhain[67] has shown that *P. malariae* can be transmitted intravenously from man to the chimpanzee and maintains its virulence and specific character for man; also the *malariae type* of plasmodium of the naturally infected chimpanzee is transmissible to man, producing a malaria fever of the quartan type.

Plasmodium ovale Stephens 1922 is the cause of a mild form of tertian fever in East Africa and probably South America. The name indicates the oval shape which is generally assumed by the parasite as well as the parasitized erythrocyte. The infected corpuscles may become somewhat enlarged. The pigment is dark and granular and "Schüffner's dots" are present in all stages. The merozoites range from 8 to 12 in number.

Life Cycle of the Plasmodia (Fig. 64). The life history of malaria parasites consists of two cycles: first, the *asexual,* also known as the blood cycle, cycle of Golgi, or schizogonic cycle; and secondly, the *sexual,* also known as the mosquito cycle, cycle of Ross, or sporogonic cycle.

The *asexual* cycle, accomplished in the blood and other tissues of man, begins with the injection of spindle-shaped *sporozoites* into the circulation with the bite of an appropriate anopheline mosquito.

It was formerly thought that the sporozoite entered the erythrocyte at once. For a number of years, however, there was much speculation as to what *did* happen in the life cycle of the *Plasmodium* between the inoculation of the sporozoite by the mosquito and the appearance of the trophozoite or signet ring in the erythrocyte. That there are pre-erythrocytic stages in the developmental cycle of *Plasmodium elongatum* Huff and *P. gallinaceum* Brumpt and other bird malaria parasites had been proved by Huff and associates;[40] the first generation following infection by sporozoites being called "cryptozoites" and subsequent generations, "metacryptozoites." These stages "require a period of development in macrophages and related kinds of cells before they invade erythrocytes." Huff[41] raised the question, "Do such stages really exist in human or simian malarial infections?" He cited indirect evidence viz.:

. . . (1) the existence of periods of inapparent parasitism followed by parasitemia in sporozoite-induced infections, and (2) the differences between sporozoite-induced infections with respect to their response to antimalarial drugs. . . . The evidence is conclusive that the sporozoites and the 3 or 4 generations of development following them do not occur in the blood during this period;

i.e., subinoculations within about half an hour of blood from a heavily sporozoite (mosquito) inoculated malaria patient may occasionally result in an infection; however, following this brief period there is a period of 7 or more days (depending apparently on the species of *Plasmodium*) when subinoculations will *not* result in infection.

Levaditi and Schoen (Levaditi[51]) in 1931 had observed, without realizing what they were seeing, the cysts of the exoerythrocytic stage of *Plas-*

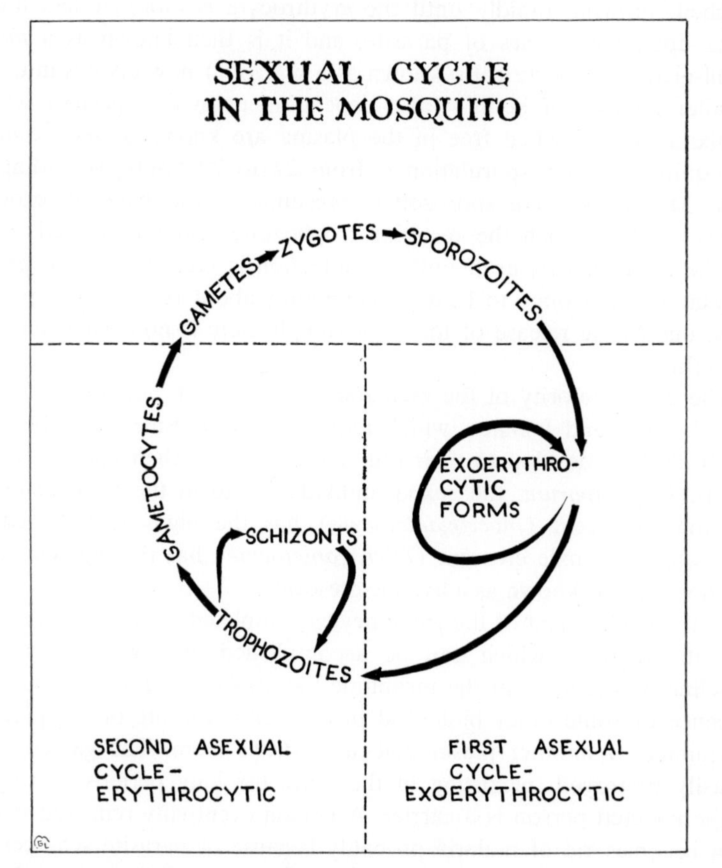

Fig. 64. Diagrammatic life cycle of *Plasmodium*. (Redrawn from Levaditi, after Sergent.)

modium kochii in the liver of a lemur, *Cynocephalus babuin*. In 1948, Garman recognized the true nature of these cysts, and Garman, Shortt, and their associates demonstrated, in 1948 and 1949, the presence of the exoerythrocytic stage of *Plasmodium vivax* and *P. falciparum* in man. This discovery explained several phenomena, particularly the nature of relapses, the "incubation" period following inoculation of the human host by the bite of the mosquito, and the lack of response to antimalarial drugs during this period.

The exoerythrocytic stage is passed in the reticuloendothelial system of such organs as the liver, spleen, heart, and brain, where the sporozoites develop into cryptozoites, assuming a spheroid shape and increasing in size through repeated nuclear divisions. Reproduction takes place through spore formation (schizogony), the resulting sporozoites then entering epithelial or macrophage cells and becoming metacryptozoites, which again undergo schizogony. After three or four generations, the parasites, as trophozoites, enter the blood; after having parasitized an erythrocyte the "signet ring" stage is reached, growing rapidly until the erythrocyte is more or less filled, depending upon the species of parasite, and it is then known as a *merocyte*. The full-grown merocyte (also known as a *schizont*) now divides into a larger or smaller number of bodies (also depending upon the species) which are then liberated, and when free in the plasma are known as *merozoites*. The time required for this sporulation is from 24 to 72 hours, according to the species. Merozoites, like sporozoites, presumably also have an exoerythrocytic cycle, after which the resulting trophozoites enter other red cells, and again the cycle repeats itself until the infection is great enough to produce a paroxysm, i.e., in from 6 to 12 days, commonly about 10 days. The paroxysms may be due to the release of toxins, although there is no clear evidence concerning this.

The great majority of the merozoites are asexual, but some of them are potential males and females, which require a longer time, probably not less than 10 days, to develop to their full growth and are then known as gametocytes. In *P. falciparum,* the sexual individuals are in the form of *crescents*. The female crescent (*macrogametocyte*) has the pigment collected at the center, while the male crescent (*microgametocyte*) has the pigment scattered throughout, and is known as a hyaline crescent.

With development of the gametocytes completed, all is ready for the next cycle (the sexual), which can be accomplished only within the body of anopheline mosquitoes. In the meantime the asexual cycles are repeated until senescence or some other biological process ends the life of the parasites or until quinine or another plasmodiacide destroys them. The gametocytes are not easily destroyed, persisting in the body for long periods, during which time the infected person is a carrier. A person eventually removed from reinfection becomes rid of malaria probably because of parasite senescence. Rejuvenation of the parasite brood and consequently relapses even after many years of latency may perhaps result from the exoerythrocytic cycle referred to earlier.

The *sexual cycle,* the cycle of Ross, has been observed only in female anopheline mosquitoes, in the stomach of which flagellation of the male gametocyte takes place. After a peripheral arrangement of the chromatin (in clumps corresponding to the number of flagella) there are extruded from three to six long slender filaments (flagella), each of which separates from the parent body (exflagellation), forming the male *gamete* (*microgamete*), corresponding in function to the spermatozoon of higher animals. The female gametocyte, now known as the *macrogamete,* having been taken into the stomach of the mosquito with the microgametocytes in the act of sucking blood, also undergoes certain changes (maturation), becoming rounded or oval in form with the chromatin mass centrally located. In this condition and still in the stomach of the mosquito, the microgamete conjugates with the macrogamete, producing the *zygote,* which soon becomes motile and is then known as the *ookinete* or vermiculus, in which stage the epithelium of the stomach is penetrated, and a position is shortly taken up just beneath the peritoneal membrane. Based on his studies of the plasmodia of birds, Huff[42] points out that this penetration of the stomach wall:

> . . . is not a boring process, for this zygote has lost its pointed ends long before the penetration begins. When the ookinetes are first found in the vicinity of the stomach wall, they are lying parallel to it in the serous mucoid layer adjacent to the cells of the stomach wall. As the parasite grows, it becomes relatively thicker and gradually forces two of the stomach cells apart. It gradually becomes more spherical and forces the stomach cells apart nearer and nearer the outside of the stomach wall. The stomach cells now begin to come back to their original position on the inner side. Finally the parasite, now an oocyst, comes to lie under the outer envelope of the stomach.

In this position the parasite grows enormously, forming an *oocyst* (Fig. 65) in which many nuclei appear in from 4 to 5 days. These tiny nucleated bodies give rise to hundreds of spindle-shaped organisms (*sporozoites*), which are shed into the body cavity of the mosquito in from 24 to 48 hours (Fig. 66). The majority of the sporozoites eventually collect in the salivary glands, remaining there until the mosquito bites again, when many of them may be injected with the saliva into the wound. The time required for the completion of the sexual cycle varies from 7 to 10 days under favorable conditions. Once infected, the mosquito probably remains infected and infective for the rest of its life. In making malaria surveys one should be proficient in detecting plasmodial infections in anophelines.[43]

What makes a mosquito a good natural vector? Conclusive experimental evidence indicates that the plasmodia of human malaria do not develop within the bodies of culicine mosquitoes even though gametocytes are ingested. Whether all anopheline species are infectible is, of course, not known; many

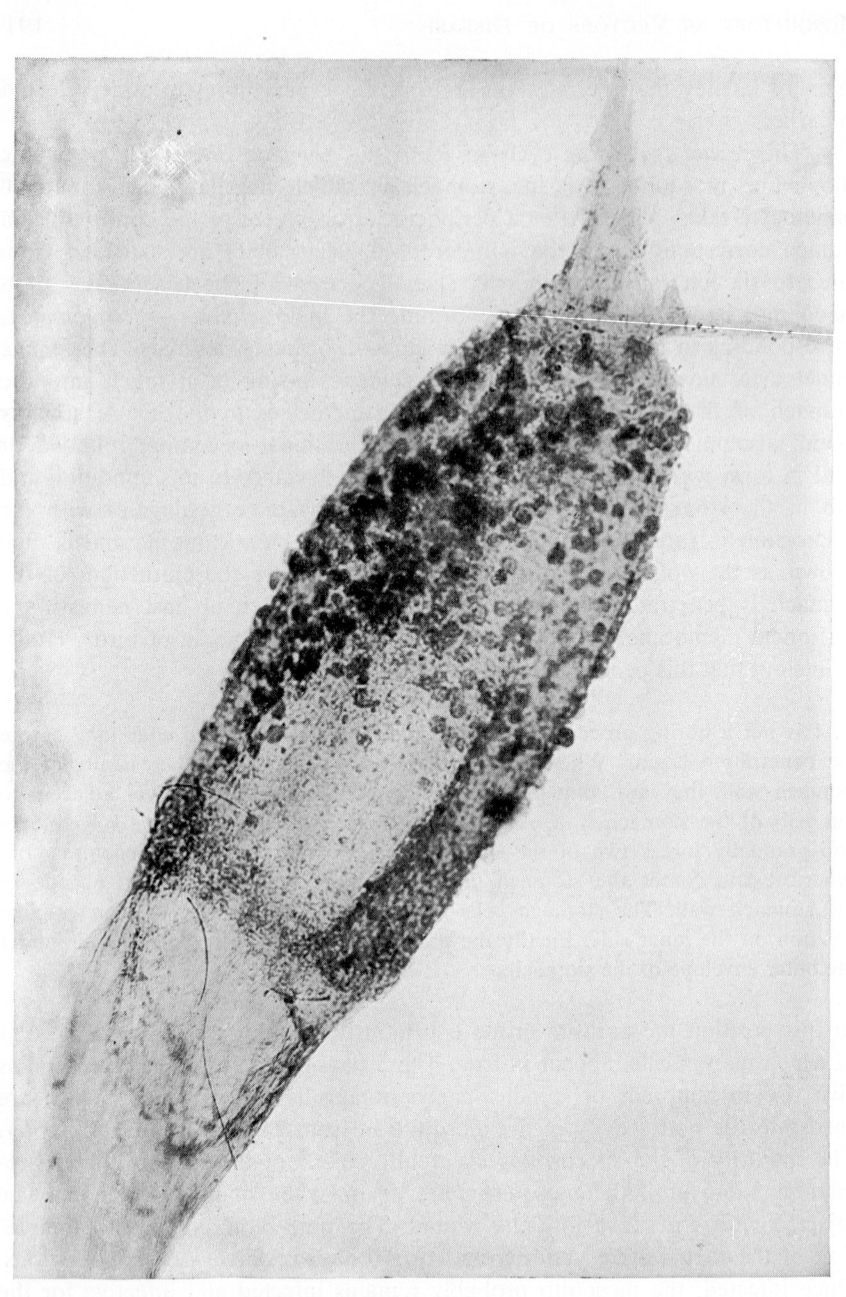

Fig. 65. Stomach of female *Anopheles* mosquito with numerous plasmodial cysts. (Photograph by Mayne.)

malariologists are of the opinion that laboratory tests tend to prove that it is a matter of degree only, that no anopheline is completely refractory to the plasmodia of human malaria. Only 85 of the approximately 400 known species of *Anopheles* have been definitely incriminated as vectors of malaria.[26] There is not only a variation in the degree of mosquito species hospitality to plasmodia but also a variation in the species of plasmodia. For example, *A. quadrimaculatus* is susceptible to both *Plasmodium vivax* and *P. falciparum,* while *A. punctipennis,* though equally susceptible to *P. vivax,* seems to be refractory to certain strains but not to others of *P. falciparum.*[9]

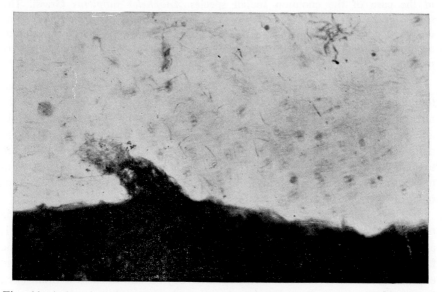

Fig. 66. A bursting plasmodial cyst on the stomach of a mosquito. Spindle-shaped sporozoites are being liberated. (Greatly magnified.) (Photograph by Mayne.)

A good natural vector is an *Anopheles* species which is freely and abundantly infectible by the several species of human plasmodia, offers a favorable environment for development to the sporozoite state, avoids loss of sporozoites in unsuitable places, breeds successfully and abundantly, is a house invader, and takes human blood repeatedly, i.e., is anthropophilous. The maintenance of close and constant contact between an anthropophilous mosquito and its source of food supply is an important factor in endemicity. The life expectancy of the mosquito is also an important factor; unless the mosquito lives long enough to mature viable sporozoites in sufficient numbers and to bite a second time, its infective capacity is lost. The concept of species sanitation is based on a knowledge of the factors referred to above. An anopheline may be common, even abundant, yet of little importance as a vector for one or more reasons.

Horsfall[38] lists four types of reaction of the body of the mosquito unfavorable to the plasmodium. These are: (1) failure of the zygotes to penetrate the epithelium of the gut and, consequently, their degeneration; (2) normal oocyst formation, but rupture into the lumen of the gut instead of into the haemocoel; (3) degeneration, with loss of infectiveness, of both oocysts and sporozoites; (4) the formation of "black spores" associated with degenerative oocysts.

Hindle[37] points out that:

. . . the first instance of an *Anopheles* being shown not to transmit malaria was in the case of the common Indian species *Anopheles subpictus* Grassi. This species is found quite commonly in very large numbers associated with every degree of prevalence of malaria, but it has not been shown to act as a transmitting agent (in India) under natural conditions, though it can be infected experimentally.

Epidemiology of Malaria. Hackett[31] reviewed several theories that attempt to account for "anophelism without malaria," i.e., the presence of the mosquito without the presence of the disease. This phenomenon can probably be explained, however, on the basis of: (1) lack of suitable vectors, as defined above; (2) vector density below the critical level which is sufficient to maintain the disease; or (3) climate conditions unfavorable to the maintenance of the parasite at an infective level, although favorable to the development of the mosquito.

The concept of the critical level of vector density below which malaria tends to disappear and above which the incidence of the disease increases, is an important one in the epidemiology of malaria.[76] It helps to explain some facts that have been well known but puzzling, e.g., why malaria occurs in explosive outbreaks in some areas, such as Ceylon and northwest India (i.e., is unstable), whereas it occurs in a highly endemic condition, with epidemics only in the fringes of the malarial zone, as in parts of central Africa (i.e., is stable). MacDonald[54] has attempted to make a mathematical analysis of the epidemiology of malaria. He traces the thread of malaria through the following successive elements:

(1) Those that determine the stability of the disease, viz. mosquito longevity, man-biting habits, and the mosquito cycle of the parasite.

(2) Those which determine initial transmission, viz. mosquito density and man-biting habits.

(3) Those which determine the normal season, viz. climatic factors.

(4) The inoculation rate, communal immunity expressed in reduced incidence of gametocytes, and reproduction rate of the disease expressed in terms of the critical level of vector density. In areas where the disease is stable, the ruling reproductive rate usually stands just barely above the critical level; where the disease is unstable, this rate vacillates, partly erratically and partly periodically, around it.

"This," says MacDonald, "is the picture of malaria, and the process in reverse is the picture of its control."

Whether an *Anopheles* once infected can infect more than one person without again feeding on infective blood is a matter of interest. In an instructive series of experiments, Mayne (Mitzmain[59]) reports that one mosquito proved to be the sole infecting agent in three cases. Mayne used *Anopheles punctipennis* with *Plasmodium vivax*. He also demonstrated in 11 experiments that short exposure to bites (interrupted feeding) was sufficient to cause successful transmission of the disease.

Effect of Temperature on Plasmodia in the Mosquito. In spite of the fact that all conditions appear to be favorable (i.e., presence of numerous anopheline mosquitoes together with ample human population with carriers of plasmodial gametocytes), malaria may be wholly absent in particular localities. An analysis of conditions will usually reveal the fact that the average temperature is low because the nights are cool, although the days may be fairly warm, or because of prevailing cool fogs. It is generally agreed that malaria gametocytes cannot develop successfully within the body of the mosquito host when the average temperature is below about 60° F. It is nevertheless a matter of interest to know that King[48] observed the survival of the parasite of tertian malaria in the mosquito host (*Anopheles quadrimaculatus*) at a temperature of 30° F for a period of 2 days; at 31° F for 4 days; and at 46° F for 17 days; and the parasite of estivo-autumnal malaria survived a temperature of 35° F for 24 hours.

Knowles and Basu,[49] working with the vector *Anopheles stephensi* Liston, found that the heaviest salivary gland infection of *Plasmodium vivax* was obtained at 80° F and 50 per cent relative humidity. Using the same species of *Anopheles* they found that at a temperature of 100° F and with all percentages of humidity between 50 and 100 no infection with any species of malaria parasite was obtained. The sporozoite stage of *Plasmodium vivax* was reached in the salivary glands of *A. stephensi* in 18 days at 60° F, 15 days at 70° F, 11 days at 80° F, and 9 days at 90° F. For *Plasmodium falciparum* also at 50 per cent relative humidity the time was 14 days at 70° F, 10 days at 80° F, and 9 days at 90° F. *Plasmodium malariae* has been reported to require 30 to 35 days at 67° F, with relative humidity not given.

Hibernation of the anopheline host presents the problem of the overwintering of the parasite. Mayne (Mitzmain[60]) produced evidence, which has subsequently been substantiated, that man, not the mosquito, is the overwintering or reservoir host. Anophelines overwintering in warm stables and homes may nevertheless play an important though highly circumscribed role in the transmission of malaria.

Vectors of Human Malaria. It has been abundantly proved that the causal organisms (plasmodia) of human malaria are transmitted from man to man only through the agency of mosquitoes belonging to the genus *Anopheles*. Russell, Rozeboom, and Stone[77] give identification keys to 240 species and 78 subspecies of anophelines of the world. Of this number, Russell[78] named 54 species as the chief malaria vectors. These are distributed over the world, according to various authorities, as shown in the following tabulation:

TABLE I
IMPORTANT ANOPHELINE VECTORS OF MALARIA*

COUNTRY AND SPECIES OF *Anopheles*	LOCALITY	BREEDING PLACES
United States and Canada		
quadrimaculatus Say	Eastern, central and southern United States (Gulf to Ontario)	Sunlit, impounded water, marshes, swamps, rice fields
freeborni Aitken	Rocky Mountains, New Mexico, Pacific coast	Sunlit seepage water, irrigation ditches, rice fields (in part)
Mexico, Central America, West Indies		
albimanus Wiedemann	Mexico to Colombia and Venezuela, West Indies	Sunlit lagoons (brackish and fresh), swamps, pools
p. pseudopunctipennis Theobald	Southern United States to Argentina	Sunlit streams with green algae, seepage, pools, etc.
darlingi Root	Central America to Argentina	Sunlit fresh waters, marshes, etc.
aquasalis Curry	Central America to Brazil, West Indies	Brackish marshes, irrigation seepages, etc.
punctimacula Dyar and Knab	Mexico to Brazil, West Indies	Shaded pools, swamps, streams
bellator Dyar and Knab	West Indies to Brazil	Water at bases of leaves of bromeliads
aztecus Hoffmann	Mexico	Sunlit pools with green algae
South America (*See also* Mexico, etc.)		
cruzii Dyar and Knab	Brazil	Water at base of leaves of bromeliads
albitarsus Lynch-Arribálzaga	Argentina	Rice fields, marshes, overflows, etc.
gambiae Giles	Imported into Brazil, now exterminated[87]	All sorts of collections of fresh water

* *See also* Herms and Gray.[35]

TABLE I (*Continued*)

COUNTRY AND SPECIES OF *Anopheles*	LOCALITY	BREEDING PLACES
Europe		
l. labranchiae Falleroni	Mediterranean, Europe, and North Africa	Upland streams, rice fields, brackish coastal marshes
labranchiae atroparvus van Thiel	England and Sweden to Spain and northeastern Italy	Sunlit pools and brackish marshes, swamps, etc.
maculipennis messeae Falleroni	Norway, Russia, Siberia, Manchuria	Fresh-water pools, ponds, marshes
superpictus Grassi	Spain, southern Europe, Greece, Asia Minor	Pools in stream beds, irrigation canals, seepages, etc.
sacharovi Favre (= *elutus*)	Balkans, Russia	Sunlit coastal marshes, fresh or brackish water
North Africa and Middle East (*See also* Europe)		
claviger Meigen	Ukraine, Asia Minor, North Africa	Rock pools, wells, cisterns, marshes
pharoensis Theobald	North Africa, Palestine	Rice fields, swamps
sergenti Theobald	North Africa, Palestine, Turkey, Syria	Rice fields, irrigation canals, borrow pits, seepage water
superpictus Grassi	Asia Minor	Stream bed pools, irrigation canals, seepage water, hill district
Central and South Africa		
funestus Giles	Tropical Africa	Stream margins, swamps, ditches, seepage water
gambiae Giles (*See also* South America)	Tropical Africa, Egypt, Arabia	Puddles, pools, sluggish streams, all sorts of collections of water
moucheti Evans	Uganda, Congo, Cameroons	Stream margins, swamps
pharoensis Theobald (*See also* North Africa)	Widely distributed in Africa, Palestine	Rice fields, swamps
nili Theobald	Widely distributed in central Africa	Shade loving, stream margins
pretoriensis Theobald	Widely distributed, central and south Africa	Sunlit rock pools, stream beds, hoofprints, ditches

TABLE I (*Continued*)

COUNTRY AND SPECIES OF *Anopheles*	LOCALITY	BREEDING PLACES
Philippine Islands		
minimus flavirostris Ludlow	Many islands, Java, Celebes	Foothill streams, ditches, wells
mangyanus Banks	Many islands	Stream beds, irrigation ditches
Japan, North China, Korea		
sinensis Wiedemann	Widely distributed	Open clear water, rice fields, swamps, ponds, slow streams
pattoni Christophers	Northern China	Beds of hill streams, rock pools
South and Central China, Burma, Taiwan		
minimus Theobald	Hilly regions, southern China, Taiwan, Burma	Sunlit, slow-moving streams, rice fields, irrigation ditches
sinensis Wiedemann	Plain of central China, Burma	*See* North China
jeyporiensis var. *candidiensis* Koizumi	Hong Kong area	Rice fields in hilly country
culicifacies Giles	Burma	Stream breeder, irrigation ditches
maculatus maculatus Theobald	Burma, southern China	Stream and river bed breeder, rice fields, pools, lake margins
philippinensis Ludlow	Burma, Indo-China	Rice fields, borrow pits, swamps, ditches, tanks
India and Ceylon		
culicifacies Giles	India, Ceylon, Thailand	*See* Burma, etc.
stephensi Liston	India	Wells, cisterns, roof gutters, temporary water receptacles
m. maculatus Theobald	India, Ceylon	*See* Burma, South China, etc.
fluviatilis James	India, Thailand	Foothill stream edges, springs, irrigation canals
minimus Theobald	Eastern and northern Ceylon	*See* South China, etc.
philippinensis Ludlow	India	*See* Burma, Indo-China, etc.

TABLE I (*Continued*)

COUNTRY AND SPECIES OF *Anopheles*	LOCALITY	BREEDING PLACES
Thailand, East Indies, Malaya (*See also* India and Ceylon)		
aconitus Dönitz	East Indies, Malaya, Indo-China	Rice fields, irrigation ditches, pools in creek beds, reservoirs
nigerrimus Giles	Malaya, East Indies	Rice fields, impounded water, borrow pits, sluggish streams
maculatus maculatus Theobald (*See* South China, etc.)	Thailand, Malaya, East Indies	Stream and river bed breeder, seepage water, lake margins
subpictus subpictus Grassi	Malaya, East Indies	Borrow pits, buffalo wallows, all sorts of temporary or permanent collections of water
sundaicus (Rodenwaldt)	Thailand, Malaya, East Indies	Sea-water lagoons and swamps
umbrosus Theobald	Malay, Indo-China, East Indies	Shaded jungle pools, mangrove swamps
Australia, Melanesia, Polynesia		
farauti Laveran (= *moluccensis*)	New Guinea, Solomons, New Hebrides	Fresh or brackish water, all sorts of natural or artificial collections of water, clear or polluted
punctulatus punctulatus Dönitz	New Guinea, Solomons	Rain pools, stream margins, hoofprints, etc.
bancrofti Giles	New Guinea, northern Australia	Shallow, slow-moving streams

Malaria Control and Eradication. Prior to the end of World War II, malariologists were content to keep the disease under control—to hold onto gains and to reduce the incidence of the disease, particularly in highly populated areas, to a low level. The release of DDT for civilian use, together with spectacular advances in our knowledge of the bionomics of anophelines, led to a new concept, eradication. This does not necessarily mean eradication of the mosquito vector. If its numbers are reduced below the critical level of density, so that all transmission of the human parasite is eliminated for a period of two or three years, the disease will disappear spontaneously from the human host. If reintroduction can be prevented, an extensive area, such as the continental United States, can be freed completely from the disease. Thus, even though we may not be able to eradicate the mosquitoes involved, "anophelism without malaria" may persist over a continent and ultimately, it is hoped, over the world.*

This is an amazing concept. It is still far from being realized; in 1955 there were an estimated 200,000,000 cases of malaria in the world, with 2,000,000 deaths.[75] Technical difficulties stand in the way of malaria eradication from, in particular, many parts of Asia and Africa. The possibility that jungle primates may serve as a reservoir, as they do for yellow fever, must be considered; experimental infections of man by *Plasmodium* species parasitic on monkeys (e.g., *P. kochi*) and vice versa have been effected, and the human and monkey plasmodia are closely related. Nevertheless, world eradication of malaria is a feasible objective.[85]

Malaria control and eradication programs must take into consideration the broad aspects of the ecology of the disease, its vector, and its victim. These are well expressed in the Russell formula,

$$(X + Y + Z)\ b\ e\ p\ t\ i = \text{Malaria incidence},$$

whereby the chain of malaria infection, human carrier (X) to the mosquito vector (Y) to the human victim (Z) is modified by the following factors:

b = bionomics of man and mosquito
e = environment of man and mosquito
p = plasmodia, species, and strains
t = therapy and control measures
i = the immune factors in man and mosquito

Russell[75] sums up very effectively the steps that lead to malaria eradication. First, there is a preparatory phase, including an initial survey, planning, and preliminary operations. (For modern survey methods, consult MacDonald.[54]) This is followed by the phase of attack, with total spraying coverage, until malaria transmission has ceased and until the parasite has been virtually eliminated from the reservoir host. For *P. vivax* and *P. falciparum,* this means 2 1/2 to 3 years. The phase of consolidation begins with the wiping out of any residual pockets that may remain. This is the difficult phase; discovery of isolated cases and the application of antimalarial drugs takes first priority. Surveillance must be maintained over the entire area, however. The final phase of maintenance must last as long as malaria exists anywhere in the world. Under ordinary circumstances it will not be difficult, however, since local health agencies can be on the alert for the reintroduction of ma-

* This is an optimistic view which is not shared by many malariologists, particularly since many factors involving human relationships, etc., complicate the effective application of technical advances.

laria, which may be considered an exotic disease in an ever increasing area of the world.

Animal Malarias

Avian Malaria. Blood protozoa were first reported from birds in 1885 by Danilewsky from the Russian Ukraine. Herman[34] lists 178 species and subspecies of North American birds in whose blood protozoon parasites have been found; 62 of these protozoon infections are listed as plasmodial. The species of avian plasmodia, of which there are many, can be divided roughly into two groups, based on whether they produce an elongate or a round type of gametocyte. Among those belonging to the elongate type is *Plasmodium elongatum* Huff, and among those belonging to the round type are the following well-known species: *Plasmodium gallinaceum* Brumpt, *P. cathemerium* Hartman, and *P. relictum* (Grassi et Feletti). So far as is known, avian plasmodia are transmitted in nature by culicine mosquitoes, among them *Culex pipiens, C. pipiens quinquefasciatus,* and *C. tarsalis.* Numerous species of mosquitoes are susceptible to infection in the laboratory, including *Anopheles quadrimaculatus.* For laboratory purposes, *Aedes aegypti* is an excellent vector of *Plasmodium gallinaceum* Brumpt, as in *Aedes atropalpus* (Coquillett), according to Trembly.

Other malarialike infections of birds are caused by *Haemoproteus,* e.g., *Haemoproteus columbae* Celli and San Felice, of pigeons and doves, transmitted by a louse fly, *Pseudolynchia canariensis* (Macquart); also quail malaria caused by *Haemoproteus lophortyx* O'Roke carried by *Lynchia hirsuta* Ferris, the louse fly of quail. (See Chapter 14.) A malarialike disease of ducks is caused by *Leucocytozoon simondi* Mathis and Leger and is carried by a simuliid fly, *Simulium rugglesi* Nicholson and Mickel (see p. 131).

Simian Malaria. Among the several species of the genus *Plasmodium* peculiar to monkeys are *P. knowlesi* Sinton and Mulligan, *P. cynomolgi* Mayer, *P. kochi* (Laveran), *P. inui* Halberstadler and Prowazek, and *P. brasilianum* Gonder and Berenberg-Glossler. These plasmodia differ but slightly from the human species, and when *P. knowlesi* is introduced (as the paresis treatment) into the blood of man, a clinical *vivax* malaria response obtains.[58] *Anopheles quadrimaculatus* is reported to be highly susceptible to *P. cynomolgi.* Clark and Dunn,[20] in Panama, were able to infect certain species of Panamanian anophelines with this parasite.

Saurian and Amphibian Malaria. Plasmodia have long been known in lizards of the family Iguanidae; among these are *Plasmodium agamae* Wenyon, *P. diploglossi* Aragão and Neiva, *P. giganteum* Theiler, and *P. floridense* Thompson and Huff. Bullfrogs and toads have recently been shown to have plasmoidal infections, viz.: *P. catesbianae* Fantham, Porter, and

Richardson in the former, and *P. bufonis* Fanthem, Porter, and Richardson in the latter.

Mammalian Malarias. Bats, squirrels, buffalo, antelopes, and many other animals are hosts for plasmodial infections. There are practically unlimited opportunities in this field of research.

YELLOW FEVER

Yellow fever derives its name from the jaundiced color of the skin, mucous membranes, and sclera, which usually develops about the third or fourth day of the illness. The onset is very sudden. It begins with a severe headache, backache, and fever, with frequent vomiting. The vomit becomes very dark after 2 or 3 days because it contains blood, whence the name "black vomit." In fatal cases death usually occurs between the fifth and eighth day of the illness; if the patient survives until the seventh day, his chances for recovery are generally said to be good. One attack confers lifelong immunity. The death rate may reach as high as 50 per cent.

Yellow fever (of the jungle type) apparently existed in America in pre-Columbian days and before the introduction of *Aedes aegypti* into the New World. Mayan chronicles speak definitely of bloody vomiting (*xekik*) that ravaged Yucatan in 1484 and that took heavy tolls in populous areas of that part of the Mayan empire.[83] This disease was most probably yellow fever, but of course we cannot be certain of this. Carter[15] considers the epidemic in Yucatan, Mexico, in 1648 as the first certainly recognizable (from its description) epidemic of yellow fever. He gives 1649 as the date for the earliest introduction of yellow fever into Havana, and refers to its disappearance from Cuba after 1655 and its reintroduction from Vera Cruz in 1761. From that date until 1901 it was endemic in Havana with devastating results. The last major American urban epidemic took place in Rio de Janeiro in 1928 and 1929 with 435 recorded deaths. For nearly three centuries, yellow fever took a huge annual toll of life. Outbreaks have occurred as far north as Quebec, Canada, and as far south as Tocopilla, Chile. New York City had epidemics of yellow fever many times, as did Philadelphia.

Walter Reed and Yellow Fever. Although Dr. Carlos Finlay[63] of Havana had quite early (1881) advanced a mosquito-transmission theory and had carried on what we now know to have been incriminating experiments with nonimmunes, his theory was discredited until renewed interest was given it by the work of the United States Yellow Fever Commission headed by Major Walter Reed in 1900. Reed[63] and his colleagues made a preliminary report in which they state:

> Since we here, for the first time, record a case in which a typical attack of yellow fever has followed the bite of an infected mosquito, within the usual period of incubation of the disease, and in which other sources of infection can be

excluded, we feel confident that the publication of these observations must excite renewed interest in the mosquito theory of the propagation of yellow fever, as proposed by Finlay.

The United States Senate Document No. 822 (Jan. 27, 1911) is concerned with yellow fever and contains a compilation of various publications by the Commission as well as others. The student is referred to this document for a more extensive account of the foresight, courage, and careful experimentation which established the facts of mosquito transmission of this disease. Briefly, the history of this accomplishment is as follows.

In June, 1900, Major Reed, accompanied by Acting Assistant Surgeons James Carroll, Jesse W. Lazear, and A. Agramonte, was sent to Cuba as president of a board to study the infectious diseases of the country, particularly yellow fever. The sanitary measures which had been introduced since the American occupation of the island had made no headway against yellow fever, and Reed was convinced that an insect vector was involved. The military governor of the island, General Leonard Wood, had sufficient breadth of mind and specific scientific training to appreciate Reed's arguments, so he granted full authority to proceed and made the necessary money available. Volunteers from the army provided subjects for experimentation.

In consideration of the times and circumstances, the experimental procedure was remarkably thorough. Complete records were kept of each man to be experimented on, and movements of men into and out of the experimental areas were carefully controlled. The mosquitoes used were bred from the eggs and kept in a building screened by wire netting. A completely mosquito-proof building was divided into two compartments, and infected mosquitoes which had been allowed to feed on yellow fever patients were released in one of these compartments only. The disease was contracted only by individuals who remained in that compartment for a period of time or who otherwise allowed infected mosquitoes to bite them; all attempts to transmit the infection by means of bedding, clothes, or by objects otherwise handled by the patient, or by the handling of filthy objects, failed. Infection was accomplished, however, by injecting blood drawn directly from a yellow fever patient into the body of a nonimmune; even the blood serum, after having passed through a bacteria-proof filter, remained infective.

In the course of the experiments, only one human life was lost. Dr. Lazear will always be remembered as the man who gave his life in order that the curse of yellow fever could be conquered.

The conclusions reached by the Commision follow:

1. The mosquito (*C. fasciatus,* =*Aedes aegypti*) serves as the intermediate host for the parasite of yellow fever.

2. Yellow fever is transmitted to the nonimmune individual by means of the bite of the mosquito that has previously fed on the blood of those sick with this disease.

3. An interval of about 12 days or more after contamination appears to be necessary before the mosquito is capable of conveying the infection.

4. The bite of the mosquito at an earlier period after contamination does not appear to confer any immunity against a subsequent attack.

5. Yellow fever can also be experimentally produced by the subcutaneous injection of blood taken from the general circulation during the first and second days of this disease.

6. An attack of yellow fever, produced by the bite of the mosquito, confers immunity against the subsequent injection of the blood of an individual suffering from the nonexperimental form of this disease.

7. The period of inoculation in 13 cases of experimental yellow fever has varied from 41 hours to 5 days and 17 hours.

8. Yellow fever is not conveyed by fomites, and hence disinfection of articles of clothing, bedding, or merchandise, supposedly contaminated by contact with those sick with this disease, is unnecessary.

9. A house may be said to be infected with yellow fever only when there are present within its walls contaminated mosquitoes capable of conveying the parasite of this disease.

10. The spread of yellow fever can be most effectually controlled by measures directed to the destruction of mosquitoes and the protection of the sick against the bites of these insects.

11. While the mode of propagation of yellow fever has now been definitely determined, the specific cause of this disease remains to be discovered.

Etiology. The search for the causal agent of yellow fever was carried on most assiduously for many years, and various discoveries were announced from time to time. Sanarelli in 1897 declared the organism to be *Bacillus icteroides;* this was amply disproved by the United States Army Yellow Fever Commission in 1900. Seidelin in 1909 described *Paraplasma flavigenum* as the causal agent, and in 1919 Noguchi came to the conclusion that a spirochete, *Leptospira icteroides* Noguchi, was the cause of yellow fever. This turned out to be the cause of Weil's disease or infectious jaundice. Yellow fever is now known to be a virus disease.

Mechanism of Transmission. The virus of yellow fever is not only present in the circulating blood during the first 3 or 4 days of the illness, but also at least 6 hours, or possibly somewhat longer, before the onset of the fever. During this short period, the vector mosquito, *Aedes aegypti,* may at one feeding ingest several thousand infective doses of the virus. The mosquito then becomes a dangerous vector for the rest of its life, which may be over 200 days. The extrinsic incubation period normally under field temperatures takes about 12 days (Carter[15]), but may be considerably shortened by increased temperature, i.e., to 4 days at 98° F or extended to 18 days at 70° F (Davis[21]). After a susceptible person has been bitten and receives an infectious dose from an infected mosquito, an incubation period of 3 or 4 days follows before the symptoms of the disease appear. Now again another source of infection, restricted as before to the short period of 3 or 4 days, is ready for other *aegypti* vectors. An epidemic may quickly develop in the presence of hordes of this rapidly multiplying species of domestic mosquito.

Pre-World War II Advances. Soper *et al.*[88] states that:

When the medical historian of the future comes to write the chapter on yellow fever, he will be obliged to devote considerable space to the developments of the decade and a half from 1926 to 1940. This short period showed how impossible of fulfillment was the dream of final eradication of yellow fever, but it saw great advances in our understanding of the etiology, epidemiology, and prophylaxis of the disease, including the discovery of animal susceptibility; the rediscovery of the virus origin; the demonstration that mosquitoes other than *Aedes aegypti* can and do transmit the virus; the development of the protection test for determining immunity; the organization of viscerotomy for the diagnosis of unsuspected fatal cases; the proof that unrecognized yellow fever has been widespread in large silent endemic areas of South America and Africa; the demonstration that the disease exists in many countries of South America as one of jungle animals, independent of the distribution of *Aedes aegypti* and of man; and finally the modification of the yellow fever virus in such a way as to make mass vaccination practical. These outstanding developments have tended to overshadow the more prosaic improvements in the organization of measures against the *aegypti* mosquito in Brazil which have transformed expensive temporary aegypti reduction campaigns for the eradication of yellow fever into economical permanent services for the species eradication of *Aedes aegypti* itself from the infested areas.

Jungle Yellow Fever. The classic type of yellow fever is an urban or house disease transmitted solely by *Aedes aegypti,* a domestic mosquito which breeds largely in artificial containers in and about human habitations. The epidemiologic pattern of urban yellow fever is relatively simple; namely, man to mosquito. Control seemed simple enough with meticulous inspection and careful application of proper control measures. The Rockefeller Foundation reported[24] that prior to 1929 the belief was expressed that yellow fever was not only fast disappearing as a human menace but that it had been practically eliminated.

In 1925 only three cases of yellow fever were reported from the entire Western Hemisphere; in the 11 months following April, 1927, no cases were reported, and it was assumed that the battle, which had cost the lives of research workers and millions of dollars, was practically won. Then almost without warning, the South American Jungle struck back (Soper and associates[86]), and in a few years' time the epidemiological strategy of the battle had to be completely altered.

It is pointed out that vast areas of the hinterland of both South America and Africa are endemic centers of yellow fever. Burke[13] studied an epidemic involving 201 cases of yellow fever of the jungle type in the absence of *Aedes aegypti* on the Planalto of Matto Grosso, Brazil, during the seasons of 1934 and 1935. He reports that the identity of the disease was definitely established, the only difference being in the condition under which infection occurs.

The paucity of human population in the infected district and the scattered distribution of cases in both time and space, together with the isolated circumstances attending many cases argue against man being the only vertebrate host involved. The sera from five *Cebus* monkeys captured for this study in known infected districts all gave positive protection test results, indicating immunity naturally acquired in the jungle. All available evidence points to infection occurring either in clearings next to uncleared jungle or in the jungle itself, especially during working hours.

Though endemic *aegypti*-transmitted yellow fever has not existed in America since 1940, jungle yellow fever must be considered as a possible permanent source of virus for the reinfection of cities and towns where high densities of *Aedes aegypti* mosquitoes are tolerated. One must remember that, clinically and pathologically, the jungle and urban types of the disease are the same, that one is as dangerous as the other, and that one may readily be transformed into the other. In jungle yellow fever the epidemiologic pattern appears to be monkey to mosquito to monkey. Man becomes infected when he goes into the forest and is bitten by infected mosquitoes. Consequently, the disease in this form is largely one affecting young adult males, rural populations, or fringe-area towns or villages; the jungle worker or traveler may bring the virus back with him when he returns to his community. There he may encounter *aegypti* mosquitoes and an epidemic of yellow fever may ensue. Epidemics which have occurred in recent years, including that of Bolivia in 1949–50 (510 cases), southern Brazil in 1951–53 (310 cases), and Costa Rica in 1951–52 (273 cases)[84] are traceable to this type of transmission. The Costa Rican epidemic, which continued to spread northward through Central America, leaving dead monkeys in its wake, should make us feel less secure concerning the safety of our position in respect to yellow fever in the United States, particularly in light of the discovery of a potential vector, *Haemagogus equinus* Theobald, in Texas, the probability that marsupials and other mammals may serve as reservoirs, and the possibility that *Aedes aegypti* may, under certain circumstances, become a tree-hole breeder.[10]

Vectors and Reservoirs. Seemingly the most important vector of jungle yellow fever in South America is *Haemagogus spegazzinii falco* Kumm *et al.*, which also serves in part as a natural reservoir for the virus.[38] This species, a tree-hole breeder, transfers the virus to nonimmune monkeys in roving bands and likewise to man upon suitable occasions. The felling of trees in the clearing of forests is particularly significant in this respect, since this procedure brings the mosquito to the ground level. Another proven vector is *Aedes leucocelaenus clarki* Galindo *et al.*, an important species in Central America. *Haemagogus equinus* Theobald has been shown to be capable of transmitting the virus in laboratory studies, and from repeated field isolations it seems to be an important vector in South and Central America. *Haemagogus mesodentatus* Komp and Kumm seems to be of importance in Central America.[66] *Sabethes chloropterus* (Humboldt) is known to harbor the virus in nature; it may be a vector of some importance.

Several mosquitoes have been incriminated as vectors of yellow fever in the tropical jungles of East Africa, among these *Aedes simpsoni* Theobald and *Aedes africanus* Theobald, both widely distributed in endemic jungle areas. The latter species is apparently highly important because of its recently discovered presence both in the forest and in the plantations. There is thus presented the possibility of introducing yellow fever to human populations directly from endemic jungle foci through the agency of one species of mosquito.[92]

Several species of mosquitoes other than those here referred to lend themselves well to laboratory transmission by the bite; among them is a common and widespread Nearctic species *Aedes triseriatus* (Say)[6] in which the monkey, *Macaca rhesus,* was used as the host. It is of interest to note that the more important species of mosquitoes incriminated as probable or proved vectors of the virus of jungle yellow fever are tree-hole breeders, thus sharing (perhaps roughly) the same ecologic niche with their simian hosts.

Besides those species mentioned, many others (probably more than 30) have given positive results by the bite in laboratory tests; among these are *Aedes scapularis* (Rondani), *A. fluviatilis* (Lutz), *A. luteocephalus* Newstead, *A. stokesi* Evans, *A. albopictus* (Skuse), *Culex thalassius* Theobald, *Eretmapodites chrysogaster* Graham, *Mansonia africana* (Theobald), and *Haemagogus splendens* Williston.

Prior to 1928 no experimental animal (other than man) was known to be susceptible to yellow fever. With the discovery that the Indian monkey, *Macaca rhesus,* was susceptible as well as a score of other species of monkeys, and particularly with the work of Sawyer on white mice, experimentation with various species of mosquitoes grew apace.[86]

There are evidently many species of jungle-inhabiting vertebrates which harbor the virus of yellow fever, more importantly perhaps several species of monkeys. Hedgehogs are highly susceptible animals and are of great value in laboratory investigations. Certain marsupials, also, seem to be suitable hosts. A more thorough knowledge of potential hosts is imperative if one is to ascertain the potentials of spread of sylvan yellow fever.

DENGUE FEVER

Dengue fever, also known as breakbone fever or dandy fever, is a widespread disease of tropical and subtropical regions, but it also occurs in warm temperate climates where suitable vectors are present. In an epidemic which occurred in the state of Texas in 1922, originating in Galveston during the second week in June and spreading later to other parts of the state, the number of cases of the disease was estimated at between 500,000 and 600,000.[19] Other noteworthy epidemics have occurred in Australia, Greece, Japan, Hawaii, and elsewhere.

The disease is characterized by its sudden attack, severe rheumatic pains in the joints and limbs, intense headache, backache, and high fever; a remission of 2 to 3 days follows the first attack of 3 days; the second attack lasts usually but a day and is accompanied by a rapidly spreading rash. The "saddle back" type of fever, though quite common, is not constant. The entire course may be run in 5 or 6 days. Although the disease is of much importance because of its debilitating effects and prolonged convalesence, the death rate is very low. It is caused by a virus of which two immunologically distinct types, the Hawaiian and the New Guinea, have been isolated. The virus belongs to the B group of Casals[16] along with yellow fever and certain of the encephalitides, and there is some immunologic interference between the dengue and yellow fever viruses. Immunity to the homologous strain may persist as long as 18 months,[79] but heterologous immunity is of short duration. The virus is present in the peripheral circulation during the initial stages of the disease, i.e., the first 3 to 5 days, also for about a day previous to the onset; hence, the mosquito vector must bite the patient during this short period of time in order to become infected.

Mosquito Transmission. Graham[29] (1902) was the first to demonstrate that mosquitoes transferred dengue by the bite. Transmission experiments conducted by Chandler and Rice[19] with *Aedes aegypti* were successful in 4 out of 6 cases, the mosquitoes having fed on patients in the second to fifth days of the disease. The mosquito is able to transmit the infection after an incubation period of 8 to 14 days. Infected mosquitoes remain infected as long as they live. *Aedes aegypti* has been shown to be infective for as long as 174 days and has been kept alive for 7 months.[83] Transovarian transmission is not known to occur.

Aedes aegypti is the only proven vector of dengue in the Western Hemisphere, and studies of the epidemiology of the disease in Panama by Rosen[69] would indicate that it is probably the only vector in the Americas. In Pacific Oceania, *Aedes albopictus* (Skuse), *A. scutellaris* (Walker), and *A. polynesiensis* Marks are proven vectors. It is perhaps significant that all these mosquitoes belong to the subgenus *Stegomyia. Culex pipiens quinquefasciatus,* formerly regarded as a vector, was shown not to be by Simmons and coworkers.[82]

Aedes albopictus breeds under urban conditions which are very similar to those of *A. aegypti,* i.e., the larvae live in fairly clear water in artificial containers; however, when away from human habitations the larvae occur in tree holes, bamboo stalks, plant axils, and stone cavities in the forests (up to 2000 feet in Hawaii). It is particularly prevalent in depressions in monuments in Japanese cemeteries, as well as in flower containers. The species is found in Oriental regions, Madagascar, New Guinea, north Australia, and the Philippine and Hawaiian Islands. The distribution of *A. scutellaris* overlaps that of *A. albopictus* in Micronesia and in Polynesia except Hawaii. It is reported to be a vector of dengue in New Guinea. *Aedes polynesiensis* has been shown to be a vector in Tahiti.[71]

The reservoir of dengue has not been determined. Certain Old World monkeys (*Macaca* and *Cercopithecus*) and chimpanzees are susceptible to the virus, and Rosen,[70] investigating the New World Callitrichidae and Cebidae, concludes that "it would seem logical to suspect that most, if not all, species of monkeys which occur in the New World are susceptible to infection with dengue virus." So although an extrahuman cycle, as in yellow fever, has not been demonstrated, it is a possibility.

MOSQUITO-BORNE VIRAL ENCEPHALITIDES

The virologist prefers to group together the causal organisms of the viral encephalitides, dengue, yellow fever, and the other viral diseases with which we are concerned as the "arthropod-borne viruses" rather than to use the encephalitis designation, since the latter categorization is partly artificial, depending as it does on the reaction of experimental hosts to infection following cerebral inoculation (W. C. Reeves, personal communication to James). A specific example of the difficulty involved is as follows. Yellow fever, the dengues, St. Louis, Japanese B, West Nile, and Russian Spring-Summer viruses (see Chapter 19) are all related antigenically. This group produces clinical diseases ranging from mild fevers through hemorrhagic fevers, and encephalitis through meningitis, hepatitis and influenzalike illnesses. An individual virus agent may produce almost this entire array of clinical diseases in the human host. Also, this single group (known as the B viruses) has both mosquitoes and ticks as vectors. On the other hand, the eastern and western equine encephalitis viruses, together with others, belong to an antigenically distinct group. Therefore, although the category of viral encephalitides is used here, for sake of convenience, it should be understood that it is not an antigenically natural group.

Equine and Human Viral Encephalitis. With the virtual elimination of malaria and yellow fever from our area, the arthropod-borne viral encephalitides have become the most important group of mosquito-transmitted disease of man in the United States. Pathologic symptoms occur in man and equines; the tick-borne louping ill of the British Isles is considered an ovine encephalitis. Etiologically, certain equine forms are identical with the corresponding forms of the human disease.

The symptoms and signs of encephalitis in horses are described as follows by Meyer, Haring, and Howitt.[57]

Preceding the onset of symptoms which attract attention, the temperature may be found to vary from 103° F to 107° F. Not infrequently when the horse shows signs of drooping of the head, sleepiness, and circling motion or other psychic and motor disturbances, the body temperature may be normal. The pulse and respiration are usually accelerated. Quite often the animal rests against the wall or corner and may show backward and sideways motions. Muscular twitchings are quite common. Many of the horses are down on the second or third day and may or may not get up when pressed to do so. Paresis of the lips and drooling are frequently noted. Mastication and swallowing may or may not be impaired, but grinding of the teeth is quite regularly observed. The conjunctiva is always infected and frequently icteric or grayish and studded with petechiae or ecchymoses. In the mild cases which were able to rise, recovery was as a rule uneventful but about half were so severe that they terminated fatally in 3 to 8 days or were destroyed for humane reasons.

In man, clinical manifestations vary considerably, depending on the type or form of encephalitis and its severity. Most infected persons show no clinical signs or symptoms. Some cases are mild and abortive, with some fever and headache; these might be missed by the diagnostician unless the abnormalities in the cerebrospinal fluid are observed. The history of such cases is often determined only by the subsequent discovery of antibodies in the blood. More severe cases are marked by fever, headache, nausea and vomiting, muscular weakness and twitching, malaise, and mental disorientation. In fatal cases, following either an abrupt or delayed onset of illness, the neck becomes stiff, there is lethargy or confusion, stupor, coma, and sometimes convulsions or paralysis. Death may follow in 2 to 4 days. In recovery, sequelae, especially in children, may include mental retardation, convulsive seizures, spasticity, or certain milder effects. Encephalitis may be incorrectly diagnosed as poliomyelitis.

Types of Mosquito-borne Encephalitides. Six types of encephalitides are known to be mosquito-borne. These are as follows:

1. *St. Louis Encephalitis* (SLE). The first recorded outbreak of this disease occurred in St. Louis and St. Louis County, Missouri, and surrounding areas, in 1933, when 1083 cases occurred in the city and county.[52] Subsequent epidemics have been recorded in Kentucky, Missouri, North Dakota, Texas, Colorado, California, Washington, and elsewhere. In general, the distribution of the disease includes the western half of the United States plus Illinois, Indiana, Ohio, Kentucky, and Tennessee.[2] Aitken[1] has recorded it from Trinidad. The disease is generally not considered equine in nature, although it does occur as a subclinical infection in horses and has caused death in experimental cases. Mortality in human beings is variable, usually 10 to 30 per cent, although west of the Rocky

Mountains the mortality is decidedly lower, possibly the result of a less virulent strain.[27] *Culex tarsalis* is considered the most important vector in the west; in the central United States *C. pipiens* and *C. p. quinquefasciatus* are considered to be the normal vectors.

2. *Western Equine Encephalitis* (WEE). This type of encephalitis occurs chiefly in the United States and Canada west of the Mississippi and in Illinois and Wisconsin, although the virus has been recorded as far eastward as Rhode Island[2] and Florida. The virus of Argentina equine encephalomyelitis seems to be identical with it. Since the isolation by Hammon *et al.*[32] of the virus from wild *Culex tarsalis* at Yakima, Washington, in 1941, a discovery that has been confirmed repeatedly at Yakima and elsewhere since that time, *Culex tarsalis* has been considered the chief vector. The virus has been isolated in nature from at least seven other mosquitoes distributed through the genera *Aedes, Anopheles, Culex,* and *Culiseta.* Some of these are obviously involved in transmission, since the virus is more broadly distributed, geographically, than the commonly accepted vector. It seems significant, however, that in North America the area where the disease is strongly endemic and where it occurs as outbreaks or epidemics corresponds with the area occupied by *Culex tarsalis.* Mortality in human beings, once clinical symptoms appear, is lower, in general, than in the St. Louis type.

3. *Eastern Equine Encephalitis* (EEE). This disease was first identified as a separate etiologic type in 1933. Its distribution is chiefly along the states of the Atlantic seaboard and Gulf coast, from Massachusetts to Texas, although scattered isolations of the virus have been made as far inland and northward as Kansas and Wisconsin. It also occurs in Mexico, Panama, Brazil, the Dominican Republic, and Cuba. The virus has been isolated from *Mansonia perturbans* (Walker), *Culex salinarius* Coquillett, *Culiseta melanura* (Coquillett), and *Aedes sollicitans* (Walker). The disease is contracted less frequently by man than the western and St. Louis types, but it is more severe; an outbreak in Massachusetts in 1938 involved 34 human cases, of which 25, or 74 per cent, were fatal, and 10 of 13 cases in the same area terminated fatally in 1956.[2] The disease also affects pheasants and some passerine birds, often with fatal consequences.

4. *Venezuelan Equine Encephalitis* (VEE). This disease, known since 1935, occurs among horses in Ecuador, Colombia, Venezuela, Panama, and Trinidad. *Mansonia titillans* (Walker) has been shown to be a vector. In man, the symptoms and signs of the disease are mild.

5. *Japanese B Encephalitis* (JAP). This disease, so called in order to distinguish it from "Japanese A" (which is identical with the nonarthropod-borne Von Economo's disease), has been known since 1871. It occurs in the Far East, particularly on the Japanese mainland. *Culex tritaeniorhynchus* Giles and perhaps other species of mosquitoes are considered to be vectors. The disease has a high incidence of mortality. In the epidemic of 1924 in Japan 6000 human cases were reported with a 60 per cent mortality. In this epidemic, it cannot be ascertained whether the diagnosis was accurate in all cases, but in another epidemic in Japan in 1948, there were about 8000 cases with a 30 per cent mortality. Horses and swine are also affected by this virus.

6. *Murray Valley Encephalitis* (MVE). This disease, which occurs in northern Australia and New Guinea, is similar to St. Louis and western equine

encephalitis. *Culex annulirostris* Skuse appears, on epidemiologic bases, to be the most likely vector in Australia; this opinion is strengthened by the fact that the virus will increase 10- to 100-fold in the closely related *Culex tarsalis,* in which an intrinsic incubation period of 13 days, at temperatures of about 78° F, has been demonstrated under experimental conditions.[74]

The possible importance of other arthropod-borne encephalitides should not be overlooked. The California (Hammon-Reeves) virus has to date been associated with three human cases of encephalitis, and Ilheus virus has been associated with a febrile illness in man. To date (personal communication to James from Reeves, 1959), a total of 79 viruses have been recognized in the arthropod-borne group. In addition to the above mentioned, these include such mosquito-transmitted encephalitis viruses as Anopheles A, Anopheles B, Wyeomyia, and others. These viruses should not be dismissed summarily as unimportant. Cases of encephalitis of unknown etiology may, in some instances, be traceable to these unknown or insufficiently known agents, or pathogenic strains may develop which may play a part in increasing or inducing pathogenicity. For tick-borne viruses, see Chapter 19.

For a classification of the arthropod-borne viruses based on antigenic relationships, the student should consult Casals and Reeves.[16]

Mosquito Transmission of the Viral Encephalitides. The year 1933 is outstanding in the developments that affected our knowledge of the American encephalitides and their relation to mosquito transmission. It was in that year that the St. Louis epidemic occurred, followed by Lumsden's report (unpublished until 1958)[52] in which mosquitoes, specifically *Culex pipiens* and *C. p. quinquefasciatus,* were indicated as probable vectors. In this year, also, eastern, western and St. Louis encephalitides were recognized as diseases with separate virus etiologies. (cf. Ferguson[23] for an interesting tabulation of the historical highlights with reference to the American encephalitides and for a bibliography covering the period 1930–51.) Finally, there were the now classical researches of Kelser[45] on mosquito transmission.

Kelser proved that the WEE virus can be transmitted by *Aedes aegypti,* not only from infected guinea pigs to normal guinea pigs, but also to a horse which contracted the disease and died within 5 days after the onset of clinical signs. Blood which was drawn from the horse at the height of the fever and injected into a guinea pig induced the disease, and mosquitoes which fed upon the horse during the period of high temperature and subsequently fed on a normal guinea pig likewise transmitted the disease. The largest percentage of deaths among the guinea pigs bitten by infected mosquitoes occurred on the sixth day following the infective mosquito bite. The mosquitoes were found to be capable of transmitting the disease as early as 6 days and remained infectious for at least 36 days. Kelser pointed out that it is possible that the mosquitoes, when once infected, may remain infectious the rest of their lives as is the case in yellow fever and dengue.

Subsequent years witnessed intensive investigations of mosquitoes, particularly *Aedes* spp., as well as of other arthropods, including *Dermacentor* ticks and conenose bugs. The discovery of Hammon and his co-workers[32] that the viruses of both SLE and WEE occur in nature in *Culex tarsalis* led to the subsequent establishment of the position of that mosquito as the principal vector of the WEE and an important vector of the SLE virus. These viruses have been isolated from a number of species of mosquitoes in nature, including *Aedes dorsalis, Anopheles freeborni, Culex pipiens, Culex restuans* Theobald, *Culex tarsalis, Culiseta melanura,* and *Mansonia perturbans.*[23] A number of additional species, largely *Aedes* and *Culex* but including at least five other genera, have been used with at least some success in transmission, either directly (through the bite of the mosquito) or indirectly (through artificial techniques).

Originally, the normal transmission of viral encephalitides was thought to be man-or-horse to mosquito to man-or-horse. In 1938, following the suggestion of Ten-Broeck[93] that birds may serve as reservoirs, the EEE virus was isolated from pheasants and from the brain of a pigeon in nature. Many birds, including the domestic fowl, prairie chickens, redwing blackbird, magpie, and purple grackle, as well as poultry lice and mites, are now known to harbor a variety of viruses in this group. Birds are now generally considered to be the reservoir, although there is some evidence that would connect certain types of encephalitis with bats,[50] snakes, and perhaps other vertebrates. Mosquito-borne encephalitis, therefore, seems to be an infection of birds, asymptomatic or subclinical except for EEE in pheasant and some other birds, maintained in its reservoir by bird-biting mosquitoes, but pathogenic when transferred to horses or man.

Chamberlain[17,18] has summarized the virus-vector-host relationships of the North American arthropod-borne encephalitides. EEE infection is associated with swamp areas (not necessarily coastal) where the reservoir is found in swamp-dwelling birds. The maintenance cycle is a low-level one and transmission is effected by mosquitoes, like *Culiseta melanura,* which show a distinct preference for avian blood. Mosquito populations need not rise above what is considered a normal level. It is not likely that man or horses will be bitten until the virus infection passes beyond this stage in its epidemiology. When an exceptionally high population of a susceptible mosquito occurs, associated with a general low level of immunity in the bird population, feeding specificity becomes a less important factor. The vertebrate host range is now extended, and man and horses may be included in it. Such outbreaks are self-limiting, fortunately; they cease with the decline of mosquito populations and the development of a high incidence of immunity in the bird populations.

Culex tarsalis serves excellently as both an endemic and epidemic vector of WEE; this mosquito is widely distributed and abundant, feeds freely on man, horses, and birds, is exceptionally susceptible to infection, and transmits with high efficiency. The epidemiologic pattern of WEE is, therefore, somewhat different from that of EEE, but in areas from which *C. tarsalis* is absent, the pattern of WEE becomes much like that of EEE. In the eastern part of its range, SLE occurs essentially as urban epidemics, with peak incidence in the 40- to 70-year age groups and with a relatively high mortality; in the west, epidemics are more often rural, more commonly in the under-10 age group, and with a low mortality.[23,27] Vector relationships may furnish the explanation of this difference: *Culex tarsalis,* the western vector, is rural in its breeding habits, whereas *C. pipiens* and *C. p. quinquefasciatus* are domestic breeders found in urban and suburban situations. Passage of the virus through different vectors might lead to minor strain variations, with no antigenic differentiation, which might account for the differences in host susceptibility and pathogenicity. The WEE and EEE viruses, unlike the SLE virus, do not appear to be susceptible to successful transmission by *C. pipiens* or *C. p. quinquefasciatus.*

Many problems concerned with mosquito transmission, some of them as yet unsolved, involve the ecology of the mosquito, the viruses, the hosts, and the reservoirs. Some of the more pertinent facts are as follows.[17] The mosquito-infecting potential for different hosts will vary considerably; similarly, some mosquitoes will become infected at a much lower concentration of virus in infected hosts than will others. Even when mosquitoes are given a virus meal of high concentration, well above the threshold of ordinary infection, some species prove to be far more susceptible than others. Also, some can transmit the infection much more effectively than others. Successful transmission depends on several factors. For example, the virus must circulate and either accumulate or multiply in the salivary glands; the barrier to transmission in poor or refractory mosquito vectors may reside here, rather than in the gut or elsewhere. Multiplication of the virus in the mosquito has been shown to be as high as a millionfold (SLE in *Culex tarsalis*). The extrinsic incubation period, which is dependent upon the multiplication of the virus to an effective level and its translocation, varies inversely with the temperature, and is also affected by differences in physiology of the mosquito species; it may range from less than a week to about a month.

The overwintering of the virus is still an unsolved problem. The studies of Reeves and co-workers[5,64,65] throw considerable light on the problem; for example, in an unheated cellar WEE virus was shown to remain infective in *Culex tarsalis* for 113 days and SLE in *C. p. quinquefasciatus* for 116 days. Where winters are mild, or where chickens or other suitable hosts are available to relay the virus infection, its maintenance in this fashion is a distinct possibility. At least one virus of the arthropod-borne group (WEE) has been shown to persist in the avian host for as long as 10 months, and that virus has been shown to recirculate in the blood subsequent to the period of active viremia.[65] These facts do not, by any means, invalidate the possibilities that the virus has survived in the avian or other reservoir host or that it has been reintroduced with the advent of the new season.

The problem of viral encephalitides, like that of many other arthropod-borne diseases, needs to be considered from a world-wide standpoint. As Alexander and Murray[2] point out:

A real problem today resides in arthropod-borne encephalitides that are not now seen in the United States but might be imported. For example, in 1956 an illness in an individual, who became sick on arrival in California from Okinawa, was later diagnosed as Japanese B encephalitis, and in 1955 a case of Venezuelan encephalitis was reported in a laboratory worker in Washington, D. C. The public health hazard in such instances is the possibility of mosquitoes becoming infected, permitting survival and propagation of the virus locally. This, plus the possible introduction of infected mosquitoes, points up the need for increased knowledge and surveillance of arthropod-borne viruses by those responsible for the public health.

OTHER MOSQUITO-BORNE VIRUSES

West Nile Infection. This is a denguelike, febrile childhood disease, apparently self-limited, and rarely associated with definite manifestations of encephalitis.[91] It occurs in Egypt, the Sudan, the Belgian Congo, Uganda, Israel, and India. The virus has been isolated from *Culex univittatus* Theobald, which, on epidemiologic and ecologic grounds, seems to be the most probable vector; isolations have also been made from *Culex antennatus* (Becker), and experimental transmission has been obtained by the use of *C. pipiens, C. tritaeniorhynchus,* and *Aedes albopictus* (Skuse).

Rift Valley fever, or enzootic hepatitis, an acute viral disease which affects many animals including mice, sheep, cattle, antelopes, and man, has a wide distribution throughout South Africa; the virus has also been isolated in Kenya and in Japan. In man, the disease is characterized by an acute onset after a short incubation period, fever, prostration, pain in the extremities and joints, abdominal discomfort, and a low leucocyte count in the peripheral blood stream. The mortality rate is low and recovery confers lasting immunity. In lambs mortality may reach 100 per cent, and epizootics may be severe; an estimated 1,000,000 animals were lost in the epizootic of 1955 in South Africa, according to Alexander (cited by Steyn).[89]

Aedes (*Ochlerotatus*) *caballus* (Theobald) is the experimentally determined vector in South Africa. It is of interest to note that the subgenus *Ochlerotatus* is represented in North America by 50 species, including *A. dorsalis, A. nigromaculis, A. sollicitans,* and other common forms. *Aedes caballus* readily bites man and animals in the daytime and is easily spread by automobiles, trains, airplanes, and the transportation of animals. The life history of this mosquito and its relation to Rift Valley fever are discussed by Steyn. The virus has been isolated from wild-caught females of *Aedes demeilloni* Edwards, *A. tarsalis* Newstead, and *Eretmapodites* spp.[26]

Rabbit myxomatosis, also known as "big head" of rabbits, produces lesions in the skin, lymph glands, tunica vaginalis, testicle, spleen, and lungs. The disease runs a rapid course, and death ensues within a week or two. Rabbits are the only known susceptible hosts, but the disease seriously affects only the European wild rabbit, *Oryctilagus,* being mild or asymptomatic in the American *Lepus* and *Sylvilagus.* In 1943 Aragão[3] reported successful transmission of the virus by mosquitoes, *Aedes scapularis* (Rondani) and *A. aegypti.* Other mosquitoes as well as other bloodsucking arthropods have been incriminated in transmission.

The disease has been introduced into Australia in an attempt to combat the problem of the introduced European rabbit. According to Button[14] the mosquitoes chiefly involved as the vectors are *Aedes* spp., *Culex annulirostris* Skuse, and *Anopheles annulipes* Walker. The virus is apparently capable of being transmitted by a wide range of bloodsucking arthropods, including fleas, lice, and conenose bugs.

Fowl pox, an important viral disease of poultry, while spread in various ways, such as contact between diseased and healthy birds, may also be spread, according to Brody,[11] by *Aedes stimulans* (Walker) by intermittent feeding, harboring the virus in or on its body for at least 2 days following an infective meal, and by *Aedes aegypti,* which can definitely transmit the virus more than once during its lifetime. The latter species is able to transmit the disease within one hour after an infective meal and continues to be infective for at least 40 days.

FILARIASIS

Wuchereria Filariasis. Infection with nematode worms belonging to the family Filariidae is known as filariasis. The larval worms of this family are commonly known as microfilarae and occur in the circulatory and lymphatic systems, connective tissue layers, and serous cavities of the vertebrate hosts.

Bancroft's filaria, *Wuchereria bancrofti* (Cobbold), is a widely distributed parasite of man, being indigenous to Polynesia and Melanesia, where advanced elephantiasis is frequently encountered; the disease is found in many tropical and subtropical areas of the globe, such as central Africa, southeast coastal China, and the Far East. In the United States only one endemic area has been known in the past, a small area including Charleston, South Carolina.[25] Puerto Rico is reported to be one of the best-known endemic areas of filariasis in the Western Hemisphere, although the disease is not regarded as a major health problem there.[90] The infection also exists in the northeast coastal portions of South America.

The sheathed microfilariae, first noted by Bancroft in 1876, measures about 300μ in length and from 7.5 to 10μ in diameter (Fig. 67). As observed by Manson in 1877–78, they occur in the peripheral blood, particularly at night. In the daytime most of the microfilariae are concentrated in the pulmonary vessels, the capillaries of the heart, and other visceral organs. This nocturnal periodicity[36] enables night-flying mosquitoes such as *Culex pipiens quinquefasciatus* to suck up the parasites while biting. Manson called attention to this adaptation and believed that mosquitoes served as "nurses" for the filariae, and that when the mosquitoes dropped into water and disintegrated, the organisms were liberated, and infection of human beings resulted from drinking infected water.

Life Cycle. The fully grown, very slender, sexually mature worms, the females reaching a length of 80 to 100 mm and the males about 40 mm,

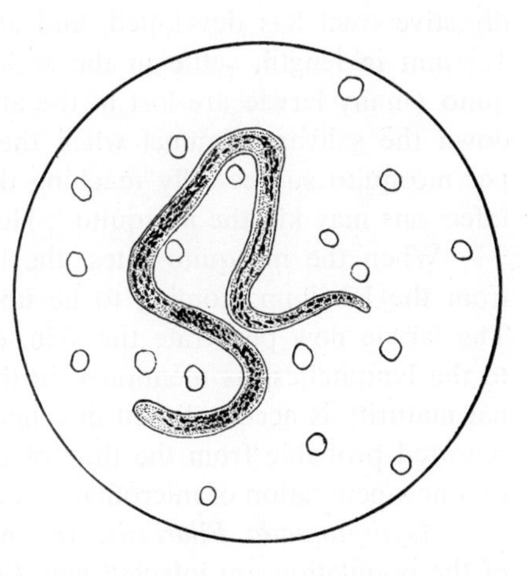

Fig. 67. *Wuchereria bancrofti,* in human blood. × 333.

are often found (postmortem) in tangles in nodular dilations of the distal lymphatics, in lymphocytic varices, and in the glands themselves, or even in the thoracic duct. Here great numbers of minute microfilariae are born, each in a sheath or sac. Although many remain in the lymph, others following a normal circulatory course will reach the peripheral circulation. Brown[12] reports an infection of 23,240 microfilariae per milliliter of blood in a Virgin Islander (except for a slight general glandular enlargement, there were no symptoms referable to this infection). In the so-called classic filariasis, the microfilariae manifest a nocturnal periodicity, i.e., they are present in the peripheral blood of infected persons principally during the hours from 8 P.M. to 2 A.M. There is, however, a nonperiodic form of *bancrofti* in the South Pacific area. In either instance the microfilaries are available to appropriate species of mosquitoes, i.e., anthropophilous night feeders in the case of "filaria nocturna," and day biters in the case of "filaria diurna." Many species of mosquitoes belonging to four common genera, *Culex, Aedes, Mansonia*, and *Anopheles*, have been incriminated as vectors, some species being more readily infective than others. The more numerous the individual mosquitoes in a large population of infected human beings, the more dangerous is the situation.

It must be remembered that this is an infection referred to earlier in which the pathogen does not multiply within the body of the vector; the mosquito must imbibe one microfilaria from the blood of an infected person for every filarial worm transmitted to a new victim. Having successfully reached the stomach of the mosquito, the tiny worm now loses its saclike sheath and in a matter of hours forces its way through the stomach wall and works its way through the thoracic muscle, becoming somewhat "sausage-shaped" by the fourth or fifth day.

There are two molts, and by the end of the twelfth to fourteenth day the digestive tract has developed, and at least some infective larvae, now about 1.5 mm in length, settle in the region of the head and labium of the mosquito (many larvae are lost in the abdomen) awaiting an opportunity to slip down the salivary channel when the mosquito bites. The number of larvae per mosquito successfully reaching this stage is evidently quite small (heavy infections may kill the mosquito); Hu and Yen[39] report an average of 3.9.

When the mosquito bites, the larvae slip down the labium and escape from the labellum, coming to lie upon the warm skin of the person bitten. The larvae now penetrate the skin, enter the lymph stream, and are carried to the lymphatics, as mentioned in the beginning, where development to sexual maturity is accomplished in a matter of months; from 12 to 18 months is reported probable from the time of infection to the maturity and appearance of a new generation of microfilariae in the peripheral blood.

Asymptomatic Filariasis. In endemic areas a considerable percentage of the population are infected with the parasite, as shown by blood smear examination: thus Murray[61] reported 19.1 per cent positive for *microfilaria* in a survey of 5144 Samoans, and Kessel[46] reports that 30 per cent of the population of Tahiti harbor microfilariae, whereas only 20 per cent show symptoms or signs of acute filariasis, and 5 to 10 per cent exhibit some degree of elephantiasis. Brown[12] states that on physical examination the infected person, though unaware of the infection, may exhibit a general glandular enlargement especially of the inguinal lymph glands.

Inflammatory Filariasis. The inflammatory, or acute phase, is accompanied by a fever of 101° to 104° F, often with chills, more or less severe toxemia, and swollen lymphatics. Recurrent attacks of inflammatory filariasis may occur many months after exposure to infection. Brown[12] suggests that these inflammatory reactions "may be an allergic phenomenon due to a sensitivity to the products of the worms or to a superimposed bacterial infection, usually streptococci."

Obstructive Filariasis (Elephantiasis). The obstructive types of filariasis (grossly enlarged scrotum, vulvae, breasts, or legs) usually follow years after the original long exposure to mosquito bites in endemic areas and are the exception rather than the rule. Microfilariae are frequently absent from the blood, although Murray[61] states that he found that, in American Samoa, persons afflicted with elephantiasis were much more likely to have microfilariae than those without this condition.

Brug's filaria, Wuchereria malayi Brug, the causal organism of *filariasis malayi* is very similar to that of Bancroft's filariasis. It occurs in India, Ceylon, Thailand, the East Indies, the Philippines, and New Guinea. In some areas such as portions of coastal China and the islands of the East Indies, the two *Wuchereria* infections overlap; the behavior of the worms in the mosquito vector, as well as in man, and the effects on the human host are very similar. *Wuchereria malayi,* which is essentially nocturnal in periodicity, differs from *W. bancrofti* only in minor details. The morphology of the sheathed microfilariae differs chiefly in the cephalic space, which is twice as long as broad, and the posterior extremity of the worm has a slight bulb at the tip with two minute terminal nuclei. While there is little difference in the causal organisms, it is important to note that the vectors involved in their transmission are different.

Mosquito Species Involved. Throughout the filarial belt of the world (between 30° N and 32° S latitude) some 60 species of mosquitoes belonging to half a dozen genera have been implicated in greater or lesser degree as vectors of the infection. *Culex pipiens quinquefasciatus,* the chief vector in India and a widely distributed tropical and subtropical species, heads practically all lists of vectors; it is, however, significant that in the Samoan area experimental evidence disclosed that only 29 per cent of *C. p. quinquefasciatus* could be infected from a single blood meal, whereas 90 per cent of *Aedes polynesiansis* Marks[56,71] become infected; also it is reported that only 1 per cent of the former developed microfilariae to the infective stage in contrast to 18 per cent in the *Aedes* species. A similar subordinate role is occupied by *C. p. quinquefasciatus* in other parts of the Pacific (Rosen[68]) and likewise in Africa south of the Sahara Desert, where, according to Hawking,[33] *Anopheles gambiae* and *A. funestus* Giles are the chief vectors. The possibility is mentioned by both Hawking and Rosen that different strains of either mosquito or the filaria may be involved. Successful transmission by *C. p quinquefasciatus* seems to involve the periodic, rather than the nonperiodic, form of the parasite.

Aedes polynesiensis Marks is the chief vector over widespread areas in Polynesia; wherever it coexists with nonperiodic filaria, it is the chief or sole vector (cf. Jachowski[44]). In several island groups of the South Pacific (among them Solomon, New Hebrides, Fiji, and Samoa) a primary vector is *Anopheles farauti* Laveran which often becomes tremendously infected and dies as a result; as many as 96 eight- to ten-day-old larvae have been observed (Reiber). Only 11 per cent of the total number of infected mosquitoes survived long enough to transmit larvae. Under natural conditions this percentage would no doubt be still lower.

In the China area *Anopheles hyrcanus sinensis* Wiedemann and *Culex pipiens pallens* Coquillett are proven vectors, as they are also in Japan together with *Aedes togoi* (Theobald).

In testing the susceptibility of North American species of mosquitoes to *Wuchereria bancrofti* (Bora Bora strain) Eyles and Most[22] found that development to advanced or infective stage occurred in the following species: *Culex p. pipiens, C. p. quinquefasciatus, C. erraticus* (Dyar and Knab), *C. salinarius* Coquillett, *Anopheles walkeri* Theobald, *A. punctipennis, Aedes triseriatus* (Say), *A. aegypti, Aedes atropalpus* (Coquillett), and *Mansonia perturbans* (Walker). In the following species development did not proceed beyond the first larval stage: *Anopheles quadrimaculatus, Anopheles freeborni, Aedes tormentor* Dyar and Knab, and *Psorophora ferox* Humboldt.

With only three specimens of *Culex tarsalis* tested, Scott, Richards, and Seaman[81] found that one of these developed infective stages of *W. bancrofti* in the thorax, head, and proboscis. The principal vector mosquitoes of *W. malayi* are members of the *Mansonia* group in which the wrigglers attach themselves to submerged aquatic plants such as *Pistia* and *Eichornia,* as described in the preceding chapter. *Mansonia* (*Mansonoides*) *annulifera* Theobald is considered to be the principal vector, although several other related species (e.g., *M. uniformis* Theobald in India and *M. longipalpis* Wulp in Malaya) are proven vectors. Certain anophelines, e.g., *Anopheles sinensis* Wiedemann, are implicated.

Reservoir Control. The discovery of a relatively safe and orally administrable drug, diethylcarbamazine,[80] together with vector control, has reduced the incidence of filarial infection in areas where intensive campaigns have been carried out. Kessel[46] reports that in Tahiti the use of diethylcarbamazine, in a four-year period, reduced acute filariasis by 84 per cent; the effects on the chronic form, because of the length of time involved in its development, were hard to judge, but no cases were observed. The effect of the drug on the adult worm has not been determined. Methods of vector control vary, being different for such mosquitoes as *Culex quinquefasciatus* and *Aedes polynesiensis;* this illustrates the importance of determining what species are involved as important vectors.

Heartworm of Dogs. *Dirofilaria immitis* (Leidy), a cosmopolitan species, occurs in dogs and occasionally cats, as well as in various wild carnivores. The adult worms invade the heart (right ventricle) and pulmonary artery of the host, where they often form tangled knots, and may cause death as the result of embolism, asphyxia, and dilation of the heart. This parasite has become widely distributed in the United States. *Culex pipiens* and *Aedes* *aegypti,* as well as a number of other species of mosquitoes, are known to be vectors. The problem of heartworm in dogs has been confused by reported transmission by fleas, but Newton and Wright have shown that a species belonging to a different genus, *Dipetalonema,* is involved in flea transmission (see Chapter 18).

Other Filarial Worms. Among other species belonging to the family Filariidae are *Mansonella ozzardi* (Manson) and *Acanthocheilonema perstans* (Manson), transmitted by *Culcicoides* (see Chapter 9); *Loa loa* (Cobbold) transmitted by *Chrysops* (see Chapter 13); *Onchocera volvulus* Leuckart, transmitted by black flies (see Chapter 9).

REFERENCES

1. Aitken, Thomas H. G., 1958. "Entomological aspects of the Trinidad virus research program," *Proc. 10th Internat. Congr. Entomology,* **3:**573–86.

2. Alexander, E. Russell, and Murray, Walter A., 1958. "Arthropod-borne encephalitis in 1956," U. S. Public Health Service, *Pub. Health Rep.,* **73:**329–39.

3. Aragão, H. B., 1943. "O virus do mixoma coelho do mato (Sylvilagus), sua transmissão pelos *Aedes scapularis* e *aegypti," Mem. Inst. Oswaldo Cruz,* **38:**93–99.

4. Bass, C. C., and Johns, F. M., 1912. "The cultivation of malaria plasmodia *in vitro," J. Exper. Med.,* **16:**567–79.

5. Bellamy, R. E.; Reeves, W. C.; and Scrivani, R. P.; 1958. "Relationships of mosquito vectors to winter survival of encephalitis virus. II. Under experimental conditions," *Am. J. Hyg.,* **67:**90–100.

6. Bennett, Byron L.; Baker, Fred C.; and Sellards, Andrew W.; 1938. "The behavior of the virus of yellow fever in the mosquito, *Aedes triseriatus," Science,* **88:**410–11.

7. Boyd, Mark F., 1941. "An historical sketch of the prevalence of malaria in North America," *Am. J. Trop. Med.,* **21:**223–44.

8. Boyd, Mark F., 1950. *Malariology.* Philadelphia: W. B. Saunders Co. 2 vols. 1643 pp.

9. Boyd, M. F., and Kitchen, S. F., 1936. "The comparative susceptibility of *Anopheles quadrimaculatus* and *Anopheles punctipennis* to *Plasmodium vivax* and *Plasmodium falciparum," Am. J. Trop. Med.,* **16:**67–71.

10. Breland, Osmond P., 1957. "Some factors that might influence the reintroduction of yellow fever into the United States," *Texas J. Sc.,* **9:**262–66.

11. Brody, Arthur L., 1936. *The Transmission of Fowl Pox.* Ithaca: Cornell Univ. Agric. Exp. Sta., Memoir no. 195. 37 pp.

12. Brown, H. W., 1945. "Current problems in filariasis," *Am. J. Pub. Health,* **35:**607–13.

13. Burke, A. W., 1937. "An epidemic of jungle yellow fever on the Planalto of Matto Grosso, Brazil," *Am. J. Trop. Med.,* **17:**313–34.

14. Button, J. A., 1952. "The insect vector in relation to myxomatosis in Australia," *J. Dept. Agric. W. Australia,* (3) **1:**819–21, 823, 825, 827–29.

15. Carter, Henry Rose, 1931. *Yellow Fever—an Epidemiological and Historical Study of its Place and Origin.* Baltimore: Williams and Wilkins Co. xii + 308 pp.

16. Casals, Jorki, and Reeves, William C., 1959. *Arthropod-Borne Animal Viruses,* in Rivers, Thomas M., and Horsfall, Frank L., *Viral and Rickettsial Infections of Man.* Philadelphia: J. B. Lippincott Co. pp. 269–85.

17. Chamberlain, Roy W., 1958. "Vector relationships of arthropod-borne encephalitis in North America," U. S. Public Health Service, *Pub. Health* Rep., **73:**377–79.

18. Chamberlain, Roy W., 1958. "Virus-vector-host relationships of the American arthropod-borne encephalitides," *Proc. 10th Internat. Congr. Entomology,* **3:**567–72.

19. Chandler, Asa C., and Rice, Lee, 1923. "Observations on the etiology of dengue fever," *Am. J. Trop. Med.,* **3:**233–62.

20. Clark, H. C., and Dunn, L. H., 1931. "Experimental efforts to transmit monkey malaria to man," *Am. J. Trop. Med.,* **11:**1–10.

21. Davis, Nelson C., 1932. "Effect of various temperatures in modifying extrinsic incubation period of yellow fever virus in *Aedes aegypti,*" *Am. J. Hyg.,* **16:**163–76.

22. Eyles, Don E., and Most, Harry, 1947. "Infectivity of Pacific island *Wuchereria bancrofti* to mosquitoes of the United States," *Am. J. Trop. Med.,* **27:**211–20.

23. Ferguson, Frederick F., 1954. *Biological Factors in the Transmission of American Arthropod-Borne Virus Encephalitis.* Washington: *Pub. Health Monograph* no. 23. 37 pp.

24. Fosdick, Raymond B., 1937. *The Rockefeller Foundation: A Review for 1936.* pp. 13–17.

25. Francis, Edward, 1919. *Filariasis in Southern United States.* U. S. Public Health Service, *Hygienic Lab. Bull.,* no. 117. 34 pp., 9 plates.

26. Foote, Richard H., and Cook, David R., 1959. *Mosquitoes of Medical Importance.* U. S. Dept. Agric., Agric. Handbook no. 152. 158 pp.

27. Giddings, Luther E.; Smith, Lee W.; Beaver, Margaret E. N.; and Sooter, Clarence A.; 1959. "St. Louis encephalitis outbreak during 1956 in Grand Junction, Colorado," U. S. Public Health Service, *Pub. Health Rep.* **74:**372–75.

28. Golgi, C., 1886. "Sulla infezione malarica," *Arch. Sc. Med.,* **10:**110.

29. Graham, H., 1902. "The dengue: a study of its pathology and mode of propagation," *Med. Rec.,* **61:**204–07.

30. Grassi, B.; Bignami, A.; and Bastianelli, G.; 1899. "Ciclo evolutivo delle semilune nell' *Anopheles claviger* ed altri studi sulla malaria dall' ottobre 1898 al maggio 1899," *Atti Soc. Studi d. Malaria,* **1:**14–27. (Cited by Ross, 1910.)

31. Hackett, L. W., 1937. *Malaria in Europe: An Ecological Study.* London: Oxford Univ. Press. Humphrey Milford. xvi + 336 pp.

32. Hammon, W. M.; Reeves, W. C.; Brookman, B.; Izumi, E. M.; and Gjullin, C.; 1941. "Isolation of the viruses of western equine and St. Louis encephalitis from *Culex tarsalis* mosquitoes," *Science,* **94:**328–30.

33. Hawking, D. M., 1957. "The distribution of bancroftian filariasis in Africa," *World Health Organ. Bull.,* **16:**581–92.

34. Herman, Carlton M., 1944. "The blood protozoa of North American birds," *Bird Banding,* **15:**89–112.

35. Herms, W. B., and Gray, H. F., 1944. *Mosquito Control: Practical Methods for Abatement of Disease Vectors,* 2nd ed. New York: The Commonwealth Fund. viii + 419 pp.

36. Hinman, E. Harold, 1936. "Attempted reversal of filarial periodicity in *Dirofilaria immitis," Proc. Soc. Exper. Biol. & Med.,* **33:**524–27.

37. Hindle, Edward, 1914. *Flies in Relation to Disease—Bloodsucking Flies.* London: Cambridge Univ. Press. xv + 398 pp.

38. Horsfall, William R., 1955. *Mosquitoes: Their Behavior and Relation to Disease.* New York: The Ronald Press. 723 pp.

39. Hu, Stephen M. K., and Yen, Chia-Hsien, 1933. "Studies on the susceptibility of *Culex pipiens* Linn. var *pallens* Coq. to experimental infections with *Wuchereria bancrofti* Cobbold in Shanghai area," *Chinese M. J.,* **47:**1359–66.

40. Huff, Clay G., *et al.,* 1948. "Symposium on exoerythrocytic forms of malaria parasites, Parts I–VI," *J. Parasitol.,* **34:**261–320.

41. Huff, Clay G., 1948. "Exoerythrocytic stages of malarial parasites," *Am. J. Trop. Med.,* **28:**527–31.

42. Huff, Clay G., 1934. "Comparative studies on susceptible and insusceptible *Culex pipiens* in relation to infections with *Plasmodium cathemerium* and *P. relictum," Am. J. Hyg.,* **19:**123–47.

43. Hunter, George W., 3rd.; Weller, Thomas H.; and Jahnes, William G., Jr.; 1946. "An outline for teaching mosquito stomach and salivary gland dissection," *Am. J. Trop. Med.,* **26:**221–28.

44. Jachowski, Leo A., 1954. "Filariasis in American Samoa. V. Bionomics of the principal vector, *Aedes polynesiensis* Marks," *Am. J. Hyg.,* **60:**186–203.

45. Kelser, R. A., 1933. "Mosquitoes as vectors of the virus of equine encephalomyelitis," *J. Am. Vet. M. A.,* n.s. **35:**767–71.

46. Kessel, John F., 1957. "An effective programme for the control of filariasis in Tahiti," *World Health Organ. Bull.,* **16:**609–32.

47. King, A. F. A., 1883. "Insects and disease, mosquitoes and malaria," *Pop. Sci. Monthly,* **23:**644–58.

48. King, W. V., 1917. "The effect of cold upon malaria parasites in the mosquito host," *J. Exper. Med.,* **25:**495–98.

49. Knowles, R., and Basu, B. C., 1943. "Laboratory studies on the infectivity of *Anopheles stephensi," J. Malaria Inst. India,* **5:**1–30.

50. LaMotte, Lewis C., Jr., 1958. "Japanese B encephalitis in bats during simulated hibernation," *Am. J. Hyg.,* **67:**101–08.

51. Levaditi, C., 1951. "La phase exo-érythrocytaire des hématozoaires du paludisme," *Rev. Paludisme & Med. Trop.,* **9:**121–38.

52. Lumsden, L. L., 1958. "St. Louis encephalitis in 1933," U. S. Public Health Service, *Pub. Health Rep.,* **73:**340–53.

53. MacCallum, W. C., 1898. "On the haematozoan infections of birds," *J. Exper. Med.,* **3:**117–36.

54. MacDonald, G., 1957. *The Epidemiology and Control of Malaria.* London: Oxford University Press. 201 pp.

55. Manson, Patrick, 1909. *Tropical Diseases.* London: Cassel and Company, xx + 876 pp.

56. Marks, E. N., 1951. "The vector of filariasis in Polynesia: a change in nomenclature," *Ann. Trop. Med. & Parasitol.,* **45:**137–40.

57. Meyer, K. F.; Haring, C. M.; and Howitt, B.; 1931. "Newer knowledge of the neurotropic virus infections of the horse," *J. Am. Vet. M. A.,* n.s., **32:**376–89.

58. Milam, D. F., and Kusch, Ernest, 1938. "Observations on *Plasmodium knowlesi* malaria in general paresis," *South. M. J.,* **31:**947–49.

59. Mitzmain, M. B., 1916. "An attempt to determine the number of persons one mosquito can infect with malaria," U. S. Public Health Service, *Pub. Health Rep.,* **31:**2325–35.

60. Mitzmain, M. B., 1916. *Is Mosquito or Man the Winter Carrier of Malaria Organism?* Washington, D. C.: Govt. Print. Office, in Pub. Health Bull., no. 84. 32 pp.

61. Murray, William D., 1948. "Filariasis studies in American Samoa," *Nav. Med. Bull.,* **48:**327–41.

62. Reed, A. C., 1937. "Ultimate prognosis of hookworm disease, malaria, and amebiasis," *Proc. 27th Annual Meeting Medical Section of American Life Convention,* pp. 176–206.

63. Reed, Walter; Carroll, James; Agramonte, A.; and Lazear, Jesse W.; 1900. "The etiology of yellow fever—a preliminary note," *Proc. 28th Annual Meeting, Amer. Public Health Assn.,* Indianapolis, Oct. 22–26.

64. Reeves, W. C.; Bellamy, R. E.; and Scrivani, R. P.; 1958. "Relationships of mosquito vectors to winter survival of encephalitis viruses. I. Under natural conditions," *Am. J. Hyg.,* **67:**78–89.

65. Reeves, W. C.; Hutson, G. A.; Bellamy, R. E.; and Scrivani, R. P.; 1958. "Chronic latent infections of birds with western equine encephalomyelitis," *Proc. Soc. Exper. Biol. & Med.,* **97:**733–36.

66. Rodaniche, Enid de, and Galindo, Pedro, 1957. "Isolation of yellow fever virus from *Haemagogus mesodentatus, H. equinus,* and *Sabethes chloropterus,* captured in Guatemala in 1956," *Am. J. Trop. Med. & Hyg.,* **6:**232–37.

67. Rodhain, J., 1948. "Susceptibility of the chimpanzee to *P. malariae* of human origin," *Am. J. Trop. Med.,* **28:**629–31.

68. Rosen, Leon, 1955. "Observations on the epidemiology of human filariasis in French Oceanea," *Am. J. Hyg.,* **61:**219–48.

69. Rosen, Leon, 1958. "Observations on the epidemiology of dengue in Panama," *Am. J. Hyg.,* **68:**45–58 .

70. Rosen, Leon, 1958. "Experimental infection of New World monkeys with dengue and yellow fever viruses," *Am. J. Trop. Med. & Hyg.,* **7:**406–10.

71. Rosen, Leon; Rozeboom, Lloyd E.; Sweet, Benjamin H.; and Sabin, Albert B.; 1954. "The transmission of dengue by *Aedes polynesiensis* Marks," *Am. J. Trop. Med. & Hyg.,* **3:**878–82.

72. Ross, R., 1897. "Observations on a condition necessary to the transformation of the malaria crescent," *Brit. M. J.,* **1:**251; also, "On some peculiar pigmented cells found in two mosquitoes fed on malarial blood," *ibid.,* **2:**1786–88.

73. Ross, R., 1910. *The Prevention of Malaria.* New York: E. P. Dutton & Co., xx + 669 pp.

74. Rozeboom, Lloyd E., and McLean, D. M., 1956. "Transmission of the virus of Murray Valley encephalitis by *Culex tarsalis* Coquillett, *Aedes polynesiensis* Marks, and *A. pseudoscutellaris* Theobald," *Am. J. Hyg.,* **63:**136–39.

75. Russell, Paul F., 1958. "Malaria in the world today," *Amer. J. Pub. Health,* **47:**414–20.

76. Russell, Paul F., 1959. "Insects and the epidemiology of malaria," *Ann. Rev. Entomol.,* **4:**415–34.

77. Russell, Paul F.; Rozeboom, Lloyd E.; and Stone, Alan; 1943. *Keys to the Anopheline Mosquitoes of the World with Notes on their Identification, Distribution, Biology, and Relation to Malaria.* Philadelphia: Amer. Entomol. Soc. 152 pp.

78. Russell, P. F.; West, L. S.; and Manwell, R. D.; 1946. *Practical Malariology.* Philadelphia: W. B. Saunders Co. 684 pp.

79. Sabin, Albert B., 1952. "Research on dengue during World War II," *Am. J. Trop. Med. & Hyg.,* **1:**30–50.

80. Santiago-Stevenson, D.; Oliver-Gonzales, J.; and Hewitt, R. I.; 1947. "Treatment of filariasis bancrofti with 1-diethylcarbamyl-4-methylpiperazine hydrochloride (Hetrazan)," *J.A.M.A.,* **135:**708–12.

81. Scott, O. K.; Richards, C. S.; and Seaman, E. A.; 1945. "Experimental infection of Southern California mosquitoes with *Wuchereria bancrofti,*" *J. Parasitol.,* **31:**195–97.

82. Simmons, J. S.; St. John, Joe H.; and Reynolds, F. H. K.; 1931. *Experimental Studies of Dengue.* Philippine Bur. Sc., Monograph no. 29. 489 pp. (3 plates).

83. Soper, Fred L., 1955. "Yellow fever conference," *Am. J. Trop. Med. & Hyg.,* **4:**571–661.

84. Soper, Fred L., 1958. "The 1957 status of yellow fever in the Americas," *Mosq. News,* **18:**203–16.

85. Soper, Fred L., 1958. "More about malaria eradication," *Mosq. News,* **18:**53–58.

86. Soper, Fred L.; Penna, Cardosa E.; Serafim, J., Jr.; Frobisher, M., Jr.; and Pinheiro, J.; 1933. "Yellow fever without *Aëdes aegypti:* Study of a rural epidemic in the Valle do Chanaan, Espírito Santo, Brazil, 1932," *Am. J. Hyg.,* **18:**555–87.

87. Soper, Fred L., and Wilson, D. Bruce, 1943. *Anopheles gambiae in Brazil 1930 to 1940.* New York: The Rockefeller Foundation, xviii + 262 pp.

88. Soper, Fred L.; Wilson, D. Bruce; Lima, Servulo; Antunes, Waldemar Sá; 1943. *The Organization of Permanent Nation-wide Anti-Aedes aegypti Measures in Brazil.* New York: The Rockefeller Foundation. xiii + 137 pp.

89. Steyn, J. J., 1958. "The South African vector of Rift Valley fever," *Proc. 10th Internat. Cong. Entomology,* **3:**629–32.

90. Tampi, M. K., 1931. "A study of filariasis in Porto Rico," *Porto Rico J. Pub. Health & Trop. Med.,* **6:**435–41.

91. Taylor, R. M.; Work, T. H.; Hurlbut, H. S.; Rizk, Farag; 1956. "A study of the ecology of West Nile virus in Egypt," *Am. J. Trop. Med. & Hyg.*, **5**:579–620.

92. Taylor, R. M., and Theiler, Max, 1948. "The epidemiology of yellow fever," *Proc. 4th Internat. Cong. Trop. Med. & Malaria,* Washington, D. C. (Abstracts).

93. Ten-Broeck, C., 1938. "Birds as possible carriers of the virus of equine encephalomyelitis," *Arch. Path.*, **25**:759.

94. Wilcox, Aimée, 1942. *Manual for the Microscopical Diagnosis of Malaria in Man.* Washington, D. C.: U. S. Public Health Service, in Nat. Inst. Health Bull., no. 180. ix + 39 pp. (16 plates).

Chapter 12

MOSQUITO ABATEMENT

Historical. Stage[37] has reviewed very concisely the development of mosquito abatement programs, methods, and materials. The following account is drawn largely from his discussion.

Ancient Greeks and Romans believed there was some etiologic connection between intermittent fevers and swamps, hence the use of *drainage methods* in Greece and especially Rome to overcome the "poisoning effects" of stagnant water. Lancisi, the greatest Italian physician of his time, published a treatise on swamp fevers in 1717, according to Russell, in which he suggests that since malaria disappeared after drainage, the poison was probably transmitted by mosquitoes which also came from the swamps.

The use of larvicides dates back to about 1793 when oil (probably whale oil) was used in Philadelphia on rain barrels to kill mosquito larvae. The general application of oil as a mosquito larvicide was delayed a century, however. L. O. Howard, in 1892, and Ronald Ross, in 1900, recommended the use of kerosene and paraffin on mosquito-infested waters. By 1900 several communities had adopted this method of destruction of mosquito larvae.

Howard's first public address on mosquito abatement, delivered in New Jersey in May, 1901, marked the beginning of a wide-scale concerted effort against mosquitoes in the United States. John B. Smith in New Jersey had already started a program which, under the subsequent direction of T. J. Headlee, was to culminate in a monumental piece of research in the control of salt-marsh mosquitoes. By 1912 the organization of mosquito abatement districts was under way, and managers had begun to emphasize the need for effective larvicides which could be used safely where fish, plants, and warm-blooded animals were concerned.

Several larvicides were tested during the earlier years of the twentieth century, but it was the discovery by M. A. Barker and T. Haynes, in 1921, that Paris green could be used effectively and economically against *Anopheles,* that revolutionized malaria control. In 1923 W. V. King, and G. H. Bradley tested the application of Paris green by airplane. Within a few years *Anopheles* control by Paris green had become standard procedure, and it remained so until the advent of DDT.

Another advance in mosquito control came in 1930 when the biochemist, J. M. Ginsburg, published a report on the use of pyrethrum–oil emulsion as a larvicide. This material has remained to the present time the only safe insecticide for use on fishponds and ornamental pools.

During World War II, the need for mosquito repellents, larvicides, and adulticides became critical. At the U.S.D.A. Orlando, Florida, laboratory, more than 6000 chemicals were evaluated between 1942 and 1945. DDT emerged as the chemical in wide use in early postwar days. The first sample had been released through the Surgeon General's office in August, 1942, and had been tested the following October. The use of DDT brought a new concept to medical entomology—control over a prolonged period of time from a single application (residual effect) and through the application of a relatively small amount of insecticide.

Subsequent research has been directed toward the discovery of insecticides still more practical than DDT, of insecticides that would replace DDT when resistance to that chemical is encountered, and toward better methods of application. In some cases, as in pastures where the problem of contamination exists, it has become necessary to resort to a nonresidual chemical such as parathion. An important step in the development of better methods of application dates back to 1940 when W. N. Sullivan, L. D. Goodhue, and J. H. Fales published their first report on a new method for dispersing insecticides in air. The development by Goodhue of the aerosol bomb proved to be a revolutionary concept in the field of insecticide dispersal, particularly when DDT became available for this purpose.

In respect to ecologic control, it should be noted that in many areas mosquito breeding has shifted largely from natural areas to artificial ones attributable to current water resources development and manifested through irrigated agriculture, industrial liquid wastes, and community liquid wastes. In this regard, natural sources of mosquitoes, other than those associated with snow melt in mountainous areas, are becoming largely neutralized through reclamation and land development. Thus, mosquito problems are frequently created as a result of insufficient provision for their prevention.

Thousands of repellents have been tested. During World War II three of these, dimethyl phthalate, ethyl hexanediol (Rutgers 612), and Indalone (*n*-butyl mesityl oxide oxalate), or a combination of these, known as 6-2-2, became standard. In 1958 a much more effective repellent, diethyltoluamide, came into use.

ORGANIZATION AND PERSONNEL

Organization for Abatement Work. Before actual abatement work is undertaken, it must be well planned and organized.[18] There must be an adequate preliminary survey. The services of an experienced and practical mosquito-abatement expert should be secured to make the survey. The expenses for the survey may be defrayed from funds raised by public subscription or by any other means.

The preliminary report should include information and recommendations on the following matters:

1. The boundaries of the area which should be included within the project.
2. The population, area, and assessed valuation of the proposed district.
3. The location and areas of the principal breeding situations, such as marshes, etc.
4. Tentative suggestions as to the best method of control for each principal breeding area.
5. The amount and types of domestic breeding, and measures for abatement.
6. The particular species of mosquitoes involved, with a brief discussion of their breeding habits and behavior.
7. The probable organization that will be required, including personnel and equipment.
8. Detailed preliminary estimates of cost, both for the permanent work (including capital outlays) and for regular maintenance. With these should be submitted comparative costs for currently operating districts of similar size and condition.
9. The economic losses caused by mosquitoes in the proposed district, and the estimated economic savings which should result from adequate mosquito abatement.
10. Where a mosquito-borne disease is involved, statistical material of epidemiologic importance should be included.

Personnel. The general supervision of organized mosquito control work, particularly as to policies and finance, is usually in the hands of a board or commission appointed in various ways in different states. The proponents of the undertaking should make the proper representations to the appointing power or powers, so that only citizens of outstanding character and ability are chosen. It is desirable that the members of the board or commission serve without compensation, except that expenses incurred in the performance of duty be defrayed. In making selections it is well to include any combination of the following: a public-minded attorney, a respected educator, an outstanding physician, an able sanitary or civil engineer, a competent agriculturist, and a successful businessman—all should have a deserved reputation for unselfish public service.

The most important duty of the board or commission is the selection of the executive officer, who for the larger districts should have at least the following qualifications: (1) agreeable personality and honesty; (2) successful experience in mosquito abatement work; (3) administrative ability; (4) training in medical entomology and sanitary engineering. For very small districts this officer may well be of the working-foreman type.

A group of responsible citizens whose duty it is to administer the expenditure of considerable sums of local tax money for mosquito control is not likely to appoint as manager or executive officer a man who is simply brimful of so-called personality on the assumption that he will make a good "public relations" man. A good personality is an important asset, but the tax-paying public is particularly concerned with the man's ability to "deliver the goods." Thorough familiarity with the goods, in this case mosquito control, is essential to good public relations.[17] The manager of a mosquito control district is the key man to the success of an effective program; therefore careful selection is of considerable importance.

In large districts it is necessary to subdivide the force into divisions which can be handled by a responsible *foreman* or *inspector* and a staff of operators. The foreman should be a full-time employee, active, energetic, interested in his work, and able to supervise his men in all sorts of mosquito control operations. As he is in immediate contact with the public, he must have a good personality and must be able to get along with people. He will require much "backbone," plus self-restraint and patience. He must be physically equal to sustained activity in the field, for the work is frequently arduous. The regular operators should be carefully selected and kept on a year-round basis, with temporary additions during the peak of the breeding season.

Adequate office facilities must be provided, inclusive of clerical and telephone service, for public contact and business purposes. Detailed maps of the district must be available, a reporting system, and a bookkeeping system in conformance with legal requirements must be developed. The office should maintain a skillful and continuous program of publicity and public education.

Training of Personnel and Education of the Public. In order to secure a high level of performance in mosquito control operations, the administrative and operational staff of a mosquito abatement district must be properly trained in control techniques. Mosquito control involves highly technical skills and complicated procedures which unless correctly administered may constitute a public health hazard and in agricultural areas may prove injurious to agriculture. Also, in order to secure full cooperation of the public, there must be a program of public education. One or more members of the staff should be trained to carry this out; in fact, the nature of mosquito control is such that all members of the staff, and operators as well, are in constant contact with the public while on duty; hence, all have a measure of responsibility in this regard; even a minor "slip-up" may cause a "breakdown" in public relations.

Public health agencies in various states maintain mosquito control training programs designed to provide the operational personnel with the fundamentals of mosquito control. Training teams should include both entomologic and operational instructors who have had field experience and top training, since many of those receiving instruction can be expected to have had experience themselves. Instruction should include lectures, laboratory work, and field demonstrations in the use of insecticides and equipment. Experienced operators can profit greatly by occasional refresher courses.

Mosquito Surveys. The simplest form of mosquito survey on which policy and action can be based has as its minimum objective the accurate *determination of all species* of mosquitoes present in a given locality, along with an estimate of their relative *abundance,* a mapping of their *distribution,* and a designation of their respective *breeding places.* The survey will delimit the boundaries of the area which should be included within the program; it should ascertain the population and assessed valuation of the area; it should specify in general the best method of control for the principal breeding areas and the probable organization that will be required (personnel and equipment); it should furnish estimates of cost both for permanent control work and regular maintenance.

Surveys must be done intelligently (i.e., by qualified persons) and with adequate means; they are intended to guide policy and action, usually involving considerable sums of public money. Adequate maps are required to show topographic details. Surveys in greater detail should secure the following information concerning the area under consideration: (1) *meteorologic conditions* (by the month), rainfall, humidity, temperature, winds, etc.; (2) *topography,* soil, vegetation, drainage, water courses, ponds, lakes, springs, swamps, salt marshes, ditches, etc.; (3) *agricultural crops,* methods of farming, major crops, irrigation practices, rice culture, etc.; (4) additional specific epidemiologic information with regard to encephalitis, malaria, and other mosquito-borne infections, if present, such as sporozoite rate and oocyst rate in dissected anopheline mosquitoes; numerical prevalence of different species of adult anophelines in houses, privies, pig pens, barns, etc.; spleen rate and parasite index in blood; malaria morbidity, incidence, etc.; presence of arthropod-borne encephalitis calls for additional technical details (see Chapter 11).

CONTROL THROUGH MODIFICATION OF THE LARVAL HABITAT

Essentials of Mosquito Abatement. In view of the fact that no mosquito ever came into existence without water in which its larval stages were completed, and that a very small quantity may serve the purpose, the control of all collections of suitable water available to mosquitoes is a matter of basic importance. The study of water management is highly important. The objective of mosquito abatement operations is the elimination of mosquito production. Usually this means elimination at their source and while they are in the larval stage. It is much simpler to treat such restricted water areas than to await the migration of the adults over large tracts of agricultural and residential lands where their control is more uncertain and more complicated. The abatement method must fit the offending species of mosquito. Marsh drainage or the usual larvicidal treatments would be ineffective in the control of tree-hole species such as *Aedes sierrensis* (Ludlow) where specialized treatment is required.

Nothing can take the place of regular and detailed inspection to locate mosquito larvae. By no other means can the operator be sure whether larvae are present or approximately when they emerge as adults. Even under temperate-zone conditions the work of mosquito abatement is a continuous year-round program, with special alertness in the spring to curb the first brood of larvae, and intensive larviciding through the summer. At the end of the breed-

Fig. 68. Breaks in the irrigation ditch are responsible for considerable inundation, producing favorable breeding places for mosquitoes. Similarly, seepage from such ditches into borrow pits or low-lying areas may be highly productive of mosquitoes. The rapidly running water in the ditch is unfavorable for breeding.

ing season, efforts should be intensified to reduce the last brood as far as possible so as to have fewer overwintering mosquitoes to start the following year's brood. An intensive adulticiding program is in order. Use the winter months for maintenance work on drainage systems; for construction of new drains and permanent structures; for maintenance of moving equipment; and for planning the following year's work. Permanent corrective work should be the aim.

Water Management. Anyone concerned with mosquito control operations soon learns that much mosquito breeding is due to mismanagement of water intended for useful purposes. Irrigation systems so essential to crop production in arid regions too often do not provide the proper drainage, or the canals and ditches may be so situated or so constructed as to permit seepage resulting in ideal breeding places for potent malaria vectors such as *Anopheles freeborni* or the transmitter of encephalitis, *Culex tarsalis* (Fig. 68). Improper flooding of rice fields or uncontrolled flooding, as well as improper irrigation practices in the production of alfalfa or ladino clover, may be productive of numerous mosquitoes. Irrigated pastures, particularly, may be a source of many mosquitoes. Water impoundment (Fig. 69) may result

Fig. 69. Seepage water below impoundment (O'Sullivan Dam, Grant County, Washington; the dam is out of the picture, to the left). Seepage water, producing large numbers of *Anopheles freeborni,* is encroaching upon a road where, 2 or 3 years before, the dominant vegetation was sagebrush. (Photograph by Harry G. Davis.)

in the production of important malaria vectors such as *Anopheles freeborni* and *A. quadrimaculatus* in the United States, *A. minimus* in the far East, and *A. gambiae* in Africa. The significance of impounded water, so far as malaria is concerned, depends upon the presence or absence of vector *Anopheles* adaptable to such breeding conditions. Mosquito production is due in large part to man's carelessness and indifference, so well illustrated by the ubiquitous borrow pits formed by the removal of earth for highway and railroad embankments and fills, and by the drainage ditch improperly constructed with respect to slope or outlet (see King[24]).

Irrigation. Where irrigation is properly practiced with due attention to the economical use of water and good agricultural practice, there need be little or no mosquito breeding and consequent threat of mosquito-borne disease. However, when seepage results from breaks in ditches and particularly from side-hill canals, ideal swampy areas are produced, and cattle and horses leave water-filled hoofprints, an ideal breeding situation for *Anopheles freeborni* and *Culex tarsalis* in the western United States (Fig. 70). Because of the breeding habits of these important western disease-bearing mosquitoes, poorly constructed and improperly operated or leaking irrigation ditches have commonly been known to account for malaria or encephalitis in the neighborhood.

Fig. 70. Hoofprints around puddles, ponds, and streams are good breeding places. The water in the hoofprints shown here produced 60 to 80 larvae, mostly *Culex tarsalis,* per pint; much greater productivity often occurs in similar breeding areas. (Photograph by Harry G. Davis.)

Wilson[46] points out that:

. . . malarial effects are not attributable directly to the results of irrigation where it is economically and properly practiced—where care is taken to irrigate only land which has an open soil and such slopes and natural drainage as to prevent waterlogging, no unhealthy effects will result. . . . It is desirable, in order to mitigate the possible evil effects of irrigation, to keep the canal as much as possible within soil so that its surface level may be low, and thus only raise the subsurface water plane to the least height practicable; that earth wanted to complete embankments be never taken from excavations or borrow-pits except where such localities admit readily of drainage.

An excellent reference to irrigation practices and mosquito production is contained in a progress report by that name and released by the California Department of Public Health, the United States Department of Agriculture, and the California Mosquito Control Association.[2] In this report, where water application efficiency is defined as "the fraction of the water delivered to the farm that is stored in the root zone for use by the crop, expressed as per cent," it is concluded that:

. . . certain specific relationships exist between water management and adult mosquito production in irrigated pastures with fine textured soil:

1. There is an inverse relationship of increasing mosquito production with decreasing application efficiency.
2. Fields with water application efficiencies above 66 per cent will not produce mosquitoes.
3. Fields with water application efficiencies below 66 and above 57 per cent will generally produce a few adult mosquitoes and this production may be sporadic and difficult to predict.
4. Moderate mosquito production appears to be associated with water application efficiencies which range between 35 and 45 per cent.
5. High mosquito production is generally found in fields with efficiencies below 35 per cent.
6. Success in the management of fields with fine textured soils is more dependent upon irrigation and other management factors than upon the soil type itself.
7. Certain conditions can occur, such as coarse textured soil, shallow hardpan, poor field design, or irregular topography, which may change the degree of relationship between application efficiency and mosquito production. These factors can be recognized and evaluated separately, and should not distract from the usefulness of the general relationships which have been established.

It may be pointed out that there is a distinct difference between agricultural drainage and mosquito abatement drainage as applied to irrigation districts. Agricultural drainage is concerned merely with the problem of lowering the ground water level to the point where crops can be raised successfully. Frequently considerable quantities of mosquito-breeding water remain, often in the drains themselves (Fig. 71). Such drainage consists usually of large deep main drains with comparatively few laterals. Mosquito abatement drainage, on the other hand, is a matter of more careful attention to detail, with great care to obtain uniform grades and smooth bottoms for the drains, so as to avoid mosquito breeding.

Impounded Water. The storage of water in deep, clean, and steep-walled reservoirs seldom presents a mosquito problem; neither does storage of water in steep-sided reservoirs in rocky canyons. As pointed out by Bishop et al.:[4]

The impoundage of flowing streams profoundly alters the biology of the affected waters. One of the changes may be a vast increase in the potential for anopheline mosquito production unless appropriate control works and procedures are planned, designed, and operated. The choice is, therefore, between the probability of a disastrous "man-made" increase in transmission of malaria or a successful resolution of the continuing conflict between adverse biological pressures and control practices.

The magnitude of operations by the Tennessee Valley Authority begun in 1933, based on water management (control), is indicated by the fact that these involved 10,000 miles of reservoir shore line in a region of widely varying topography. The impounding of a lake in a region of flat topography within the Tennessee Valley produces a wide variety of breeding places of *Anopheles quadrimaculatus*. There a huge food supply of microorganisms is provided in the flotage as well as optimum protection against enemy fish and other aquatic predators. One of the important ways to control mosquito breeding in this situation is *water level* management. The effect of water level manipulations on anopheline larvae is both direct and indirect; direct in that as a result of drawing water out of the marginal vegetation the larvae are exposed to an open and clean water surface wherein few can survive; and indirect in that the water is removed from the marginal plants, drift, and flotage which provide food and protection for the mosquito larvae. One of the most important elements in water level management is periodic water level fluctuations. Complicated biological study and engineering features beyond the scope of this book are involved in accomplishing the desired results.

Fig. 71. Drainage water resulting from faulty irrigation, a source of numerous mosquitoes.

The foregoing applies also to impoundments for irrigation purposes throughout the western states where *Culex tarsalis* has become an encephalitis threat.

Fig. 72. (*A*) Willow flat along the lower Columbia River offers shelter and breeding places for floodwater mosquitoes. (*B*) Same willow flat cleared of shade and other protection and thus freed of mosquitoes. Regular maintenance is necessary to prevent their return. (After Stage, Gjullin, and Yates; U.S.D.A. photographs.)

Reclamation of mosquito-breeding areas may have an important side effect. Stage[36] states "There are numerous instances across the United States where mosquito breeding swamps have been made over into recreational lakes by dredging and impounding of open water unsuitable for mosquitoes."

Controlled reflooding may be successfully employed in the control of *Aedes* mosquitoes (Fig. 72). The eggs of *Aedes* do not all hatch at any one flooding; some eggs do not hatch until there have been a number of successive wettings. It is at least theoretically possible ultimately to hatch out all mosquito eggs in a given reclaimed area by purposeful flooding of the land, holding the water there for several days until a brood of larvae appears, and then draining the land rapidly before the larvae develop into adult mosquitoes. The land is then allowed to remain unwatered until a subsequent flooding. As no adults have been permitted to emerge, no new eggs are deposited, and thus by successive wettings all eggs should be hatched eventually without additions of new eggs. Thus actually thousands of acres of salt marsh on Suisun Bay near San Francisco have been freed of *Aedes dorsalis* (Meigen), so that these marshes can now be flooded or dried out at the will of the owner without hatching hordes of mosquitoes. From 7 to 10 successive floodings and drainings were necessary to accomplish this.

Flushing. Several species of *Anopheles* mosquitoes, particularly *A. minimus flavirostris* (Ludlow), the principal vector of malaria of the Philippine Islands, breed in the running water of small upland streams, the larvae being able to hold fast against the current by means of small hooks; other anophelines breed in stream-bed pools. Flushing devices, either automatic or hand-operated, can be installed at intervals along the breeding length of such streams so as to release suddenly a relatively large quantity of water accumulated behind a dam. The mosquito larvae are swept downstream forcibly and are destroyed by stranding and crushing (see Herms and Gray[18]).

Salinification. *Anopheles albimanus* Wiedemann, the principal malaria vector of the West Indies, breeds prolifically in certain brackish coastal lagoons. Hurlbut[23] showed that where the salinity remains between 15 and 25 per cent sea-water, breeding is abundant, while collections made concurrently where the salinity was 70 to 80 per cent were entirely negative. Breeding of this species can be eliminated by increasing the salinity to about 75 per cent by making adequate sea connections, thus subjecting the marginal lagoons to tidal action.

Russell reports that Knipe and Hackett used tide gates in reverse position at Durazzo, in Albania (Jugoslavia), to transform a brackish swamp into a sea-water lagoon to inhibit the breeding of *Anopheles sacharovi*.

Creeks and Small Streams. Except for flood water left behind during overflow from floods, great rivers themselves rarely afford opportunity for mosquito breeding. Flood water left behind when rivers recede may become a prolific breeding place for certain species of mosquitoes such as *Aedes vexans,* and in some instances in appropriate regions a malaria or encephalitis hazard may be created in that a breeding place for *Anopheles* or *Culex tarsalis* may result. In many parts of the country, as creeks and smaller streams recede during the rainless summer, numerous sunny pools are left behind which will soon become green with algae (e.g., *Spirogyra*), among which vast numbers of mosquito larvae occur; also quiet deeper pools occur along the banks shaded by willow and other vegetation, in which certain mosquitoes find suitable breeding places. Pools along the banks can frequently be drained off or can at least be thoroughly larvicided.

Small streams or creeks that border communities or flow through the town frequently become clogged with rubbish and eventually become prolific mosquito breeders. Communities should not permit rubbish to be thrown into stream beds. By neatly channelizing such stream beds and planting the banks with shrubbery, an eyesore and mosquito hazard may be rendered attractive and harmless.

Drainage. The removal or control of collections of water which produce mosquitoes presents a distinct problem in nearly every case. The type of drainage required in many instances will generally not require technical engineering skill. There are, however, drainage projects of considerable proportions for which engineering skill is necessary; such skill is eminently necessary for large-scale salt-marsh drainage operations where land reclamation calls for dikes, drainage canals, pumps, tide gates, and the like. Unless the executive officer is himself an engineer, properly qualified engineering services must be secured to obtain effective control.

In the case of a swamp caused by springs, a system of deep circumferential cut-off drains is recommended in order to intercept the seepage water and conduct it around the wet area. Where streams debouch from the hills onto a flat plain or valley, water from heavy rains, particularly in the spring, tends to spread out and leave temporary pools which may produce mosquitoes. Usually these temporary pools can be more economically controlled by larviciding; but, in some cases at least, drains may be dug which lead back into the main stream at a lower elevation. These ditches will usually require considerable maintenance.

Mosquito breeding in rolling country is commonly due to artificial obstructions, particularly railroad or highway embankments with improperly placed culverts. Usually culverts are set too high so that pools or swamp areas are formed on the upper side of the embankment. Corrections are usually not speedily made, if at all; hence, heavy larviciding is a necessary remedy.

In some swampy situations because of small or negative gradients, drainage becomes very difficult or impossible. In such cases *sumpage ditches* or *sumpage wells* may be constructed (Fig. 73), and the collected water may then be heavily larvicided. Surface water may also persist because of hardpan (impervious soil, etc.), in which case *vertical drainage* may be resorted to by digging sumpage wells or by blasting.

Drain Ditches. The purpose of laying out drain ditches is to secure effective and economic drainage. Although open drain ditches are most commonly used in mosquito control operations, subsurface drainage with the use of tile, or bundles of saplings laid in the ditches may at times be appropriate. Where the general slope of the ground is appreciable to the eye, this is usually a simple matter, i.e., following the low points to a place where the drainage water can be disposed of into some natural water course or other situation where there is sufficient fall to carry the water away. Laterals are then run from the main drain by the shortest distance to connect with low spots or wet areas. The bottom of the main drain ditch must be kept deep enough so that the laterals can reach all the low spots in the area to be drained.

For most of the ordinary ditching for mosquito control, transit and level are unnecessary. All that one needs are a few stakes, 500 feet or more of

Fig. 73. Storage sump collects extra irrigation water to be used again. This prevents water from standing in fields in shallow puddles. (Photograph by Roy McCarrell; courtesy of the Delta Mosquito Abatement District, Visalia, California.)

stout chalk line or strong cotton cord for line, and a hand level with a 10-foot board marked in feet and inches. If drains of considerable size and yardage are to be excavated, the usual surveying methods are employed, and the work should be done under contract with power machinery unless such equipment is owned or otherwise available to the district.

Hand labor, with pick and shovel, serves many purposes very well. Mattocks may be found useful in some soil. In many cases more or less dense vegetation has to be cut down and cleared before ditching can be performed with any speed or economy. Heavy grass or weeds may be cut with scythe, sickle, or machete (a dangerous tool in the hands of a man not accustomed to its use). In open fields a horse or power-drawn hay mower may be economical. For brush, axes, brush hooks, or machete may be used.

Dense grass and some forms of brush may be killed by applying stove distillates or diesel oils, which are toxic to vegetation, or standard weed killers such as 2,4-D. After killing and drying, the vegetation can be burned. Arsenical weed killers such as sodium arsenite or an acid solution of arsenious chloride may be used where there is no danger to cattle or other herbivorous animals. However, in any agricultural community the use of arsenical weed killers should be avoided in mosquito control operations.

Weed burners, capable of throwing a flame several feet, can be used fer clearing dense vegetation, but the general experience seems to be that they are more expensive than other methods of clearing. If burning is to be done, due consideration must be given to the nesting season and nesting habits of wild life.

Ditching with Dynamite. Swampy ground may often be economically ditched with dynamite. Special directions will have to be followed, and trial shots will be necessary as a rule to determine the correct depth of holes, their distance apart, and the amount of dynamite per hole. The most satisfactory results are obtained by using 50 to 60 per cent straight dynamite, fired by self-propagating detonation.

Dynamite ditch construction is advantageous in that a ditch can be blown through land with stumps, boulders, etc., without first removing these obstructions; it is only necessary to place heavier loads at these points.

Maintenance of Ditches. After the drainage ditch is constructed, it must be maintained in effective working order. Three main conditions making constant maintenance necessary are:

1. Growth of vegetation;
2. Caving or sloughing of banks;
3. Artificial obstructions.

Under some conditions, growth of vegetation in and adjacent to ditches is not a problem, but as a rule ditches will require clearing several times a year in order to keep them free from obstructing growths. In tropical or semi-tropical countries the problem of keeping drains free from vegetation is most difficult, and the source of considerable maintenance expense.

While weed killers may be helpful under some conditions, dependence must be placed in most cases on hand labor in cutting down and clearing out vegetation. The frequency of clearing will depend, of course, on local soil and climatic conditions, and it will be difficult as a rule to estimate in advance what the annual cost of maintenance of ditches will be.

Caving or sloughing of ditches is apt to occur in new ditches, for the first year or two. After that the banks usually become fairly stable, and but little further trouble is encountered, unless cattle are pastured along the ditches. In that case the animals may break down the ditch banks and cause some trouble.

Artificial obstructions are as a rule frequent only in the vicinity of public roads near a city or town. It is surprising how many will haul refuse away from their homes out into the country and dump it, usually *in* a ditch close to a road and thus block the ditch completely or partially. The ditch thereupon becomes a mosquito breeder.

Frequent inspections of drainage ditches, say at least once every two or three weeks during the breeding season, should be carried on and all objects that obstruct the flow, whether natural or artificial, removed promptly. During the winter, all ditches should be gone over carefully and trimmed to grade, and the proper side slopes remade, so that all will be in first-class order at the beginning of each breeding season.

Salt-marsh Drainage. Salt-marsh drainage requires special study and experience because of tidal action, soil conditions, differences in behavior of salt-marsh mosquitoes, and other factors. The rich reward in comfort and reclaimed land has given incentive to salt-marsh mosquito abatement. Strong public-spirited organizations have given marked support to this work on the Atlantic coast as well as on the Pacific, particularly in New Jersey, Florida, Texas, and California.

These marshes include vast areas of tidal marshes affected by salt or brackish water along the shores of oceans and particularly the various bays, sounds, and estuaries. The effect of daily (diurnal) and spring tides resulting in fluctuations of water level is the principal feature distinguishing these from fresh-water marshes, although other characteristics, such as the salt-marsh vegetation, are of importance.

While salt marshes appear to be flat, there is a gradual slope between low tide level and the adjacent dry land. For practical purposes these marshes may be divided into two main areas, the area subject to daily tidal action, where mosquito breeding seldom occurs, and the area between the elevation of mean high tidal water and the elevation of the extreme high tides. It is in the latter area that practically all the breeding of salt-marsh mosquitoes occurs. Mosquitoes such as *Aedes dorsalis* may breed in potholes left by the receding tide: if these potholes are connected to the main channel by ditches, these mosquito breeding areas can often be eliminated.[38]

Mosquito control operators concerned with projects involving salt marshes must acquaint themselves thoroughly with tidal phenomena. These vary in range and type in different parts of the world. The so-called "spring" tides, one or two of which occur each month, are the tides which fill pools along the upper portions of the marshes, and in these pools the principal salt-marsh mosquito breeding takes place.

The dates, times, and heights of the monthly highest tides are important in their bearing on the approximate time of emergence of a new crop of salt-marsh mosquitoes. It should be the invariable practice during the salt-marsh mosquito breeding season to inspect all known or suspected marsh breeding areas, beginning about 2 days after the highest tide and completing the inspection within 6 or 7 days. The delay of two days is for the purpose of giving the larvae opportunity to develop to a sufficient size to be easily seen with the unaided eye. Since, under favorable conditions in salt marshes, the time from egg hatching to emergence may be as short as 8 days, it is obvious that if a flight is to be prevented, the inspection and necessary control measures must be completed before the time of emergence.

Because salt-marsh mosquito control involves the location of dikes and tide gates, the knowledge of the dates, times, and heights of both the lowest tides and the highest tides, particularly of "storm tides," the combined effect of "spring tides" and piling up of water on shore due to high winds and river flood waters, as well, is important.

Marsh vegetation is often very dense and interferes with inspection and larviciding; hence, burning is usually recommended. But it must be borne in mind that peat deposits commonly occur, and if the water level has been lowered as a result of drainage, which is usually practiced, dry peat may ignite and cause a peat fire. Peat fires can be extinguished only by flooding, which may be expensive. An additional hazard which may follow drainage is the shrinkage of the soil and the formation of "cracks." These cracks may be several feet long and may contain water in which mosquitoes will breed in abundance. Such cracks are difficult and expensive to larvicide, though hand or airplane applications of DDT are helpful. An area of marsh that has cracked due to drainage operations should be disked so as to break up the surface and fill in the cracks. An occasional disking after the initial treatment may be necessary. For mosquito abatement purposes it is desirable to lower the water level only to the point where the water is drawn from breeding areas in dense vegetation but not to the extent that cracking of the soil occurs or a peat fire hazard is created. Drainage and burning must also be done with due regard for wildlife conservation.

Types of Salt-marsh Drainage. These are two principal methods of marsh drainage: (1) open marsh drainage, and (2) reclamation. In open marsh drainage the marsh is opened up by ditches to the free ebb and flow of tides so as to eliminate *standing* water suitable for mosquito breeding. In the reclamation type the area to be drained is surrounded on the low sides by a dike which is pierced in one or more places by outlet structures, tide gates, which permit water behind the dike to run at low tides, but prevent the return flow at high tides. Suitable drainage ditches are dug to conduct water to the outlets. The reclaimed marsh may be used for agricultural purposes.

Filling and Pumping. In almost all mosquito abatement, low wet areas will be encountered which cannot be economically drained. Although some such places may be ponded and the water stocked with top minnows, usually the most satisfactory method is filling (Fig. 74). Most smaller holes, such

Fig. 74. Upper figure shows a pond, adjacent to a railroad, caused by obstruction of the natural drainage, a source of many mosquitoes every year. Larviciding, while serving the purpose of mosquito control, requires the repeated expenditure of time, labor, and money. The lower figure shows the same spot after it had been permanently corrected by the railroad company.

as borrow pits, can be filled in by hand shoveling; larger holes may be filled by means of power scrapers. If sanitarily handled, municipal garbage and refuse may be used in a "fill and cover" method. Such fills are covered with earth and compacted so as to prevent fly breeding and to some extent rat breeding.

Salt marshes may be filled by hydraulic dredges, which suck mud and sand from the bottom of an adjacent bay and pump the mud and water mixture through a pipe and discharge it on the marsh. Where harbor or channel improvements are being made by hydraulic dredging, very satisfactory arrangements may often be made to use the mud and sand to fill a nearby mosquito-breeding marsh.

LARVAL CONTROL IN SOME SPECIAL HABITATS

Mosquito Breeding in Rice Fields. The control of mosquito breeding in rice fields is obviously a matter that must have the attention of those concerned with rice culture (agronomists) as well as the mosquito control experts. Much of the breeding can be controlled by proper management with respect to the habits of mosquitoes. Many species of mosquitoes are involved, some of which are malaria vectors. In the extensive rice-growing areas of Arkansas, 98 to 99 per cent of the population of noxious mosquitoes consist of four species, *Psorophora confinnis* (Lynch-Arribálzaga) and *P. discolor* (Coquillett), both flood-water breeders, constituting 83 to 94 per cent, and *Culex erraticus* Dyar and Knab and *Anopheles quadrimaculatus* Say, a malaria vector, constituting the rest (Horsfall[22]). In some newly developed areas, the introduction of rice culture on a large scale is characterized by hasty, haphazard methods (quick returns at minimum cost), with utter disregard of sound agronomic practice. Poorly constructed irrigation systems and even poorer drainage methods result in a veritable bog adjacent to rice fields. Too often as much as half of the mosquito production is due to poor practices and could be largely controlled by improved methods of water management. Growing rice in very porous soil requires much replenishment of water, and the continuous freshening by replenishment may in certain areas invite abundant breeding of malaria vectors, e.g., *Anopheles freeborni* Aitken in California. Where rice growing is an old established practice, great care is normally exercised in the matter of water management, particularly so in the vicinity of communities. People must learn to live in such an environment, and it is folly to endure mosquitoes which may be produced by rice fields.

Several authors have recommended intermittent irrigation, e.g., Hill and Cambournac[20] in Portugal, and Russell, Knipe and Rao[33] in South India. The latter recommend a cycle of 5 wet days and 2 dry days, particularly for the control of the vector, *Anopheles culcifacies* Giles.

In 1948 Cambournac and Fonseca,[5] reporting on anopheline and malaria control in the rice-growing regions of Portugal, pointed out that the control of anopheline larvae in rice fields by the use of DDT emulsions is both economical and practical. They recommend 5 liters of a 1 per cent emulsion per hectare, i.e., about 5.28 quarts to about 2.5 acres, poured in the irrigation ditches and thus automatically dispersed in the plots.

Anopheles Control in Bromeliads. *Anopheles bellator* Dyar and Knab is regarded as the most important vector of malaria in Trinidad (West

Indies), where it breeds in the rain water collected in the axils of the leaves of epiphytic bromeliads, particularly the large so-called "tank plants," *Gravisia aquilega* and others. These plants are found in great profusion on immortelle trees which are planted to shade cacao; hence, the problem of anopheline control is bound up with the cacao industry. Attempts at anopheline control on the island were unsuccessful until this very specialized habitat was discovered. Manual removal of the bromeliads is costly. Gillette[9] reports that the spray killing of bromeliads by the mechanical application of copper sulfate

Fig. 75. Motorcycle sidecar equipped for larviciding. (Photograph by H. F. Gray.)

is the method of choice. He states that one application of 0.25 per cent to 0.5 per cent solution may suffice for a 10-year period. The instance is cited of the treatment of about 1500 acres in a district of 30,000 population resulting in a spleen rate reduction from 28 per cent in 1945 to 5 per cent in 1947.

Sewer Inlets and Catch Basins. In the newer types of street inlets, little opportunity is afforded for water to collect and remain standing for mosquito breeding. Most of the old types of inlets and catch basins, especially those connecting with a combined sewer (for domestic sewage and storm water), are apt to produce mosquitoes, particularly *Culex pipiens*. Larviciding is most economically done by means of a motorcycle sidecar (Fig. 75). One filling with 25 gallons of larvicide with air pressure to 50 pounds per square inch will suffice for a day's work, i.e., from 200 to 300 catch basins.

Public Utilities Street Vaults. In practically all urban areas, the various public utilities, such as telephone, power and light, gas, electric railway, telegraph, and water, have numerous vaults in streets which are frequently the source of a severe local infestation of *Culex pipiens* and *Culex tarsalis* during the breeding season.

Cesspools, Privies, Liquid Manure Pits. Where pit privies are built in wet areas, water collects and prolific mosquito breeding (*Culex pipiens quinquefasciatus, Culex p. pipiens,* and *C. tarsalis*) may result. Where liquid wastes are disposed of in leaching cesspools, mosquito production may be very great if mosquitoes have access to them. Even small knot holes or vent pipes afford a ready means of entrance. If necessary repairs are made so the egress is cut off, a larvicide need not be applied; otherwise appropriate treatment must be practiced.

Liquid manure pits in connection with greenhouse and plant nurseries commonly produce prodigious numbers of *Culex pipiens* and *Culex tarsalis.* Only larvicides which are not dangerous to plants may be used.

Tree Holes. In wooded areas and on estates tree-hole mosquitoes, such as *Aedes sierrensis,* often cause great annoyance. Tree holes, particularly in oaks, collect water in which mosquito larvae thrive. Liberal applications of DDT larvicide are recommended; the larvicide should be applied not only to the water but also liberally swabbed on the wood above the water line to repel egg-laying female mosquitoes. The practice of tree surgery on estates has greatly reduced mosquito breeding in tree holes. Heavy applications of DDT, chlordane, heptachlor, or lindane aerosal have been effective in canyons or narrow valleys.

Cemetery Urns, Other Receptacles, and Sundry Nuisances. Urns and other types of receptacles intended for flowers on graves may stand partly filled with water for considerable lengths of time without changing and may furnish breeding places for many species of mosquitoes. *Culex pipiens* and *Aedes aegypti* often compose a high percentage of the mosquitoes breeding in such a habitat. Aarons[1] in 1948 obtained excellent control by the use of DDT aerosol, 5 per cent emulsion in diesel oil, applied at about three-week intervals. Each treatment (made before 7 A.M.) required only about one hour, whereas previously over 200 man-hours were required for hand treatment.

Water-holding receptacles of many kinds may prove suitable for mosquito breeding and must not be overlooked by the "mosquito man." However, it sometimes happens that an overemphasis of the tin can results in attracting the attention away from more important matters, such as dripping hydrants, stagnant ditches, etc. Indeed the water in tin cans unless in shady situations usually becomes too hot for mosquitoes during most of the summer. Heaps of broken gourds commonly are teeming with mosquito larvae; tubs and barrels of water frequently produce many of these pests, even certain species of anophelines. Stagnant water in poorly constructed street gutters is often a serious menace. Dripping faucets may result in pools of water suitable for mosquito breeding.

CHEMICAL CONTROL OF LARVAE*

Routine Inspections for Mosquito Breeding. Inspections for the purpose of finding breeding places in organized mosquito abatement districts are made either upon the receipt of complaints or for routine purposes. The inspector should be guided by the nature of the complaint: (1) mosquitoes annoying at night or affecting sleep, and (2) mosquitoes annoying during the daytime or toward evening, while working in the garden or watering the lawn. In the first instance it is probably a domestic fresh-water species, breeding on the premises or in the immediate vicinity. In the second instance it is a salt-marsh species, if salt marsh is near, or it may be a flood-water or tree-hole *Aedes*. In a previous chapter (p. 154) exceptions to this rule are discussed, particularly the dispersal flights of some species of *Anopheles*. Obviously the inspector must have a thorough knowledge of the species of mosquitoes and be well informed concerning breeding habits. When complaints are received, the inspector should visit the premises and if possible capture mosquitoes for positive identification, so as to simplify inspection for larvae and to ensure effective abatement.

In searching for adult mosquitoes for species determination, it is important to remember that only certain species are active during the day; hence, if they are not active, one must search for them in dark, cool and moist places, under houses, in basements and cellars, behind pictures, in closets and dark corners. A flashlight is very useful in these operations. *Aedes dorsalis* and other day fliers often hide in shrubbery and may be found by shaking bushes and vines or kicking weeds. The mosquitoes may be collected in small cyanide bottles or by means of an aspirator with an extension rubber tube.

Inspections, whether due to complaint or as a matter of routine, must be thoroughly and intelligently carried out; the breeding may be occurring in a rain barrel, a lily pond, an eaves trough, or a concealed cesspool; it may be taking place in a concealed chamber fed by a natural spring, in an abandoned well, a broken or clogged sewer or drain; floor boards may have to be removed.

* A valuable manual for the mosquito control operator is Vannote *et al.*, 1952. *Ground Equipment and Insecticides for Mosquito Control.*[42]

The work of routine or house-to-house inspection must be properly organized for efficient and economical coverage. The inspectors must be intelligent, well trained technically, and capable of meeting all sorts of people.

In inspecting large tracts of marsh to locate the precise producing areas, it is always advisable to mark off the marsh into definite sections, which can be examined one at a time, so that no portion is overlooked. Breeding areas, when located, are marked by setting up stakes in the center of the breeding area for the crew or larviciders which follow, or for future reinspection. Frequently both inspection and larviciding may be done concurrently by the same man.

Larvicides. All too commonly mosquito control is thought of as the practice of applying larvicides to the surface of stagnant water. Too often this is done without actually knowing mosquito larvae are present. Larvicides have a useful place in mosquito abatement operations; however, all properly conducted operations should look upon larviciding as secondary to the methods set forth previously in this chapter. The correct use of larvicides should be observed at all times. These chemicals, even the safest of them, are poison and have a varying degree of toxicity to man, domestic animals, and useful wildlife. Toxicity to useful plants must also be considered. Finally, there is the problem of resistance; it should be kept in mind that no mosquito has ever become resistant to the destruction of its breeding grounds.

Inorganic Larvicides and Botanicals. *Oiling,* for many years the standard method of larval control, is rarely, if ever, used today. Petroleum oils now find their place in mosquito control chiefly as diluents of more effective insecticides. Any oil which may be used on water to destroy the aquatic stages of mosquitoes must, of course, be lethal, at least in time, to all larvae and pupae; it must conform to standard specifications which may be determined by consulting the older literature on the subject. Crankcase oil should not be used; combustion has destroyed the elements of chief insecticidal value which it contained.

Paris green has long been used successfully against the surface-feeding anopheline larvae. This material, diluted with road dust, hydrated lime, finely powdered charcoal, finely powdered talc, or other finely powdered material, was suitable for airplane dusting on a large scale as well as for application with hand dusters. It apparently acts as a stomach poison, the small particles of Paris green being ingested with larval food.

With the advent of synthetic organic insecticides, the use of Paris green was virtually discontinued. There is an indication, however, that the development of new formulations, combined with the resistance problem, may bring about a revival of the use of Paris green and, perhaps, other inorganic insecticides. Such a formulation has been investigated by Rogers and Rathburn.[30] Its preparation involves the use of a granular base consisting of vermiculite from which dust-sized particles had been removed by screening; this base was subsequently sprayed with an oil emulsion sticker and then blended with Paris green. The completed formulation is then allowed to dry. When applied to the water, the vermiculite floats, but the Paris green begins immediately to be released; it settles slowly to the bottom, but some remains on the surface for several days. Thus both surface and subsurface-feeding larvae are affected. Cost of treatment can be made to compare favorably with that of using the chlorinated hydrocarbons.

Concerning the dangers from the use of this poison, Rogers and Rathburn[30] state:

> Considering the many problems attendant on the use of organic compounds as larvicides, especially the potential hazards to fish and other beneficial forms of life and the ever-increasing "resistance" problem it would appear that thorough investigation of Paris green, as well as other inorganics, offers one of the most promising approaches for the future in control of mosquitoes with chemicals. The literature leaves no doubt that Paris green was used as an anopheline larvicide for more than 30 years with a good margin of safety to man, domestic animals, fish, and other animals. Also, to the authors' knowledge, no "resistance" to this chemical by mosquitoes was reported in its long history as a larvicide.

Botanicals. Pyrethrum extract, especially when fortified with piperonyl butoxide, is very toxic to mosquitoes in the larval as well as adult stages. Vannote and Ginsburg[41] prepared an emulsion of kerosene (extracted from 1 pound of pyrethrum flowers per gallon of petroleum solvent) emulsified with water and soap (66 per cent kerosene extract with 34 per cent water containing 3 per cent of soap). This stock emulsion was diluted 1 to 10 with water for the field spray. Using in excess of 50 gallons of the dilution per acre, Ginsburg obtained a complete kill of larvae on salt marsh. This is the insecticide of choice where valuable and delicate plants are growing. Formulations made of pyrethrins, which give a rapid knockdown, and insecticides such as DDT with long residual effect and heavy kill are desirable.

The Chlorinated Hydrocarbons. *DDT* has been rigidly tested by many mosquito control agencies in large-scale field operations in practically all parts of the world. Both as a larvicide and adulticide, it has been proved a superior culicicide. Its use is not "foolproof"; it is a poisonous chemical, and care must be exercised when using it in the presence of food and food containers in the homes and in barns and stables. Furthermore, since DDT is practically insoluble in water, solvents are employed in the preparation of DDT sprays. The solvents are inflammable and explosive; hence, when using such sprays indoors or in enclosed places without emulsifying in water, caution must be exercised. Some of the solvents are toxic to man.

DDT-oil Solutions. Diesel oil, kerosene, and fuel oil will dissolve DDT in about 24 hours at temperatures of about 70° F. To make a 5 per cent solution, add about 2 pounds (2 1/8 pounds for a true 5 per cent weight-per-volume solution) of technical DDT to each 5 gallons of oil. Used as a larvicide, control can be obtained with 5 quarts per acre of a 1 per cent

DDT-oil solution. Oil without DDT for similar control would require from 15 to 25 gallons per acre. Using a 5 per cent DDT-oil solution, as little as 1 to 2 quarts per acre will be effective when applied with pressure spray equipment under ideal conditions.

Emulsion. An emulsion concentrate may be made of 25 per cent DDT, 10 per cent Triton X-100, and 65 per cent xylene or other solvent. Concentrates are available commercially. Emulsions are made by adding the required amount of concentrate slowly to water with continuous stirring. To prepare a 5 per cent emulsion of DDT, for example, 1 volume of the concentrate is mixed with 4 volumes of water. When used in the field as a larvicide the emulsions should be applied at the rate of 0.1 to 0.2 pounds of DDT per acre of water surface. Since DDT is not a strong pupacide, treatments must be made with this in mind or formulations must be employed which include pupacides.

Wettable DDT powder has advantages over emulsifiable concentrates of oil solutions in that it is packaged dry in a more concentrated form and in that there is no solvent problem or fire hazard. It is used extensively as a residual, especially in tropical climates.

DDT dust larvicide is employed for anopheline control, especially where long distance drifting is needed to control breeding areas. Against the larvae of *Anopheles* it is said to be about 25 times as toxic as Paris green dust, which was formerly used for the same purpose. It is applied as a 10 per cent DDT dust in pyrophyllite, talc, or other inert dust at the rate of 0.1 to 0.2 pound DDT per acre, i.e., 1 pound dust mixture. Where there is abundant vegetation, the dosage must be increased. For the control of *Culex* and *Aedes* species, a larger dosage is also required.

BHC or its 99.5 pure gamma isomer, *lindane,* may be used against DDT-resistant mosquitoes, at 0.05 to 0.1 pound per acre. Lindane is preferable to BHC because of several factors; it lacks the disagreeable odor of the latter, it is less toxic to man, and it contains a high concentration of the effective gamma isomer, which may vary considerably in the parent compound. It is, on the other hand, more expensive to manufacture. *Dieldrin* is used at the same concentrations.

In applying the chlorinated hydrocarbons to forage pastures or to alfalfa hay crops after irrigation, one must bear in mind the residue factor. Even though the amount of insecticide so applied may not produce clinical symptoms in livestock, it may become evident in milk or meat products in excess of the legal limit. BHC is more persistent than dieldrin, and dieldrin more so than DDT; consequently, of the three, DDT is the least hazardous to use, in this respect, where contamination of food for cattle is a problem.

The Phosphorus Compounds. In areas where mosquito resistance to the chlorinated hydrocarbons has developed or is threatening, a shift to larvicides of a different chemical group may be indicated. The phosphorus compounds, which may be considered derivatives of phosphoric acid, are frequently used in this case. Of those in wide use, *malathion* is the safest so far as toxicity to man and warm-blooded animals is concerned. It may be used at the rate of 0.4 to 0.5 pound per acre for mosquito control. It is in general as effective, and much safer to use, than parathion, although much more costly.

Parathion, another insecticide of this group, may be used at the rate of 0.05 to 0.1 pound per acre, applied as emulsions, solutions, or granular insecticides against DDT-resistant mosquitoes, but *it is dangerously toxic to man through inhalation, through skin absorption, or by mouth,* and must be used only with the observation of extreme precautions. The lack of residual action of parathion does, however, make it possible to apply it to pastures by airplane, if the proper precautions are observed. The use of phosphorus compounds is not the final answer to the problem of resistance; mosquitoes have been reported as becoming resistant to malathion and even to parathion.[28]

At present, phosphate insecticides, malathion and parathion, receive acknowledgement as culicicides only as a sort of desperation resort in the event of resistance to chlorinated hydrocarbon insecticides. Experience in California (personal communication, R. F. Peters to James) is that parathion, particularly, is an outstandingly effective insecticide for mosquito control, and *when used in accordance with safety procedures* has proved to be the most economical insecticide ever available.

Carbamates. At the present time, *Sevin* (1-naphthyl *N*-methylcarbamate) shows great promise as a larvicide.

Applications of Larvicides. Methods of applying larvicides will, of course, depend upon the materials used, i.e., whether liquids or dusts, and whether large areas are involved or only a few catch basins. For relatively small areas or for numerous small and widely separated areas, hand application is both economic and convenient.

Hand spraying equipment such as the compressed air sprayer or the knapsack spray pump (Fig. 76) has had almost universal use. This type of equipment partly atomizes the larvicide, resulting in a better spread and a better coverage of the water surface and is at the same time more economical in the use of larvicide and in labor. Compressed air sprayers consist of closed metal cylinders of 1 to 5 gallons' capacity, fitted with a brass plunger pump which forces air into the container until a strong air pressure is built up. To the outlet pipe, which extends to the bottom of the container, are attached a piece of flexible hose and a spray nozzle. A fan-type spray nozzle is usually attached to the end of a 1/4–inch metal pipe; it is usually supplied with an assortment of nozzle disks, each with air aperture of different size or shape, which produces spray patterns of varying coarseness. Compressed air sprayers operate at pressures of 30 to 50 pounds. The knapsack sprayer has a liquid pump, instead of the air type, which permits development of pressures in the range of 80 to 180 pounds. In operation the tank is filled about three-quarters full with larvicide. A hand level extending over one shoulder when the sprayer is strapped on the back operates the pump plunger. The container should be provided with a lip about 1 1/2 inches high extending around and above the tip of the can to prevent the larvicide from spilling down the back of the operator. One man with a knapsack sprayer can spray about 5 acres per day of 8 hours under open field conditions.

Power Equipment to Apply Culicides. Enormous strides have been made in the development of power equipment designed to give efficient distribution of the newer insecticides in field practice. Many problems have had to be met. It has been pointed out that in order to capitalize on the increased toxicity

Fig. 76. Knapsack spray pump in use in mosquito control.

and the heretofore unheard-of residual properties of these products, a much finer break-up of the insecticides is demanded as well as a more widespread and uniform distribution. Since applicators for larval control are in general of the same types as those used for residual adult control, they will be discussed under that heading.

Aircraft in Mosquito Control. The use of aircraft in the distribution of insecticides for mosquito control became almost world-wide during World War II. DDT in various formulations was the insecticide of choice in these operations. The American Mosquito Control Association has issued a valuable illustrated brochure[32] which presents practical information on when, where, and how aircraft may be used to distribute mosquito insecticides, chiefly DDT, and on appropriate methods for appraising results. All agencies using aircraft for mosquito control purposes should have this brochure available to the personnel concerned.

clouds, mists, fog, fumes, atomized oil in oil burners, smoke screens, etc., in which air constitutes the continuous external dispersion medium and the fine particles form the internal or dispersed phase.

The main object of aerosol spraying is to disperse insecticides, such as mosquito larvicides and adulticides, etc., in such a fine state of subdivision and in such a way that they remain suspended or floative in the air for long periods of time, thereby prolonging their effectiveness. The work of Ginsburg[11] in the development of pyrethrum aerosols for use out of doors is well known. DDT aerosols are now widely used as adulticides. Airplane thermal exhaust aerosols are commonly employed in rice fields and other large-scale

Fig. 78. Application of a residual spray: an example of perfect deposit made with a wettable powder applied to a wall surface. Droplets are large, coverage thorough, with no running of liquid. (After Stage; U.S.D.A. photograph.)

mosquito control operations. Numerous types of equipment are available for producing aerosols, among them the engine exhaust of a "jeep," which is inexpensive and effective (Fig. 79).

Household space sprays that utilize the aerosol principle usually contain, as their active ingredients, DDT plus either pyrethrins or allethrins fortified by piperonyl butoxide.

Residual Treatment. *Duration of Toxicity of Residual Insecticides.* Early treatments with DDT greatly reduced mosquito populations for two weeks or more, with residual effects in some cases lasting as long as 135 days. In later tests with other chlorinated hydrocarbons, lindane, BHC (40 per cent gamma), and dieldrin have proven much superior, dieldrin being somewhat less effective than lindane or BHC. The development of resistance may be a factor in the apparently reduced effectiveness of DDT. For outdoor treatment, residual insecticides may be applied to low vegetation and ground litter. Supplementary pyrethrum or allethrin sprays may be necessary to provide protection against migrating mosquitoes.

Indoor residual spraying to destroy adult mosquitoes is accomplished by treating all the wall surfaces and ceilings, undersurfaces of tables, beds, etc., with a 5 per cent DDT-oil emulsion spray, using either a hand or air-pressure sprayer. The object is to deposit a residuum of about 200 mg of DDT per square foot. One thorough treatment may last in excess of 3 months. Rooms should be ventilated during spraying and DDT should not be allowed to fall on food, food preparation surfaces, dishes, or cooking utensils.

Fig. 79. Aerosol equipment in adulticiding operations. (Photograph by E. A. Smith.)

The residual effectiveness of DDT (190 mg of 5 per cent DDT emulsion per sq ft) applied indoors to adobe walls and straw-thatched roofs under subtropical conditions is shown in a report by Downs *et al.,*[8] who noted residual action 29 months after application.

Gray[14] points out that this residual effect of DDT and its analogs gives us not only a completely new technique in mosquito control, but an entirely new concept, particularly in the control of disease vectors.

Repellents. There is little doubt that through the centuries man has tried to protect himself from mosquito bites by using herbs and smoke smudges, probably with little success. Oriental punk has long been widely employed; considerable quantities were used in the tropics by the armed forces of both sides during World War II. During World War I troops who were forced to operate in mosquito-infested regions were often advised to smear themselves with so-called "bamber oil" (among other ointments), a mixture of citronella oil, kerosene, and coconut oil, with a little carbolic acid added. Relief was probably not marked.

Early during the World War II period, steps were taken to develop repellents with some effect. Granett[13] at Rutgers University (New Jersey) and Kipling and Dove[26] at the United States Bureau of Entomology and Plant Quarantine, Orlando, Florida, laboratories, in cooperation with the armed forces and other agencies (some commercial), developed the widely used repellents known as Rutgers 612, dimethyl phthalate, and Indalone. Ethyl hexanediol (Rutgers 612) is most effective against *Aedes* species, while dimethyl phthalate is most effective against *Anopheles quadrimaculatus.*

By far the best repellent for mosquitoes, as well as for chiggers, fleas, ticks, and biting flies, that has been developed so far is diethyltoluamide. Three isomers are present; arranged in order of the effectiveness of their repellency they are meta, ortho, and para. Optimum repellency is obtained when the chemical is formulated with about 70 per cent of meta isomer and 30 per cent of the other two combined. The repellent remains effective for several hours, is strongly resistant to rub-off, and may be applied to the skin or to clothing and other fabrics.

Screens to Exclude Mosquitoes. Where there is no control of mosquitoes or only incomplete control, particularly in the presence of disease-transmitting species, sleeping quarters, living quarters, porches, etc., should be adequately screened against intruding mosquitoes. The best size mesh for all purposes is No. 18, i.e., 18 strands to an inch. The screens must be suited to exposure and to the climatic conditions of the situation where they are used. They must be protected or reinforced against mechanical breakage at points of stress. Painting screens on both sides with a 5 per cent oil emulsion of DDT is a good practice.

MISCELLANEOUS CONSIDERATIONS

Duck Clubs. In most states the duck-shooting season does not begin until November 1, or later. By that time, cold weather usually stops mosquito breeding. However, many duck clubs start flooding their duck ponds long before this, perhaps to have the ponds ready to attract the earlier migrants. These slowly filled shallow ponds may prove to be a mosquito menace. Some clubs keep their ponds well flooded throughout the year, and if the banks are steep, and top minnows have access to all parts of the pond, there is no mosquito problem. The ponds which are most difficult to handle are those that are drained off in January or February, after the duck season is over, and are allowed to remain dry during the summer, being again flooded in late summer or early autumn while the weather is still warm. Breeding is certain to occur. *Aedes* eggs, such as those of *Aedes dorsalis* (Meigen), from preceding years promptly hatch, and a plague of mosquitoes soon appears.

The following rules in dealing with mosquito control in connection with duck clubs are suggested:

1. Continuous all-year flooding of ponds is permissible and approved, provided that the ponds are stocked with mosquito fish at all times.
2. Intermittent maintenance of ponds is permissible, provided (a) the water is effectively removed early in the spring before breeding occurs, and (b) the water is not put in during autumn until the weather is cool enough to prevent mosquito breeding.
3. Ponds must have sound, tight banks and bottoms to prevent wet areas due to seepage.
4. Ponds must have sufficient depth throughout to permit mosquito fish to penetrate freely all parts.
5. Ponds must not be overgrown with vegetation, especially along and near the margins, so that mosquito fish may have free access to all parts.
6. If the water is pumped, the supply and equipment should be adequate to fill the ponds with reasonable speed.
7. Duly authorized inspectors of mosquito abatement districts in which the ponds occur should be permitted to inspect the area frequently to determine whether or not mosquito breeding is taking place.
8. If in spite of all precautions mosquito larvae do occur, a larvicide should be applied, but only where breeding is actually in progress. Parathion at 0.1 pound per acre has been used successfully without adverse effect to wildlife, since it has no residual properties.

Mosquito Control and Wildlife Conservation. Mosquito abatement operations if intelligently conducted need not be detrimental to wildlife, though no doubt they have been so at times. In conducting control operations in suburban and rural areas, an understanding of wildlife ecology is urged, and a modification of measures to suit the situation is necessary. It is regrettable if wildlife has been harmed; but there have also been unfounded complaints on the part of misinformed and intolerant wildlife conservationists which have made it distinctly difficult for mosquito abatement officials to perform their proper function. It is important that the seemingly divergent viewpoints of conservationists and duck club interests be harmonized with mosquito abatement officials. No doubt each group will need to make reasonable concessions.

Cooperation between responsible mosquito abatement officials and the representatives of wildlife interests is only made difficult when one side or the other sets itself upon a pedestal. Properly trained experts in mosquito control are just as truly biologists as are wildlife authorities; the only difference is usually in the fact that the former are trained in the field of invertebrate zoology and the latter in the field of vertebrate zoology. Both should be ecologists and have training in limnology. Fortunately, most authorities in the field of mosquito control have had training not only in the ecology of aquatic invertebrates, but for obvious reasons also in vertebrate ecology. Entomologists trained in mosquito control and ecology, and wildlife conservationists equally well trained in ecology ought to be able to see "eye to eye" as biologists. Working thus together as biologists on an equal footing, the aims and objectives of both sides will be advanced.

A comprehensive study of the relationship of pesticides to wildlife has been made by Rudd and Genelly;[31] this work should be consulted by anyone planning mosquito larvicidal programs in areas where wildlife is involved. The authors point out that losses are usually the result of failure to follow recommended procedures of application. Sometimes these losses are irretrievable; for example, on the island of Cyprus a rigorous *Anopheles* control campaign eliminated malaria, but it also exterminated all indigenous freshwater fish and devastated, if it did not destroy, invertebrate populations. Even in noninsular areas, an entire ecologic type, e.g., in rice fields, might be involved. DDT can be used safely at 0.1 to 0.2 pound per acre; some fish will be killed even at these concentrations, but recovery of populations is rapid. Crustaceans are in general very sensitive even to these low concentrations, and their populations may be severely affected. The destruction of crabs may, therefore, have considerable economic significance. Dieldrin is more toxic to fish than DDT; treatment of 2000 acres of Florida east coast tidal marsh with dieldrin pellets at one pound per acre, for *Culicoides* larvae, virtually exterminated fishes and crustacea from that area.[15] Parathion and malathion are not hazardous to fish; they are far less toxic than the chlorinated hydrocarbons.

Natural Enemies of Mosquitoes. There are probably no other insects that have a greater number of natural enemies than mosquitoes. In spite of this, a review and summary of the literature dealing with "Predators of the Culicidae" by Hinman[21] indicates that, excluding fish, the chances of finding satisfactory predators is not very encouraging. Among the natural enemies of mosquitoes, few are so frequently referred to as dragonflies (also known as "mosquito hawks"), bats, and surface-feeding fish. Dragonflies, order Odonata, are predaceous in both the nymphal and adult stage. The aquatic nymphs are commonly found in quiet, shallow, permanent pools suitable also for mosquito breeding, and both may flourish in the same pool in spite of the fact that the dragonfly nymphs, usually relatively few in number, may feed on mosquito wrigglers.

Since the nymphs feed in the mud and debris at the bottom, probably few wrigglers are captured. If the wrigglers are easily available, the nymphs will feed on mosquito larvae voraciously. Warren[43] reported a nymph of *Pantala* consuming by 7 o'clock in the evening 75 full-grown mosquito larvae which he had placed in a glass half-full of water in the morning. Adult dragonflies are exceedingly adept at capturing mosquitoes on the wing just before and at sunset. However, here again the number of dragonflies, which also feed on other insects, is no match for the mosquitoes. Dragonflies do not fly at night when night-flying mosquitoes are on the wing.

The role of larvae of the Chaoboridae[7] and of the mosquito subfamily Toxorhynchitinae has been mentioned previously (Chapters 9 and 10). The latter group is of distinct significance in the destruction of tree-hole breeding haematophagous mosquitoes.

Bats are insectivorous and feed freely on mosquitoes; as many as 250, it is said, may be captured by one bat in a night, but with many other species of crepuscular and night-flying insects available, bats are not effective enough to be a large factor in control, even though one might tolerate them in large numbers near the home. Bat roosts have been established to accommodate bats for the purpose of mosquito control, but the bats have not reduced the mosquitoes to an appreciable degree.

Fish of various species have been advocated for many years. In *Nature* for December, 1891 (pp. 223–24), there is this item:

> An Englishman living on the Riviera, according to a correspondent, having been troubled by mosquitoes, discovered that they bred in the large tanks kept for the purpose of storing fresh water, which is rather a rare commodity at this Mediterranean resort. He put a pair of carp in each tank and succeeded in this way in extirpating the insect pest.

The most useful of all fishes for mosquito control is the top minnow or mosquito fish, *Gambusia affinis* (Baird and Girard),[34] a hardy, rapidly breeding, prolific surface-feeding fish which within its range normally inhabits shallow water suitable for mosquito propagation. It is viviparous and may produce as many as 6 to 8 broods in a season with an average of 40 to a brood. The size of the fish ranges from 1 1/4 inches in length in the male to nearly 2 inches in the female. This fish is easily propagated and adapts itself to a variety of conditions with ease. It has been introduced into various parts of the world, even over great distances, for example, from Texas to the Hawaiian Islands and thence to the Philippines. Transportation of top minnows can be done satisfactorily in 10-gallon milk cans with tops punched with holes and water kept below the point where the top of the can begins to narrow. Although as many as 500 fish may be transported for an hour's trip with only moderate loss, not over 200 young fishes per can should be shipped on longer trips, and special care must be exercised to remove dead fish at intervals and freshen the water.

For garden pools 10 square feet in diameter, 20 top minnows will be ample, and no artificial feeding will be necessary. The *Gambusia* will more or less regulate their own numbers according to the food supply available.

Top minnows will evidently not feed on mosquito larvae when these are motionless, hence are not markedly effective in the control of mosquitoes whose larvae are sluggish; e.g., the usually motionless larvae of *Anopheles quadrimaculatus* do not attract the attention of top minnows as readily as do the more active larvae of *A. freeborni;* hence, the minnows are not so effective in control. Several other species of top minnows and killifish (families Cyprinodontidae and Poeciliidae) have been found useful. The International Health Board of the Rockefeller Foundation has issued (1924) a comprehensive treatise entitled "The Use of Fish for Mosquito Control."

In Guayaquil, Equador, the problem of the yellow fever mosquito was solved, according to Connor,[6] by the use of fish. Connor states that at the time of his writing the domestic water supply was delivered to the house daily and was stored in tanks and other receptacles, such as barrels, oil cans, earthenware bowls, etc. In these various containers yellow fever mosquitoes developed in countless numbers. Experimentation with several species of fish finally resulted in the selection of the "chalaco" (*Dormitator latifrons,* family Eleotridae). These fish, furnished to the Yellow-Fever Service by local fisherman, were placed in a specially prepared well, the conditions of which approximated those of the stream from which the fish were taken. After a few days the fish were removed to a second well, the water of which was the same as that used by the city. They were then made available for public use. Connor writes:

> More than 30,000 water receptacles have in this way been purged of mosquito larvae in a relatively short time and at a minimum of expense. With the continued use of fish it is believed that the yellow-fever mosquito can be reduced to such small numbers that, should a few cases of the disease be introduced into the community, it would not spread.

Transportation of Exotic Mosquitoes by Airplane. The accidental importation of exotic mosquitoes may result in severe epidemics of disease with heavy loss of life and may necessitate expensive campaigns to root out the evil. Particularly noteworthy is the malaria epidemic in Brazil following the introduction of *Anopheles gambiae* Giles from Africa, which caused catastrophic epidemics of malaria and posed a threat to all the Americas until the mosquito was finally eradicated.[35] Such dangers, particularly importation of the vector of yellow fever, have long been recognized as possible through air transportation. Various amendments have been made to the "International Sanitary Convention for Aerial Navigation of April 12, 1933," signed by the United States in April, 1934, according to Miller, Burgess, and Carpenter.[29] Article 54, (a 1944 amendment) reads:

In view of the special risk of conveying insect vectors of malaria and other diseases by aircraft on international flight, all such aircraft leaving affected areas will be disinsected . . . further disinsectization of the aircraft on or before arrival may be required if there is reason to suspect the importance of insect vectors.

The ever-increasing use of ordinary airplanes for transportation of passengers, baggage, and freight has added to the severity of the problem.[16] Mosquitoes apparently cannot survive passage in unheated, unpressurized areas of jet planes.[40] In continental areas it is probable that air transportation is of little importance along north-south lines, although along lines of latitude the danger is very real.[3] The same is true of isolated islands. Hawaii, for instance, with its limited fauna of three haematophagous mosquitoes, must maintain constant vigilance against introduction of species new to the islands. Rigid inspection and treatment of incoming aircraft, and treatment of actual and potential breeding areas in the vicinity of the air field, as practiced at the RNZAF Station at Whenuapai, New Zealand[27] may be necessary to prevent disastrous introductions.

REFERENCES

1. Aarons, Theodore, 1948. "Cemetery mosquito control by aerosol," *Proc. & Papers 16th Annual Conf. Calif. Mosq. Control Assn.,* Berkeley, pp. 84–85.

2. Anonymous, 1956. *The Relationship between Irrigation Practices and Mosquito Production.* State of California, Dept. of Public Health; U. S. Dept. of Agric.; and Calif. Mosquito Control Assn. Processed. 101 pp.

3. Bates, Marston, 1949. *The Natural History of Mosquitoes.* New York: The Macmillan Company. xv + 379 pp.

4. Bishop, E. L.; Hollis, M. D.; Mansur, C. I.; *et al.;* 1947. *Malaria Control on Impounded Water.* Washington, D. C.: U. S. Public Health Service and Tennessee Valley Authority. xiii + 422 pp.

5. Cambournac, F. J. C., and Fonseca, A. E. da, 1948. "Experiments on the control of anopheline larvae and malaria in rice-growing regions of Portugal," *Proc. 4th Internat. Cong. Trop. Med. & Malaria* (Abstracts), Washington, D. C.

6. Connor, Michael E., 1921. "Fish as mosquito destroyers," *Natural History,* **21:**279–81.

7. Cook, Edwin F., 1956. *The Nearctic Chaoborinae (Diptera: Culicidae).* St. Paul: Univ. Minn. Agric. Exp. Sta., in Tech. Bull. 218. 102 pp.

8. Downs, W. G.; Iris, R. C.; and Gahan, J. B.; 1948. "Residual effectiveness of DDT in the third season after application," *Am. J. Trop. Med.,* **28:**741–45.

9. Gillette, H. P. S., 1948. "The control of bromeliad malaria in Trinidad, B. W. I.," *Proc. 4th Internat. Cong. Trop. Med. & Malaria* (Abstracts), Washington, D. C.

10. Ginsburg, J. M., 1931. "Airplane application of larvicide on mosquito breeding places inaccessible from land," *New Jersey Agric. Exper. Sta., Annual Rept.* (1930–1931), **19:**173–76.

11. Ginsburg, J. M., 1935. "Larvicides and a method of temporary protection from adult mosquitoes in limited areas," *Proc. New Jersey Mosq. Extermination Assn.*, **22**:147–51.

12. Ginsburg, J. M., 1943. "Aerosol sprays for killing and repelling mosquitoes," *Proc. New Jersey Mosq. Extermination Assn.*, **30**:211–17.

13. Granett, Philip, 1943. "The significance of the development of mosquito repellents for the protection of military and civilian populations," *Proc. New Jersey Mosq. Extermination Assn.*, **30**:203–10.

14. Gray, H. F., 1948. "Some new ideas in mosquito control," *Bol. Ofic. San. Panam.*, **27**:321–25.

15. Harrington, Robert W., and Bidlingmayer, William L., 1958. "Effects of dieldrin on fishes and invertebrates of a salt marsh," *J. Wildlife Management*, **22**:76–82.

16. Herms, W. M., 1946. "Wartime aviation quarantine. Pests and their control," *J. Pest Control Industry*, **14**:24–25.

17. Herms, W. B., 1948. "Public relations in mosquito control operations," *Proc. and Papers 16th Annual Conf. Calif. Mosq. Control Assn.* (Berkeley), pp. 51–54.

18. Herms, W. B., and Gray, H. F., 1944. *Mosquito Control: Practical Methods for Abatement of Disease Vectors*, 2nd. ed. New York: The Commonwealth Fund. viii + 419 pp.

19. Hewitt, C. G., 1919. "The use of the aeroplane in entomological work," *Agric. Gaz. Canada*, **6**:877.

20. Hill, Rolla B., and Cambournac, F. J. C., 1941. "Intermittent irrigation in rice cultivation, and its effect on yield, water consumption and *Anopheles* production," *Am. J. Trop. Med.*, **21**:123–44.

21. Hinman, E. H., 1934. "Predators of the Culicidae (mosquitoes)," *J. Trop. Med. & Hyg.*, **37**:129–34, 145–50.

22. Horsfall, William R., 1942. *Biology and Control of Mosquitoes in the Rice Areas*. Fayetteville: Univ. Arkansas, in Agric. Exper. Sta. Bull., no. 427. 46 pp.

23. Hurlbut, Herbert, 1943. "Observations on the use of sea water in the control of *Anopheles albimanus* Wied.," *J. Parasitol.*, **29**:356–60.

24. King, W. V., 1948. "Man-made malaria," *Proc. 4th Internat. Cong. Trop. Med. & Malaria* (Abstract), Washington, D. C.

25. King, W. V., and Bradley, G. H., 1925. "Airplane dusting controls malaria mosquitoes," *Aero Digest*, **7**:652–53.

26. Knipling, E. F., and Dove, W. E., 1944. "Recent investigations of insecticides and repellents for the armed forces," *J. Econ. Entomol.*, **37**:477–80.

27. Laird, M., 1951. *Insects Collected from Aircraft Arriving in New Zealand from Abroad*. Wellington, New Zealand: Victoria Univ., in Zool. Pub., no. 11. 30 pp.

28. Lewallen, Lawrence L., and Bradley, John H., 1958. "Parathion resistant *Aedes nigromaculis*," *Calif. Vector Views*, **5**:56.

29. Miller, Albert; Burgess, Robert W.; and Carpenter, Stanley J.; 1947. "Potentialities of transportation of exotic anophelines by airplane," *J. Nat. Malaria Soc.*, **6**:227–43.

30. Rogers, Andrew J., and Rathburn, Carlisle B. Jr., 1958. "Tests with a new granular Paris green formulation against *Aedes, Anopheles,* and *Psorophora* larvae," *Mosq. News,* **18:**89–93.

31. Rudd, Robert L., and Genelly, Richard E., 1956. *Pesticides: Their Use with Toxicity in Relation to Wildlife.* Sacramento: Calif. Dept. Fish & Game, Game Bull. 7. 209 pp.

32. Russell, P. F.; Bradley, G. H.; Hess, A. D.; Mulrennan, J. A.; and Stage, H. H.; 1948. *The Use of Aircraft in the Control of Mosquitoes.* American Mosquito Control Association, in Bull. no. 1. 26 pp. (45 plates).

33. Russell, Paul F.; Knipe, Fred W.; and Rao, H. Ramanatha; 1942. "On the intermittent irrigation of rice fields to control malaria in South India," *J. Mal. Inst. India,* **4:**321–40.

34. Seale, A., 1917. "The mosquito fish, *Gambusia affinis* (Baird and Girard), in the Philippine Islands," *Philippine J. Sc.,* **12:**177–89.

35. Soper, Fred L., and Wilson, D. Bruce, 1943. *Anopheles gambiae in Brazil, 1930 to 1940.* New York: The Rockefeller Foundation. xviii + 262 pp.

36. Stage, Harry H., 1943. "Relation of the Bonneville Dam to mosquito control along the Columbia River," *Proc. New Jersey Mosq. Extermination Assn.,* **30:**197–202.

37. Stage, Harry H., 1952. *Mosquitoes.* Washington, D. C.: Yearbook of Agriculture, 1952, pp. 476–86.

38. Stage, H. H.; Gjullin, C. M.; and Yates, W. W.; 1952. *Mosquitoes of the Northwestern States.* Washington, D. C.: U. S. Dept. Agric., Agric. Handbook no. 46. 95 pp.

39. Stivers, John O., 1958. "The airplane as the primary spray tool in a large scale mosquito control program," *Calif. Vector Views,* **5:**11–16.

40. Sullivan, W. N.; DuChanois, F. R.; and Hayden, D. L.; 1958. "Insect survival in jet aircraft," *J. Econ. Entomol.,* **51:**239–41.

41. Vannote, R. L., and Ginsburg, J. M., 1931. "Practical application of pyrethrum mosquito larvicide," *Proc. New Jersey Mosq. Extermination Assn.,* **18:**111–20.

42. Vannote, Robert L., *et al.* 1952. *Ground Equipment and Insecticides for Mosquito Control.* Amer. Mosq. Control Assn., Bull. 2. 116 pp.

43. Warren, Alfred, 1915. *A Study of the Food Habits of the Hawaiian Dragonflies or Pinau with Reference to Their Economic Relation to Other Insects.* Honolulu: College of Hawaii Publications, Bull. no. 3. 45 pp.

44. Weick, Fred E., and Roth, George A., 1957. "Aerial application of insecticides," *Ann. Rev. Entomol.,* **2:**297–318.

45. Williams, L. L. Jr., and Cook, S. S., 1927. "Paris green applied by airplane in the control of Anopheles production," U. S. Public Health Service, *Pub. Health Rep.,* **62:**459–80.

46. Wilson, H. M., 1909. *Irrigation Engineering,* 6th ed. New York: John Wiley and Sons, Inc. 625 pp.

Chapter 13

HORSE FLIES, DEER FLIES, AND SNIPE FLIES

Order Diptera; Suborder Brachycera

The suborder Brachycera, aside from the Tabanidae, does not contain many flies of medical importance. However, the genus *Symphoromyia* of the family Rhagionidae includes a number of species of vicious bloodsuckers; and *Hermetia illucens* (Linnaeus), family Stratiomyidae, is sometimes involved in myiasis, on the one hand, yet may, as a larva, be a predator on house fly larvae, on the other. The following key will separate the three groups.

1. Third segment of antenna (flagellum) enlongated, annulated but not aristate 2
   Third segment of antenna kidney-shaped, without evident annuli and with a subterminal arista; wing venation with neither of the peculiarities described in couplet 2. . Genera *Suragina* and *Symphoromyia* (Rhagionidae)
2. Antenna terminating in a broad, elongated vanelike style; wing veins crowded toward the anterior margin of the wing, R_5 ending before the wing apex; mouth parts fitted for lapping.......................
   ....*Hermetia illucens* (Linnaeus) (Stratiomyidae)
   Antenna terminating in a slender, several-segmented style; wing veins normally spread, but veins R_4 and R_5 broadly diverging and enclosing the apex of the wing between them; females of medically important species with mouth parts fitted for piercing and lapping........Family Tabanidae

HORSE FLIES AND DEER FLIES

Family Tabanidae

To this large and cosmopolitan family of the order Diptera, comprising about 2500 species, belong the avidly bloodsucking flies commonly known as horse flies, deer flies, breeze flies, greenheads, or mango flies. These flies are usually quite large and heavy bodied, measuring in length from 7 to 10 mm in the smaller species to from 20 to 30 mm in the larger species. They are strong fliers and notorious pests of horses, cattle, deer, and many other warm-blooded animals, and are at times annoying to man, particularly the persistent members of the genus *Chrysops*. The males feed on vegetable sap and some may suck juices of soft-bodied insects, but they do not bite. The eyes are very large and widely separated (dichoptic) in the females, and contiguous (holoptic) in the males. The antennae are short (though fairly long in some genera such as *Chrysops*) and are porrect, consisting of three segments, the terminal one, or flagellum, being elongated and annulated but not bearing an arista. The wing venation is characteristic in that the branches of vein R_{4+5} diverge broadly, thereby enclosing the apex of the wing between them. The mouth parts of the female are bladelike and function as cutting instruments, though the labella are fitted for sponging (Fig. 14).

Since most of the species are aquatic or semiaquatic in breeding habits (some are able to develop in moist earth, leaf mold, or rotting logs), the

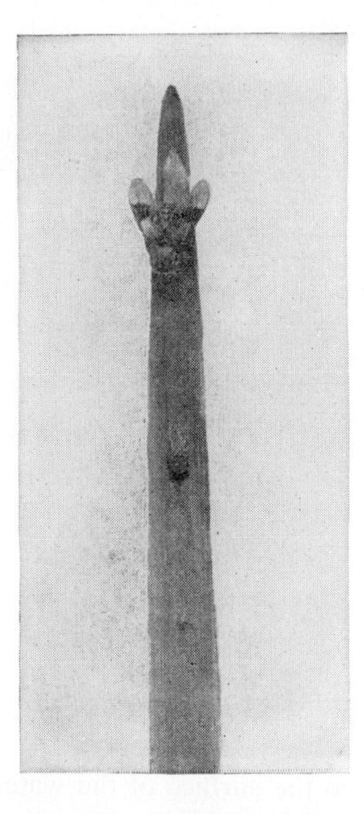

Fig. 80. A deer fly, *Chrysops* sp., in the act of oviposition. Note also an egg mass lower down on the leaf. × 1. (Photograph by Hine.)

eggs are deposited in layers on objects over water or moist situations favorable for the larvae, such as overhanging foliage, projecting rocks, sticks, and aquatic vegetation. The narrow cylindrical eggs (1.0 to 2.5 mm long) vary in numbers from 100 to 1000 and are deposited commonly in layers covered with a waterproof secretion which also binds the eggs together tightly.

The larva has a slender, cylindrical, contractile body tapering at both ends and consisting of a small head and 11 (according to some interpretations, 12) additional segments. The head is retractile, with pointed mandibles capable of inflicting a sharp bite; at the posterior end is situated a tracheal siphon which telescopes into the anal segment. The pupa resembles those of naked Lepidoptera, is obtect, abruptly rounded anteriorly, tapering posteriorly, with leg and wing cases attached to the body; the abdominal segments are free and about equal in length, segments 2 to 7 each bearing a more or less complete ring of spines near the posterior third. The adult fly emerges from the pupal case through a slit along the dorsum of the thorax, as do the rest of the Brachycera.

Breeding Habits and Life History. The eggs, numbering up to nearly a thousand, are deposited during the warmer months of the year in compact layers on objects such as the leaves of willow (Figs. 80, 81) and emergent aquatic vegetation which grows from or overhangs swampy areas, ponds, etc. The incubation period is greatly influenced by weather conditions, but during midsummer the usual range is from 5 to 7 days. On hatching the larvae fall

Fig. 81. *Tabanus punctifer*. Egg mass on willow leaf, larva, pupa, and adult female.

to the surface of the water, upon mud or moist earth, in clumps, and quickly drop to the bottom or burrow individually into the wet or damp earth, where they begin at once to feed on organic matter. Many species are predators, sucking the juices of insect larvae, crustacea, snails, earthworms, and other soft-bodied animals; cannibalism has been observed in several species. The larvae of Tabanidae are commonly encountered buried in the mud in such places as along the edge of marshy ponds and salt marshes, roadside ditches, and the overflow from rice fields; those of certain species may be found in moist leaf mold and debris.

The larvae (Figs. 81, 82) grow rapidly during the summer and autumn, and very slowly if at all during the winter in the single-brooded species, attaining full growth in the following early spring. There is some uncertainty as to the number of larval instars; it varies, according to some authors, from 4 to 9, the first molt evidently taking place shortly after hatching. An excellent account of the early stages of Tabanidae may be found in the works of Marchand.[12]

When the full-grown larva prepares to pupate, it moves into drier earth, usually an inch or two below the surface, and in a day or two the pupal stage is reached. This stage requires from 2 to 3 weeks, varying with the species. Stone[20] reports that most *Chrysops* species emerge in less than 2 weeks, even in as short a time as 5 days. The flies emerge from the pupa case at the surface, the wings soon unfold, and the insects take refuge among nearby foliage or rest on objects near at hand; in a short time they begin to

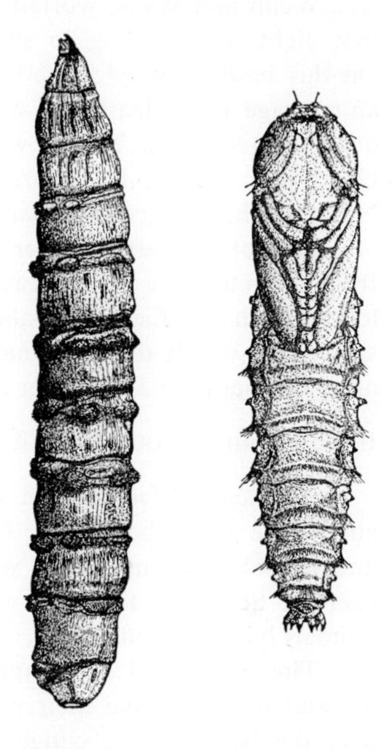

Fig. 82. Lateral view of larva (*left*) and ventral view of pupa (*right*) of *Tabanus gilanus.*

feed, the females seeking blood, and the males feeding on flower secretions and vegetable juices.

Much important information based on rearing experience with many species may be obtained by consulting various publications such as those by Stone,[20] Schwardt,[19] and Philip.[16] Schwardt, for example, reports life history records based on 202 individuals of *Tabanus lineola* (Fabricius), a common species of "greenhead," viz., average incubation period, 4 days; average larval period, 48.8 days; average pupal period, 8.1 days; average preovipositional period, 9 days; total developmental period averaging 69.9 days.

Tabanids that viciously attack man may abound in favorable mountain areas in the western United States. In the Sierra Nevada and other mountain ranges, horse flies breed in great numbers at elevations of 8000 to 9000 feet in ground made soggy by springs and water from melting snow in the summer. Deer and other wild animals suffer much from the bites of these flies.

Bites. The horse flies have broad bladelike mouth parts (Fig. 14) which inflict a deep, painful wound, causing a considerable flow of blood, which they lap up by means of their sponging labella. Man may be seriously annoyed, particularly by *Chrysops, Silvius,* and some species of *Tabanus,* but he is better able to protect himself by driving the flies away and by use of repellents than are wild and domestic animals. Schwardt[19] gives some pertinent information from the studies of Webb and Wells[23] and Philip:[15]

> Webb and Wells, working on *T. phaenops* O.S. in western Nevada, estimated that eight flies feeding to satiety would consume a cubic centimeter of blood. On this basis they calculated that 20 to 30 flies feeding for six hours would take an average of at least 100 cc of blood. This would amount to approximately a quart in ten days. Philip, working in Minnesota, derived a larger estimate of blood loss. Basing his figures on a somewhat heavier infestation than that in Nevada, Philip placed the daily loss of blood for each animal at 300 cc, or nearly one-third of a quart. Neither of these estimates includes the blood which exudes from the bite after the fly leaves. Philip, however, calls attention to this additional loss. The horse flies most abundant in Arkansas are comparable in size to the species on which these estimates of blood loss were made, and the infestation is often heavier than 50 flies per animal.

In describing an outbreak of gad flies in Kentucky, Garman[7] writes:

> Beef cattle had lost an average of 100 pounds as a result of the constant annoyance from them. . . . On cattle I counted from ten to nineteen. On mules and horses in harness they were a constant annoyance and even hogs were not exempt. Seven of the flies were counted on the exposed side of one of these animals lying in a puddle.
>
> The persecuted stock appeared to have given up fighting their enemies and allowed them to have their way. The switch of a cow's tail was observed to pass over the backs of the clinging flies without causing them to move. . . . During the middle of the day animals suffered so much that they refrained from grazing at all, either standing close together about the barn or else lurking singly in thickets or standing in pools formed by small streams.

The intermittent feeding habits of tabanids render them more likely to mechanical transmission of disease. A fly, interrupted in or ceasing its feeding activities on one individual, may readily pass on to another, so that sick and healthy individuals may be attacked in succession by the same fly.

Relation to Anthrax. Anthrax, also known as malignant pustule or carbuncle, wool sorter's disease, or charbon, is caused by *Bacillus anthracis.* Nearly all species of domestic mammals and man are susceptible; the herbivora and rodents are most likely to become infected.

After the inoculation of the organism into the animal, its incubation period is from 3 to 6 days. The bacilli are seen in the blood stream in advanced cases as chains of rod-shaped bodies. Entrance to the body is gained mainly in one of three ways: (1) through local pricks or lesions, i.e., *inoculation,* producing local anthrax or malignant pustule; (2) by *inhalation* of the spores, producing pulmonary anthrax; and (3) by *ingestion* with food, producing intestinal anthrax.

Horse flies relate directly to the first mode of infection (inoculation), and it is not altogether improbable that an epizootic of anthrax might thus be started and spread. Nuttall cites Bollinger (1874), who captured horse flies on a cow dead from anthrax, and saw the bacilli in preparations made from the stomachs and intestines of the insects. Two rabbits that were inoculated therewith died of anthrax.

Mitzmain[14] (Mayne), in a series of experiments with *Tabanus striatus* Fabricius, showed that direct mechanical inoculation of guinea pigs could be readily effected by the bite of the fly. He permitted the flies to feed on an inoculated guinea pig shortly before its death and transferred the flies soon thereafter (45 sec to 30 min) to a healthy guinea pig. The death of these animals followed in from 3 to 3 1/2 days.

Instances are recorded in which apparently the simple bite of an infected fly was all that was needed to produce malignant pustule in humans. Several veterinarians have related instances to the writer (Herms) in which this had occurred, notably one case in which a man was in the act of burying a cow dead of anthrax when he was bitten severely on the back of the neck by a horse fly and in due time developed a malignant pustule. Similar cases have been cited in the literature.

Tularemia. In 1919 a disease of man of hitherto unknown etiology occurring in Utah was reported by Francis[5] as deer-fly fever or Pahvant Valley plague. It was later identified by the same author with a disease reported among rodents in Tulare County, California, by McCoy and Chapin in 1912 and was given the name tularemia. It is a specific infectious disease traceable to *Pasteurella tularensis* (McCoy and Chapin). It was described by Francis as a disease of rural populations occurring during the summer months, coinciding with the prevalence of the newly discovered vector, *Chrysops discalis* Williston, a deer fly. Francis states:

> Following the fly bite on some exposed surface of the body (neck, face, hands, or legs) the onset is sudden, with pains and fever; the patient is prostrated and confined to bed; the lymph glands which drain the bitten area become tender, inflamed, and swollen, and commonly suppurate, requiring incision. The fever is of a septic type, lasting from three to six weeks, and convalescence is slow.

The disease occurs not only in the United States, but also in Canada, Alaska, northern Europe, Russia, Japan, and many other parts of the world. The pathology of tularemia is described in great detail by Lillie and Francis.[11]

In the acute form of the disease a primary ulcer (eschar) develops at the site of the inoculation. Francis and co-workers found that rabbits constitute an important reservoir for the infection and that it is transmitted from rabbit to rabbit by the *Chrysops* fly. The fly is undoubtedly merely a mechanical vector, and other species of tabanids are probably involved. It has also been found that tularemia can be transmitted from rabbit to rabbit by means of the rabbit louse, *Haemodipsus ventricosus* (Denny). *Cimex lectularius* Linnaeus, the bed bug, was also found to be a successful vector in laboratory experiments with guinea pigs, as was the mouse louse, *Polyplax serratus* (Burmeister), in the case of white mice. Mosquitoes and fleas have been shown to be able to transmit the infection. Several species of ticks are involved. *Dermacentor andersoni* Stiles is an important vector, perhaps the most important one, because the infection is transmitted transovarianly from generation to generation. Tularemia is now known to exist in nature in many species of animals; among these are meadow mice, ground squirrels, beavers, coyotes, sheep, and quail and other game birds. Infection may be acquired not only by insect bites but also by contact with infected insect feces, infected raw meat, and through contaminated water. Over 2000 cases of tularemia were reported in the United States in 1938, with a mortality of about 5 per cent.

Loiasis. The so-called mango fly, *Chrysops dimidiata* van der Wulp, has been shown by Leiper to be a vector of *Loa loa* (Cobbold), an African eye worm of man in various endemic regions in Africa, particularly the Belgian Congo. *Chrysops silacea* Austen has been proved to be a carrier of the organism by Connall and Connall,[4] who completely elucidated the life cycle not only in this fly but also in *C. dimidiata*. Microfilariae of *Loa loa* are found in the peripheral blood vessels during the daytime, showing a diurnal periodicity which gave rise to the term *Microfilaria diurna* Manson. The larvae measure about 300μ in length by 7.5μ in thickness, resembling *Wuchereria bancrofti* (Cobbold) very closely. In this stage, they are ingested by the *Chrysops* flies, and undergo development similar to that of *Wuchereria bancrofti* in the mosquito. Metamorphosis is completed in from 10 to 12 days, the larva increasing in length "tenfold." When the infected fly bites, the mature larvae issue from the proboscis, come to lie upon the skin of the host, and quickly disappear by burrowing.

The adult worms, females measuring from 50 to 70 mm in length and the males about half this length, inhabit the superficial subcutaneous connective tissue and are known to move about from place to place quite rapidly, giving rise to transient itching swellings known as Calabar swellings. The parasites have been observed in many parts of the body, such as the scrotum, penis, breast, eyelids, anterior chamber of the eye, tongue, finger, and back. The worms may be most readily excised when they travel across the bridge of the nose or conjunctiva.

Animal Trypanosomiases. Surra is a highly fatal disease of equine animals in southeastern Asia and other parts of the Far East; it occurs also in parts of Africa and of Central and South America. It was first described (1885) from India by Evans. The causal agent is *Trypanosoma evansi* (Steel). Several domestic and wild animals are involved as hosts and reservoirs. The disease may occur in a highly fatal form in dogs; in horses it is usually fatal, and camels are seriously affected. The acute form may occur in cattle and buffaloes when the parasite is introduced into a new area, but these animals are usually not seriously affected and may serve for months as reservoirs.

The trypanosomes (Fig. 83) are found in the blood of infected animals, and especially in the lymph and swollen glands, from the beginning of the first symptoms. During the early stage of the disease practically no clinical manifestations are visible save a variable appetite and an intermittent fever; there is progressive emaciation and edema of the abdomen and genitalia. Guinea pigs, white mice, and monkeys are highly susceptible laboratory animals.

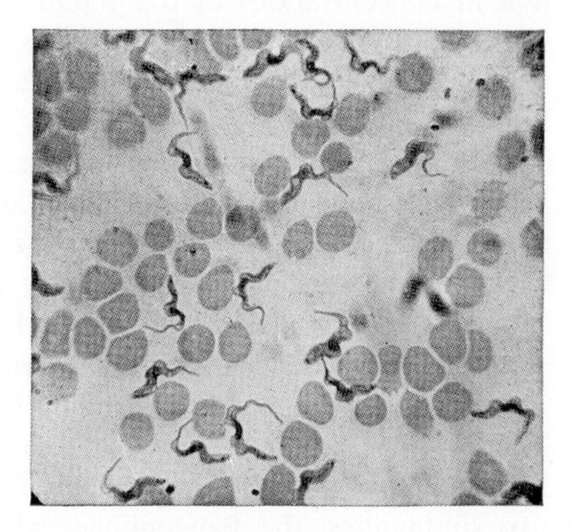

Fig. 83. *Trypanosoma evansi,* the causal organism of surra. (After Yutuc.)

Mitzmain[13] (Mayne) succeeded in transferring the infection from animal to animal through the agency of a horse fly, *Tabanus striatus* Fabricius. The transfer of the parasite took place only within 20 minutes of the infectious meal, despite the fact that the trypanosomes could survive as long as 30 hours in the intestinal tract of the fly. Other vectors, all mechanical, are bloodsucking muscids, *Ornithodorus* ticks, and (in Panama) vampire bats.

El debab is a trypanosomiasis of Algerian horses and camels traceable to *Trypanosoma berberum* Edmond and Et. Sergent (probably a synonym of *T. evansi*). This disease is evidently spread by horse flies, *Tabanus nemoralis* Meigen and *T. tomentosus* Macquart being considered the vectors.

Control. Control of tabanids has been and remains a difficult problem. One of the earlier attempts in this direction was Porchinsky's "pool of death," which involved the spreading of a film of kerosene on small pools of water where tabanids might assemble in large numbers to drink. Other methods involved control by use of predators and parasites, including the artificial dissemination of the scelionid egg parasite *Telenomus emersoni* (Girault), and modification of breeding grounds.

The use of DDT, lindane, chlordane, dieldrin, and other synthetic insecticides has brought more effective control. Lindane has proven of value against adults; it is effective when applied to vegetation where the flies congregate, and it produces a complete, though temporary, reduction when applied by air.[3] Pyrethrum plus a synergist (piperonyl butoxide or MGK 264) may, with limitations, be applied to animals as a spray. Tabanid larvae are susceptible to DDT. The larvae of *Chrysops discalis* are killed by the application in concentrations of 0.2 p.p.m. to the muck in which they breed, and *Tabanus* larvae can be controlled in salt marshes by application of granulated formulations of dieldrin at concentrations which do not seriously affect beneficial animal life.[8,9]

For protection of human beings, diethyltoluamide is an efficient repellent. Cattle may be protected by the use of butoxypolyproplene glycol (Crag fly repellent). Systemic insecticides offer a possibility in animal protection, but to date their use has not been very successful.

The Species of Tabanidae. The family Tabanidae is a fairly large one of almost world-wide distribution. There are 2500 to 3000 species distributed in from 30 to 80 genera, depending upon the interpretation of the authority. The Nearctic forms have been treated in the monographs of Stone[21] and Brennan,[2] and have been catalogued by Philip.[17] The family is divided into two subfamilies, the Pangoniinae, which includes all Tabanidae with apical spurs on the hind tibiae, e.g., the species belonging to the genera *Silvius, Chrysops, Goniops, Apatolestes,* and *Pangonia;* and the subfamily Tabaninae, in which the apical spurs are lacking, as in *Tabanus* and *Chrysozona.* Some of the more important Nearctic species are as follows.

Tabanus atratus Fabricius (Fig. 84), the black horse fly, measures from 16 to 28 mm in length. It is distributed over most of the United States east of the Rocky Mountains and into Mexico. The whole insect is uniformly black, and the thorax and abdomen in well-preserved specimens are thinly covered with a whitish pollen, or dust, which is easily rubbed off if the specimens are not cared for properly. In certain lights the abdomen shows a distinctly bluish cast. Curran believes, probably correctly, that this may be the "blue-tailed fly" of the well-known ballad.

Tabanus stygius Say is a black and white horse fly which is widely distributed east of the Rocky Mountains. Its length is 20 to 22 mm. It is a serious pest of livestock in much of its range. In the female the thorax dorsally is plainly whitish pollinose with more intense longitudinal lines; the thorax of the male is dorsally a uniform grayish brown. *Tabanus punctifer* Osten

Sacken (Fig. 81) is also a black and white species resembling *T. stygius* except that the front tibiae are white on the basal third and the thorax is uniformly white pollinose in both sexes; there is usually a small dark spot near the tip of the wing. It is the largest and best known species of horse fly in western North America, particularly along the Pacific coast. It seriously annoys livestock but does not attack man. *Tabanus sulcifrons* Macquart, the autumn horse fly, is a rather large species with usually a predominantly reddish-brown abdomen and with brownish-tinged wings marked by dark spots at the cross veins and at the furcation of vein R_{4+5}. *Tabanus quinquevittatus* Wiedemann (= *vicarius* Walker), the greenhead, is one of the most dreaded

Fig. 84. The black horse fly, *Tabanus atratus*. (*Left*) male, (*right*) female. × 1.5. (Photograph by Hine.)

stock pests common throughout the southern states. *Tabanus lineola* Fabricius, the striped horse fly, is also an annoying stock pest in the eastern states. In the mountains of the west, several of the mottled grayish species plague man as well as animals. Stone[21] lists 124 species of *Tabanus* (including forms sometimes segregated into the genus *Hybomitra*) in North America including Mexico.

The genus *Chrysops* (Fig. 80) contains about 80 North American species. Many members of this genus attack man readily and persistently. They are smaller than most *Tabanus* and have pictured wings which are usually definitely cross-banded. The term deer fly is usually applied to this genus.

Chrysops callida Osten Sacken is a widely distributed species, measuring from 7 to 9 mm, and is black in color with large pale yellow spots on the sides near the base of the abdomen. *Chrysops celer* Osten Sacken is black in color, the female with dense orange pile on the pleura. It measures from 8 to

11 mm in length. It appears to have a more northerly distribution. *Chrysops discalis* Williston is gray to yellowish gray in the female, with black spots on the abdomen; in the wing picture the hyaline discal cell and spot at the bifurcation of vein R_{4+5} are quite characteristic. In the male the color is predominantly black with yellow-gray spots on the abdomen. Its length is 8 to 10.5 mm. It is reported from most western states eastward to North Dakota and Manitoba.

Chrysozona americana (Osten Sacken) occurs from central Alaska to New Mexico. It is quite different in appearance from *Tabanus* and *Chrysops* in that its wings are quite characteristically and densely mottled. *Silvius pollinosus* Williston and *S. quadrivittatus* (Say), small gray species with distinctly but rather sparsely mottled wings, are viciously annoying to both man and livestock in the area just east of the Rocky Mountains.

KEY TO THE TABANID GENERA OF NEARCTIC AMERICA*

1. Hind tibiae with apical spurs; ocelli usually present. . . . . Subfamily Pagoniinae 2

   Hind tibiae without apical spurs; ocelli usually absent, if present rudimentary (Fig. 85). . . . . Subfamily Tabaninae 9

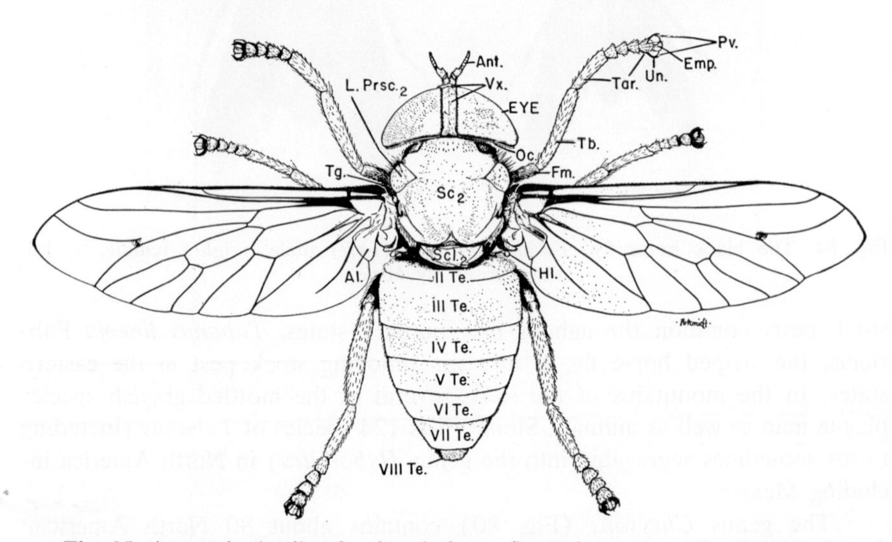

Fig. 85. Anatomic details of a female horse fly, *Tabanus punctifer*. Explanation of abbreviations: *Ant.*, antenna; *Al.*, alula; *Emp.*, empodium; *Fm.*, femur; *Hl.*, halter; *L. Prsc.*, lobe of prescutum (notopleuron); *Oc.*, occiput; *Pv.*, pulvilli; *Sc.*, scutum; *Scl.*, scutellum; *Tar.*, tarsus; *Tb.*, tibia; *Te.*, tergite; *Tg.*, tegula; *Un.*, ungues; *Vx.*, the morphologic vertex (the "front" of most taxonomic literature).

* Arranged by T. H. G. Aitken after Brennan[2] and Stone.[21] Refer also to Surcouf.[22] Philip[17] has omitted the genus *Bequaertomyia* from his recent catalog of Nearctic Tabanidae, based on the elevation by Mackerras and Fuller (1942) of this primitive group of flies to family rank (Pelecorhynchidae) in which *Bequaertomyia* appears.

2. Flagellum of antenna composed of eight annuli.................... 3
   Flagellum with five distinct annuli.............................. 7
3. Second anal vein sinuous.............................*Bequaertomyia*
   Second anal vein not sinuous...................................... 4
4. Eyes of female acutely angulate above; wings darkened anteriorly..*Goniops*
   Eyes of female rounded (normal); wings of uniform color........... 5
5. Palpi short, stubby, about equal in length to proboscis, which is conspicuously shorter than head.............................*Apatolestes*
   Palpi slender, distinctly shorter than proboscis, which is often as long or longer than head.. 6
6. Cell R_5 petiolate.......................................*Esenbeckia*
   Cell R_5 open..*Stonemyia*
7. Pedicel of antenna about half as long as scape.................*Silvius*
   Pedicel of antenna more than half as long as scape, often nearly as long 8
8. Wings evenly infuscated; abdomen globose, much wider than thorax; antennae very slender and elongate; a stump at bifurcation of vein R_{4+5}..*Neochrysops*
   Wings irregularly infuscated, exhibiting a variety of patterns (entirely hyaline in *C. hyalina* Shannon); abdomen normal; antennae variable; bifurcation of vein R_{4+5} without a stump (except rarely adventitiously) .... *Chrysops*
9. Scape of antenna considerably longer than thick; frons of female widened below, broader than high, with a velvety-black spot to each side at angle made by eye and subcallus;* flagellum of antenna with four annuli; wing gray, with small white maculations.............*Chrysozona*
   Scape of antenna usually scarcely longer than thick; frons of female not broader than high, without velvety-black spots; flagellum of antenna usually with five annuli; wing pattern, if any, not as in *Chrysozona*.. 10
10. Eye bare; subcallus very swollen and shiny; genae denuded; dorsal angle of flagellum small and blunt; wing at least partially infuscated...... 11
    Without above combination of characters; if the subcallus is large and denuded, the eye is densely pilose............................... 12
11. Scape of antennae swollen, at least below; apical half of vein R_4 turned abruptly forward; wing, at least anteriorly, infuscated with a crescent-shaped, hyaline apex; tibiae somewhat swollen...........*Bolbodimyia*
    Scape of antenna not noticeably swollen; vein R_4 not turned abruptly forward; apex of wing not hyaline; tibiae not swollen......*Whitneyomyia*
12. Flagellum of antenna with no dorsal angle; frons of female very narrow, the median callus a very slender line; no ocellar tubercle; wing with at least a subapical brown spot; eye bare....................*Diachlorus*
    Not with this combination of characters.......................... 13

* That part of the frons below the level of the lower, inner angle of the eye and above the antennae is termed the *subcallus;* the frons proper (just dorsad) usually possesses two denuded calli, one at the lower margin, the *basal callus,* and the *median callus,* usually narrow and frequently broadly joined to the *basal callus.* The terms *scape* and *pedicel* are applied to the first and second segments, respectively, of the antenna; the complex "third segment" is the flagellum.

13. Basal portion of antennal flagellum with a prominent, forward-projecting tooth reaching nearly to the base of the annulate portion; eye pilose . . . . *Dicladocera*
    Basal portion of antennal flagellum with or without a prominent dorsal angle, but if this is produced forward the eye is bare 14
14. Basal callus in female lacking or very much reduced, separated from eye by a considerable space; neither palpus black nor abdomen with a narrow dorsal stripe 15
    Basal callus of female as wide, or nearly as wide, as frons, or, if narrowed, still considerably wider than median callus; either palpus black or abdomen with a narrow dorsal stripe 17
15. Eye distinctly pilose; no distinct ocellar tubercle (eye of female usually with a single, diagonal, purple line which often shows even in dried specimens) . . . . *Atylotus*
    Eye bare or very sparsely pilose; ocellar tubercle present or absent (frons of female about five times as high as width at base) 16
16. Basal callus a swelling at base of a slender raised ridge; a distinct ocellar tubercle present in female; abdomen brownish, with white bands, the apex compressed . . . . *Leucotabanus*
    No basal or median calli or ocellar tubercle present; bright green or yellow species, the abdomen not distinctly compressed apically . . . . *Chlorotabanus*
17. Annulate portion of antennal flagellum hairy; no ocellar tubercle; second palpal segment short and stout; with erect hair; proboscis short. . *Anacimas*
    Not agreeing entirely with above, the hair of antennal flagellum very inconspicuous if present 18
18. Rather small species, with bare or sparsely pilose eye, scarcely any angle, and no dorsal excision on flagellum of antenna, and frequently a stump from vein R_4 . . . . *Stenotabanus*
    Eye bare or pilose, but if a stump vein from vein R_4 is present either the dorsal angle of the antennal flagellum is distinct or the eye is densely pilose, or both . . . . *Tabanus*

SNIPE FLIES

Family Rhagionidae (Leptidae)

Snipe flies belong to the dipterous family Rhagionidae, formerly known as Leptidae. The family comprises nonbloodsuckers as well as bloodsucking species. Leonard[10] characterizes it as follows:

> Flies of moderate to large size usually more or less elongate and nearly bare to moderately pilose, rather than densely hairy, never, however, with distinct bristles. Males usually holoptic; more rarely dichoptic. Empodium pulvilliform, there being three pads of about equal size between the claws. . . . Veins of the wing distinct, not crowded anteriorly; third longitudinal [vein]* furcate; basal cells large; five posterior cells usually present.

* Leonard says "cell" (lapsus).

Two American genera, *Suragina* (e.g., *S. longipes* (Bellardi) of Mexico) and *Symphoromyia*[1] contain bloodsucking species. In both of these the antenna, which are highly variable in the family as a whole, are three-segmented, the third segment (flagellum) being kidney-shaped (sometimes concave in dorsal profile below the arista and then not quite kidney-shaped) with a subterminal arista. The wings of *Suragina* are banded whereas those of *Symphoromyia* are clear. The Australian genus *Spaniopsis,* which also sucks blood, has an elongated third antennal segment which terminates in a style.

The females of several species of *Symphoromyia* are vicious biters, behaving somewhat as do the tabanid flies belonging to the genus *Chrysops.* They alight on the exposed parts of the body quite silently and singly, and inflict a sudden painful bite usually before their presence is known. Some

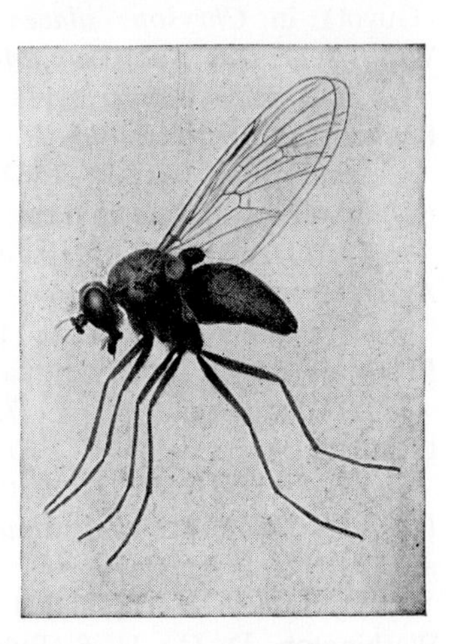

Fig. 86. A snipe fly, *Symphoromyia hirta.* (Adapted after Hearle.)

species may readily be mistaken at first for stable flies. Among the severe biters are *Symphoromyia atripes* Bigot, a western species measuring 5.5 to 8 mm in length, black with black legs; *S. pachyceras* Williston, particularly a Pacific coast species, measuring a little larger (6 to 9 mm in length), also almost wholly black; *S. kincaidi* Aldrich, a similar species but with yellow palpi; and *S. plagens* Williston, a robust species about the size of a house fly, with an orange-colored abdomen. *Symphoromyia hirta* Johnson is shown in Figure 86.

The mouth parts are of the tabanid type, the strongly sclerotized piercing and cutting structures being enclosed in a retractile labial sheath; as in the tabanids, blood is lapped up by the labella. The mouth parts have been studied in detail by Ross.[18]

Very little is known about the breeding habits and life history of the species of *Symphoromyia.* Frohne[6] recovered two newly emerged females of *S. atripes* in a Dove type emergence trap in Alaska; the larvae probably lived in wet peaty soil. Frohne describes the breeding area, particularly from the standpoint of its vegetation, in detail. The rhagionids as a group breed mostly in moist soil, where there is decaying vegetation; the larvae are predaceous.

REFERENCES

1. Aldrich, J. M., 1915. "The dipterous genus *Symphoromyia* in North America," *Proc. U. S. Nat. Mus.,* **49:**113–42.

2. Brennan, J. M., 1935. "The Pangoniinae of Nearctic America, Diptera: Tabanidae," *Univ. Kansas Sc. Bull.* **22:**249–402.

3. Brown, A. W. A., and Morrison, P. E., 1955. "Control of adult tabanids by aereal spraying," *J. Econ. Entomol.,* **48:**125–29.

4. Connall, A., and Connall, S. L. M., 1922. "The development of *Loa loa* (Guyot) in *Chrysops silacea* (Austen) and in *Chrysops dimidiata* (van der Wulp)," *Tr. Roy. Soc. Trop. Med. & Hyg.,* **16:**64–89.

5. Francis, Edward, 1919. "Deer fly fever or Pahvant Valley plague," U. S. Public Health Service, *Pub. Health Rep.,* **34:**2061–62.

6. Frohne, W. C., 1957. "Habitat and males of Alaskan snipe fly pests (Symphoromyia: Rhagionidae)," *Mosquito News,* **17:**94–96.

7. Garman, H., 1910. *An Outbreak of Gadflies in Kentucky.* Kentucky Agric. Exper. Sta., in Bull., no. 151.

8. Hansens, Elton J., 1956. "Granulated insecticides against greenhead (Tabanus) larvae in the salt marsh," *J. Econ. Entomol.,* **49:**401–03.

9. Jamnback, H., 1957. "Control of salt marsh *Tabanus* larvae with granulated insecticides," *J. Econ. Entomol.,* **50:**379–82.

10. Leonard, M. D., 1930. *A Revision of the Dipterous Family Rhagionidae (Leptidae) in the United States and Canada,* in Mem. Amer. Entomolog. Soc., no. 7, 181 pp. (3 plates).

11. Lillie, R. D., and Francis, Edward, 1936. *Pathology of Tularaemia.* Washington, D. C.: U. S. Public Health Service, in Nat. Inst. Health Bull., no. 167. 217 pp.

12. Marchand, Werner, 1920. *The Early Stages of Tabanidae (Horseflies).* New York: Rockefeller Institute for Medical Research, in Monograph no. 13. 203 pp. (15 plates).

13. Mitzmain, M. B., 1913. "The mechanical transmission of surra by *Tabanus striatus* Fabricius," *Philippine J. Sc.* 8:223–29.

14. Mitzmain, M. B., 1914. "Summary of experiments in the transmission of anthrax by biting flies." U. S. Public Health Service, *Pub. Health Bull.,* no. 94, pp. 41–48.

15. Philip, C. B., 1928. "Methods of collecting and rearing the immature stages of Tabanidae," *J. Parasitol.,* **14:**243–53.

16. Philip, C. B., 1931. *The Tabanidae (Horseflies) of Minnesota, with Special Reference to their Biologies and Taxonomy.* St. Paul, Minn.: in Univ. Minn. Tech. Bull., 80. 132 pp. (4 plates).

17. Philip, C. B., 1947. "A catalog of the bloodsucking fly family Tabanidae (horseflies and deerflies) of the Nearctic region north of Mexico," *Amer. Midland Naturalist,* **37:**257–324.

18. Ross, H. H., 1940. "The Rocky Mountain 'black fly', *Symphoromyia atripes*," *Ann. Entomol. Soc. Amer.*, **33**:254–57.

19. Schwardt, H. A., 1936. *Horseflies of Arkansas*. Fayetteville: Univ. Arkansas, in Agric. Exper. Sta. Bull., no. 332. 66 pp.

20. Stone, Alan, 1930. "The bionomics of some Tabanidae (Diptera)," *Ann. Entomol. Soc. Amer.* **23**:261–304.

21. Stone, Alan, 1938. *The Horseflies of the Subfamily Tabaninae of the Nearctic Region*. Washington, D. C.: Dept. Agric., in Misc. Publ., no. 305. 171 pp.

22. Surcouf, J., 1921. *Diptera, Family Tabanidae*. Brussels: Genera Insectorum (P. Wytsman), Fasc. 175.

23. Webb, J. L., and Wells, R. W., 1924. *Horseflies: Biology and Relation to Western Agriculture*. Washington, D. C.: Dept. Agric., in Bull., no. 1218. 36 pp.

Chapter 14

THE SYRPHID FLIES, MUSCOID FLIES, AND LOUSE FLIES

Suborder Cyclorrhapha

Special Structural Characteristics of Adults. In the higher Diptera, certain anatomic structures peculiar to this group are used as a basis for the construction of keys and descriptions. The most important of these will be considered here.

The most conspicuous feature of the head (Fig. 87) is the pair of large *compound eyes* which, though widely separated from each other in the female, are often contiguous or very narrowly separated in the male, thereby greatly constricting the areas that lie between them. The *ocelli* are located on an *ocellar* or *frontal triangle* which is usually clearly demarcated; in the Chloropidae, this triangle is very large and may occupy most of the vertex and a considerable area of the front. The median area extending from the ocelli to the base of the antennae is the *frontal stripe* or *frontale;* to each side, adjoining the eye, lie the *parafrontals* which, below the base of the antennae, become the *parafacials.* The central part of the face, set off by a suture which extends above the base of the antennae, terminates below an area called the epistoma, which may be produced forward over the *oral margin.* The ridges between the center of the face and the parafacials are called the *facialia* or *facials.*

The *antenna* (Fig. 41) is three-segmented; the second segment is set at a distinct angle to the first, so that the antenna is pendant rather than porrect, as in most insects. The second antennal segment, in the calyptrate muscoids, is partially divided by a seam or suture that runs most of the length of its outer dorsal side. The *arista,* a large bristlelike structure arising high on the third segment, actually consists of several terminal segments of the antenna which have migrated onto a dorsal position and fused. The arista may be bare or hairy; the hairs may be situated above and below (plumose) or above only; if the latter, they may be simple (cf. Fig. 111) or, as in the tsetse flies (Fig. 106), plumose.

Chaetotaxy (the arrangement of macrochaetae or bristles) is important in the taxonomy of the muscoid flies. That of the head is shown in Figure 87; that of the thorax in Figure 88. The more important bristles mentioned in this text are the *vibrissae* (an unusually strong bristle on the lower part of each facial) and the following thoracic bristles: the *notopleurals, dorsocentrals, acrostichals, sternopleurals, hypopleurals,* and *scutellars.* These, as well as others not mentioned here, may be identified from Figures

88A and 88B. The bristles of the abdomen are not so important, but the median marginals, i.e., erect bristles at the apices of the segments and near the median line (measured from left to right), will be mentioned in subsequent descriptions.

In addition to the chaetotaxy, mention should be made of the following thoracic structures. The two *thoracic spiracles* have been shown to be the

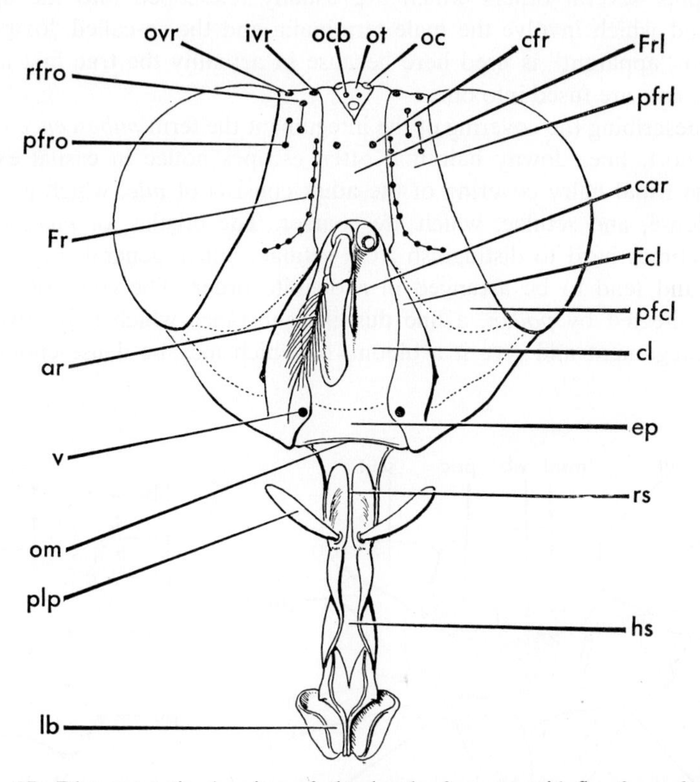

Fig. 87. Diagrammatic drawing of the head of a muscoid fly, from front view. Explanation of abbreviations; *ar,* arista; *car,* facial carina; *cfl,* cruciate frontal bristle (scar); *cl,* clypeus; *ep,* epistoma; *fcl,* faciale; *fr,* frontal row (bristle scars); *frl,* frontale (frontal stripe or vitta); *hs,* haustellum; *ivr,* inner vertical bristle (scar); *lb,* labella; *oc,* ocellus; *ocb,* ocellar bristle (scar); *ot,* ocellar triangle; *ovr,* outer vertical bristle (scar); *pfcl,* parafaciale; *pfrl,* parafrontale; *pfro,* proclinate fronto-orbital row (bristle scars); *plp,* palpus; *rfro,* reclinate fronto-orbital row (bristle scars); *rs,* rostrum; *v,* vibrissa. (Drawing by Arthur Cushman; U.S.D.A. photograph.)

mesothoracic and *metathoracic,* respectively (Fig. 88, *mss* and *mts*). The *propleuron* lies in front of the mesothoracic spiracle; whether its centrally depressed area is hairy or not may be of good taxonomic significance. In the calyptrate muscoids, a well-defined *mesonotal suture* is present, and the area between the wing base and the side of the scutellum, known as the *postalar callus,* is well differentiated. Two pairs of *squamae* are present, one (the *alar*) more closely associated with the wing, and the other (the *lower* or *thoracic*) closer to the wall of the thorax. The latter may be hairy above, and this may be of taxonomic significance. The *postscutellum* (Fig. 88) in some of the calyptrate muscoids is strongly produced as in the figures; in others, it is inconspicuous or undeveloped.

The abdomen of a muscoid fly usually consists of four apparent segments, plus several others which are usually telescoped into the apparent fourth and which involve the male terminalia and the so-called "ovipositor." The term "apparent" is used here because in actuality the true first and second segments are fused into one.

In describing the covering of the integument the term *pubescence* refers to a very short, fine, downy hair that often escapes notice in casual examinations; the usual hairy covering of the adult consists of *pile,* which is soft and rather dense, and setulae, which are coarser. The bristles, or *macrochaetae,* are sometimes hard to distinguish from setulae, but in general they are quite distinct and tend to be arranged in a definite order. The color of the body may be affected by *pollen,* a fine dustlike substance which may cover parts of the integument and give it a bloom, or which may be dense enough even

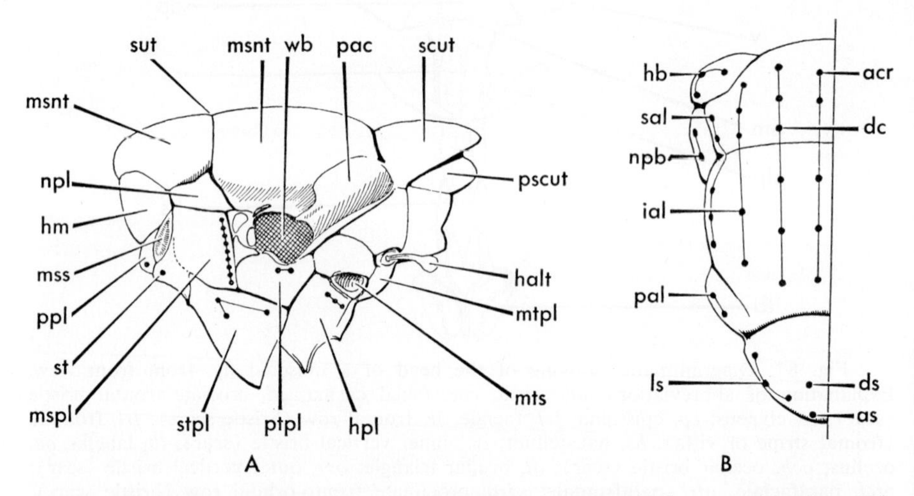

Fig. 88. Diagrammatic drawing of the thorax of a muscoid fly. (*A*) Side view; (*B*) left half, dorsal view. Abbreviations of areas and bristle scars: *acr,* acrostichal row; *as,* apical scutellar; *dc,* dorsocentral row; *ds,* discal scutellar; *halt,* halter; *hb,* humeral row; *hm,* humerus; *hpl,* hypopleuron; *ial,* intra-alar row; *ls,* lateral scutellar row; *msnt,* mesonotum; *mspl,* mesopleuron; *mss,* mesothoracic spiracle; *mtpl,* metapleuron; *mts,* metathoracic spiracle; *npb,* notopleural row; *npl,* notopleuron; *pac,* postalar callus; *pal,* postalar row; *ppl,* propleuron; *pscut,* postscutellum; *ptpl,* pteropleuron; *sal,* supra-alar row; *scut,* scutellum; *st,* stigmatal; *stpl,* sternopleuron; *sut,* mesonotal suture; *wb,* wing base. Bristle scars not labeled are named in accordance with the sclerite on which they are located (propleural, sternopleural, mesopleural, hypopleural, pteropleural). (Drawing by Arthur Cushman; U.S.D.A. photograph.)

to conceal the ground color. The term *pollen* in Latin means a "fine dust," and the aptness of its application also to the microspores of seed plants is obvious.

The following keys will aid in the identification of some of the higher Diptera of greater medical importance. To make identifications below the generic level, the student will need to consult specialized works that deal with the family and geographic area in question. Several useful manuals of recent date are James,[11] Van Emden,[35] Eldridge and James,[7] and Shtakelberg;[30] the last mentioned is an excellent work that will be useful even in dealing with the Nearctic fauna, but its use depends on the student having a reading knowledge of Russian.

KEY TO THE FAMILIES OF HIGHER DIPTERA (CYCLORRHAPHA) THAT CONTAIN FORMS OF MEDICAL IMPORTANCE* (ADULTS)

1. Body strongly flattened in a dorsoventral axis and with a tough leathery or horny integument; coxae widely separated at the base, the legs attached laterally and spreading away from the body (except in some Streblidae); ectoparasitic forms, frequently without wings. (Section Pupipara) 2
   Body usually not flattened and without an especially tough integument; coxae close together, the legs attached ventrally and not particularly spreading; wings present, with rare exceptions. (Section Myodaria).. 4
2. Head small, when at rest folded back into a groove on the dorsum of the thorax; prosternum produced.......... Family Nycteribiidae
   Head larger, not folding back into a groove on the dorsum of the thorax; prosternum not produced.......... 3
3. Palpi leaflike, broader than long, and not ensheathing the proboscis .... Family Streblidae
   Palpi elongated, forming a sheath for the proboscis... Family Hippoboscidae
4. Wing with a spurious vein, that is, a veinlike fold in the membrane between the radius and the media and transversing the cross vein r-m; anal cell closed very close to the wing margin........ Family Syrphidae
   Wing without a spurious vein; anal cell not prolonged toward the wing margin 5
5. Wing with only the veins toward the fore margin thickened, the others weak, oblique, and not connected by cross veins........ Family Phoridae
   Wing not as described, but with the normal muscoid type of venation.. 6
6. Mouth parts nonfunctional, reduced to three knoblike structures (the two palpi and the rudimentary proboscis); bot and warble flies...... 7
   Mouth parts well developed and functional.......... 10
7. Postscutellum distinctly formed; squamae large; apical cell greatly narrowed or closed at its apex.......... 8
   Postscutellum undeveloped; squamae large or small, apical cell open, sometimes narrowed.......... 9

* The more important myiasis-causing flies can be determined with the use of this key. An exception is *Hermetia illucens* (L.), which belongs to the Brachycera.

8. Apical cell closed and petiolate........................Family Oestridae
   Apical cell open..............................Family Hypodermatidae
9. Squamae small; apical cell gradually broadening to the wing margin
   ....Family Gasterophilidae
   Squamae large; apical cell greatly narrowed at its apex..Family Cuterebridae
10. Second antennal segment with a longitudinal seam or suture extending along its outer upper edge; squamae usually large; postalar callus distinct 11
    Second antennal segment without a longitudinal suture; squamae usually small; postalar callus not differentiated......................... 13
11. Hypopleural bristles present; apical cell greatly narrowed toward its apex 12
    Hypopleural bristles absent; apical cell sometimes narrowed toward its apex but often broadly open.......................Family Muscidae
12. Two strong notopleural bristles present; if there is a weak third, the abdomen is metallic blue, green, or coppery, and the depression of the propleuron is hairy; base of the radius before the humeral cross vein often hairy posteriorly..........................Family Calliphoridae
    At least three or four notopleural bristles present,* abdomen, in medically important forms, black (often reddish at the apex) with grayish or silvery pollen; depression of the propleuron bare; base of radius before the humeral cross vein bare posteriorly..Family Sarcophagidae
13. Subcosta distinctly differentiated from vein R_1 and ending independently in the costa.. 14
    Subcosta absent or only partially developed, not reaching the costa.... 15
14. Metathoracic spiracle with one to several hairs (visible only under high magnification) on its border; palpi, vestigial; head, spherical; slender, wasp-waisted, somewhat resembling winged ants........Family Sepsidae
    Metathoracic spiracle with only ordinary soft pubescence; palpi well developed; eyes round; bristles of the front confined to the upper part and consisting of at most two pairs...............Family Piophilidae
15. Frontal triangle very large, often occupying a large part of the front; vein Cu_1 with a slight, though quite distinct, crook or curvature near the middle of the discal cell; species of medical importance with a spur, usually curved, at the apex of the hind tibia. (*Hippelates*)....
    ....Family Chloropidae
    Frontal triangle small; vein Cu_2 without a noticeable crook or curve at the middle of the discal cell; hind tibia without a curved spur at its apex ....Family Drosophilidae

KEY TO THE GENERA OF MUSCIDAE (IN THE BROAD SENSE) OF MEDICAL IMPORTANCE (ADULTS)

1. Arista bare or virtually so; apical cell broadly open at its apex; second anal vein short and the third anal vein curved forward in such a way that, if the second were produced, the two would intersect.......*Fannia*
   Arista long-haired, at least above; apical cell narrowed at its apex; anal veins not as in *Fannia*.................................. 2

* *Wohlfahrtia* usually has only two.

2. Proboscis fitted for bloodsucking, long, slender, rigid, with small labella, (Fig. 15) 3
   Proboscis shorter, fleshy, with well-developed labella, at most with rasping labellar teeth, which may be fitted for lapping but not for siphoning blood (Fig. 16); arista with hair above and below 6
3. Arista with hair above and below .... *Haematobia*
   Arista with hair above only 4
4. Proboscis thin, with a strongly developed bulb at the base of the lower portion (haustellum) (Fig. 107); hairs of arista in turn plumose; discal cell of wing shaped like a meat cleaver .... *Glossina*
   Proboscis somewhat thicker, enlarged but not bulbous at the base of the haustellum (Fig. 15); hairs of arista simple; discal cell not shaped like a meat cleaver 5
5. Palpi short and small, not nearly as long as the haustellum; flies of about the same size as the house fly (Fig. 111) .... *Stomoxys*
   Palpi very prominent, about as long as the haustellum and ensheathing it in life; size considerably less than that of the house fly (Fig. 111) . . *Siphona*
6. Vein M_{1+2} broadly rounded at its bend; longest hairs of arista not half so long as the terminal aristal segment .... *Muscina*
   Vein M_{1+2} angularly rounded at its bend; longest hairs of arista almost as long as the terminal aristal segment .... *Musca*

KEY TO THE GENERA OF CALLIPHORIDAE OF MEDICAL IMPORTANCE (ADULTS)

1. Base of the radius (before the humeral cross vein) with a row of hairs posteriorly on the upper surface 2
   Base of the radius bare posteriorly on the upper surface 6
2. Hind coxa with a row of hairs posteriorly; green to violet-green species, with three prominent black longitudinal stripes on the mesonotum 3
   Hind coxa bare posteriorly; green to bluish-black species, sometimes with transverse bands or 2 narrow longitudinal stripes or both on the mesonotum, but never marked as above 4
3. Palpus short and filiform, not nearly reaching the margin of the epistoma .... *Callitroga*
   Palpus elongated and clavate, almost reaching the margin of the epistoma .... *Paralucilia**
4. Lower squama hairy above .... *Chrysomya*
   Lower squama bare .... 5†
5. Mesonotum convex; mesothoracic spiracle with bright orange hair, preacrostichal bristles well developed .... *Phormia*
   Mesonotum flattened on the disc; mesothoracic spiracle with dark hair; preachrostichal bristles absent or very poorly developed ..... *Protophormia*

* *Paralucilia* is included in the key because *P. wheeleri* (Hough) of the western United States might easily be mistaken for *Callitroga.*

† Nestling bird parasites of the genus *Protocalliphora* (= *Apaulina*) will also trace to this couplet.

6. Depression of the propleuron bare; yellow, brown, or gray species..... 7
   Depression of the propleuron pilose; abdomen blue, green, or violet, except in some Australian *Calliphora*........................ 9
7. Prosternum hairy; lower section of proboscis (haustellum) somewhat swollen; yellowish species with only ordinary hairs and bristles on the thorax.. 8
   Prosternum bare; lower section of proboscis not at all swollen; blackish species with abundant crinkly yellowish hairs (except when they are abraded) on the sides and dorsum of the thorax................*Pollenia*
8. Vein R_5 with a row of erect hairs extending nearly to cross vein r-m; eyes of both sexes broadly separated; second abdominal segment especially long ....*Auchmeromyia*
   Vein R_5 with a row of erect hairs extending less than half-way to cross vein r-m; eyes of the male nearly contiguous; second abdominal segment of ordinary length ....*Cordylobia*
9. Lower squama bare above 10
   Lower squama hairy above 11
10. Subcostal sclerite with only soft pubescence not interspersed with stiff black hairs ....*Phaenicia*
    Subcostal sclerite with wiry, erect black hairs in addition to the fine pubescence ....*Lucilia*
11. Abdomen shining, but the sheen somewhat dulled by overlying pollen; scutellum usually with four or more strong lateral bristles on each side ....*Calliphora*
    Abdomen brilliantly shining, without overlying pollen to dull the sheen; scutellum with three strong lateral bristles on each side ......*Cynomyopsis*

KEY TO THE GENERA OF SARCOPHAGIDAE OF MEDICAL IMPORTANCE (ADULTS)

1. Arista with only pubescence; abdomen with constant markings which are independent of the light incidence ....*Wohlfahrtia*
   Arista plumose; abdomen with checkered black and gray markings which become reversed with changing light incidence .*Sarcophaga* (broad sense)

Identification of Cyclorrhaphous Larvae. The typical muscoid larva, called a maggot, is legless, more or less cylindrical but strongly tapering anteriorly and truncated posteriorly; it is distinctly segmented, with 12 visible segments including the so-called "cephalic" segment (Fig. 89). Some muscoid larvae differ from this general pattern, however; the cattle grub and sheep grub, for example, are robust and more oval, and the larva of *Fannia* is flattened with conspicuous processes extending from the body. Fully grown larvae differ greatly in length according to species, ranging from less than 5 mm to about 35 mm.

At the narrow, somewhat pointed anterior end the *mouth hooks* are prominent, unless the mouth parts are nonfunctional, as in the tsetse fly or the mature cattle grub. The mouth hooks form a part of the *cephalopharyn-*

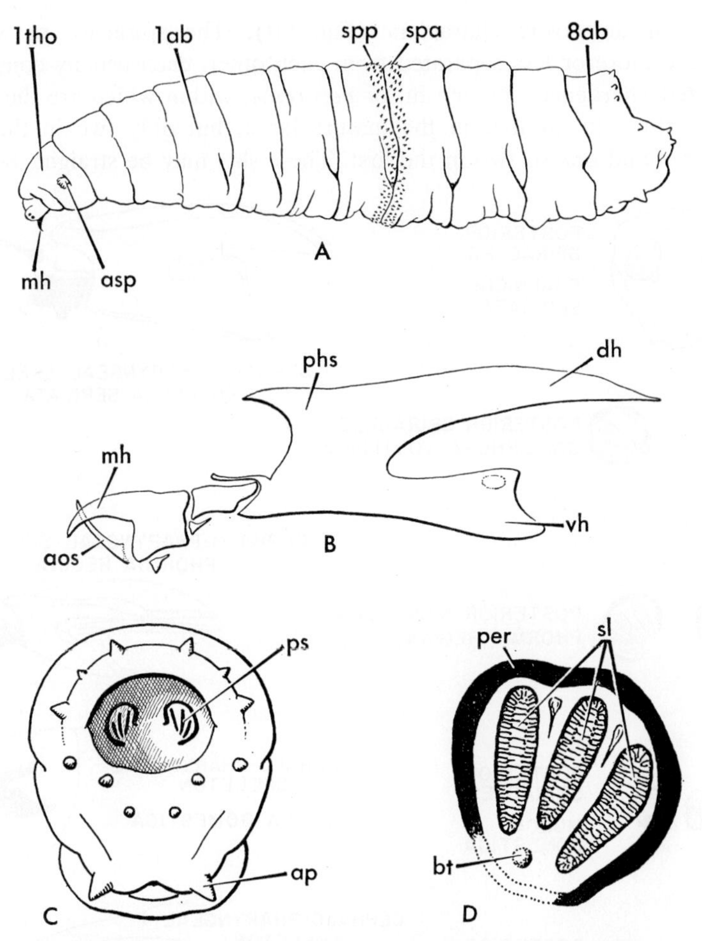

Fig. 89. Diagrammatic drawing of the mature larva of a muscoid fly. (*A*) Lateral view; (*B*) cephalopharyngeal skeleton; (*C*) posterior view; (*D*) a posterior spiracle. Explanation of abbreviations: *ab*, abdomen; *aos*, accessory oral sclerite; *asp*, anterior spiracle; *bt*, button; *dh*, dorsal horn of the pharyngeal sclerite; *mh*, mouth hooks; *per*, peritreme; *phs*, pharyngeal sclerite; *ps*, posterior spiracle; *sl*, slits of the posterior spiracle; *spa*, spines of the anterior margin of the segment; *spp*, spines of the posterior margin of the segment; *tho*, thorax; *vh*, ventral horn of the pharyngeal sclerite. (Drawing by Arthur Cushman; U.S.D.A. photograph.)

geal skeleton, the form of which may be useful in the identification of larvae (Fig. 90). In some Calliphoridae, an *accessory oral sclerite,* lying below the basal part of the mouth hooks, may be of taxonomic importance. The *anterior spiracles,* located on the posterior part of the second segment (first thoracic) are used in taxonomic discrimination; so are the *spines* of the body, which may be fine or coarse, and located in rows, in particular areas, or generally distributed over the body.

At the blunt or posterior end are found the *posterior spiracles* which afford useful diagnostic characters (Fig. 90). The spiracles, or *stigmatal plates,* are more or less separated from each other; each usually consists of a sclerotized (hardened) outer rim, or *peritreme,* within which are the *spiracular slits,* three in number in the mature larva, but only two in the second stage larva and one or two in the first. These slits may be straight, bowed, or

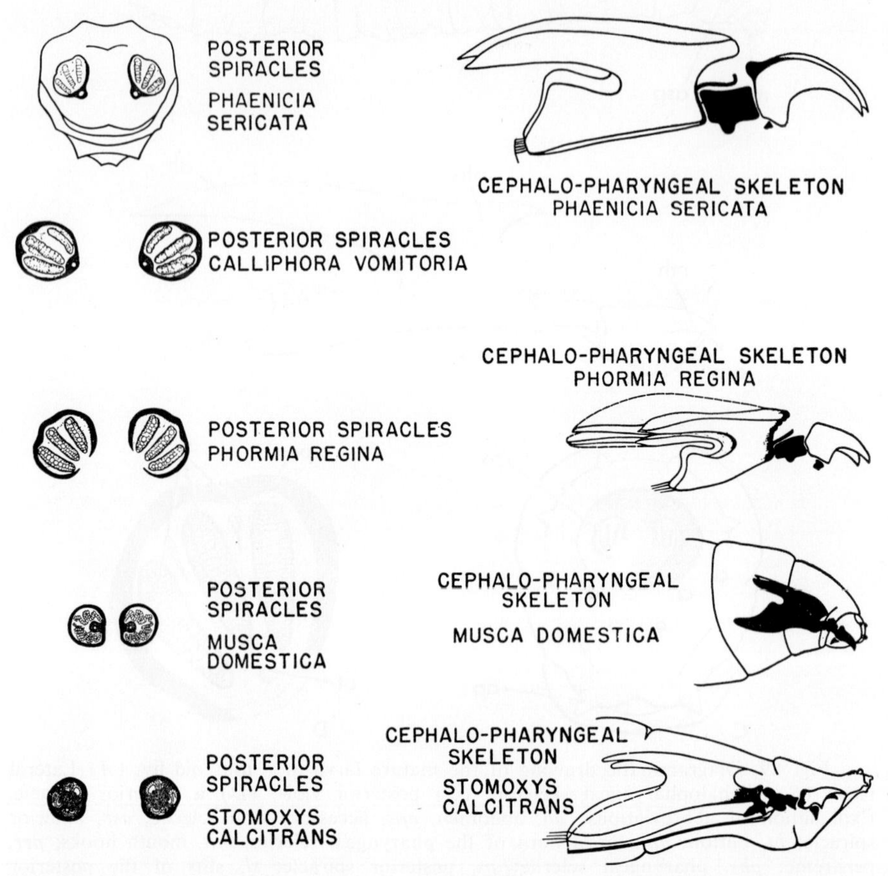

Fig. 90. Taxonomic details used in the classification of muscoid fly larvae. (Redrawn after various authors.)

highly sinuous; sometimes, as in *Hypoderma,* the slits are replaced by multiple small round openings. A prominence known as the *button* is often present in the peritreme or the area that would ordinarily be enclosed by an incomplete peritreme; it may be absent or variously situated depending on the species, and therefore has taxonomic value.

In using the posterior spiracles for purposes of classification the following characters are to be noted: (1) diameter of the stigmatal plate, the space occupied by one stigmatal plate on a line drawn through the center of both; (2) the distance between the plates; (3) the general form and shape of the plates; (4) presence or absence of a button; (5) the form of the peritreme, whether complete or broken, regular or irregular, its thickness, and its relation to the button; (6) the form of the spiracular slits, if present, and their relation to one another and to the peritreme and the button; (7) the location of the plates in respect to the segment that bears them, for example, whether they lie flush with the posterior wall of the segment or whether they are sunken into concavities.

The following keys, based largely on James[11] but taken in part from other sources, will aid in the identification of the mature (third stage) larvae of the higher Diptera.

KEY TO THE FAMILIES OF HIGHER DIPTERA (CYCLORRHAPHA) THAT CONTAIN FORMS OF MEDICAL IMPORTANCE (MATURE LARVAE)

1. Free larval stage of very brief duration or lacking (that is, developing larva retained within body of female) .... Family Muscidae (in part, *Glossina*, etc.); Pupipara
   Free larval stage present 2
2. Conical maggots, the body broad and truncated behind, tapering to a narrow anterior end, without prominent tubercles or processes on any segment but the last (Fig. 89); posterior spiracles flush with the posterior face of the anal segment or sunken into a concavity or depression. 3
   No such larvae; that is, the body either not conical (Fig. 124), or with lateral or dorsal spinous processes (Fig. 97), or with the posterior spiracles at the end of two processes or of a respiratory tube 5
3. Posterior spiracles deeply sunken into a rounded concavity; inner slits of posterior spiracle directed away from the median line ventrally .... Family Sarcophagidae
   Posterior spiracles flush with the posterior face of the anal segment; or, if they are sunken into a shallow slitlike concavity, their inner slits are directed toward the median line ventrally 4
4. Slits of posterior spiracles either sinuous or short and radially arranged.. .... Family Muscidae (in part)
   Slits of posterior spiracles long and slender, more nearly parallel to one another .... Family Calliphoridae (in part)
5. Body robust, ovate or pear-shaped, without fleshy protuberances or stalked posterior spiracles 6
   Body, if ovate, flattened and not robust, and with either fleshy protuberances or stalked posterior spiracles 11
6. Each posterior spiracle with three distinct slits 7
   Each posterior spiracle with numerous small openings, but without well-defined slits 9
7. Larva either nude, wrinkled, with the posterior spiracles separated by several times the diameter of each (*Auchmeromyia*), or the slits sinuous (*Cordylobia*) .... Family Calliphoridae (in part)
   Larva spine-bearing, the slits in the posterior spiracle not sinuous 8

8. Pear-shaped species; spiracular slits straight and elongated, deeply sunken into a concavity (*Dermatobia*) .... Family Cuterebridae (in part)
   Ovate species; spiracular slits bent at the middle and at most a shallow concavity .... Family Gasterophilidae
9. Mouth hooks rudimentary .... Family Hypodermatidae
   Mouth hooks well-developed 10
10. Body with spines weak and located on the ventral surface only or on the anterior margin of each segment dorsally; integument only moderately tough .... Family Oestridae
    Body with spines stronger or in the form of spinose plates and more evenly distributed; integument very tough .. Family Cuterebridae (in part)
11. Body with tubercular, fleshy, or spinous processes dorsally and laterally on the segments 12
    Body without such processes 14
12. More or less cylindrical larvae with short or moderately short, unbranched, lateral and dorsal tubercles on the segments 13
    Flattened larvae with long, filiform processes which are branched at least basally and may appear feathery, on the dorsum and sides of the segments; posterior spiracles borne on stalks, each stalk with four lobes on which are found the three slits and the button (*Fannia*) .... Family Muscidae (in part)
13. Small, dirt-white, slightly flattened larvae, measuring up to 4 mm, with short processes on the dorsal and lateral surfaces; posterior spiracles on brown, hardened tubercles, each with a narrow opening. Family Phoridae
    Larger, more nearly cylindrical larvae, with longer, pointed fleshy processes laterally and dorsally; posterior spiracles in a cleft on the posterior face of the last segment and consisting of flattened plates perforated by three slits (*Chrysomya,* in part) .... Family Calliphoridae (in part)
14. Posterior spiracles at the end of a long retractile respiratory tube which, when extended, is longer than the length of the body proper; rat-tailed maggots .... Family Syrphidae
    Posterior spiracles on short tubercles or a short respiratory process which is much shorter than the body length 15
15. Posterior spiracles situated at the end of the branches of a forked respiratory process .... Family Drosophilidae
    Posterior spiracles situated at the apices of short cones 16
16. Last abdominal segment with a pair of fingerlike processes on the sides ventrally; mature larvae do not skip .... Family Sepsidae
    Last abdominal segment with a pair of processes on the sides ventrally which are tapered and point slightly upward; mature larvae move in a skipping fashion .... Family Piophilidae

KEY TO THE GENERA OF MUSCIDAE (IN THE BROAD SENSE) OF MEDICAL IMPORTANCE (MATURE LARVAE)

1. With only brief free stage prior to pupation; mouth hooks lacking; posterior end with a very sharply demarcated collar posterior to which are two shiny, black lobes separated by a deep cleft or pit .... *Glossina*

With a distinct free stage during which at least most of the larval development takes place; larvae not as described above 2
2. Larvae of the normal muscoid shape (cylindrical, tapering anteriorly), without lateral processes 3
Larvae flattened, with prominent lateral processes ....*Fannia*
3. Slits of posterior spiracle strongly sinuous.......................... 4
Slits of posterior spiracle arcuate (with a simple bow) ....*Muscina*
4. Slits of posterior spiracle each with three or more loops, usually W-shaped ....*Musca*
Slits of posterior spiracle each with two loops, S-shaped 5
5. Posterior spiracles triangular, separated from each other by 1.5 to 2 times the diameter of a spiracle 6
Posterior spiracles kidney-shaped, separated from each other by 1/4 to 1/3 the diameter of a spiracle ....*Siphona*
6. A ventral tubercle, covered with small spines, present behind the anus .*Stomoxys*
No such tubercle present ....*Haematobia*

KEY TO THE GENERA OF CALLIPHORIDAE OF MEDICAL IMPORTANCE (MATURE LARVAE)

1. Robust larvae, oval in outline, not noticeably tapering anteriorly 2
Slender larvae, tapering anteriorly 3
2. Cuticle bare of obvious spines, with numerous longitudinal and horizontal folds; posterior spiracles very widely separated, each with three straight, short, outwardly directed slits ....*Auchmeromyia*
Cuticle armed with obvious spines; posterior spiracles not widely separated, each with three sinuous slits ....*Cordylobia*
3. Peritreme of posterior spiracle incomplete, not enclosing the button, which may be weakly defined 4
Peritreme of posterior spiracle complete, enclosing the button 5
4. Posterior spiracle without a definite button ....*Callitroga, Paralucilia*
Posterior spiracle with a button ....*Chrysomya, Phormia, Protophormia*
5. Peritreme of posterior spiracle weakly sclerotized ....*Pollenia*
Peritreme of posterior spiracle strongly sclerotized 6
6. Accessory oral sclerite present ....*Calliphora, Cynomyopsis*
Accessory oral sclerite absent ....*Lucilia, Phaenicia*

HIPPELATES FLIES—EYE GNATS

(*Family Chloropidae*)

Hippelates Flies. These flies are members of the Chloropidae, the family of the frit flies and related forms. Members of the genus are as a rule very small flies (1.5 to 2.5 mm in length); they are frequently called "eye gnats" or "eye flies" because they are attracted to mucous secretions, also sebaceous secretions, pus, and blood. Some species are attracted to exposed genital organs of mammals (e.g., *Hippelates pallipes* clustered around a dog's penis), and others are attracted to sores on the lower limbs (e.g., *H. flavipes* on yaws sores). They may be distinguished from most members of the same family by the presence of a distinct shining black apical or subapical spur on the hind tibia. They are extraordinarily persistent and if brushed away will quickly return to continue engorging themselves. They are nonbiting; however, the labella are provided with spines, which have been thought by some authors to act as scarifying instruments capable of producing minute multiple incisions, likely to assist pathogenic organisms carried by the insects in gaining a foothold.[9]

Unlike the gnats discussed in Chapter 10, all of which are Nematocera, the Chloropidae have short aristate antennae and are more like the house fly in form and structure though much smaller. The pomace flies, *Drosophila,* resemble some *Hippelates,* but they have a distinctly feathered arista, whereas that of *Hippelates* is at most pubescent. A distinct feature which will distinguish the Chloropidae from related families is the very large frontal triangle, the sclerotized plate on which the ocelli are situated. The larvae of many Chloropidae live in grass and other plants (stem maggots); however, those of the genus *Hippelates* develop in a wide variety of materials such as decaying vegetables and animal matter, incorporated into the soil during farming operations.

Relation to Conjunctivitis. *Siphunculina funicola* de Meijere is known as the "eye fly" of India, Ceylon, and Java, and is believed to be responsible for the spreading of conjunctivitis in these countries. Roy[24] gives a chart which shows that the seasonal prevalence of this fly in Assam coincides closely with epidemic conjunctivitis.

Hippelates flies have long been looked upon with suspicion in certain parts of the southern United States as possible vectors of a form of conjunctivitis commonly known as "sore eye," "pinkeye," etc. At a meeting of the Entomological Society of Washington held October 11, 1894, Schwarz[28] presented notes on *Hippelates pusio* Loew in the southern states. He stated that it was particularly abundant in Florida and annoying to man and animals, and that it is attracted to eyes and to the natural openings of the body as well as to infected wounds. In an article in *Insect Life* (1895), Schwarz[29] throws much suspicion on *Hippelates* flies as vectors of "sore eye."

For a number of years, at least since 1912, there have been numerous cases of catarrhal conjunctivitis apparently of the follicular type in the Coachella Valley of California where a veritable pest of *Hippelates* flies flourishes in season. Recently, high populations of eye gnats have been encountered in other desert and foothill sections of southern California. Intensive farming practices in these areas have provided optimum conditions for breeding of eye gnats. Several papers dealing with the biology and public health importance of eye gnats were published following investigations in the Coachella Valley. More recent studies in the same area include those of Burgess,[4] Tinkham,[33,34] Mulla, [16,17] and Mulla and Barnes.[19]

At the time of the Coachella investigations, the flies were identified as *Hippelates flavipes* Loew. In a letter dated May 19, 1927, J. M. Aldrich writes: "The species which you sent from Coachella Valley, California, is *pusio* Loew. It is the same species which was identified as *flavipes* Loew by Malloch, *Proc. U.S.N.M.* **46,** 1913, p. 245. His variety *pusio* on page 246 is a different form." In the same letter Aldrich also writes: "In the Proceedings of the California Academy of Sciences, Vol. 4, 619, Townsend described *Oscinis collusor* from Lower California which he said was reported to cause irritation of eyes of travelers and the 'mal de ojo' of natives." The identity of the Coachella Valley species was finally established by Sabrosky,[26] as *collusor* (Townsend), a close relative of the true *pusio,* and the name has been used in reports of recent investigations. The name *flavipes* applies to quite a different fly, a neotropical species inhabiting Mexico, Central and South America, and the West Indies.

The literature dealing with the Chloropidae as vectors of conjunctivitis has been reviewed with great care by Graham-Smith.[9] This review indicates a paucity of experimental evidence but a large amount of circumstantial evidence involving flies as spreaders of conjunctivitis in Egypt, the West Indies, India, Ceylon, Java, and the United States. Tinkham has shown that circumstantial evidence has closely related *H. collusor* abundance with incidence of pinkeye among grade-school children in the Coachella Valley from 1924 to 1951.

Relation to Yaws. As pointed out in Chapter 1, flies have for many years been suspected as vectors of yaws (framboesia tropica), and some experimental evidence has been advanced from time to time; however, the evidence collected by Kumm[13] in Jamica with *Hippelates flavipes* Loew (as *pallipes* Loew) is most convincing. Kumm, as well as others, has shown that it is relatively easy to demonstrate motile *Treponema pertenue* Castellani in the "vomit drops" of eye gnats after they have fed on infectious lesions of yaws. He found, however, that the spirochetes were presumably digested in the midgut and hindgut of the gnats very soon after they were ingested, none being seen after an interval of two days. There was no evidence of cyclical development.

The gnats receive the infection most readily by feeding on available primary lesions which exude freshly infected serum with large numbers of spirochetes. Inoculation is affected mechanically, i.e., the unchanged spirochetes are deposited in "vomit drops"[14] when infected gnats feed on exuding serum from wounds, excoriated areas, or susceptible surfaces. The manner in which the gnats receive the infection and their general feeding habits are well described by Kumm, Turner, and Peat.[15]

Bovine Mastitis. Sanders[27] reports investigations at the Florida Agricultural Experiment Station which incriminate *Hippelates* (species not given) as well as the house fly, *Musca domestica,* as vectors of bovine mastitis. *Hippelates* flies were seen to hover around natural openings of calves, yearlings, pregnant heifers, and lactating cows. They fed on lachrymal fluid, fatty body secretions, milk droplets accidentally spilled, and on secretion at the tip of the teats of animals in herds where mastitis has prevailed. Exposure tests were made with flies feeding alternately on infected material and the teat orifice; also the teat orifice was exposed to flies taken directly from premises where mastitis prevailed. "Mastitis developed in each of the experimental animals by the exposure technique employed."

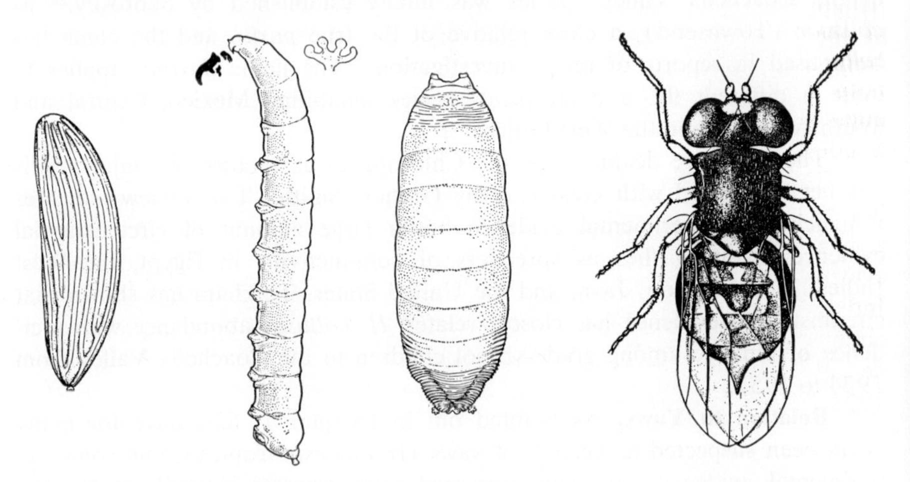

Fig 91. *Hippelates collusor.* From *left to right:* egg; larva, showing cephalopharyngeal skeleton and anterior spiracle; pupa; adult. (After Herms and Burgess, except adult fly which is redrawn after D. G. Hall.)

Life History of Hippelates Collusor. This species and the closely related *H. pusio* Loew, with which it has been confused in the literature, have, collectively, a wide distribution in the southern United States where the winters are mild. The adult flies are present throughout the year in the desert and foothill region of California, and are particularly annoying during April through November. During the peak months the adults are noticeable early in the morning and late in the afternoon, and then in deep shade, such as densely planted shrubbery, in date gardens, and in the shade of the house. The fluted, distinctly curved eggs are about 0.5 mm. in length (Fig. 91). They are deposited on or below the surface of the soil; the average incubation period under optimum conditions (90° F) is about 2 days. The larvae feed on a great variety of decaying organic matter including excrement, provided the material is rather loose and well aerated. According to Burgess[4] the larvae will not develop naturally in closely compacted soil or putrid material, neither will they breed in excrement unless it is mixed with loose earth. The larval stage under optimum conditions requires about 7 to 11 days. During the winter months the larval and pupal stages may last for many weeks.

Pupation takes place close to the surface of the material in which the larvae develop. The prepupal stage requires about 1 day, the pupal about 6, and the preovipositional adult about 7, giving a total of about 21 days from egg to adult fly, or about 28 days from egg to egg. Eggs are deposited in batches up to 50, usually followed by a second but smaller batch after about 7 days.[4] In the Coachella Valley, the development of all stages is slowed down in the winter season. The gnats breed during the cool months, but at a much lower rate. With the onset of warm weather the gnats become more active, and larger numbers emerge from the pupae. Experiments performed by Hall[10] show that the larval stage averaged about 11.4 days on human excrement, 8.7 days on dog manure, and about 17 days on decaying oranges. Burgess[4] and Mulla[16] point out that the majority of *Hippelates* gnats are bred in light, well-drained sandy soils that are freshly plowed (i.e., plowed not over 3 weeks before) and contain abundant humus or vegetable matter (cover crops, manure) and sufficient moisture. The disturbed soil habitat is characteristic also of the true *H. pusio* and the related *H. bishoppi* Sabrosky.[6]

Hippelates eye gnats are generally strong fliers. They fly with and against the general direction of the wind, although wind velocities of 5 miles or more per hour considerably reduce the flight activity of eye gnats. In the desert regions of California flight activity is more noticeable in the early morning and the late afternoon hours when the temperature is over 100° F. In the spring and fall months the gnats probably fly throughout the day and infest residential areas, golf courses, schoolyards, motels, and the like.

In a recent study, Dow[5] investigated the dispersal of *H. pusio* in Georgia with the use of phosphorus-32. The insect was found to fly as far as one mile from the release point. In a more extensive study on the flight range and dispersal pattern of *H. collusor* in the Coachella Valley of California, Mulla and March[22] tagged a large number of this eye gnat with radioactive phosphorus. Thousands of labeled gnats were released in each of two experiments in two different areas of the Valley. The gnats were found to distribute and infest a whole community within 4 to 6 hours from the time of release. In both the experiments the insects traveled as far as 4 to 4.5 miles from the release point.

Classification. Sabrosky[25] gives a valuable review of the *Hippelates* of the United States. In addition to the stout and distinct tibial spur, the following characteristics will assist in the identification of this genus: cephalic bristles short, weak, and not conspicuous; ocellars very short, erect, and convergent or cruciate; fronto-orbital hairs minute, slightly reclinate; no intrahumeral bristles present. The species which are most important from the medical standpoint belong to the *pusio* group; in this group the body color is black, and the thorax is polished and shiny, with at most a trace of pollen at the base of the wing. Sabrosky places *H. pusio* Loew, *H. flavipes* Loew, *H. pallipes* (Loew), *H. bishoppi* Sabrosky, *H. collusor* (Townsend), and two other species in this group. *Hippelates flavipes* and *H. pallipes* have been confused with each other in the literature, but *H. flavipes* is a tropical species and *H. pallipes* belongs to the temperate regions.[26] The information published by Kumm on "pallipes," therefore, properly relates to *flavipes*. Some members of other groups of *Hippelates* may be seriously annoying, but some species (e.g., *hermsi* Sabrosky) do not attack man.[34]

Control of Hippelates Flies. Control is difficult, and much more information concerning the breeding habits and behavior of these flies is needed to provide a sound basis for permanent control.[16] Tests made with DDT and lindane as adult sprays have proven ineffective. Tinkham[34] obtained 95 per cent control of *H. collusor* in date and orange groves in the Coachella Valley by disking aldrin and heptachlor in the form of emulsifiable concentrates into infested soil. Subsequent investigations by Mulla[18] and Mulla *et al.*[20] proved these materials to yield poor control. In these later studies, DDT and endrin proved more promising. In chemical treatment, the problem of possible resistance must be faced; moreover, soil chemistry and temperatures must be taken into consideration. Tinkham[33] advocates noncultivation, when feasible, as a permanent control measure against *H. collusor*. He points out that noncultivation of date and orange groves may be carried on without adverse and probably with beneficial results so far as agriculture is concerned, with the saving of the labor and cost of cultivation, and with elimination of the eye gnat problem. However, recent information has indicated a large number of *H. collusor* to breed in noncultivated crop land,[16] and the advocacy of noncultivation alone would not alleviate the situation. Moreover, standard farm production operations in Coachella Valley call for extensive cultivation and are not in favor of noncultivation schedules.

Attractants. A powerful attractant for *Hippelates* eye gnats could be employed in obtaining population prevalence in baited traps. It could also be used in combination with insecticides to draw the gnats to the poison in a selected area. All the attractants known thus far against eye gnats are of animal and plant origin and proteinaceous in nature. No synthetic chemical has been found that would manifest appreciable attractancy to eye gnats.

Among the proteinaceous materials, Mulla[16] found fermenting egg and lactalbumin peptone to have the highest attractancy against *H. collusor* from a group of 11 protein hydrolyzates of animal and plant origin. For more systematic studies on the attractants and baits of *Hippelates* eye gnats, a simple and sensitive olfactometer has been devised.[21] This tool has made it possible to pursue the field of chemical attractants with establishing routine screening programs.

LOUSE FLIES AND BAT FLIES

(*Series Pupipara*)

Characteristics of Hippoboscidae. Four families of flies constitute the Pupipara, three of which attack warm-blooded animals: (1) Hippoboscidae (louse flies); (2) Nycteribiidae (spiderlike bat flies); and (3) Streblidae (bat flies). The bloodsucking parasitic flies belonging to the family Hippoboscidae are readily recognized as Diptera when winged. The larvae are retained within the body of the female, being nourished by special glands within the mother until time for pupation is reached; they are then extruded, and pupation quickly follows, whence the term, "pupipara." The adult flies are described as follows by Williston:

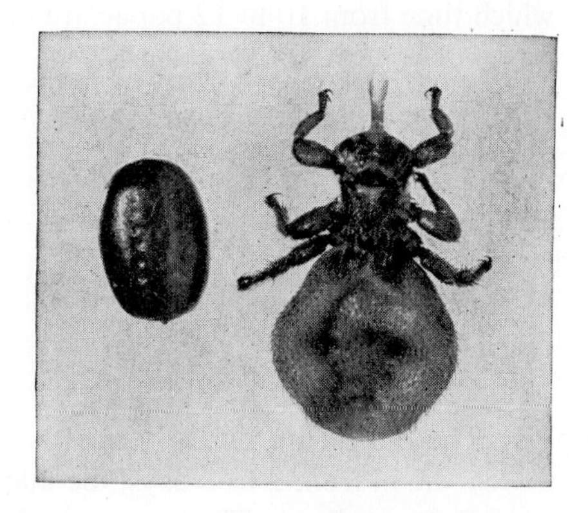

Fig. 92. The sheep "tick" or louse fly, *Melophagus ovinus.* (*Left*) pupa; (*right*) adult. × 4.5.

Head flattened, usually attached to an emargination of the thorax; face short, palpi forming a sheath for the proboscis, not projecting in front of the head; antennae inserted in pits or depressions near the border of the mouth, apparently one-jointed, with or without a terminal bristle or long hairs. Eyes round or oval, ocelli present or absent. Thorax flattened, leathery in appearance; scutellum broad and short. Halteres small or rudimentary. Abdomen saclike, leathery in appearance, the sutures indistinct. Legs short and strong, broadly separated by the sternum; tarsi short; claws strong and often denticulated.

The members of this family are all parasitic in the adult stage upon birds or mammals. There are about 400 species widely distributed throughout the world. They range in size from 2.5 to 10 mm. The American species have been admirably monographed by Bequaert.[2]

The sheep "tick" or ked, *Melophagus ovinus* (Linnaeus), is a wingless bloodsucking species, reddish brown in color, about 5 to 7 mm in length. It is a world-wide parasite of sheep and goats. The head is short and sunken into the thorax, the body saclike, leathery, and spiny (Fig. 92).

Life History. The eggs are retained and hatch within the body of the female ked, where the larvae develop in about 7 days and are extruded fully grown ready to pupate. The extruded larva pupates during the course of a few hours, becoming chestnut brown in color; the secretion with which it is covered hardens and serves to glue the pupa firmly to the wool of the host. The pupae are commonly found on infested animals in the region of the shoulders, thighs, and belly. Pupae may be found on sheep at all times of the year, although the time required for development in the winter is longer than in the summer. Swingle,[32] who has observed this insect very carefully, states that pupae require from 19 to 23 days to hatch in the summer, whereas 19 to 36 days are required during the winter on sheep kept in the barn and probably 40 to 45 days on sheep out of doors. The time required for the females to reach sexual maturity is from 14 to 30 days and over, when they begin extruding young at the rate of one about every 7 to 8 days. Swingle considers about 4 months as the average life of the insect, during which time from 10 to 12 pupae are deposited.

Fig. 93. Louse fly of the deer, *Lipoptena depressa,* showing wingless and winged forms. × 5.

The entire life of the ked is spent on its host; when off the sheep, the insects die in from 2 to 8 days, the majority in about 4 days.

Damage Done. The presence of a few louse flies on the body of a sheep does not materially affect it. In heavy infestations the presence of the insect is indicated by the fact that the animal rubs itself vigorously, bites the wool, and scratches. Badly infested animals show emaciation and general unthriftiness. The injury to lambs is especially marked.

Control. The use of pyrethrum with a synergist added (piperonyl butoxide or MGK 264) or rotenone has proven effective as a spray or dip. Certain chlorinated hydrocarbons and organophosphorus compounds have been recommended, but they are not considered safe for use on milk goats or sometimes under other circumstances. Pfadt and DeFoliart[23] recommend power dusting with dieldrin for control on sheep, provided that the animal is not slaughtered for at least 86 days after application.

Other Louse Flies of Mammals. *Lipoptena depressa* (Say) and *Neolipoptena ferrisi* (Bequaert) are common parasites of deer in North America. These species are smaller than *Melophagus ovinus,* but otherwise resemble it; they are wingless when etablished on the host, but have well-developed filmy wings on emergence from the pupal stage (Fig. 93). The parasites have been found in chains, three or four individuals attached to one another, the first fly drawing blood from the host, the second with its proboscis thrust into the abdomen (dorsally) of the first, the third drawing on the second, and so on to the last individual. *Lipoptena cervi* (Linnaeus), known as the "deer ked," is reported to be a common species on European deer, and according to Bequaert[2] has become naturalized in the northeastern United States on the Virginia white-tailed deer and on wapiti. *Lipoptena mazamae* Rondani occurs on deer in South and Central America and in the southeastern United States.

Nine species of the genus *Hippobosca* are recognized as valid by Bequaert.[1] The wings are always well developed in the genus and are functional throughout adult life. With the exception of the ostrich louse fly, *H. struthionis* Janson, the species of the genus are ectoparasitic on mammals. *Hippobosca equina* Linnaeus, known in England as the "forest fly" is usually found on horses, mules, and donkeys, sometimes on cattle and other animals; *H. longipennis* Fabricius is commonly found on domestic dogs in the Far East and in many parts of the Mediterranean region; *H. variegata* von Mühlfeld occurs on domestic cattle and equines and is widespread in distribution; *H. camelina* Leach is a parasite of the camel and dromedary. No species of *Hippobosca* seem to be established in America.

Louse Flies of Birds. The pigeon fly, *Pseudolynchia canariensis,* is an important parasite of domestic pigeons throughout the tropics and warmer regions of the world. It is found throughout the southern United States and northward along the Atlantic Coast to New England. The dark brown flies have long wings, 6.5 to 7.5 mm, and are able to fly swiftly from the host, but usually alight near by. They move about quickly among the feathers of the host and bite and suck blood from parts that are not well feathered.

The mature larvae, at first pale yellow and later jet black in color, are deposited on the body of the bird while it is quiet, but they soon roll off and collect in the nests. Bishopp[3] gives the duration of the pupal stage at from 29 to 31 days when the mean daily temperature is about 73° F. Thus, the thorough and regular cleaning of the nests at intervals not to exceed 25 days is probably the most important single step in control. The pupae are very resistant; hence, ordinary insecticides are of little use. Bishopp states that "one of the most effective and easily applied treatments for squabs is *fresh* pyrethum powder, one to three pinches (depending upon the size of the squab) scattered among the feathers."

In addition to its evil effects as a bloodsucking parasite, the pigeon fly is the vector of pigeon malaria caused by *Haemoproteus columbae* (Celli and San Felice), the parasite undergoing sporogeny in the body of the insect and consequently requiring it as a link in its life cycle. Also, bird malaria in the California valley quail (caused by *Haemoproteus lophortyx* O'Roke) is transmitted by *Lynchia hirsuta* Ferris and *Stilbometopa impressa* (Bigot), and other bird hippoboscids may be involved in transmission of other species of *Haemoproteus.*

Hippoboscids Attacking Man. This subject has been reviewed critically by Bequaert.[2] No known hippoboscid has man as its normal or habitual host, but at least 13 species, including *Hippobosca equina* Linnaeus, *H. camelina* Rondani, *H. variegata* Megerle, *H. longipennis* Fabricius, *Melophagus ovinus* (Linnaeus), *Iipoptena cervi* (Linnaeus), and *Pseudolynchia canariensis* (Macquart), have been authentically reported as biting man. The sheep ked may become quite annoying to persons employed in shearing sheep or handling wool, but repeated bites tend to cause the skin to cease reacting. The pigeon fly may readily attack persons who handle squabs and adult birds; the bite is said to be as painful as a bee sting and its effects may persist for 5 days or more.[31]

Bat flies are pupiparous bloodsucking parasites belonging to the family Streblidae; they are all parastic on bats in tropical and subtropical climates. Little is known about the life history of these insects. The species of the family Streblidae have been reviewed by Kessel.[12] Spiderlike bat flies belong to the family Nycteribiidae. They are very small (2 to 3 mm long), wingless, spiderlike parasites of bats. Except for a very few species described from North and South America, they are primarily parasites of Old World bats. Ferris[8] has reviewed the New World species. The fact that vampire, fruit-eating, and insectivorous bats are involved in the epidemiology of rabies is of interest in this connection, since, until proven otherwise, there exists the possibility that bat parasites may help to maintain the virus in bat populations.

REFERENCES

1. Bequaert, Joseph, 1937. "Notes on Hippoboscidae, 5, The American species of Lipoptena," *Bull. Brooklyn Entomol. Soc.*, **32:**91–101.

2. Bequaert, Joseph C., 1953–1957. "The Hippoboscidae or louse-flies (Diptera) of mammals and birds. Part I. Structure, physiology, and natural history. Part II. Taxonomy, evolution, and revision of American genera and species," *Entomologia Amer.*, **32** (n.s.):1–209; **33** (n.s.):211–442; **34** (n.s.):1–232; **35** (n.s.):233–416; **36** (n.s.):417–611.

3. Bishopp, F. C., 1929. "The pigeon fly, an important pest of pigeons in the United States," *J. Econ. Entomol.*, **22:**974–80.

4. Burgess, Robert W., 1951. "The life history and breeding habits of the eye gnat, *Hippelates pusio* Loew, in the Coachella Valley, Riverside County, California," *Amer. J. Hyg.*, **53:**164–77.

5. Dow, Richard P., 1959. "Dispersal of adult *Hippelates pusio,* the eye gnat," *Ann. Entomol. Soc. Amer.*, **52:**372–81.

6. Dow, Richard P.; Bigham, John R.; and Sabrosky, Curtis W.; 1951. "Sequel to 'Hippelates (eye gnat) investigations in the Southeastern States' by John T. Bigham," *Proc. Entomol. Soc. Wash.*, **53:**263–71.

7. Eldridge, Bruce F., and James, Maurice T., 1957. "The typical muscid flies of California (Diptera: Muscidae, Muscinae)," *Bull. Calif. Insect Survey,* **6:**1–17 (3 plates).

8. Ferris, G. F., 1924. "The New World Nycteribiidae (Diptera: Pupipara)," *Entomol. News,* **35:**191–99.

9. Graham-Smith, G. S., 1930. "The Oscinidae (Diptera) as vectors of conjunctivitis, and the anatomy of their mouth parts," *Parasitology,* **22:**457–67 (1 plate).

10. Hall, David G., 1932. "Some studies on the breeding media, development, and stages of the eye gnat, *Hippelates pusio* Loew," *Am. J. Hyg.,* **16:**854–64.

11. James, Maurice T., 1948. *The Flies that Cause Myiasis in Man.* Washington, D. C.: Dept. Agric., in Misc. Publ., no. 631. 175 pp. (1947).

12. Kessel, Q. C., 1925. "A synopsis of the Streblidae of the world," *J. N. Y. Entomol. Soc.,* **33:**11–34 (4 plates).

13. Kumm, Henry W., 1935. "The natural infection of *Hippelates pallipes* Loew with spirochaetes of yaws," *Tr. Roy. Soc. Trop. Med. & Hyg.,* **29:**265–72.

14. Kumm, Henry W., and Turner, T. B., 1936. "The transmission of yaws from man to rabbits by an insect vector, *Hippelates pallipes* Loew," *Am. J. Trop. Med.,* **16:**245–62 (5 plates).

15. Kumm, Henry W.; Turner, T. B.; and Peat, A. A.; 1935. "The duration of motility of the spirochaetes of yaws in a small West Indian fly, *Hippelates pallipes* Loew," *Am. J. Trop. Med.,* **15:**209–23.

16. Mulla, Mir S., 1958. "Recent developments in the biology and control of *Hippelates* eye gnats," *Proc. & Papers Calif. Mosq. Control Assn.,* **26:**78–82.

17. Mulla, Mir S., 1959. "Some important aspects of *Hippelates* gnats, with a brief presentation of current research findings," *Proc. & Papers Calif. Mosq. Control Assn.,* **27:**48–52.

18. Mulla, Mir S., 1960. "Chlorinated hydrocarbon insecticides as soil treatments against the eye gnat *Hippelates collusor* (Townsend) in the laboratory," *J. Econ. Entomol.,* **53:**367–72.

19. Mullla, Mir S., and Barnes, Martin M., 1957. "On laboratory colonization of the eye gnat *Hippelates collusor* (Townsend)," *J. Econ. Entomol.,* **50:**814–16.

20. Mulla, Mir S.; Barnes, Martin M.; and Garber, M. J.; 1960. "Soil treatments with insecticides for control of the eye gnats *Hippelates collusor* and *H. hermsi,*" *J. Econ. Entomol.,* **53:**362–65.

21. Mulla, Mir S.; Dorner, Robert W.; Georghiou, George P.; and Garber, M. J.; 1960. "Olfactometer and procedure for testing baits and chemical attractants against *Hippelates* gnats," *Ann. Entomol. Soc. Amer.,* **53:**529–37.

22. Mulla, Mir S., and March, Ralph B., 1959. "Flight range, dispersal patterns and population density of the eye gnat *Hippelates collusor* (Townsend)," *Ann. Entomol. Soc. Amer.,* **52:**641–46.

23. Pfadt, R. E., and DeFoliart, G. R., 1957. "Power dusting to control the sheep ked," *J. Econ. Entomol.,* **50:**190–94.

24. Roy, D. N., 1928. "Report on investigation into aetiology and prevention of Naga sore in Assam," *Indian Med. Gaz.,* **63:**673–87.

25. Sabrosky, Curtis W., 1941. "The *Hippelates* flies or eye gnats: preliminary notes," *Canad. Entomol.,* **73:**23–27.

26. Sabrosky, Curtis W., 1951. "Nomenclature of the eye gnats (*Hippelates* spp.)," *Amer. J. Trop. Med.*, **31**:257–58.

27. Sanders, D. A., 1940. "*Musca domestica* and *Hippelates* flies, vectors of bovine mastitis," *Science*, **92**:286.

28. Schwarz, E. A., 1894. "Notes on *Hippelates pusio* in the southern states," *Proc. Entomol. Soc. Washington*, **3**:178–80.

29. Schwarz, E. A., 1895. "The Hippelates plague in Florida," *Insect Life*, **7**:374–79.

30. Shtakelberg, A. A., 1956. "Synantropnye Dvukrylye Fauny S. S. S. R." (transliteration); (Synanthropic Flies of the Fauna of the U.S.S.R.). Moscow: Academy of Sciences of the U. S. S. R. 164 pp.

31. Soroker, Robert H., 1958. "Pigeon fly problem in southern California," *Calif. Vector Views*, **5**:46.

32. Swingle, Leroy D., 1913. *The Life History of the Sheep Tick, Melophagus ovinus*. Laramie: Univ. of Wyoming, Agr. Exper. Sta Bull., no. 99.

33. Tinkham, Ernest R., 1952. "The eye gnats of the Coachella Valley with notes on the 1951 larvaciding program," *Calif. Mosq. Control Assn., Proc. & Papers*, **20**:83–84.

34. Tinkham, Ernest R., 1953. "Control of eye gnats by soil larvicides," *Calif. Mosq. Control Assn., Proc. & Papers*, **21**:67–68.

35. Van Emden, F. I., 1954. *Handbooks for the Identification of British Insects. Diptera Cyclorrhapha. Calyptrata (I). Section (a). Tachinidae and Calliphoridae*. London: Royal Entomological Society. 133 pp.

Chapter 15

THE HOUSE FLY AND ITS RELATIVES

Order Diptera, Superfamily Muscoidea

House-invading Flies. Many species of robust flies belonging to various families of Diptera are commonly found indoors. Some of these are an actual or potential menace to human health in that they habitually enter the house and come in contact with human food or drink, after breeding or feeding in excrement or dead animal material. These same flies, and others which have no relationship to the transmission of pathogenic organisms, may be of further importance because of their annoyance and interference with human comfort. Flies of such character belong chiefly to the Muscidae (including the Anthomyiidae), Sarcophagidae (flesh flies), and Calliphoridae (blow flies).

The bionomics of the house fly and related forms of medical and sanitary importance have recently been treated in an admirable monograph by West,[47] and a condensed account of the relationship to disease, with an extensive list of citations, has been presented by Lindsay and Scudder.[29]

The Family Muscidae. The family Muscidae, to which the house fly and several other house-invading species belong, is characterized by Curran[5] as including:

> . . . flies of medium to small size, usually dull colored, with the squamae large or of medium size, *the hypopleural bristles absent,* the second antennal segment grooved above. Arista plumose, pubescent, bare, or pectinate, eyes approximate or widely separated in the males, the front rarely narrowed in both sexes; frontal bristles always present, intrafrontals frequently present; orbitals developed but rarely in the males. . . . Male genitalia usually not prominent but sometimes conspicuous; fifth sternal lobes sometimes prominent. [*Italics* authors'.]

The House Fly. Hewitt's[21] description (translation from Schiner) of *Musca domestica* Linnaeus (Fig. 94), the house fly, will serve our purposes:

> Frons of male occupying a fourth part of the breadth of the head. Frontal stripe of female narrow in front, so broad behind that it entirely fills up the width of the front. The dorsal region of the thorax dusty gray in color with four equally broad longitudinal stripes. Scutellum gray with black sides. The light regions of the abdomen yellowish, transparent, the darkest parts at least at the base of the ventral side yellow, the last segment and a dorsal line blackish brown. Seen from behind and against the light the whole abdomen shimmering yellow, and only on each side of the dorsal line on each segment a dull transverse band. The lower part of the face silky yellow, shot with blackish brown. Median stripe velvety black. Antennae brown. Palpi black. Legs blackish brown. Wings

tinged with pale gray with yellowish base. The female has a broad velvety black, often reddishly shimmering, frontal stripe, which is not broader at the anterior end than the bases of the antennae, but becomes so very much broader above that the light dustiness of the sides is entirely obliterated, the abdomen gradually becoming darker. The shimmering areas of the separate segments generally brownish. All the other parts are the same as in the male. Mature insect 6–7 mm. in length, 13–15 mm. across the wings.

Fig. 94. Developmental stages of the house fly, *Musca domestica.* (*Upper left*) eggs; (*upper right*) larvae; (*lower left*) pupae; (*lower right*) adult. (Courtesy California Bureau of Vector Control; photograph of adult by Edward S. Ross; others by Arthur C. Smith.)

Musca domestica has the central region of the propleura clothed with, or at least bearing a few, fine hairs. This is not true of all species of *Musca.*

Of a total of 23,087 flies collected by Howard[23] in dining rooms in different parts of the United States, 22,808 (about 99 per cent of the whole number) were *Musca domestica.* However, there are extensive areas in the United States today where other muscoids, for example *Fannia* or certain blow flies, predominate. The changes which have accompanied progress have evidently altered the composition of the domestic fly fauna since Howard's time. As West[47] points out, "In many parts of the United States today *Musca domestica* is less a housefly than a 'picnic fly,' 'park fly,' 'dairy fly,' or 'stable fly,' but wherever found, it is almost certain to be the availability of human food or drink which brings it there." *Musca domestica* is almost cosmopolitan, but in some parts of the world its place is taken by other species, particularly *Musca sorbens* Wiedemann.

In order to determine the distribution of the sexes of *Musca domestica,* Herms made observations in June, 1909, under two different conditions: first, six sweepings with an insect net were made over a pile of horse manure on which many flies had gathered; second, all but about 6 flies were collected in one house, giving a fairly representative lot for indoors, even under screened conditions. The netted samples yielded 811 flies, 729 of which were *Musca domestica;* of these, however, 697, or 95.6 per cent, were females. Thus, it is clear that it is the "instinct" to oviposit that mainly attracted these flies to the manure. Observations made in the near vicinity of the manure piles, proved that certainly the same percentage (over 95 per cent) of the flies clinging to the walls of the stable, boxcs, and so on, were males.

Of the flies collected indoors, 202 out of 214 were *Musca domestica;* of these, 86 were males and 116, or about 57 per cent, were females. This would, it seems, indicate that males and females are equally attracted to the house by odors issuing therefrom. The sexes of flies emerging from puparia taken at random are approximately equal.

Life History of the House Fly. The house fly passes through a complex metamorphosis, i.e., egg, larva (maggot), pupa, and adult or fully winged insect (Fig. 94). Under warm summer temperatures, under what may perhaps be considered representative conditions, the egg stage requires 8 to 12 hours, the larval stage about 5 days, the pupa 4 to 5 days, a total of about 10 days from egg to adult insect. This allows for the development of from 10 to 12 generations in one summer. Under more nearly ideal conditions, the length of the life cycle may be shortened and the number of annual generations consequently increased. In California the minimum time from egg to adult is estimated at 7 days (Arthur C. Smith, personal communication), with 2 to 3 generations a month in warm weather.

From 75 to 150 eggs are deposited singly, piled up into masses, and there are usually several such layings at intervals of 3 or 4 days. Female flies begin depositing eggs from 9 to 12 days after emerging from the pupa case. Dunn,[7] reporting on his observations in Panama, states that as many as 159 eggs may be deposited in one batch, that large batches are sometimes deposited at intervals of but 36 hours, and that one female may deposit as many as 21 batches, or a total of 2387 eggs, in 31 days after emergence. He also states that oviposition may take place as early as 2 1/4 days after emergence and that one successful copulation seems to be sufficient to fertilize the female for her lifetime. Copulation may occur within 24 hours after emergence. These numbers are much larger, and the periods of time much shorter, than those reported in at least most other studies available. Under usual laboratory conditions house flies reach sexual maturity in 3 or 4 days, and begin depositing eggs on the ninth day after emergence from the puparium. Sunshine stimulates their breeding. Egg laying may continue throughout the lifetime of the fly, i.e., for more than 2 months.

The larval stage is the growing period of the fly, and the size of the adult will depend entirely upon the growth that the larva attains. An underfed larva will result in an undersized adult. The growing stage requires from 4 to 6 days, after which the maggots usually crawl away from their breeding place, many of them burrowing into the loose ground beneath the manure pile, or under boards or stones, or into dry manure collected under platforms and the like. One and three-quarter pounds of dry manure, taken from beneath a platform, were recorded by the author (Herms) as containing 2561 pupae. The larvae spend 3 or 4 days in the prepupal or migratory stage before actually pupating.

As in the case of other muscoids, the adult fly, when transformation is completed, pushes the end of the puparium open by means of the ptilinum; then, by alternate expansion and contraction of this organ, the fly opens a passageway through the loose soil and debris to the surface. Compaction of the soil impedes its progress.[3]

When the fly emerges from the pupal case, the wings are folded in tight pads, and change in size is due to expansion and addition in weight and not to growth. Stomach contents or development of eggs in the female add to weight. This is why no "young" house flies are seen, i.e., young in the sense of being small. Little flies are not "baby" flies; they are either a different and smaller species or are undersized. One can influence the size of the adult fly by underfeeding it in the larval stage.[17]

With one adult fly depositing from 120 to 150 eggs per lot, with at least 6 lots at intervals of from 3 to 4 days, Hodge[22] gives us the following statement: "A pair of flies beginning operations in April may be progenitors, if all were to live, of 191,010,000,000,000,000,000 flies by August. Allowing one-eighth of a cubic inch to a fly, this number would cover the earth 47 feet deep."

Authorities differ in their opinions as to how the house fly hibernates. The largest group, according to West,[47] believes that the hibernating pupae are the most important in providing for the continuance of the species for the following year. Probably the situation varies from one locality and climate to another; this assumption would explain the variation in factual findings and in general opinions of specialists. Under tropical conditions there is no interruption in breeding.

Influence of Temperature on Life History. Temperature influences materially both the survival of the immature stages and the time required for the development from the egg to the adult. The temperature of an average manure pile to which material is added daily varies from 18° to 66° C. Young growing larvae are most numerous where temperatures vary from 45° to 55° C. Below 45° C, half-grown and full-grown larvae occur; above 55° C, the temperature seems to become too great.

Herms kept records of laboratory rearing of flies at temperatures of from 16° to 30° C. At 16° C, the egg stage required 36 to 40 hours for its completion; the larval stage, 11 to 26 days; and the pupal stage, 18 to 21 days. These figures progressively decreased as temperature increased; the comparable figures at 30° C being 8 to 12 hours for the egg, 5 to 6 days for the larval, and 4 to 5 days for the pupal stage. The average time required to develop from egg to adult, at the various temperatures, were: 16° C, 44.8 days; 18°, 26.7 days; 20°, 20.5 days; 25°, 16.1 days; and 30°, 10.4 days. The shortest time required for the development of *Musca domestica* may, depending on local conditions, be less than the minimum time observed above. In California, for example, this minimum time may be as low as 7 days. The determination of the minimum time for any locality may be an important consideration in fly control.

Breeding Places. Excrement is one material upon which *Musca domestica* habitually deposits its eggs, the larvae feeding on this material and the contained microorganisms. To gain an estimate of the number of larvae developing in an average horse-manure pile, Herms took samples after 4 days' exposure to flies, with the following results: first sample (4 lb) contained 6873 larvae; second sample (4 lb), 1142; third sample (4 lb), 1585; fourth sample (3 lb), 682; total, 10,282 larvae in 15 pounds. All larvae were nearly or quite fully grown. This gives an average of 685 larvae per pound. The weight of the entire pile was estimated at not less than 1000 pounds, of which certainly two-thirds was infested. A little arithmetic gives us the astonishing estimate of 455,525 larvae (685 × 665), or in round numbers 450,000.[18]

Horse manure is a favorite larval food, and at one time it was regarded as the chief factor in the production of house flies in many rural and village areas in the United States. Cow manure is frequently an important factor in the development of flies. Flies will also breed in hog manure, but the swarm of flies around pig pens usually originates in the waste feed, slops, etc. Chicken manure is the most important factor in the breeding of flies in poultry districts, and hosts of blow flies in such areas may be the result of dead birds being buried in shallow pits or simply disposed of by being thrown into a gulley or a corner. Human excrement is a very dangerous substance, and if exposed to flies in open privies becomes a very prolific breeding medium; this consideration emphasizes the need for making privies flyproof or for using other means to prevent flies from breeding in them.

In this day of automobiles and tractors, however, other sources of breeding may be vastly more important than excrement. Smith,[42] studying conditions in dairy barns in California, concludes that "the fly-breeding potential of these enormous amounts of organic waste materials [chicken and cow manure, garbage, etc.] is far greater than it could possibly have been back in the horse-and-buggy days." He further says (personal communication): "Perhaps the greatest numbers of house flies I have seen came from lima bean waste in the field. I have seen nearly as great numbers from celery waste, tomato waste, etc." Wet grain from flooded granaries has been known to produce enormous plagues of flies.

Fig. 95. Fresh trash and garbage on an open dump may be a prolific breeding ground for flies. (Courtesy California Bureau of Vector Control; photograph by Arthur C. Smith.)

Great swarms of flies are often found around feed troughs; the animals (hogs and cattle) may be literally covered with them. An examination of the waste feed behind or beneath the troughs or in and about the mixing vats will almost invariably reveal numerous maggots. Storage receptacles for slops sometimes present a wriggling mass of maggots. The correction of such fly breeding manifestly depends in large part upon greater care in handling the mash, wet or dry.

It frequently happens that brewers' grain or spent hops, bran mash, and ensilage are only partly consumed by the animals, and the waste is thrown out into the fields in heaps. Such heaps of waste are commonly a source of enormous numbers of flies (nearly all *Musca domestica*) about dairies where otherwise conditions may be good and where no apparent reason for the swarm of flies exists. Commercial wastes and freeze plant wastes, when used as feed for beef and dairy cattle, may likewise constitute a major problem.

Garbage heaps, particularly when fermentation and decomposition begin, are commonly sources of many flies of several kinds (Fig. 95). Heaps of de-

Fig. 96. An uncovered, ill-kept garbage can may breed flies even when "empty." An examination of the bottom of this can revealed larvae of the house fly, the lesser house fly, the greenbottle fly, and the drone fly. (Courtesy California Bureau of Vector Control; photograph by Edgar A. Smith.)

caying onions and other vegetables, fruits, etc., as well as decaying straw and weeds, may become infested with maggots, often the larvae of the biting stable fly, *Stomoxys calcitrans*. Meat scraps in garbage commonly produce blow flies. The fly-breeding potential of a garbage can, under certain circumstances, is amazing (Fig. 96). In experiments conducted in Contra Costa County, California, single garbage cans have produced more than 20,000 larvae within a week's time (Arthur C. Smith, personal communication).

In the country, in the absence of sewers or septic tanks, the dishwater from the kitchen is frequently piped from the sink to a ditch in the back yard. On many occasions these ditches become clogged and vile smelling, and an examination will reveal numerous maggots developing in the muck—a source of flies which is commonly overlooked. Also, maggots may be found in countless number in the soft sludge mat covering the liquid in defective septic tanks, chiefly those of older construction.

Hewitt[21] has recorded *Musca domestica* as either breeding in or being attracted for oviposition to a wide range of materials other than those mentioned above, and West,[47] chiefly from the literature, has added others. The Bureau of Vector Control of the California State Department of Public Health has been making extensive studies of breeding media for the house fly and other species of nuisance flies. The student of the subject would do well to consult their reports issued in mimeographed form or published in their periodical, *California Vector Views,* and through other publishing media.

Range of Flight. Ordinarily under city conditions it may be safely said that where flies are abundant they have bred in the immediate vicinity. The house fly can, however, use its wings effectively and may also be carried by the wind, although it usually seeks protection very quickly when there is a strong breeze. The use of radioactive isotopes as markers has indicated that flies can fly as far as 20 miles from their source and that under certain conditions they may migrate from 1 to 4 miles in considerable numbers; the dispersion capacity, however, is usually limited to a distance of 0.5 to 2 miles (Schoof and Siverly[39]). Where houses are situated close together, flies have the opportunity to travel considerable distances by easy flights, and they are often carried on garbage vehicles and on animals.

Longevity of Flies. In order to determine the longevity of flies, it is necessary to keep the same individual under observation from the time of emergence from the puparium to the time of death. The writer (Herms) has done this by keeping each pupa in a separate vial, noting the time of emergence to the hour and spotting each fly lightly with Chinese white on the thorax. The spots can be arranged singly and in combinations so that many different flies can be kept under observation at the same time. After marking, flies were liberated in bobbinet-covered cages (size of cages never more than 8 × 10 × 18 in.). Each cage was provided with sugar water and a receptable of horse manure. A full set of experiments under sufficiently varying conditions indicates an average life of close to 30 days, with a maximum life of something over 60 days during the summer months. In hibernation, flies may live over winter, i.e., from October to April, in the eastern and central United States. In California, flies emerge from their pupal cases throughout the winter, and their life history is then considerably longer than in summer.

Other House-invading Muscids. There are many species (74, including subspecies, according to West[47]) belonging to the genus *Musca,* but only a few of these are comparable in their habits to *M. domestica.* The most important of these are *M. vicina* Macquart (probably best considered a subspecies of *M. domestica*), the common house fly of the Orient: *M. nebulo* Fabricius, a tropical or subtropical species; and *M. sorbens* Wiedemann, widespread and important in the Orient, the Pacific Islands, and Australia.

Musca autumnalis De Geer, the face fly, (formerly called *M. corvina* Fabricius) has somewhat different habits. It is described by Austen as follows:

> . . . though agreeing approximately with the house fly in length, is a bulkier, more compactly built and thick-set insect . . . often decidedly larger. In the male the upper surface of the abdomen has a black base, from which there is a backward prolongation in the shape of a longitudinal, median stripe, both base and stripe being sharply defined, and presenting a well marked contrast to the cinnamon-buff of the remaining ground color; in the female the upper surface of both thorax and abdomen is grey, with darker markings. In the case of both sexes, however, the surest criteria for distinguishing *Musca autumnalis* from *M. domestica* are those presented by the upper surface of the head. Whereas in the male *Musca autumnalis* the eyes are so close together as to be almost or actually in contact at one spot, in the male house fly the space between the eyes is always much broader, and, as already indicated, may be nearly equal to one-fourth of the total width of the head. As regards the opposite sex, in the female of *Musca autumnalis* the black longitudinal area (frontal stripe) in the center of the space between the eyes is approximately equal in width to the grey border on each side, separating it from the corresponding eye. In the female house fly, however, the frontal stripe is much broader, and its width greatly exceeds that of the border, yellowish-golden in front and below, blackish above, on each side of it. The resting position of the wings in *Musca autumnalis* is the same as in *M. domestica.* In the autumn, in country districts in the British Islands, *Musca autumnalis* frequently enters houses and public buildings, sometimes in large numbers, and subsequently hibernates in attics, roof-lofts, towers, in the folds of curtains in disused rooms, and in similar retreats.

In Curran's[5] key to the genera to Muscidae, *Musca autumnalis* runs to *Orthellia* because of the propleura which, unlike those of *M. domestica,* are bare; the only North American species of *Orthellia,* however, is metallic green in color.

Vockeroth[45] has recently pointed out that this species occurs in Nova Scotia, where it may collect in considerable numbers in houses; it has invaded the United States at least as far south as Virginia. Vockeroth says: "The larvae live in cow dung; the adults suck blood and other exudations from the surface of mammals, but cannot pierce the skin, and, like the adults of *Pollenia rudis* (Fab.), the cluster fly, they hibernate in large numbers in houses." It was at first thought that this recent invader of the New World was relatively harmless, but Vockeroth (personal communication) states that it is a serious pest of cattle and horses in various parts of southeastern Canada and the eastern United States, and that it is a potential vector of disease of both man and domestic animals.*

Fannia canicularis (Linnaeus), the lesser house fly (or little house fly), is frequently seen hovering in mid-air or flying hither and thither in the middle of the room. Whereas the house fly is encountered most abundantly in the kitchen or dining room, particularly on food, the lesser house fly will be seen as frequently in one room as another, and very seldom actually on the spread table. These little flies are commonly observed to dance weirdly in the center of a room midway between the floor and the ceiling. Various observers have estimated that flies of this species constitute from 1 to 50 per cent of the total population of flies in the average house.

James[24] describes the fly as follows:

> This is a slender fly, in large part blackish, but with the abdomen usually more or less extensively yellow, the yellow regions being especially prominent in the male and characteristically in the form of three, sometimes four, pairs of spots. The middle tibia of the male is not deformed. The thorax has three brown stripes, which are fairly evident in unrubbed specimens. Length about 6–7 mm.

It is easily distinguished from *Musca* by the broadly open cell R_5 and by the characteristic forward bend of vein 3rd A, which would intersect the 2nd A if the latter were produced.

The eggs of this species are deposited chiefly on decaying vegetable matter and excrement, particularly of chickens, humans, horses, and cows. The larvae emerge in about 24 hours and may be recognized as compressed, spiny organisms about 6 mm long when full grown (Fig. 97). The pupal period lasts about 7 days under favorable conditions. The complete life cycle requires from 15 to 30 days.

Fannia scalaris (Fabricius), the latrine fly, is very similar to the foregoing. In size the two flies are about the same, if anything the latrine fly is somewhat the larger. The thorax and abdomen are bluish black; the antennae, palpi, and legs are thick. The abdomen has a dark median stripe which, with segmentally arranged transverse bands, produces a series of dorsal triangular markings. In contrast to the preceding, the middle tibia of the male is provided with a distinct tubercle.

The eggs of this fly are deposited chiefly on excrement of humans, horses, cows, etc., also on decaying vegetable matter. The egg stage lasts

* Since the above was written, Teskey (1960. "A review of the life-history and habits of *Musca autumnalis* DeGeer [Diptera: Muscidae]," *Canad. Entomol.*, **92:** 360–67) has given much valuable information on the distribution, life history, habits, and medical and veterinary significance of this fly. Although this fly has not been proven to be a vector of any disease, there is evidence to suggest that it might be involved in transmission of leprosy, pinkeye, conjunctivitis, infectious abortion of cattle, and mammalian eye worm, *Thelazia* spp. (It is an intermediate host of *T. rhodesi* Desmarest in Russia.) It has also been reported in one case of human enteric myiasis.

about 24 hours, the larval stage about 6 days and over, and the pupal stage about 9 days.

While the larva of the latrine fly resembles that of the lesser house fly in general, it is readily distinguishable because its lateral protuberances are distinctly feathered (Fig. 97).

Both *Fannia canicularis* and *Fannia scalaris* are Old World, as well as New World, in their distribution. Other similar species, with similar breeding habits and likewise found in both hemispheres, are *F. manicata* (Meigen) and *F. incisurata* (Zetterstedt). *Fannia benjamini* Malloch, an American species, not only enters houses, but may also cause annoyance by darting constantly about the eyes, ears, and mouths of persons who may enter its habitat

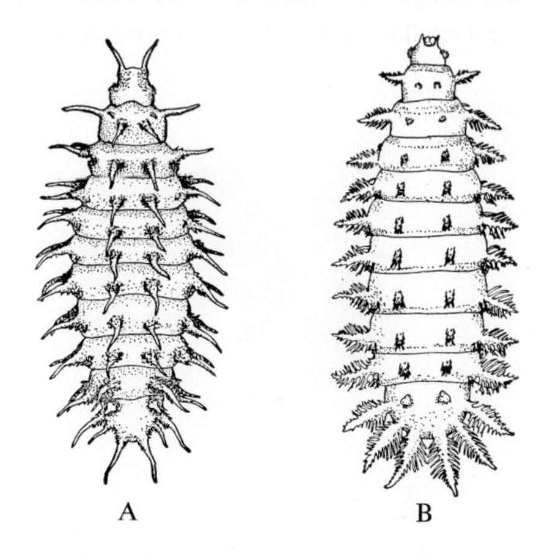

Fig. 97. (*A*) Larva of *Fannia canicularis;* (*B*) *larva of Fannia scalaris.* × 6. (Redrawn and adapted after Hewitt.)

(Arthur C. Smith, personal communication). There is some possibility that this fly might be involved in disease transmission.

Muscina stabulans (Fallén), the false stable fly (nonbiting stable fly) is larger and more robust than the house fly, varying in length from 7 to nearly 10 mm. Its general appearance is dark gray. The head is whitish gray, the antennal arista bears setae on both the upper and lower sides. The thorax is gray with four longitudinal black lines, the scutellum is yellowish broadly along its apex; the abdomen is almost black in color, covered with gray in places, which gives it a blotched appearance. The legs are slender and are largely reddish gold or cinnamon in color. The wings are folded like those of *Musca domestica;* vein M_{1+2} is not elbowed and converges but gently toward the vein before it (R_{4+5}). The eggs of this species are laid upon decaying organic matter and excrement, including human feces and rotting cow dung, in which the larvae develop. The complete life cycle is said to require from 5 to 6 weeks. *Muscina assimilis* (Fallén), a similar species with wholly black legs, has much the same habits.

Family Calliphoridae (Blow Flies). The blow flies, comprising the bluebottles and greenbottles, as well as the flesh flies (Sarcophagidae), are placed in the family Metopiidae by Curran; however, most authorities do not accept this classification. The Calliphoridae are characterized by James[24] as follows:

The arista is plumose, the hairs being usually long and extending almost to its apex; there is no postscutellum except in some genera of little medical importance; hypopleural and pteropleural bristles are present; there are three sternopleurals, two in front and one behind; there are two notopleurals, rarely an adventitious third; vein M_2 bends strongly forward, greatly narrowing but usually not closing the apical cell; and the first abdominal sternite overlaps the lateral margins of the tergites.

The larvae usually feed on dead animals or meat-containing garbage; less frequently they are scavengers on excrement and plant materials; some are facultative or obligatory parasites. An extensive study of the life histories

Fig. 98. A common blow fly, *Calliphora vomitoria.*

and nutritional requirements of several common species has been made by Kamal.[26] The adults of most species, at least in the New World and Europe, are partly to largely metallic blue, green, coppery green, or greenish black. A notable exception to this is the cluster fly *Pollenia rudis.*

Calliphora. Among the several species of bluebottle flies (metallic blue in color), two are quite common, namely, *Calliphora vomitoria* (Linnaeus) (Fig. 98), which has black genae clothed with golden-red hairs, and *C. vicina* Robineau-Desvoidy (= *C. erythrocephala* [Meigen]), which has fulvous genae clothed with black hairs. The eggs of these species hatch in from 6 to 48 hours; the growing larvae feed on the flesh for from 3 to 9 days, and after attaining full growth leave the food and bury themselves in loose earth or debris. This period (prepupal) lasts from 2 to 7 days, after which pupation takes place. The pupal period varies considerably according to temperature, lasting from 10 to 17 days, commonly 11 days. Thus, the life history of the blow fly requires from 16 to 35 days, usually 22 days. The life of the adult is about 35 days on an average.[19]

Phaenicia (= *Lucilia*) *sericata* (Meigen) is of a yellowish green or cupreous green metallic color with the abdomen varying from metallic blue and green to copper. It may occur indoors but is typically a scavenger. The palpi are yellow. There are usually three (occasionally four) postachrostical bristles present on each side. The apparent second abdominal segment is devoid of *erect* dorsal marginal bristles (these are present in the similar *Bufolucilia sylvarum* [Meigen] which also has black palpi). At a temperature of 80° ± 2° F, with beef lung or fish as food, the entire life cycle of *P. sericata,* from the deposition of the egg to emergence of the fly, requires about 12 days, broken down as follows: egg stage (the egg hatching the same day if deposited during early morning), about 8 hours; larval stage (feeding period), about 2 ½ days; prepupal stage (migrating larva), about 3 days; pupal period, about 6 days. It is the most abundant species of the genus in North America, particularly in the northern United States and Canada.[15] Also, it is highly domestic. *Phaenicia sericata* lends itself well to rearing in large numbers for experimental purposes. Rearing procedures are described by Dorman, Hale, and Hoskins.[6]

The size of the flies and the sex ratio[20] vary according to the amount of food available during the larval or feeding stage. The sex ratio (2.8–3.1 males to 6.9–7.2 females) for flies resulting from larvae which fed until they left the food voluntarily, i.e., from 72 to 78 hours, is reversed (6.2–6.5 males to 3.5–3.8 females) in flies in which the larvae were permitted to feed only 30 to 36 hours, i.e., were underfed.

Lucilia illustris (Meigen) is a holarctic species, widely distributed in North America; it is common in the midwestern portion of the United States where it ordinarily deposits its eggs on carcasses of animals in competition with *Phaenicia sericata.* It appears to be an open woodland and meadow species. North American authors have heretofore not fully recognized the fact that they were quite surely dealing with *L. illustris* and not with *L. caesar* (Linnaeus), as they often stated. The two species resemble each other very closely. Hall[15] states that *L. caesar* is not known to occur in North America. The thorax of *L. illustris* is metallic blue-green with bronze and purple reflections; the legs are black; the normal number of lateral scrutellar bristles in *Lucilia* is three pairs.

Phormia regina (Meigen), known as the black blow fly, is a widely distributed holarctic species; it is found throughout the United States and as far south as Mexico city. It commonly deposits its eggs in the wool of sheep. It is a cold-weather fly, occurring more abundantly during the early spring months and becoming less abundant as hot weather approaches. The thorax is black with a metallic bluish-green luster; there are darker black longitudinal stripes on the dorsum extending somewhat beyond the suture; the legs are shining black; the abdomen is olivaceous or bluish-green to black, and shining; the length of the fly is 6 to 11 mm.

Pollenia rudis (Fabricius), the cluster fly, may be distinguished from other common blow flies with domestic habits, at least in Europe and America, by its pollinose, nonmetallic abdomen. According to Austen,[1] it measures normally about one-third inch (8 mm) in length; it is thus as a rule a much larger insect than the house fly, which it superficially resembles. It is more heavily built and slower in its movements. Austen continues the description:

The upper surface of the dark greyish-olive middle region of the body (thorax) is clothed with a thick coat of fine, silky, recumbent, yellowish or golden-yellow hair, easily visible to the naked eye, and, though readily rubbed off, still recognizable with the aid of a lens even in a much damaged specimen. The iron grey upper surface of the posterior division of the body (abdomen) is mottled with shimmering metallic patches of lighter gray. (In 1908) Dr. D. Keilin, working in Paris, made the extraordinary discovery that the maggot of the cluster-fly is an internal parasite of a small earthworm (*Allolobophora chlorotica*, Sav.) [which like the fly itself, is exceedingly common and widely distributed in Europe, North America, and elsewhere]. The popular name of the insect (namely cluster fly) is due to the habit of this fly of clustering together, sometimes in very large numbers like a swarm of bees, when hibernating in houses or other buildings.

Family Sarcophagidae (Flesh Flies). This family contains a variety of biotic types, including the familiar medium-sized grayish flies found around carrion and excrement. The abdominal pattern in the more familiar types consists of a tessellated gray-and-black, i.e., a checkerboard pattern in which the spots change from black to gray and back with the light incidence; an exception in a medically important group occurs in the myiasis-producing *Wohlfahrtia*. The arista of the antenna is bare or, if hairy, the plumosity does not reach the apex; there are usually three or more notopleural bristles. The larvae may breed in carrion, excrement, or decaying vegetable matter; some parasitize grasshoppers, Lepidoptera, snails, and other invertebrates, and a few parasitize vertebrates, including man.

Sarcophaga haemorrhoidalis Fallén, one of the numerous species of flesh flies, occurs throughout North America as well as Europe. It measures 10 to 14 mm in length; in color it is gray. The terminalia of the male are red. It reminds one of an overgrown house fly, but it is lighter gray, the eyes are brighter reddish-brown in color, and it is larviparous. The larvae have a wide range of feeding habits, being, however, primarily scavengers. They feed on dead insects, carrion, mammalian excrement, etc.

The larvae may be deposited on the hand of a person holding a female fly. The life cycle in the presence of ample food and warm temperature requires from 14 to 18 days. The growth of the larva is very rapid after extrusion when food such as carrion is available. The larval stage may be completed in about 3 days, followed by the prepupal or migratory stage, which usually lasts about 3 days. The pupal stage requires from 8 to 10 days. *Sarcophaga carnaria* (Linnaeus), measuring 10 to 16 mm in length, is another widely distributed and common species of flesh fly.

FLIES AND HUMAN WELFARE

Flies as Pests. Lindsay and Scudder[29] have pointed out the importance of flies as nuisances or pests "in an age when those who enjoy a high standard of living are spending progressively more and more for creature comforts." There is no reason why we should tolerate a fly nuisance (Fig. 99), any more than that we should endure hordes of biting mosquitoes. This is particularly true in an age in which we can recognize more and more the importance of mental, as well as physical, health.

Control of fly nuisances must, like mosquito control, be a public responsibility. An outstanding, as well as pioneering piece of work in this direc-

Fig. 99. Such a fly nuisance as this is intolerable. (Courtesy California Bureau of Vector Control; photograph by Edgar A. Smith.)

tion, has been done by California's Bureau of Vector Control and by the Health Department of Santa Clara County; these agencies have thoroughly recognized the importance of the nuisance aspect and of public responsibility in its abatement.

One can only speculate as to what effect buzzing flies in the home may have on mental health. It is an established fact that some persons have a pathological fear of insects (entomophobia), real or imaginary. The effect on more normal persons is unknown, but any outside influence that increases tension should, if possible, be eliminated.

Germ Carriers. The house fly, *Musca domestica,* is by accident of habit and structure an important and dangerous disease-transmitting insect. In habit the house fly is revoltingly filthy, feeding indiscriminantly on excrement, vomit, and sputum, and is, on the other hand, equally attached to the daintiest food of man. The house fly's proboscis is provided with a profusion of fine hairs which serve as collectors of germs and filth; the foot of the fly, when examined under a microscope, presents an astonishing complexity of structure. Each of the six feet is equally fitted with bristly structures and pads which secrete a sticky material, adding thus to their collecting ability. When the fly feeds, it regurgitates droplets used in liquefying solid food and extrudes droplets of excrement as well. Its structure, added to its naturally vile habits, makes the house fly an ideal transmitter of filth diseases.

The house fly has long been known to contaminate food but was, nevertheless, regarded as a scavenger, and thus a beneficial insect. Leidy[28] in 1871 expressed an opinion that flies were probably a means of communicating disease to a greater degree than was generally suspected. From what he had observed in one of the large military hospitals, in which gangrene had existed during the Civil War, he thought flies should be carefully excluded from wounds. The real menace of the fly became evident in 1898, during the Spanish-American War, and shortly later Howard[23] vociferously accused the house fly, which he called the "typhoid fly," of mechanical dissemination of disease. The period from the beginning of the present century to the beginning of World War I was chiefly one of education of the public to the dangers of the house fly to human health (West[47]) and was culminated by the publication of the classical monograph of Hewitt.[21] Then followed a period of "false security" (West) until, with the advent of World War II, the need for house fly control again became suddenly and spectacularly apparent.

If there remains any doubt in the mind of the reader as to the harmfulness of the house fly, let him take the time to make a few careful observations for himself. In order to show that the house fly can carry "germs" of a known kind, a simple test can be made with a culture of *Staphylococcus aureus*. After the fly is allowed to walk about in the culture tube, it is transferred to a sterile agar plate upon which it is permitted to walk for about 3 minutes. The plate is then incubated for 24 hours. Figure 100 shows the trail of the fly in one test; every place the foot touched is plainly marked by a vigorous bacterial growth.

Esten and Mason[8] in an article entitled "Sources of bacteria in milk" state:

The numbers of bacteria on a single fly may range all the way from 550 to 6,600,000. Early in the fly season the numbers of bacteria on flies are comparatively very small, while later the numbers are comparatively very large. The place where flies live also determines largely the number that they carry. *The average for 414 flies was about one and one-fourth million bacteria on each.* It hardly seems possible for so small a bit of life to carry so large a number of organisms. The objectionable class coliaerogenes type was two and one-half times as abundant as the favorable acid type.

A significant study was made by Yao, Yuan, and Huie[48] in Peiping, China. This was based on a total of 384,193 flies, of which 98.4 per cent were *Musca domestica,* 1.1 per cent were *Fannia canicularsis* and *F. scalaris,* 0.31 per cent were *Lucilia caesar,* 0.16 per cent were *Calliphora vicina* and *C. vomitoria,* and 0.03 per cent were *Sarcophaga carnaria.* The authors found an average of 3,683,000 bacteria per fly in the slum district, and an

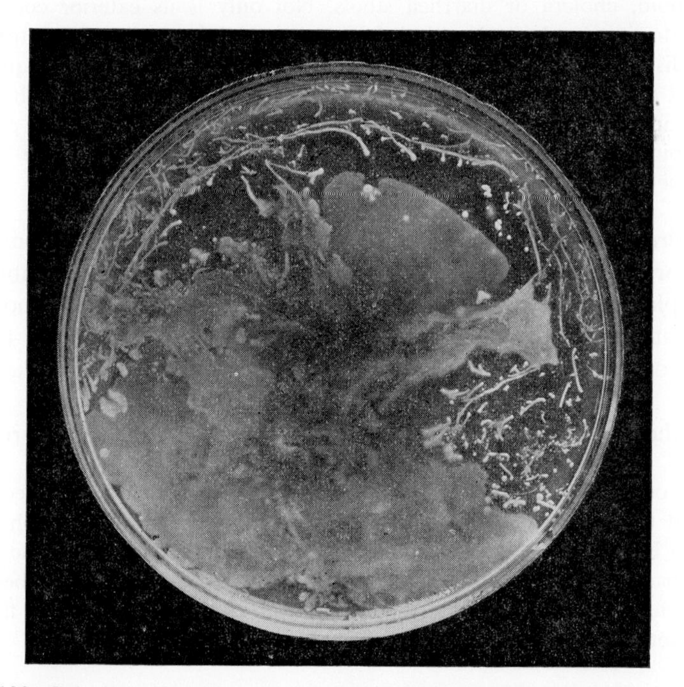

Fig. 100. Cultures of *Staphylococcus aureus* (along with certain air-contaminating bacteria) transferred by a house fly to a sterile agar plate upon which it was allowed to crawl for 3 minutes. Incubation period was 24 hours.

average of 1,941,000 for the cleanest district. They found eight to ten times as many bacteria inside the flies as on the outside.

The fly usually acquires infection by walking over infectious materials, both its feet and wings being contaminated. The intestinal contents of flies also become charged with infection when feeding, and this is dejected in the fly specks and vomit droplets. It seems plausible that in some cases flies might become infected in the larval stage by developing in infectious fecal matter, and that newly emerged and unfed flies would be dangerous. Under experimental conditions Graham-Smith[13] has produced infected blow flies by feeding the larvae on meat infected with spores of *Bacillus anthracis*. He found that the blow flies remained heavily infected for at least 2 days after emerging, and that the bacilli could be cultivated either from the legs and wings or intestinal contents of flies more than 15 or 19 days old.

The opportunity for flies to become infected is so great in all communities, even the most sanitary, that no fly should be trusted to alight on food prepared for human consumption. The following quotation is from Nuttall and Jepson:[31]

> It should be remembered that a fly may cause relatively gross infection of any food upon which it alights after having fed upon infective substances, be they typhoid, cholera or diarrhea stools. Not only is its exterior contaminated, but its intestine is charged with infective material in concentrated form which may be discharged undigested upon fresh food which it seeks. Consequently, the excrement voided by a single fly may contain a greater quantity of the infective agents than, for instance, a sample of infected water. In potential possibilities the droppings on one fly may, in certain circumstances, weigh in the balance as against buckets of water or of milk.

Gastrointestinal Diseases. The house fly is primarily a food contaminator and vector of filth diseases because of its feeding and breeding habits, as already explained. Pathogenic organisms are collected on feet and mouth parts and ingested while feeding, then deposited mechanically while the fly is crawling on human food or deposited by regurgitation or with the fly's excrement.

Of the house fly's ability to transmit typhoid bacilli, Jordan writes:[25]

> Not only may bacilli stick to the legs and wings of these insects, but if swallowed they may survive the passage of the alimentary tract. Typhoid bacilli have been isolated from house flies captured in houses in Chicago, in the neighborhood of badly kept privy vaults used by typhoid patients, and it has been shown experimentally that living bacilli may remain in or upon the body of flies for as long as twenty-three days after infection.

It is in respect to gastrointestinal diseases that the role of the house fly in disease transmission has been most firmly established. The results of studies on bacillary dysentery, or shigellosis (causative organisms, *Shigella dysenteriae* and *S. paradysenteriae*), are particularly enlightening. The work of Watt and Lindsay[46] in semiarid, subtropical Texas near the mouth of the Rio Grande, where shigellosis is so highly prevalent and endemic in some areas that a reduction of 50 per cent in rate would be readily detectable in a sample of feasible size, has given particularly significant results. Lindsay and Scudder,[29] citing that work, say:

> Through cooperation with the Texas State Health Department, fly control was achieved with DDT spraying in five out of nine similar towns. It resulted in substantial reduction in (a) *Shigella* infections, as determined by rectal swab cultures in representative groups of children under 10 years of age, (b) reported attacks of diarrheal disease, and (c) reported deaths of children under two years of age. Fly control operations were routinely established early in 1946, a few weeks in advance of the establishment of direct epidemiological measurements. Thus differentials between reported illnesses and actual infections were evident when first measured, although reported deaths of infants under two years of age prior to fly control were essentially at the same rate in the two groups of towns. In September, 1947, after nearly 20 months of fly control in five of the nine study towns, the treatment order was reversed, and the four previously untreated towns were subjected to fly measures with DDT. This change in schedule coincided with the normal seasonal increase in flies in the area and within a few days the Scudder fly grill indices for the previously treated towns had risen sharply. This was followed a few weeks later by a comparable condition in the rates of cultured infections of *Shigella* and of reported diarrheal disease. Concurrently with these rising trends, fly indices for the currently treated towns abruptly declined. This reversal in trends, coinciding with the change in fly controlled areas, decisively eliminated the possibility of chance and demonstrated the role of flies in vectoring a human disease in this study area and under the conditions involved.

Transmission of typhoid fever (causative organism, *Eberthella typhosa*) and the two strains of paratyphoid (*Salmonella paratyphi,* = *Bacillus paratyphosus* A, and *Salmonella schötmulleri,* = *Bacillus paratyphosus* B), is by fecal contamination of food and drink. Faichnie[10] in a study of the etiology of enteric fever came to the conclusion that comparatively little typhoid is carried on the feet of flies, but he found that both *E. typhosa* and *S. paratyphi* multiplied in the intestines of flies fed on infected excrement. The epidemiologic picture, together with repeated isolation of the bacteria from flies, points strongly to the incrimination of flies, particularly in "air-borne" sources of infection. Nevertheless, evidence such as we have in respect to shigellosis is absent.

Salmonella enteritis (pathogen, *Salmonella* spp.) has been considered in part a fly-borne disease. However, in the studies of Watt and Lindsay, as well as in subsequent studies in Georgia, the transmission of salmonellosis bacteria was not established, although *Salmonella* infections in livestock were common in the area studied. Either the vectoring potentiality of the fly is low, or the host qualifications of man are unnatural, or both (Lindsay and Scudder[29]). It is probable that the low dosage transmission of the fly removes it from serious consideration as a vector and that human cases of the disease, even in areas where domestic animal infection rate is high, are due to consumption of food contaminated by other agencies.

Cholera, the causative organism of which is the bacillus *Vibrio comma,* was among the first diseases in which the house fly was incriminated as a carrier. Tizzoni and Cattani in Bologna in 1886 isolated cholera vibrios from flies caught in cholera wards. Simmonds in 1892 captured flies in the post-mortem morgue in Hamburg and isolated cholera vibrios from these in large numbers. "Upon the surface of vegetables and fruits kept in a cool moist place, experiments have shown that the spirillum may retain its vitality for from four to seven days" (Jordan).

In their study of the epidemiology of cholera, Gill and Lal[11] found evidence to support the startling suggestion that possibly one phase of the life cycle of the cholera vibrio may be passed in the body of the house fly. The results of their work show that the vibrios disappeared from the body of the fly after about 24 hours but reappeared on or about the fifth day, at which time the fly was capable of infecting food by its feces.

Yaws (Frambesia) is caused by the spirochaete *Treponema pertenue* Castellani. The disease is widely distributed in the tropics. The spirochetes are found in the superficial ulcers on the hands, feet, face, and other parts of the body. The following statement by Nuttall and Jepson[31] presents evidence showing that *Musca domestica* is amply able to transmit this infection:

> Castellani (1907) tested the matter of fly transmission of yaws by experimental methods. He allowed *M. domestica* to feed (1) upon yaws material (scraping from slightly ulcerated papules), and (2) upon semi-ulcerated papules on the skin of these yaws patients. In both cases he was able to discover the *Treponema* (*Spirochaeta*) *pertenue* in microscopic preparations made from the flies' mouth parts and legs. Furthermore, he allowed *M. domestica* to feed on yaws material (1 and 2 above) and afterwards transferred them to scarified areas upon the eyebrows of monkeys. Of 15 monkeys thus experimented upon, three developed yaws papules at the places which had been contaminated by the flies.

The work of Satchell and Harrison[38] in Samoa indicates quite convincingly that wound-feeding flies, particularly *Musca domestica* and *M. sorbens,* are involved in the transmission of yaws in that area.

Ophthalmia. Evidence concerning the role of the house fly in the transmission of eye infections is conflicting, but the following bits of information are pertinent.

In commenting on ophthalmia as carried by flies, Howard[23] has the following to say:

> Dr. Lucien Howe of Buffalo informed the writer [Howard] that in his opinion the ophthalmia of the Egyptians is also transferred by flies and presumably by the house fly. . . . Doctor Howe called attention to the fact that the number of cases of eye disease always increases when the flies are present in the greatest numbers and the eye trouble is most prevalent in the place where the flies are most numerous. In the desert, where flies are absent, eyes as a rule are unaffected. He made an examination of the flies captured upon diseased eyes and found on their feet bacteria which were similar to those found in the conjunctival secretions. Flies captured in Egypt swarming about the eyes of ophthalmia patients and sent to Washington, D. C., were identified as *Musca domestica.*

The role of the house fly in the transmission of conjunctivitis is apparently not as great as was once supposed. In the United States, *Hippelates* gnats are much more important than house flies in the transmission of that complex of bacillus-caused infections known as "pinkeye" and "sore eye." The more serious trachoma of the Near East, a viral disease, which frequently results in blinding, is, according to Siniscal,[41] a family disease resulting from poor sanitary practices under crowded conditions. Lindsay and Scudder[29] believe that "if his [Siniscal's] conclusions are sound, flies would seem very unimportant as carriers during ordinary levels of the disease."

Poliomyelitis. Flies, biting and nonbiting, as well as mosquitoes, have long been under suspicion as vectors of the virus of poliomyelitis. Since it has been established that poliomyelitis is an infection of the food canal that becomes secondarily localized in nervous tissue, suspicion now rests only on the filth-breeding and filth-feeding flies. Its virus has been isolated repeatedly from human stools and sewage, and its presence has been demonstrated in flies collected in the field during both urban and rural epidemics by various investigators. Sabin and Ward[36] state that there is no longer any doubt that flies can carry the virus. The virus was isolated from 1 of 3 batches of flies (in Atlanta), more than 95 per cent of which were *Musca domestica.* Isolation of the virus was made from 7 out of 12 batches of flies collected in Cleveland, Ohio (fresh meat was added to the banana and sugar); from 90 to 95 per cent of these flies were Calliphoridae (blow flies). Hall,[15] who identified the flies, points out that all of the positive samples of flies contained *Phaenicia* (*Lucilia*) *sericata* and *Phormia regina.* Just where and how these flies originally obtained the virus is an unsolved problem, as Hall remarks. Positive experimental evidence was secured by intraperitoneal inoculation into *Cynomolgus* monkeys of etherized fly extract; unetherized material was given both intranasally and by mouth.

Some information is available as to the viability of the virus on carrier flies. Trask, Paul, and Melnick[44] found positive flies only in lots collected within 10 days of the onset of a local case, although the virus is known to persist in the stools of rhesus monkeys for 1 to 2 months. Bang and Glaser[2] were able to recover the virus only when the adult flies had been fed on infective material, never from flies reared from infected larvae. Persistence of the virus on and in the fly seems to vary with the strain of the virus, but ranges from about 48 hours to 12 days or more, ample time for the fly to contact the food of a susceptible person.

The conclusion that not only the house fly but also certain flesh flies and blow flies, particularly *Phaenicia sericata* and *Phormia regina,* can harbor the poliomyelitis virus and, under proper circumstances, can transmit it either by external contamination or by internal passage following ingestion, seems quite secure. However, proof is lacking. When, for example, a poliomyelitis epidemic occurred in southern Texas in the test area where Watt and Lindsay were conducting their now classical experiments on shigellosis, results of fly control in relation to the incidence of the disease were negative.

Consequently, it is still unclear what role, if any, flies may play in the *transmission* of poliomyelitis to human beings; that flies might serve as a link in the infection of animal reservoirs is of course not impossible. Since it is known that muscoid flies may harbor the virus of poliomyelitis, every effort should be made to control flies by any means possible, be it by environmental sanitation or by the use of insecticides, which normally should be only supplementary to good sanitation. Fly control needs encouragement. However, in the face of evidence that poliomyelitis can be spread by human carriers and since evidence of transmission by flies is incomplete, fly campaigns recommended as a means of poliomyelitis control, particularly the community-wide spreading of residual or other insecticides by airplane, only creates false hope and false security. It must be borne in mind, too, that such treatment affects only the adult population; the residual effects are not likely to influence in any large measure the following broods of flies.

Tuberculosis. Investigations by Dr. C. Andre of the University of Lyons were reported at the Anti-Tuberculosis Congress at Washington, in 1908, as follows:

> Flies are active agents in the dissemination of Koch's bacillus because they are constantly going back and forth between contagious sputa and feces, and foodstuffs, especially meat, fruit, milk, etc., which they pollute by contact with their feet, and especially with their secretions.
>
> The experimental researches of the author show the following:
>
> 1. Flies caught in the open air do not contain any acid-fast bacilli that could be mistaken for the bacillus of Koch.
>
> 2. Flies that have been fed on sputum evacuate considerable quantities of bacilli in their excretions. The bacilli appear six hours after ingestion of the sputum, and some may be found as long as five days later. These flies, therefore,

have plenty of time to carry these bacilli to a great distance, and to contaminate food in houses apparently protected from contagion, because not inhabited by consumptives.

3. Food polluted by flies that have been fed on sputa contains infective bacilli and produces tuberculosis in the guinea pig.

4. Flies readily absorb bacilli contained in dry dust.

5. Flies caught at random in a hospital ward produced tuberculosis in the guinea pig.

The means by which the infection was carried to the guinea pig in the above experiments was not stated.

No conclusive work has established the relationship of flies to the transmission of tuberculosis. Lamborn (cited by West), working with *Musca sorbens* in Nyassaland, found that the tubercle bacilli might remain viable in the body of the fly for a week.

As an experimental procedure Lamborn injected a guinea pig intraperitoneally with the gut contents of three flies that had fed eight days previously on positive sputum. The animal died four months later of generalized tuberculosis, as did a second animal injected five days after the flies had fed.[47]

Intestinal Protozoa. Roubaud[34] found that the cysts of *Entamoeba coli* (Grassi), *Entamoeba histolytica* (Schaudinn), and *Giardia lamblia* Stiles passed through the intestine of the fly uninjured, and that free amebae (both *coli* and *histolytica*) when fed to flies were found dead in the fly's intestine in less than an hour. The supposed role of the house fly in the transmission of *Entamoeba histolytica* cysts has been supported by the research of other workers. Pipkin[32] believes that the external carriage of both trophozoite and cyst of *E. histolytica* is of no significance in the transmission of amebiasis except where sanitary conditions are generally ignored, but that transmission by way of the alimentary tract is important on a community basis, especially in backward areas. Root[33] found mobile *Chilomastix mesnili* (Wenyon) in a fly's feces 7 minutes after it had fed on an infectious stool.

Eggs of Parasitic Worms. Extensive and careful work on the dispersal of eggs of parasitic worms by the house fly has been done by Nicoll.[30] The following is a summary of his investigations. Flies feed readily on excrement in which eggs from parasitic worms occur. Eggs may be conveyed by flies from excrement to food in two ways, namely, on the external surface of the body and in the intestines. The latter is possible only when the diameter of the eggs is under 0.05 mm. Eggs with a diameter of up to 0.09 mm may be conveyed on the external surface; however, those adhering eggs are usually gotten rid of by the fly within a short time, while those harbored in the intestine may remain for several days. It was found that material containing eggs of parasites, and in particular gravid segments of tapeworms, remains a source of infection through flies for as long as two weeks.

The eggs of the following parasitic worms were shown experimentally to be capable of transmission by *Musca domestica: Taenia solium* Linnaeus, *Taenia pisiformis* (Bloch), *Taenia hydatigena* Pallas, *Hymenolepis nana* (von Siebold), *Dipylidium caninum* (Linnaeus), *Diphyllobothrium latum* (Linnaeus), *Enterobius vermicularis* (Linnaeus), *Trichocephalus* (*Trichurus*) *trichiurus* (Linnaeus), both internally and externally; *Necator americanus* (Stiles), *Ancylostoma canium* (Ercolani), *Ascaris equorum* Goeze, *Toxascaris leonina* (von Linstrow), *Hymenolepis diminuta* (Rodolphi), externally only. No trematode parasites were experimented with, and the observations of Stiles that the larval fly can ingest ascarid eggs and pass them on to the adult were not confirmed. In addition to the above, West lists *Ascaris lumbricoides* Linnaeus, *Ancylostoma duodenale* (Dubini), *Hymenolepis nana* (von Siebold), and the hydatid *Echinococcus granulosus* (Batsch) as being transferred in the egg stage by the fly.

Diseases of Domestic Animals. House flies are thought to be one means by which murrina, a trypanosomiasis of horses, mules, and burros in Panama, can be transmitted. The causative organism is *Trypanosoma hippicum* Darling. Bovine mastitis, a streptococcal infection in cattle caused by *Streptococcus agalactiae,* was thought by Sanders[37] to have *Musca domestica* as well as hippelates gnats for natural vectors, although Ewing[9] did not consider the house fly an important natural agent.

Larvae of the nematode *Habronema* may cause persistent ulcerations, or summer sores, on the lower portions of bodies of horses, and also *habronemic conjunctivitis,* which manifests itself as sores on the eyes. Adults of *Habronema muscae* Carter occur in the stomach of the horse, where they lay their eggs, which pass out with the feces. The newly hatched larvae find their way into the bodies of the fly larvae which are evidently true intermediate hosts, and in which further development of the nematode occurs. The worm larvae escape from the adult fly and attack the host, or the fly may be accidentally ingested.

Domestic fowls are commonly infested by tapeworms, several of which may have the house fly or the stable fly as intermediate host. This relationship was first demonstrated by Guberlet.[14] The most important of the fowl tapeworms is *Choanotaenia infundibulum* (Bloch). Parasitized flies may be ingested in food, such as buttermilk, which is attractive to both chickens and flies.

FLY CONTROL

Fly Control. Effective fly control is based on a knowledge of the habits and life history of the particular offending species. First the breeding places must be found, and then the appropriate remedy applied. The presence of flies always denotes defective sanitation, particularly in the disposal of manures, garbage, sewage, slops, food wastes, ensilage, brewers' grain, spent hops, wet mash, dead animals, etc. The prevention of fly breeding requires good housekeeping practices in the broad sense.

Fly control involves (1) reduction of fly populations to a minimum through sanitation and good management of potential breeding areas, and (2) chemical control to attempt to eliminate those flies which are still able to develop. The two methods need to be used hand in hand, but emphasis should be placed on the first. In many areas and under certain conditions, sanitation and management of wastes may suffice without, or with limited, reliance on chemical methods. When critical conditions exist, as in areas where wastes are difficult to control or where epidemics of shigellosis threaten, the use of every effective method available is justified. Fly control in most communities has not achieved the status of mosquito control because fly problems are largely the result of neglect of the sanitary aspects and, consequently, the greater threat is to those social and economic strata of mankind where such neglect is tolerated.

> The social significance of diarrheal disease has always been slight, because those attacked are in the lower stratum of society, and the morbidity and mortality are chiefly infant. Were the disease one that struck indiscriminantly through our population as did the mosquito-borne diseases, more public support for fly abatement would probably be available (Lindsay and Scudder[29]).

Rural Fly Control. Since the principal *rural* breeding places of house flies are usually in and about barns and stables, particular attention must be paid to these as well as to barnyards and corrals, with special reference to the disposal of manures and the prevention of accumulations of manure in such locations. Proper construction of barns, with special reference to the floors, is important. Directions for sanitary, flyproof construction are available through the various state and federal experiment station publications. Floors should be so planned that removal of manure is facilitated and liquid wastes are drained off so that they will not be permitted to accumulate. If concrete stall floors are covered with wood to prevent animals from coming into direct contact with the concrete, the superfloor should be so made that it can be lifted while the concrete is being cleaned. If the crevices of the wood floor are not also frequently cleaned, fly larvae will develop in these also.

Manure Disposal. Piling manure in a barnyard results in a loss of manurial value because of leaching and chemical changes of an undesirable nature; it is also conducive to fly breeding and the survival of pathogens. Methods of treating manure piled in stacks may further decrease the value of the product as a fertilizer or may render it wholly unfit for this purpose. On the other hand, humus resulting from properly composted manure, night soil, garbage, and other organic matter contains nitrogen, phosphorus, and potash, which are vital to the continuing fertility of the soil, as well as certain trace elements which are known to be essential for optimum plant growth. Also, proper composting of wastes prevents fly breeding and results in the destruction of pathogenic bacteria, protozoa, and helminth ova, as well as weed seeds (see Fig. 101).

Whenever manure is piled up and accessible to flies, these insects are afforded an opportunity to breed. In about 4 days, after the larvae have reached full growth, they begin to migrate into the drier portions of the heap and crawl out into nearby debris, beneath platforms, into soil under and around the stack, etc. Fly control, in such a stack, can be obtained by the use of chemicals, which is generally undesirable, or by frequent turning of the

Fig. 101. Properly composted manure may be piled without producing any fly breeding. This "manure mountain," in southern California, bred no flies except in one small seepage area along its edge. (Courtesy California Bureau of Vector Control; photograph by Arthur C. Smith.)

stack, which involves considerable labor. Scattering the animal wastes in the field, although a means of preventing fly breeding, again involves considerable labor and results in loss, particularly of nitrogen, from the drying of raw fecal material.

Composting pits are frequently maintained on farms and truck gardens where quantities of rotted manure are used for fertilization purposes. Such pits, if properly constructed, will take care of farm wastes and will produce, without loss of essential soil nutrients and without successful fly breeding, a humus free from pathogenic organisms and weed seeds. The pit should be built of concrete or masonry, on a concrete or masonry slab. At one corner the pit should drain into a sump which may also be used to collect the urine and liquid manure from the barns. If feasible, the pit may be covered with wood so constructed as to exclude flies and mosquitoes (the latter sometimes breeding in the liquids collected in the sump). If the pit is not covered, fly breeding must be controlled, but this will be limited to approximately the upper 3 in. and the area adjacent to about the upper foot of wall. Turning will take care of this area of fly breeding; the labor involved will be much less than that required for an entire stack.

Open pits may be covered with a polyethylene tarpaulin or with a tarred cloth stretched tightly to prevent fly emergence; or insecticides, such as crude naphthalene, may be sprayed on the upper layers. It should be borne particularly those concerned with labor saving, may be encountered. Some of the organisms involved in the composting process.

One pit may suffice for four or fewer farm animals; for a larger number, two or more pits should be constructed so that one can be finishing the composting process during the period that the others are being filled. With larger numbers of animals, or in large poultry ranches, special problems, particularly those concerned with labor saving, may be encountered. Some of the problems of fly control in chicken houses are discussed by Hart.[16]

The fundamentals of composting, including a discussion of fly control, and directions for the construction of composting pits are given by Gotaas.[12]

General Recommendations. Bohart *et al.*[4] make the following representative suggestions for decreasing the potential of wastes on farms for becoming fly-breeding sources:

1. Weekly distribution in a thin layer on fields.
2. Composting in compact piles with insecticidal treatment of the surface or composting in fly-tight bins.
3. Weekly removal by a central agency for rapid mechanical composting or storage in an open pit silo or sanitary fill.
4. Farm construction to aid rapid drying of manure through free air circulation and sunlight.
5. Adequate drainage and protection from wetting organic wastes by rain, ground water, or leaky watering devices.
6. Incineration or deep burial of animals or birds or utilization of insecticides if immediate disposal of carcasses is not feasible.
7. Maintaining poultry on deep litter where fly breeding is greatly reduced by rapid turnover of droppings in the dry litter.
8. Maintaining laying flocks in single-bird, wire-floored cages rather than in group wire-floored cages where manure cannot dry. This is most effective in hot, dry areas where dry cones of manure develop.
9. Manure may be stored in fly-tight manure boxes or houses or under polyethylene tarpaulins.

Community Fly Control. Among the earliest successful community-wide fly-control campaigns was one conducted by Herms[18] in Berkeley, California, in 1909–1910 during the "horse-and-buggy" days when there was really a fly problem. The population of Berkeley was about 40,000 at that time. The campaign was started with full cooperation of all city officials and the Board of Health through the health officer. Much newspaper publicity was given to the work, and bulletins on fly control were distributed by the Board of Health. Twenty students from the class in medical entomology were officially appointed sanitary inspectors. A detailed house-to-house inspection was made to locate breeding places, and advice was given as to means of control. Police officers assisted when difficult situations arose. Although insecticides were used to some extent, the campaign was based primarily on sanitary procedures.

After a few years of community interest in house fly control, there followed a lull in interest, perhaps due in large measure to conversion of livery stables into garages, a change-over from the horse to the automobile. In the late 1940's there was a widespread popular demand for fly-control programs, owing no doubt to the popular association of flies with the spread of poliomyelitis and to the enthusiastic approval of the new "miracle" killer, DDT.

Rowe[35] points out that in the conduct of the most effective and economical community fly control programs both preventive and insecticidal measures are essential. He states that too much emphasis cannot be placed upon preventive measures. These are incorporated in what are known as standard environmental sanitation practices. However, such practices must be specific and directed toward the abatement of all fly-breeding situations in so far as possible. In agricultural communities all fly-breeding hot spots should be taken into consideration; the outdoor privy may be a contributing factor; garbage and community dumps may also contribute flies; these situations are all amenable to relatively simple sanitary and insecticidal procedures.

However, according to Rowe, some of the most vexing problems in a community are created by the haphazard dumpage or the careless disposal of industrial end products and wastes. Major fly-breeding foci are often created around stockyards, stock feeding pens in connection with sugar beet refineries, abattoirs, hide and tallow plants, canneries, food and milk processing plants, etc. Vast numbers of flies—house flies, lesser house flies, and other muscids, blow flies, pomace flies, etc.—may be produced in the accumulated wastes and contaminated soil around the plants. With the contemporary trend toward suburban living, schools and homes tend to become closer in physical proximity to such fly-producing industries. Special study must be given to each situation, and a practical remedy should be employed that is adaptable to each; the program should aim at elimination of the problem whenever possible rather than at insecticidal treatment. Fly problems are man-made.

Garbage Cans. Where garbage cans are used, and certainly every household should possess a garbage receptacle that is kept tightly closed against flies, it is strongly urged that all liquids be drained from the refuse before disposing of it and that the solids be wrapped in a newspaper before they are placed in the can. The can must be kept clean. In this way fly breeding in garbage cans may be effectually prevented, and an act of mercy is done the scavenger and other handlers of garbage. It is good practice to spray the outside of the garbage can and the rack on which it stands every week or two with a residual spray.

Use of Manure on Lawns. Veritable swarms of flies may suddenly make their appearance on porches and windows and in the house after comparatively fresh manure has been spread on lawns as a fertilizer. Such manure is commonly infested with full-grown maggots or pupae which, in a few days after the fertilizer has been applied, give rise to a pest of flies. It is wise, no doubt, to use old composted manure for this purpose or to subject the manure to a thorough steaming or drenching with water at 195° F (nearly boiling) before applying it to the lawn.

Two objections are commonly raised against the steaming or drenching method of treatment: first, that the useful bacteria are destroyed, i.e., the manure may be rendered sterile; and second, that other desirable constituents are leached out by the water. Not all the useful bacteria, by any means, are destroyed by the hot water, and those remaining rapidly multiply and soon render the manure as good as ever in this respect. In the second place, the leachings may be preserved quite easily by placing the manure to be treated in a shallow, tight box similar to those used by plasterers for mixing mortar, and adding a spigot in a hole with plug from which the leachings can be drawn and used as liquid manure.

This method is also useful to mushroom growers who must use rotted manure in which certain species of fly larvae, mites, etc., may occur in great numbers.

Railroad cars laden with manure are often sidetracked in or near communities and are responsible for swarms of flies. Good results have been obtained by subjecting the entire periphery of the carload to live steam from the locomotive.

Lawn Clippings. Grass clippings from lawns are often dumped in heaps on the premises or in alleys. Hot weather soon produces a vile-smelling, decomposing, warm mass of grass which is attractive to flies, and within a few days numerous maggots, particularly of the house fly and stable fly, may be found infesting the mass. Thus again, in spite of the absence of manure and garbage, there may be a veritable plague of flies. The method of prevention is obvious: the clippings should either be composted or spread out thinly in order to dry preparatory to being burned or otherwise disposed of.

Flies from Septic Tanks. Small invasions of flies may be traced to nearby septic tanks of defective construction which permit ingress of flies. Flies may be seen coming and going through these apertures in the superstructure, and examination of the top sludge will reveal countless maggots and pupae on the surface. Elimination of these avenues of ingress will soon end the trouble.

Sewage Treatment Plants. Flies of many species, notably the house fly and blow flies, may be attracted to sewage treatment plants because of odors;

and occasionally under improper management countless numbers of flies originate in the sludge beds during the treatment process. There may also be much fly breeding in wet sludge that is applied to the soil as a fertilizer. The control of a breeding source of this kind may be accomplished by deep plowing and, of course, discontinuance of the use of wet sludge as a fertilizer.

Sewage treatment plants of modern construction do not as a rule breed flies. The methods used for fly control are various. Sewage works engineers suggest that fly breeding may be effectively prevented by quick drying of

Fig. 102. An excellently operated sanitary landfill. (Courtesy California Bureau of Vector Control; photograph by Arthur C. Smith.)

sludge. Raking procedures to remove floating debris before processing of the remaining sewage may be a cause of trouble; the rakings should be burned or buried at once before flies can get to them. Sanitary landfills (Fig. 102), if operated according to rigid specifications, may be used to alleviate the public nuisance, provided that low-value land is available without necessitating too long a haul. Incinerators may be used to avoid long hauls, but they are costly to build and operate. Chemical treatment is usually undesirable, but it may be employed under certain circumstances. The use of poison baits for adult control around sewage plants is often feasible.

A composting method of sewage disposal that has been widely used in Europe and which has been used experimentally by the United States Public

Health Service in Georgia and Arizona employs a rotary drum as the container. This is ordinarily done on a very large scale for disposing of municipal refuse, but it has been adapted to use on small premises, poultry ranches, and other animal operations (Arthur C. Smith, personal communication).

A test of the rotary drum principle as applied to urban conditions in the United States has been described by Scovel.[40] This concerns the plant at Sacramento, California (Fig. 103), in operation since 1956, which has been found thoroughly adaptable to American conditions. It combines mechanical and microbiological reduction. After the large noncompostables are removed, the remaining material is first ground and then conveyed to the "bio-stabilizer," or revolving drum, which thoroughly mixes the material, combines it

Fig. 103. The Dano plant at Sacramento, California, the first such unit in the United States. (Courtesy of Dano of America, Inc.)

with air admitted through valves, rapidly (within 24 hours) brings about sterilization of pathogenic organisms, and in about 10 days produces a very desirable compost which is nonodorous and easily handled, and which retains the desirable chemical components and microorganisms for land fertilization. Some of the advantages of this method, as pointed out by Scovel, are that it is hygienic, without production of objectionable or noxious odors; there is no smoke; flies are not bred, and rats are not fed; the process is economical, similar to landfilling and cheaper than incineration; and plants may be erected in populous areas, where limited land areas are available, and without offending the esthetic senses. Almost all natural organic products which occur as wastes may be handled by the plant.

Privies. In the absence of modern plumbing, particular attention should be paid to the location and construction of a box privy with receptacle or dug pit. No doubt many gastrointestinal diseases are traceable to insanitary privies. Two important precautions are involved: first, selection of a location which will avert pollution of wells or other water supply; and, second, choice of a type of construction which will prevent flies from gaining access to the excreta and will ensure privacy.

A sanitary privy (Fig. 104) must meet the following requirements, according to Stiles and Lumsden:[43]

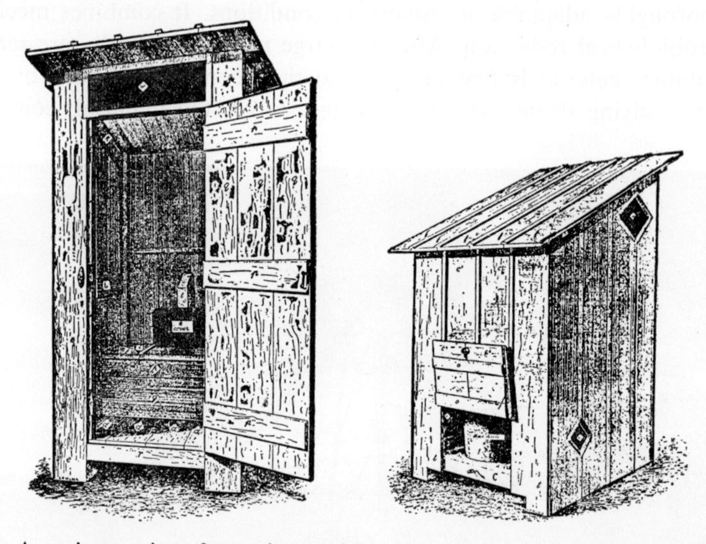

Fig. 104. A sanitary privy: front view to *left*, rear and side view to *right*. (After Stiles and Lumsden.)

(1) The excreta must not touch the ground; hence, some kind of watertight receptacle (box, pail, tub, barrel, tank, or vault) for the excreta must be used under the seat. (2) Domesticated animals must not have access to the night soil; therefore the privy should have a trapdoor in the back to exclude them. (3) Flies and other insects must not have access to the excreta; therefore the entire privy must be made rigidly flyproof, or some substance must be used in the receptacle to protect the contents from insects.

When the excreta are deposited in a pit or cesspool, great care must be exercised in banking up around the outside of the building to prevent flies from gaining access to the pit. Borax applied to the excreta is an added precaution to kill fly larvae. In deep-pit privies that are tightly constructed and fairly dry, paradichlorobenzene and orthodichlorobenzene are similarly useful. Chemical treatment with BHC, chlordane, and other chlorinated hydrocarbons cannot be recommended; for some reason as yet unknown, the use of such chemicals resulted in an *increase* in fly production, according to the investigations of Kilpatrick and Schoof.[27]

If the privy is built on skids or can otherwise be moved easily, in addition to treatment mentioned above, the accumulated excreta should be burned.

Chemical Control of Adults. In emergencies, or when methods which utilize common sanitation or which depend on the bionomics or ecologic relationships of the fly will not suffice, it is usually necessary to employ chemical means of control directed against the adults. These methods involve chiefly the use of residual sprays, space sprays, and poison baits. Insecticides, particularly the organophosphorus compounds, should be used with caution; one must not assume that, because he has handled insecticides in a careless fashion without ill results in the past, he will always be so fortunate. Insecticides, however mild, are poisons and must be treated as such. In using them for fly control, one should always use proper precautions not to contaminate human or animal food or drink or the containers for such, and it is wise to observe all printed precautions to protect oneself from the insecticides which he is applying.

Resistance to Insecticides. The miracle of DDT promised a panacea in house fly control, as well as in many other areas in medical and agricultural entomology, but with the development of resistant strains, the bubble burst. The general subject of insect resistance to insecticides has been discussed in a previous chapter, but those aspects which concern flies must be treated here.

House fly resistance to DDT, first noted in Sweden in 1946, has become so common that in many parts of the world it is useless to attempt to control *Musca domestica* by means of that chemical. Moreover, it has been shown that flies resistant to one insecticide will tend to develop resistance to other chemicals of the same group. In California, where the house fly was subjected to intensive control by the use of DDT over a period of several years, this insect developed resistance to all the chlorinated hydrocarbons, including DDT, methoxychlor, BHC, lindane, chlordane, and others; by 1957 it was beginning to develop resistance to malathion, although it was still susceptible to other organophosphorus compounds.[4] Until some solution of the resistance problem is to be had, recommendations that include residual insecticides must be made with caution and with the consideration that the development of resistance on the part of the fly may negate their value. Where resistance has not yet developed, the chlorinated hydrocarbons may be used, but with caution; in particular, if they are used as adult sprays, the same insecticides should not also be used as larvicides. Some species of flies, including apparently *Musca vicina* and *M. nebulo,* can still be controlled effectively with DDT.

There is one brighter aspect to the failure of the residual insecticides to continue to control house flies. The success of DDT had a tendency to make control operators and the general public too complacent; there is now a definite trend toward a return to the more basic, or sanitary, aspects of fly control.

Residual Sprays and Space Sprays. Residual sprays are those which, when applied to a surface in relatively small quantities, retain their effectiveness over a period of time, usually ranging from a week to a month or more. Early use of DDT in dairy barns gave phenomenal results, a single application sometimes sufficing for an entire season. In areas where resistance to the chlorinated hydrocarbons is not a problem, DDT, methoxychlor, lindane, and chlordane may still be used. Methoxychlor is not as effective against flies as DDT, but because of its relatively low toxicity to mammals it is preferred in certain situations, e.g., in dairy barns. Lindane and chlordane are more toxic to flies than DDT, but, being more volatile, they have lower residual value. DDT or chlordane should not be used for general residual spraying inside homes.

Residual sprays should be applied to areas where house flies tend to congregate. It is not always necessary to treat the entire surface. In the home, spot treatment to light fixtures, cords, windows, and other places where flies tend to light may suffice. One should be careful to avoid contamination of foodstuffs and utensils used in the preparation and serving of food. Emulsions or refined kerosene solutions are preferable on painted or papered walls in residences, since they are less visible, but wettable-powder suspensions may be applied at lower concentrations. Treatment of surfaces should be sufficiently heavy to provide an adequate residue. Sprays are usually applied to the point of initial runoff, but the amount used will depend on the nature of the surface treated. A power sprayer is advantageous, from the standpoint of both economy and results, when large areas are to be treated, but a type which can be attached to a garden hose or pump-up compressed air sprayer will serve very well.

Outside the house, residual sprays should be applied to garbage cans and other such places that may attract flies. Even in areas where house flies are resistant to the chlorinated hydrocarbons, control of such insects as *Fannia canicularis* may be obtained by spraying shrubbery, nearby weeds, and low foliage, favorite resting places of this fly.

Certain organophosphorus compounds may be used as residual sprays if sugar is added to the spray at the rate of 8 to 25 pounds per 50 gallons of water.[4] Such baited residual sprays are especially effective against the house fly which, in feeding on the sugar, may ingest a toxic dose of the insecticide. Of the organophosphorus compounds, malathion has been used most extensively, but other compounds, such as Diazinon and ronnel, have been used.

Cotton cords, impregnated with parathion plus Diazinon, may be hung well above head height in barns, poultry houses, and similar structures for long-time residual control. The cords should be handled with protective gloves while being put into place; they should not be allowed to come in contact with the bare skin. Treated cords are available commercially in many areas.

Space sprays, including aerosols, may be directed at resting flies or may be shot into the air by means of a hand applicator or with prepared pressurized dispensers when flies are numerous. Space sprays may be used in the home, in barns, and in other enclosures, but they should not be used where food can be contaminated or where there are hot surfaces or open flames. The active ingredients are usually pyrethrins, allethrins, or aliphatic thiocyanates. Pyrethrins usually have piperonyl butoxide added. This material acts as a synergist. Space spraying is particularly valuable in areas where there is a problem of resistance to residual sprays.

Poisoned Baits. The use of formaldehyde in milk, in a concentration that would be nontoxic to children and pets, has long served as a poison bait. The use of this material, along with that of such dangerous chemicals as sodium arsenite and sodium arsenate, has been virtually abandoned. The substitution of chemicals of the organophosphorus group, such as malathion and Diazinon, has, however, revived the use of baits. Baits in either dry or liquid form may be quite effective in reducing fly populations in dairy barns and poultry farms, but should not be used in the home, milk room, or in restaurants.

Bohart *et al.*[4] summarize the advantages and disadvantages of the use of organophosphorus insecticide baits as follows:

> Such baits have certain advantages over residual sprays in that they require no special application equipment, can be rapidly and easily distributed from a shaker or sprinkling can, and once initial control has been achieved are less expensive to use both from the standpoint of cost of materials and cost of labor. However, they have certain disadvantages as well since under certain conditions they do not effect as complete or as rapid control as do residual sprays; they must be applied daily in most instances until the adult population and breeding potential are reduced to a low level; and they are selective being effective principally against the house fly and not controlling a number of flies including the little house fly and biting flies such as the stable fly and horn fly which may reach high population levels.

Liquid baits utilize an attractant such as sugar, sirup, or unsulfurized molasses, mixed with the poison and water. The finished bait should contain 0.1 per cent of the insecticide and 10 per cent of the attractant. Dry sugar baits consist of granulated sugar mixed with Diazinon or malathion, 25 per cent wettable powder, with a little lampblack added to color the sugar, as a precautionary measure. A typical formula consists of 1 pound of Diazinon (25 per cent wettable powder) to 24 pounds of granulated sugar and about 2 tablespoonsful of lampblack. The addition of cornmeal, with a little peanut oil, will produce a better bait to use on moist surfaces where the sugar may dissolve. Baits may be used as needed; where sanitary conditions prevail, one application in poultry houses and dairy barns weekly may keep flies to a minimum. One should take care not to contaminate feed, mangers, litter, water, and watering troughs with the insecticide.

REFERENCES

1. Austen, E. E., 1926. "The housefly: Its life history, etc.," London: British Museum (Natural History) in *Economic Series* no. 1A, 2nd ed., pp. 5–52.

2. Bang, F. B., and Glaser, R. W., 1943. "The persistence of poliomyelitis virus in flies," *Amer. J. Hyg.,* **37:**320–24.

3. Black, Ralph J., and Barnes, Allan M., 1958. "Effect of earth cover on fly emergence from sanitary landfills," *Pub. Works Magazine,* **89:**91–94.

4. Bohart, Richard M.; Davis, Clarence S.; Deal, Andrew S.; Furman, Dean P.; March, Ralph B.; Smith, Arthur C.; and Swift, John E.; 1958: "Insecticides for control of flies on poultry ranches, dairies, homes and food processing plants," *Calif. Vector Views,* **5:**35–41.

5. Curran, C. H., 1934. *The Families and Genera of North American Diptera.* New York: The Ballou Press, 512 pp.

6. Dorman, S. C.; Hale, W. C.; and Hoskins, W. M.; 1938. "The laboratory rearing of flesh flies and the relations between temperature, diet, and egg production," *J. Econ. Entomol.,* **31:**44–51.

7. Dunn, L. H., 1923. "Observations on the oviposition of the housefly, *Musca domestica,* in Panama," *Bull. Entomol. Research,* **13:**301–05.

8. Esten, W. N., and Mason, C. J., 1908. "Sources of bacteria in milk," Storrs: in *Connecticut Agric. Exper. Sta. Bull.,* no. 51, pp. 94–98.

9. Ewing, H. E., 1942. "The relation of flies (*Musca domestica* Linaeus) to the transmission of bovine mastitis," *Amer. J. Vet. Research,* **3:**295–99.

10. Faichnie, N., 1929. "The etiology of enteric fever: Personal views and experiences," *J. M. A. S. Africa,* **3:**669–75.

11. Gill, C. A., and Lal, R. B., 1931. "Epidemiology of cholera, with special reference to transmission: A preliminary report," *Indian J. Med. Research,* **18:**1255–97.

12. Gotaas, Harold G., 1956. *Composting: Sanitary Disposal and Reclamation of Organic Wastes.* Geneva: World Health Organization. 205 pp.

13. Graham-Smith, G. S., 1911. "Further observations on the ways in which artificially infected flies carry and distribute pathogenic and other bacteria," in Reports to the Local Government Board on Public Health and Medical Subjects, London (n.s., no. 53, further reports no. 4) pp. 31–48.

14. Guberlet, J. E., 1916. "Morphology of adult and larval cestodes of poultry," *Tr. Amer. Mic. Soc.,* **35:**23–44 (2 plates).

15. Hall, David G., 1948. *The Blowflies of North America.* Thomas Say Foundation of Entomol. Soc. Amer., vol. 4. 477 pp.

16. Hart, Samuel A., 1957. "Chicken house fly control through manure handling," *Calif. Vector Views,* **4:**68–69.

17. Herms, W. B., 1907. "An ecological and experimental study of Sarcophagidae," *J. Exper. Zool.,* **4:**45–83.

18. Herms, W. B., 1911. "The housefly in its relation to the public health," Berkeley: Univ. Calif., in Agric. Exper. Sta. Bull., no. 215, pp. 513–48.

19. Herms, W. B., 1911. *The Photic Reactions of Sarcophagid Flies, etc.* Cambridge: Harvard Univ. in Contributions from Zool. Lab., Museum Comp. Zool., no. 217.

20. Herms, W. B., 1928. "The effect of different quantities of food during the larval period on the sex ratio and size of *Lucilia sericata* Meigen and *Theobaldia incidens* Thom.," *J. Econ. Entomol.*, **21:**720–29.

21. Hewitt, C. Gordon, 1910. *The Housefly.* Manchester, England: The University Press, xiii + 195 pp.

22. Hodge, C. F., 1911. In *Nature and Culture,* July, 1911.

23. Howard, L. O., 1900. "A contribution to the study of the insect fauna of human excrement," *Proc. Wash. Acad. Sc.*, **2:**541–604.

24. James, Maurice T., 1948. *The Flies That Cause Myiasis in Man.* Washington, D. C.: Dept. Agric., in Misc. Publ. no. 631. 175 pp.

25. Jordan, Edwin O., 1908. *A Textbook of General Bacteriology.* Philadelphia: W. B. Saunders Co. 557 pp.

26. Kamal, Adel S., 1958–1959. "Comparative studies of thirteen species of sarcosaprophagous Calliphoridae and Sarcophagidae (Diptera). I. Bionomics." *Ann. Entomol. Soc. Amer.*, **51:**261–71. "II. Digestive enzymology." *Ann. Entomol. Soc. Amer.*, **52:**157–73.

27. Kilpatrick, M. S., and Shoof, H. F., 1956. "Fly production in treated and untreated privies," U. S. Public Health Service, in *Pub. Health Rep.* **71:**787–96.

28. Leidy, Prof., 1871. "Flies as a means of communicating contagious diseases," *Proc. Acad. Nat. Sc. of Philadelphia,* 1871, p. 297.

29. Lindsay, Dale R., and Scudder, Harvey I., 1956. "Nonbiting flies and disease," *Am. Rev. Entomol.*, **1:**323–46.

30. Nicoll, William, 1911. "On the part played by flies in the dispersal of the eggs of parasitic worms," in Reports to the Local Government Board on Public Health and Medical Subjects, London n.s. no. 53, further reports (no. 4) on flies as carriers of infection.

31. Nuttall, G. H. F., and Jepson, F. P., 1909. "The part played by *Musca domestica* and allied (non-biting) flies in the spread of infectious diseases," in *Reports to the Local Government Board on Public Health and Medical Subjects,* London n.s., no. 16.

32. Pipkin, A. C., 1949. "Experimental studies on the role of filth flies in the transmission of *Endamoeba histolytica,*" *Amer. J. Hyg.*, **49:**255–75.

33. Root, F. M., 1921. "Experiments on the carriage of intestinal protozoa of man by flies," *Amer. J. Hyg.*, **1:**131–53.

34. Roubaud, E., 1918. "Le rôle des mouches dans la dispersion des amibes dysentriques et autre protozoaires intestinaux," *Bull. Soc., path. exot.*, **11:**166–71.

35. Rowe, John A., 1948. "Fundamentals of community fly control," *Proc. and Papers, 16th Ann. Conf. Calif. Mosq. Control Assn.* (Berkeley), pp. 11–14.

36. Sabin, A. B., and Ward, R., 1942. "Insects and epidemiology of poliomyelitis," *Science,* **95:**300–01.

37. Sanders, D. A., 1940. "*Musca domestica* a vector of bovine mastitis (preliminary report)," *J. A. Vet. M. A.*, **97:**120–22.

38. Satchell, G. H., and Harrison, R. A., 1953. "Experimental observations on the possibility of transmission of yaws by wound-feeding diptera, in western Samoa," *Trans. Roy. Soc. Trop. Med. & Hyg.*, **47:**148–53.

39. Schoof, H. F., and Siverly, R. E., 1954. "Multiple release studies on the dispersion of *Musca domestica* at Phoenix, Arizona," *J. Econ. Entomol.*, **47:**830–88.

40. Scovel, Ralph E., 1958. "The Dano method of refuse disposal," *Calif. Vector Views,* **5:**5–9.

41. Siniscal, Arthur A., 1955. "The trachoma story," U. S. Public Health Service, in *Pub. Health Rep.*, **70:**497–507.

42. Smith, Arthur C., 1956. "Fly prevention in dairy operations," *Calif. Vector Views,* **3:**57, 59–60.

43. Stiles, C. W., and Lumsden, L. L., 1911. *The Sanitary Privy*. Washington, D. C.: Dept. Agric., in Farmer's Bull., no. 463, 32 pp.

44. Trask, J. D.; Paul, J. R.; and Melnick, J. L.; 1943. "The detection of poliomyelitis virus in flies collected during epidemics of poliomyelitis. I. Methods, results, and type of flies involved," *J. Exp. Med.*, **77:**531–44.

45. Vockeroth, J. R., 1953. "*Musca autumnalis* Deg. in North America (Diptera: Muscidae)," *Canad. Entomol.*, **85:**422–23.

46. Watt, J., and Lindsay, D. R., 1948. "Diarrheal disease control studies. I. Effect of fly control in a high morbidity area," U. S. Public Health Service, in *Pub. Health Rep.*, **63:**1319–34.

47. West, Luther S., 1951. *The Housefly*. Ithaca: Comstock Publ. Co. 584 pp.

48. Yao, H. Y.; Yuan, I. C.; and Huie, Dorothy; 1929. "The relation of flies, beverages, and well water to gastrointestinal diseases in Peiping," *Nat. Med. J. China,* **15:**410–18.

Chapter 16

BLOODSUCKING MUSCOID FLIES
Tsetse Flies, Stomoxys Flies, Horn Flies

Order Diptera—Family Muscidae

TSETSE FLIES

Introduction. The genus *Glossina,* a member of the family *Muscidae,* comprises the tsetse flies of Africa. According to Buxton,[6] the word "tsetse" comes from the Sechuana language of Bechuanaland and means "fly destructive to cattle." Bequaert[2] states that the word "tsetse" was introduced into the English language by R. Gordon Cumming in 1850 in his "Five Years of a Hunter's Life in the Far Interior of South Africa," and David Livingstone in 1857 "focused the attention of the scientific world upon the ravages of the fly."

Evidently tsetse flies enjoy a wide distribution in geological times, since four species of fossil *Glossina* have been described from the Oligocene shales of Colorado. Today the tsetse flies are restricted to continental Africa south of the Tropic of Cancer where they occur in so-called "fly belts." They hold an area of about 4.25 million square miles and remain as an obstacle to the development of tropical Africa.

Fig. 105. (*Left*) *Glossina palpalis;* (*right*) *Glossina morsitans.* (After Newstead.)

Adult tsetse flies (Fig. 105), both male and female, depend on blood for their existence, and, whereas they feed on a wide variety of animals, there are host preferences among the different species. Although man is freely attacked, he is not considered a favored host. In areas where large wild animals have been greatly reduced in numbers, the flies turn freely to man. *Glossina palpalis* (Robineau-Desvoidy) favors reptiles, particularly crocodiles and monitor lizards.

Several large monographs have been published on the tsetse flies. Those of Newstead, Evans and Potts,[20] Hegh,[12] Swynnerton,[26] and, in particular, the recent work of Buxton,[6] will be especially useful to the student.

General Characteristics. The tsetses are medium-sized flies, ranging in size from that of a house fly to that of a blow fly. They are brownish in

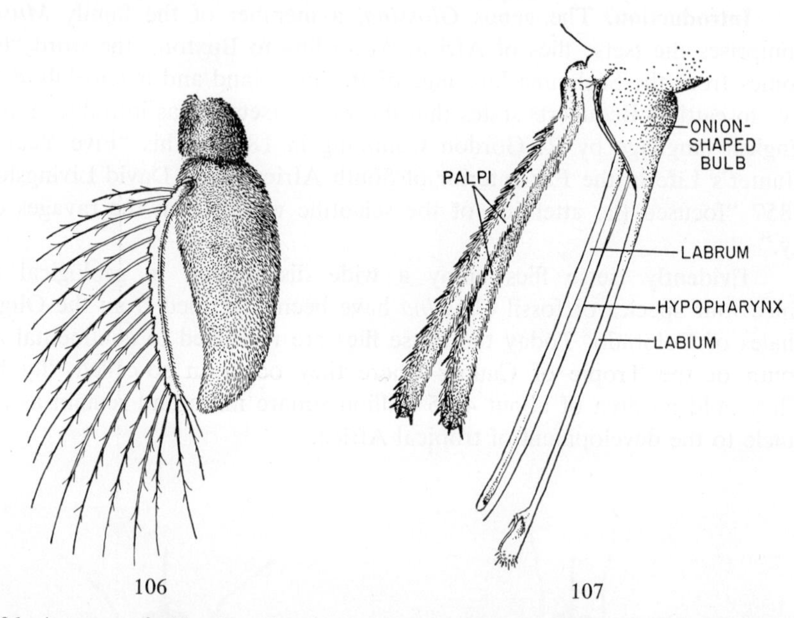

Fig. 106. Antenna of *Glossina,* showing arista with branched hairs. (Much enlarged.)
Fig. 107. Mouth parts of *Glossina.* × 17.

color; the body is wasplike, and the wings when at rest are crossed scissors-like and extend well beyond the tip of the abdomen. The wing venation is characteristic in that the fourth longitudinal vein (M_{1+2}) bends suddenly upward before it meets the anterior transverse vein, which is very oblique (Fig. 40). The discal cell is shaped remarkably like a meat cleaver and is referred to as the "cleaver cell."

The palpi are nearly as long as the proboscis, which points bayonetlike in front of the head. The antennal arista (Fig. 106) bears a series of long bilaterally branched and regularly arranged hairs only on the upper surface. This type of antenna, with its feathered aristal hairs borne on one side of the arista only, is distinctly characteristic of *Glossina* and is not known elsewhere. The mouth parts consist of the labium, which terminates in the cutting labella, the labrum, and the hypopharynx, which are ensheathed by the labium. The incision is made by the labella; the labrum and hypopharynx carry the food and salivary canals. A characteristic "onion-shaped" bulb is situated at the base of the haustellum (Fig. 107). Both sexes are avid bloodsuckers, feeding usually in broad daylight and outdoors. They are particularly attracted to moving objects.

Life History. The female tsetse fly gives birth to full-grown larvae which are extruded singly at intervals of about 10 to 15 days during the lifetime of the mother. During the intrauterine state (there are three larval stages), the larvae feed on fluid from special glands commonly referred to as "milk glands." The newly extruded larvae are creamy white to pale yellow and have a pair of intensely black, shining lobes at the posterior extremity. Thoracic spiracles are lacking. The female fly requires three blood

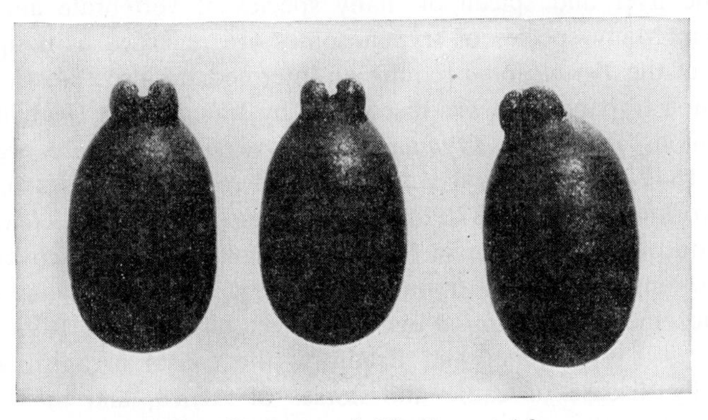

Fig. 108. Pupae of *Glossina*. × 4.8.

meals during the developmental period of each larva, the last being taken about 3 days prior to larviposition. Evidence concerning the number of larvae produced during the lifetime of one female is inconclusive, but the average number is probably 8 to 10.

The larvae are unable to crawl, as do other muscoid larvae, because of the reduced cephalopharyngeal armature and the lack of spinose pads. Lewis[17] points out that the larva moves and burrows by peristaltic movements and longitudinal contractions of the whole body. Coarse pebbly sand favors the larvae in burrowing, although a depth of only a few centimeters is reached. The behavior of the larva at this time, Lewis points out, is of great importance in determining its chances of survival. "If it is slow to penetrate the soil, it is exposed for a longer period to the possible attack of predators and parasites." Pupation takes place within an hour of larviposition. The pupa rapidly darkens to a blackish-brown color with the posterior lobes and general form as shown in Figure 108. The pupal stage lasts from

3 to 4 weeks and longer, depending much on soil temperature and soil moisture. A great deal of work has been done on the ecology of the puparium (Nash[19]).

The fly emerges from the puparium by breaking loose the end of the pupal case by pressure from the ptilinum. The flies are said to have a striking dislike for excrementous matter, and the larvae are ordinarily deposited in the root tangles of the mangrove and shade of other vegetation where the soil is not too dry and is loose. The presence or absence of organic matter seems to be immaterial (Nash).

Trypanosomiasis. The tsetse flies are important vectors of trypanosomes. The term *trypanosomiasis* applies to all infections with flagellate protozoan parasites of the genus *Trypanosoma* and includes African sleeping sickness. The *Trypanosoma* belong to the protozoon family Trypanosomidae; they invade the blood, lymph, cerebrospinal fluid, and various organs of the body, such as the liver and spleen of many species of vertebrate animals, from fish to man. Many species of trypanosomes are regarded as nonpathogenic. Nearly all of the *Tryanosoma* require an intermediate insect host.

The first trypanosome was discovered by Valentine in 1841 in the blood of the salmon. The name *Trypanosoma*[16] was given to these organisms by Gruby in 1842–43. Attention was not called to trypanosomes of mammals until the work of Lewis in 1878 on the parasites (*Trypanosoma lewisi* [Kent]) of the blood of the rat in India.* After that followed the discovery of other more important pathogenic trypanosomes, e.g., in 1880 Evans discovered the trypanosome, *Trypanosoma evansi* (Steel), of surra; in 1895 Bruce discovered *T. brucei* Plimmer and Bradford, the causal organism of nagana, the tsetse-fly disease of cattle and horses of Africa, and in 1897 Bruce[4] showed that *Glossina morsitans* Westwood transmitted the infection. In 1901 Dutton[8,9] discovered trypanosomes in a blood smear prepared by Dr. R. M. Forde from a European patient in Gambia; he also found them in the blood of a native child. Following this discovery, the organism was named *Trypanosoma gambiense* Dutton. In 1903 Bruce and Nabarro[5] proved *Glossina palpalis* to be the carrier by feeding freshly caught flies, ranging in number from 31 to 9, on a black-faced monkey daily, sometimes twice daily, beginning May 13. Trypanosomes were present in the monkey's blood on May 27. In 1903 Castellani[7] reported trypanosomes in the cerebrospinal fluid of Negroes in Uganda suffering from sleeping sickness. The trypanosomes found by Castellani were supposed to be a different species from that of Dutton (*Trypanosoma gambiense* Dutton) and were called *T. ugandense Castellani,* 1903. Kruse later gave to this trypanosoma the name *T. castellanii*. The important discoveries of Dutton and Castellani were quickly confirmed by David Bruce,

* *Trypanosoma lewisi* is transmitted from rat to rat by the rat flea, *Nosopsyllus fasciatus* (Bosc), and the rat louse, *Polyplax spinulosus* (Burmeister).

who found these trypanosomes 38 times out of 38 in the cerebrospinal fluid obtained by lumbar puncture in natives of Uganda suffering from sleeping sickness, and 12 times out of 13 in the blood. According to the rules of priority, the last two species names mentioned must give way to *Trypanosoma gambiense* Dutton. A second species of trypanosoma producing sleeping sickness in Rhodesia, Nyasaland, and adjoining territory was described in 1913 by Stephens and Fantham as *T. rhodesiense*.

Sleeping sickness is widely distributed in Africa, extending along the west coast from Senegal (in part) to Angola (in part) and eastward to the valley of the upper Nile. It has been estimated that between 1896 and 1906 from 400,000 to 500,000 natives perished from this pestilence. Dutton and Todd found that in some villages from 30 to 50 per cent of the population was infected. An epidemic, in Uganda near Lake Victoria over a five-year period took 200,000 human lives, according to Bell (1906; cited by Buxton[6]); the population of the area involved was 300,000 before the epidemic, the mortality consequently being 67 per cent. In many parts of Africa the number of cases remains high; on the other hand, as Buxton points out, there are a number of areas in East and West Africa where there are healthy people and cattle living permanently on ground from which tsetse flies have been exterminated.

Age does not affect the distribution of the malady, since children as young as 18 months to 2 years have been known to be infected. Sex does not influence the disease. Occupation and social position, however, do show a marked influence. The majority of the cases observed are among the agricultural and lower classes, where the degree of exposure to tsetse flies is greatest. In areas where *Glossina palpalis* occurs, inland fisherman in particular may be exposed to the bites of this species.

The bite of an infected tsetse appears to produce more local reaction than that of the uninfected fly. The usual duration of the incubation period is 10 to 20 days, but clinical symptoms may be delayed for as long as 2 to 5 years. In some individuals, trypanosomiasis is asymptomatic, and such persons may serve as carriers; the extent to which this condition prevails is unknown. During the first phase of the disease, which may continue for many months, the trypanosomes are in the blood, the trypanosomiasis stage; this phase is characterized by an irregular fever, glandular enlargement, debility, and languor. In the second phase, the sleeping sickness stage, the trypanosomes are constantly found in the cerebrospinal fluid; a constant accompaniment is the enlargement of the posterior cervical lymph nodes, *Winterbottom's sign;* there are a speech impairment and tremors of the tongue; there are nervousness, pronounced languor and drowsiness, which gives way to lethargy, and finally the victim falls into a comatose state, wasting rapidly, largely as a result of starvation, until death ensues. Gambian sleeping sickness, caused by *Trypanosoma gambiense,* tends to be mild and to endure for months, with the result that man is of greater importance as the reservoir of the disease; Rhodesian sleeping sickness, caused by *Trypanosoma rhodesiense,* on the other hand, progresses much more rapidly, and the patient, usually too sick to leave his village, assumes less importance as a reservoir (Buxton[6]).

Transmission. The natives of French Guinea long attributed the transmission of sleeping sickness to flies; it had already been shown by Bruce that nagana, a disease of cattle and horses, was transmitted by tsetse flies, when Dutton and Todd gave attention to the biting flies of Gambia. These investigators found that, of the flies which bite both man and animals, *Tabanus dorsovittatus* Walker and *Glossina palpalis* (Robineau-Desvoidy) were the most important. The latter is very common in western Africa, where it abounds in the mangroves which line the inland rivers during the warmer months when these insects are very troublesome.

Experiments made by these workers, however, gave negative results. It was Bruce and his collaborators who subsequently went over the matter and showed that *Glossina palpalis* is a vector. Animal experimentation showed that these flies can transmit the trypanosomes mechanically for a period of less than 48 hours; the organisms become more and more attenuated after the fly has bitten the infected individual, and it loses the power of infection in less than 48 hours. Thus, the tsetse fly may be a mechanical vector for a short period of time, during which time its soiled proboscis is involved, i.e., trypanosomes are introduced into the wound produced by the bite before the proboscis is completely cleaned. Interrupted feeding would thus be a factor. Mechanical transmission from man to man in nature is believed to be very uncommon; firm evidence as to the extent of its occurrence is lacking.

Kleine[13] in 1909, working with *Trypanosoma brucei,* causal organism of nagana, was evidently the first to demonstrate its development in the tsetse fly, *Glossina palpalis.* Robertson[21] working with the causal organism of sleeping sickness, *Trypanosoma gambiense,* reported in 1913 that it is first established in the posterior part of the midgut of the insect, where multiplication occurs, and trypanosomes of varying sizes are produced. From the tenth or twelfth day onward, slender, long forms are to be found in increasing number. These finally move forward to the proventriculus and are the dominant type. The proventriculus becomes infected as a rule between the twelfth and twentieth days. The salivary glands become infected by the slender (proventricular) type which reaches the glands by way of the hypopharynx; arriving in the glands, they become attached to the wall and assume the crithidial condition. Multiplication takes place, and trypanosomes are formed which closely resemble the blood type. The development in the salivary glands takes from 2 to 5 days before the metacyclic forms are infective.

The fly is never infective until the glands are invaded. The trypanosomes are never attached to the wall of the alimentary canal, and there is no intracellular multiplication in the gut cycle. The metacyclic forms become mature and multiply by longitudinal fission in the circulatory system of the mammalian host. The Sleeping Sickness Commission found that infectivity lasted at least 96 days. Only a small percentage of the tsetse flies become infective. The life of a female *G. palpalis* in captivity has been observed to be about 4 1/2 months.

The problem of sleeping sickness is greatly complicated in that many species of wild animals harbor the causal trypanosomes and may thus serve as natural reservoirs of the infection. Furthermore, the affinities of *Trypanosoma rhodesiense* have not yet been definitely determined. There are some who contend that this is a variant of *T. gambiense;* others contend that it is a human strain of *T. brucei,* and considerably less adapted biologically to man and his domestic animals than to wild animals, with a resulting greater virulence in respect to man. The generally accepted view, however, is that *T. rhodesiense, T. gambiense,* and *T. brucei* are morphologically indistinguishable but biologically distinct species.

The principal vectors of African sleeping sickness are *Glossina palpalis* (Robineau-Desvoidy) and *G. tachinoides* Westwood for *T. gambiense* and *G. morsitans* Westwood, *G. swynnertoni* Austen, and *G. pallidipes* Austen for *T. rhodesiense.*

Nagana. Trypanosoma brucei Plimmer and Bradford is the causal organism of classical nagana, long known to be a fatal tsetse fly–borne disease of African horses, mules, camels, and dogs. Cattle, sheep, and goats are susceptible, but usually recover (except for certain strains and when the trypanosome is transmitted by game tsetse); pigs may be chronically infected, without symptoms. Many other mammals are susceptible to the infection. Bruce[4] found that many species of wild animals harbor the trypanosome and thus form reservoirs. The disease is characterized by progressive emaciation, fever, edema of the abdomen and genitalia, and marked depression. The trypanosomes are found in the blood and especially in the lymph gland swellings from the beginning of the first symptoms.

Glossina morsitans, G. longipalpis (Wiedemann), *G. pallidipes* Austen, and, to a lesser extent, other species relate to the transmission of nagana in practically the same way that *Glossina palpalis* and other *Glossina* flies relate to sleeping sickness of man, i.e., the flies are infective for a day or two after feeding on an infected animal, then become noninfective for a period of about 3 weeks, when they again become infective and remain so for the rest of their life. The incubation period after inoculation into the body of the host is said to be about 10 days.

Other forms of nagana, also transmitted by tsetse flies, are caused by

Trypanosoma vivax Ziemann and *T. congolense* Broden. The effect on the host and the developmental histories of these trypanosomes differ in certain respects from those of *T. brucei.*

Glossina Species. Newstead *et al.*[20] recognized 20 species and 1 subspecies belonging to the genus *Glossina.* These are divided into three groups: (1) the **fusca** group, which includes the 10 largest species, viz., *Glossina brevipalpis* Newstead, *G. fusca* (Walker), *G. fusca* var. *congolensis* Newstead and Evans, *G. fuscipleuris* Austen, *G. haningtoni* Newstead and Evans *G. longipennis* Corti, *G. medicorum* Austen, *G. nigrofusca* Newstead, *G. schwetzi* Newstead and Evans, *G. severini* Newstead, and *G. tabaniformis* Westwood; (2) the **palpalis** group, which includes *Glossina caliginea* Austen, *G. pallicera* Bigot, *G. palpalis* (Robineau-Desvoidy), also one subspecies *G. palpalis fuscipes* Newstead, and *G. tachinoides* Westwood; (3) the **morsitans** group, which comprises *Glossina longipalpis* (Wiedemann), *G. morsitans* Newstead, *G. submorsitans* Westwood, *G. pallidipes* Austen, *G. swynnertoni* Austen, and *G. austeni* Newstead. *G. submorsitans* is now considered a subspecies of *G. morsitans. G. newsteadi* Austen (Group 2) and *G. vanhoofi* (Group 1), as well as several subspecies and varieties of *G. palpalis* and *G. morsitans,* have been added to the list. Recent keys to the species of *Glossina* may be found in the works of Buxton[6] and Smart.[25]

Glossina palpalis (Fig. 105) is the most important vector of Gambian sleeping sickness. It covers an enormous area in Africa, but it occurs chiefly in the Congo and West Africa. It is usually found on the shores of rivers and lakes, but it may occur far back from them; and, as Swynnerton points out, it requires a combination of several types of country, one of which must be a relatively massive woodland or thicket of more or less evergreen type. It feeds mainly on large reptiles, such as crocodiles and monitor lizards, but it can live on the blood of mammals as well. Although man is not regarded as one of its favored hosts, it will nevertheless feed freely on persons available in its riparian habitat.

Glossina morsitans (Fig. 105) is a most efficient vector of both Rhodesian sleeping sickness of man and nagana of animals. It has a wide distribution in Africa; it is of importance in the Sudan, northern and southern Rhodesia, the Belgian Congo, and many other locations. This species requires "savanna of sufficient shade value, and with sufficient logs, rocks, or tree rot holes to form a good rest-haunt and breeding-ground, and relatively open glades or plains in which to hunt for its prey." It attacks wild animals and human beings readily and hence is an important tsetse.

Glossina swynnertoni, like *G. morsitans,* is a strong vector of both Rhodesian sleeping sickness and nagana. It is largely confined to the northern part of Tanganyika, according to Swynnerton, who describes it as "the fly of the driest and most open areas and apparently unable to inhabit the more mesophytic savannas. It breeds normally in thicket, though rock suits it as well. . . . It utilizes open spaces as feeding grounds. . . . It is primarily and essentially a 'game' fly." It attacks human beings with readiness, and, like *Glossina morsitans* West, is an important tsetse.

Tsetse Fly Control. Since the memorable discoveries of Bruce and others that tsetse flies are responsible for the transmission of nagana and sleeping sickness, few insects have been so minutely studied by the most capable investigators. The practical and extended control of breeding places offers serious difficulties, not the least of these being the fact that the larvae are retained within the body of the female until fully grown, hence are not directly dependent upon an external food supply. Another complication concerns the question as to whether tsetse control in a particular area is essentially a medical or a veterinary problem, or both. The monumental work of the late C. F. M. Swynnerton gives ample testimony to the tremendous ramifications of the tsetse fly control problem.

Buxton[6] gives a comprehensive account of tsetse control. He points out that control consists of using what knowledge we have of tsetse biology to our advantage and to the fly's detriment, and that, while the status of control is still confused, principles are becoming clearer. Among the many possible modes of attack there are the following: (1) direct attack, involving the use of fly traps, insecticides, repellents, hand catching, and mechanical methods; (2) indirect attack by modification of cover; reducing or expelling wild animals, thus depriving the flies of food supply; introduction of fly barriers by setting up clearings or thickets according to the species of fly to be dealt with; reclamation; and the use of natural enemies. Recent progress in chemotherapy indicates that cattle can be successfully inoculated with drugs against tsetse.

The wide divergence in ecologic requirements complicates the control problem. Waterside tsetses, such as *Glossina palpalis,* can be eliminated from linear fly belts along the water by clearing or hand catching. In large areas of bush, such as those inhabited by *Glossina morsitans,* satisfactory results have been achieved by bush clearing, by attacking the restricted permanent habitats, and also in some instances by destruction of wild animals and control of human settlement. Insecticides such as DDT or benzene hexachloride may be used to coat potential resting places of the flies, as insecticidal "smokes" when mixed with fuel and burned, as sprays on vegetation, and perhaps in other ways. Dramatic results leading to eradication over treated areas have recently been obtained by Wilson through the use of a DDT spray on vegetation and by Du Toit and his co-workers through concentrated control on a relatively small breeding area (Fay and Kilpatrick[10]).

Tsetse fly control by clearing or burning and by destruction or control of wildlife poses some problems in relation to land and wildlife management, as well as to human relations. A good tsetse fly control program should take these aspects of the matter into consideration.

STOMOXYS FLIES

Family Muscidae, Genus Stomoxys

General Characteristics. Owing to similarity in color and size, the stable fly is often mistaken for the common house fly *Musca domestica* Linnaeus. However, the former is more robust and has a broader abdomen. In color it is brownish gray with greenish-yellow sheen; the outer of the four longitudinal thoracic stripes are broken, and the abdomen is more or less checkered. The wings when at rest are widely spread apart at the tips and are distinctly iridescent; the apical cell is open. When resting, the fly has its head thrown well up, and the wings slope decidedly toward the surface upon which it has settled. The proboscis protrudes bayonetlike in front of the head. The antennal aristae, unlike those of the house fly, bear setae on the upper side only. *Stomoxys calcitrans* enjoys practically a world-wide distribution.

Habits. Although *Stomoxys calcitrans* (Linnaeus) is commonly called the "stable fly" (the name officially adopted by the Entomological Society of America), it occurs much less abundantly (often absent) about stables than does the house fly. It is also called the "biting house fly," since it may occur indoors, especially in the autumn and during rainy weather, and bites human beings viciously. It is often very annoying along the sandy, vegetation-strewn shores of lakes. The name "dog fly" is sometimes applied to this species. The stable fly is typically an out-of-door day-biting fly and is usually to be found in abundance during summer and autumn where large numbers of domesticated animals occur, horses and cattle affording an abundant food supply. This species does not breed in excrement as does the house fly. Sunny fences, walls, light-colored canvas coverings, and light objects in general, when in the proximity of animals, are abundantly frequented by stables flies.

The stable fly is a vicious "biter" which draws blood quickly and fills up to full capacity in from 3 to 4 minutes if undisturbed, but ordinarily even when undisturbed it changes position frequently or flies to another animal, where the meal is continued. This fly feeds readily on many species of warm-blooded animals, e.g., rats, guinea pigs, rabbits, monkeys, cattle, horses, and man. Both sexes are bloodsucking. The flight of the stable fly is direct and swift and of long range, the fly sometimes traveling many miles.

Breeding Habits and Life History. Although the stable fly can be successfully reared in the manure of horses, cattle, and sheep, it may be safely said that it does not breed commonly in excrement under field conditions unless this is well mixed with straw or hay. Very good breeding places are afforded by the leftover soggy hay, alfalfa, or grain in the bottoms of or underneath out-of-door feed racks (Fig. 109) in connection with dairies and feed lots. This material becomes soggy and ferments, and here practically pure cultures of *Stomoxys* larvae may be found. The material must be moist, for dryness prevents larval development. Piles of moist fermenting weeds and lawn cuttings also furnish fairly good breeding material. Piles of decaying onions have been found by the writer (Herms) to harbor great numbers of larvae late in the autumn. Old straw piles that remain in the field through the year may produce an abundance of stable flies in the moist fermenting straw near the ground, particularly if cattle have access to it and moisten it with urine. Moist piles of fermenting peanut litter produce large numbers of

Fig. 109. Feed racks for dairy cattle afford an ideal breeding place for *Stomoxys* in that the moist lower layers of material in and under the trough furnish abundant food for the larvae.

these flies, as do beach deposits of grasses along the Florida coast. The author (Herms) has also noted this along the southern shores of Lake Erie.

The larvae (Fig. 110) of *Stomoxys* and of the house fly can readily be differentiated by the form, size, and position of the posterior spiracles; otherwise, they resemble each other closely. The pair of posterior spiracles of the *Stomoxys* larva are roughly triangular, widely separated, and situated near the periphery, while in the house fly larva they are elliptical, large, close together, and more central in position (Fig. 90).

The eggs of the stable fly are about 1 mm long, curved on one side, and straight and grooved on the opposite side. In depositing her eggs, the female fly often crawls far into the loose material, placing them usually in little pockets in small numbers, often in pairs. Egg depositions range in number from 23 to 102, usually between 25 and 50, and there are ordinarily 4 or 5 layings. Mayne (Mitzmain[18]) found in his observations made in the Philippine Islands that the maximum number of eggs produced by a single *Stomoxys* is 632 and possibly 820 and that there may be as many as 20 depositions during the lifetime of the female.

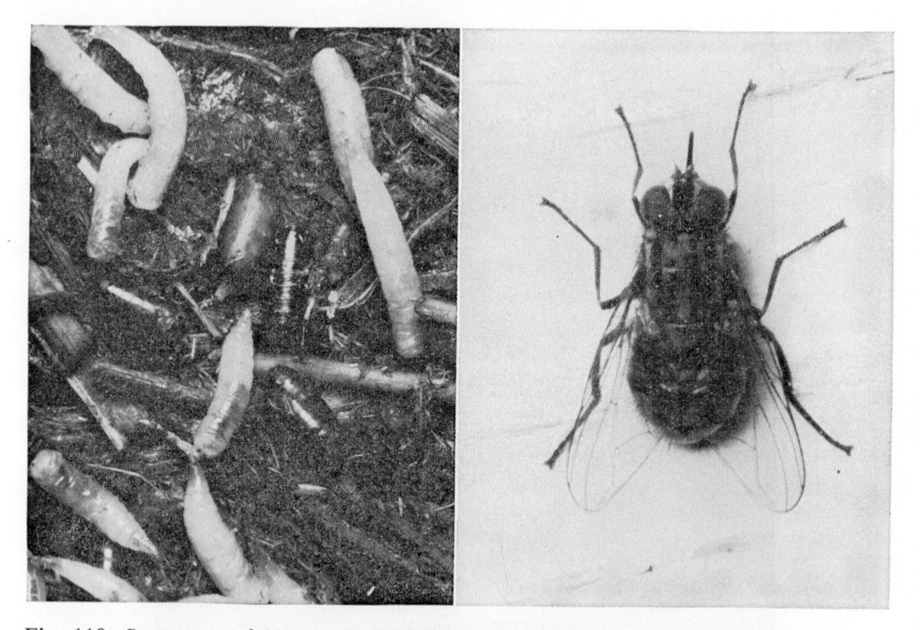

Fig. 110. *Stomoxys calcitrans.* (*Left*) larvae and pupae; (*right*) adult. (Courtesy California Bureau of Vector Control; photographs by Arthur C. Smith.)

The incubation period varies from 2 to 5 days, commonly 3 days, at a temperature of 26° C. Higher temperatures result in a shorter incubation period. The newly hatched larvae bury themselves in their food at once, thus protecting themselves against light and dryness. At a temperature of from 21° to 26° C, the larvae reach full growth in from 14 to 26 days. Mayne found that the larval stage averaged 12 days at a room temperature of 30° to 31° C.

Before pupation the larvae usually crawl into the drier parts of the breeding material, where the chestnut-colored pupae are often found in enormous numbers. The pupae are from 6 to 7 mm long and may be recognized by the posterior spiracles as in the larva. The pupal period also varies, depending largely on temperature. At a temperature of from 21° to 26° C, this period varies from 6 to 26 days, with the greatest frequency between

9 days and 13 days. At an average temperature of 29° C, Mayne found the pupal period to average 5 days.

If not handicapped, the imago emerges with astonishing rapidity, crawls away, unfolds its wings, and is ready to fly away in less than half an hour. The fact that the proboscis is temporarily attached beneath the thorax gives the newly emerged insect a very peculiar appearance, and it may then be easily mistaken for a house fly.

Summarizing the life history of the stable fly, it may be said that at a temperature of 21° to 26° C, the *shortest* periods are: egg, 2 days; larva, 14 days; pupa, 6 days; total, 22 days; the *average:* egg, 3 days; larva, 15 days; pupa, 10 days; total 28 days; the *maximum:* egg, 5 days; larva, 26 days; pupa, 26 days; total 57 days. The total time at 21° C, from the laying of the eggs to the emergence of the adults, was from 33 days to 36 days, as observed in 5 individual cases. Mayne reports the development of this fly in 12 days under optimum conditions.

Copulation takes place within a week, and egg deposition begins in about 18 days after emergence from the pupa cases at a temperature of from 21° to 26° C. Higher temperatures undoubtedly decrease this time. In warmer parts of the world the stable fly continues to breed throughout the year, slowing up the cycle during the colder months.

Longevity. With approximately 4000 flies under continuous daily observation in glass quart jars, 50 flies to a set, Herms has found that the average length of life of the stable fly under favorable laboratory conditions of feeding (i.e., daily feedings on monkeys or rabbits) is about 20 days. The maximum life under these conditions was found to be 69 days and several hours in a female. Mayne has found the maximum for a female *Stomoxys* fly to be 72 days and for a male 94 days.

The writer (Herms) has observed that a set of flies which fed only on sugar water deposited no eggs, although many of them lived 20 days or longer, whereas control flies fed on blood did lay eggs. Hence, it seems apparent that the flies must have blood in order to develop eggs.

As a Cattle Pest. Bishopp[3] regards this fly as one of the most important sources of annoyance to livestock. Injury is brought about in various ways, e.g., worry caused by the mass attacks of flies, loss of blood, and loss of flesh.

Freeborn, Regan, and Folger[11] have shown that the reduction in milk production caused by the stable fly amounted to 9.26 per cent, which for a 5 months' period means a loss of 50 gallons of milk. The total loss occasioned by the three dairy cattle pests—house flies, stable flies, and horse flies—amounted to 15 per cent.

Stomoxys and Disease. *Stomoxys* is no exception to the rule that any bloodsucking fly must be a suspect in the transmission of human and animal disease; yet there is little evidence against it. Its supposed relationship to the transmission of the poliomyelitis virus is largely of historical interest. Rosenau[23] in 1912 concluded that poliomyelitis was not a contagious disease, but on the other hand, was insect transmitted, and he apparently succeeded in transmitting the virus from infected monkeys to healthy ones through the bite of the fly. Other workers were apparently able to substantiate his findings, but Sawyer and Herms[24] were not. Taking care to use insects that had been reared for the particular purpose, rather than wild flies, they conducted seven carefully planned experiments over a period of nearly a year; about 4000 laboratory-reared flies and a large number of monkeys, rabbits, and other experimental animals were used; the results were entirely negative. Further studies have indicated that early apparent incrimination of the stable fly in the transmission of poliomyelitis was based on defective evidence. *Stomoxys,* as well as other bloodsucking flies, is now practically eliminated from consideration in this role.

The stable fly is known to have some importance in the mechanical transmission of infectious anemia of horses, a virus disease; of the anthrax bacillus; and of several forms of trypanosomiasis. It is of some importance in the transmission of surra, a disease of horses, mules, and camels caused by *Trypanosoma evansi* (Steal), and it has been shown capable of infecting animals with *T. brucei, T. rhodesiense,* and *T. gambiense.* Transmission of trypanosomes is purely mechanical and is possible for a very limited period of time. However, the restless, intermittent type of feeding characteristic of the stable fly is very conducive to this type of transmission.

On rare occasions, the stable fly becomes involved in accidental traumatic or enteric myiasis in man.

Control of Stable Flies. The more important breeding places of the stable fly can be controlled by removing moist feed wastes from feeding troughs and from feed lots, stalls, stables, etc., and scattering the wastes to hasten drying. Moisture is necessary for the development of the larvae; therefore, dry material is not suitable. Weeds, lawn cuttings, decaying onions, vegetation washed up on lake shores in the immediate vicinity of summer resorts, etc., should not be allowed to accumulate in piles long enough to ferment and decay. Bishopp[3] has shown that loosely piled strawstacks (oats and wheat) are important breeding places of the stable fly; hence, he recommends "that the straw for feeding and bedding purposes be baled and stored under cover. Where this is not practicable the stacks should be rounded up so as to make the top largely rainproof and the sides nearly vertical."

To date, the stable fly has not shown any increase of resistance to DDT, although it is naturally more resistant to this insecticide than is the house fly or the horn fly. The fact that it tends to feed on an animal for short periods of time makes the use of DDT still less effective. Better results are obtained by using pyrethrins plus a synergist (piperonyl butoxide), and repellents such as butoxypolypropylene glycol may be added. Application may be made safely to dairy cattle. As a residual spray on surfaces on which the flies may rest, Diazinon has given good results. For protection to human beings several repellents, particularly Indalone, are effective, but the recently developed diethyltoluamide is distinctly the best to date.

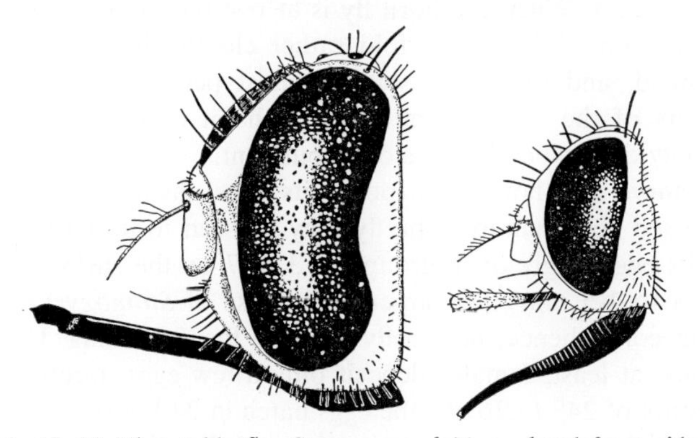

Fig. 111. (*Left*) The stable fly, *Stomoxys calcitrans,* head from side view; (*right*) the horn fly, *Siphona irritans,* same; both drawn to the same scale. (Drawings by Bruce F. Eldridge.)

THE HORN FLY

Family Muscidae

Introduction. The horn fly, *Siphona irritans* (Linnaeus), was introduced into the United States from Europe, where it has been an important cattle pest for many years. According to the United States Bureau of Entomology and Plant Quarantine, it was first reported in the fall of 1887 from Camden, New Jersey, appearing during the following year in Maryland and Virginia, probably having appeared in Philadelphia in 1886, and by 1892 was found over the entire continent from Canada to Texas and from Massachusetts to the Rocky Mountains. California cattlemen state that it made its appearance in that state in about 1893–1894. It appeared in Honolulu, Hawaii, in 1897.

The nomenclature of this species is considerably confusing to the non-taxonomist. The names *Lyperosia irritans* and *Haematobia stimulans* have been applied to it. The true *Haematobia stimulans* is a different, though closely related, European fly that is not known to occur in North America, although another similar but uncommon species, the moose fly, *Haematobia alcis* Snow, torments moose, and perhaps other members of the deer family, in Canada and the northern United States.

Characteristics. The horn fly is about half the size of the common house fly, i.e., about 4 mm long. It has much the same color and in most other respects resembles the stable fly. The mouth parts (Fig. 111) are like those of *Stomoxys* except that the labium of the horn fly is relatively heavier, and the palpi, almost as long as the proboscis, are flattened and loosely ensheath this structure. The arista is haired on the dorsal side only. The wing venation is similar to that of *Stomoxys*.

Horn flies appear early in the spring and become most abundant in late summer and autumn. When the horn fly is at rest on an animal or elsewhere, its wings lie flat on its back and fold rather closely, but when it bites, the wings are spread, and the insect stands almost perpendicularly, hidden between the hairs of the host. Apparently the habit of resting at the base of the horns is only done when flies are overabundant.

Life History. The horn fly deposits its eggs chiefly, if not exclusively, on freshly passed cow manure. The fly may be seen to dart from the animal and deposit its eggs singly or in groups of 3 to 7 on the surface of the dung. The eggs (1.3 to 1.5 mm) are larger than those of *Stomoxys;* they are reddish brown in color, hence, not easily seen on the cow dung. Under laboratory conditions, at least, females deposit only a few eggs, rarely over twenty. At a temperature of 24° to 26° C, the eggs hatch in 24 hours.

The larvae burrow beneath the surface of the droppings, reaching full growth in from 3 to 5 days, when they crawl underneath into drier parts and pupate. The pupal period requires from 6 to 8 days. Hence, the entire life history from egg to the adult requires from 10 to 14 days at a temperature of from 24° to 26° C.

Damage. The damage occasioned by the horn fly is chiefly through irritation and annoyance, which in dairy animals results in disturbed feeding and improper digestion causing loss of flesh and reducing milk production. Cattle heavily attacked by these flies may suffer a loss of 0.5 pound of flesh per day, and milk production may be reduced from 10 to 20 per cent. Range animals literally run themselves thin in trying to get away from these pests.

The actual loss of blood must be significant when literally thousands of these flies attack an animal. From 10 to 25 minutes are required for the fly to fully engorge itself; during this time it withdraws and reinserts its proboscis in the same puncture many times as in a pumping motion. Much digested blood is discharged from the anus of the fly while in the act of feeding. Unlike the stable fly, the horn fly remains with the animal constantly.

Man is only rarely attacked; the importance of the fly is chiefly veterinary rather than medical. A rather surprising case of human myiasis is on record.[14]

Control. The most effective method to prevent the multiplication of the horn fly is to scatter the droppings from cattle with a rake or other implement or simply to drag a branch of a tree over the field. Hogs allowed to run with the cattle serve this purpose very well. The manure thus scattered dries out quickly, and the larvae that are present perish, owing to the fact that they require much moisture for development. The writer (Herms) has seen this method applied successfully in various parts of California where the dry summer favors such means of handling the situation. On wide ranges this method is impracticable, but in connection with dairies it is entirely feasible.

The horn fly is much more susceptible to DDT than is the stable fly, and so far no development of resistance to that insecticide has been reported. DDT or methoxychlor used with a fly repellent (such as butoxypolypropylene glycol) gives effective results. An economical and effective means of application, in the form of a back rubber consisting of insecticide-treated burlap fastened to a chain suspended between two posts, was proposed by Rogoff and Moxon;[22] this device has been widely adopted.

The "buffalo fly," *Siphona exigua* (de Meijere), is particularly important to the cattle and dairy industries of Australia.[15] Among the animals which it attacks are buffalo, cattle, horse, dog, and man. The fly oviposits in fresh dung from buffalo and cattle in particular.

Other Species of Bloodsucking Muscoid Flies. The genus *Philaematomyia,* represented by the single species *P. crassirostris* Stein, is of particular interest because of the form of the proboscis, which is intermediate between the biting and nonbiting muscid type. *Philaematomyia crassirostris* is a widely distributed African and Oriental species resembling *Musca domestica* in size and general appearance; in fact, it is often placed in the genus *Musca.* According to Austen[1] the proximal portion of the proboscis is a strongly swollen, polished, sclerotized bulb, while the distal portion is soft and fleshy and folded back under the distal end of the bulb when not in use; when in use, its terminal section, consisting of a tubular extension, is protruded from between the labella; it is surrounded at the distal extremity with a circlet of stout sclerotized teeth. When it is not being used, the entire proboscis can be retracted within the buccal cavity. Austen states that the fly probably feeds by cutting through the epidermis with the teeth at the end of the tubular extension and then sucking up the blood.

The Ethiopian genus *Stygeromyia* (*S. maculosa* Austen and *S. sanguinaria* Austen) is said by Austen to be in some respects intermediate between *Stomoxys* and *Siphona.* It resembles *Stomoxys* in general appearance and form of the body, but is distinguished "by the relative stoutness of the short, chitinous, horizontal proboscis, and by the palpi being equal to the proboscis in length, large, expanded towards the tips, and curved upwards."

Stomoxys nigra Macquart, *S. omega* Newstead, and *S. inornata* Grünberg are all Ethiopian species and resemble *S. calcitrans* in feeding habits.

REFERENCES

1. Austen, E. E., 1909. *Illustrations of African Bloodsucking Flies Other Than Mosquitoes and Tsetse Flies.* London: Mus. Nat. Hist. 221 pp. (13 plates).

2. Bequaert, J., 1930. "Tsetse flies—past and present (Diptera: Muscoidea)," *Entomological News,* **41:**158–64, 202–3, and 227–33.

3. Bishopp, F. C., 1939. *The Stable Fly: How to Prevent Its Annoyance and Its Losses to Livestock.* Washington, D. C.: Dept. of Agric., in Farmer's Bull., no. 1097. 18 pp. (revised).

4. Bruce, D., 1897. *Further Report on the Tsetse-Fly Disease or Nagana in Zululand.* London: Harrison and Sons. 69 pp.

5. Bruce, D., and Nabarro, D., 1903. *Progress Report on Sleeping Sickness in Uganda.* Rep. Sleeping Sickness Comm. Roy. Soc. London, no. 1. 88 pp. (10 plates).

6. Buxton, Patrick A., 1955. *The Natural History of Tsetse Flies.* London: H. K. Lewis & Co. xviii + 816 pp. (47 plates).

7. Castellani, A., 1903. "Trypanosoma in sleeping sickness," *Brit. M. J.,* **1:**1218.

8. Dutton, J. E., 1902. "Trypanosoma in man," *Brit. M. J.,* **1:**42.

9. Dutton, J. E., 1902. "Note on a Trypanosoma occurring in the blood of man," *Brit. M. J.,* **2:**881–84.

10. Fay, R. W., and Kilpatrick, J. W., 1958. "Insecticides for control of adult Diptera," *Ann. Rev. Entomol.,* **3:**401–20.

11. Freeborn, S. B.; Regan, W. M.; and Folger, A. H.; 1925. "The relation of flies and fly sprays to milk production," *J. Econ. Entomol.,* **18:**779–90.

12. Hegh, Emile, 1929. *Les tsé-tsés,* vol. 1. Brussels: A. J. Engelterzi. xiv + 742 pp. (327 figs. + 15 colored plates).

13. Kleine, F. K., 1909. "Positive Infectionversuche mit *Trypanosoma brucei* durch *Glossina palpalis,*" *Deutsche med. Wochnschr.,* **35:**469–70.

14. Knapp, S. E.; Padilla, G. M.; and Philips, F. M.; 1955. "An apparent human case of myiasis by the horn fly, *Siphona irritans,*" *Parasitology,* **41:**324.

15. Kriggsman, B. J., and Windred, G. L., 1933. *Investigations on the Buffalo Fly, Lyperosia exigua de Meij.* Commonwealth of Australia: Council for Sc. and Ind. Research Pamph. 43. 40 pp.

16. Laveran, Alphonse, and Mesnil, Felix, 1904. *Trypanosomes et Trypanosomiasis.* Paris. xi + 417 pp. Translated by D. N. Nabarro, 1907. Chicago Medical Book Co.

17. Lewis, D. J. 1934. "The behavior of the larvae of the tsetse flies before pupation," *Bull. Entomol. Research,* **25:**195–99 (1 plate).

18. Mitzmain, M. B., 1913. "The bionomics of *Stomoxys calcitrans* (Linnaeus); a preliminary account," *Philippine J. Sc.,* **8** (Sec. B):29–48.

19. Nash, T. A. M., 1939. "The ecology of the puparium of *Glossina* in northern Nigeria," *Bull. Entomol. Research,* **30:**259–84.

20. Newstead, R.; Evans, A. M.; and Potts, W. H.; 1924. *Guide to the Study of Tsetse Flies.* Liverpool: School Trop. Med., in Memoir no. 1, n.s., 272 pp. (28 plates, 4 maps).

21. Robertson, Muriel, 1913. "Notes on the life history of *Trypanosoma gambiense,* with a brief reference to the cycles of *Trypanosoma nanum* and *Trypanosoma pecorum* in *Glossina palpalis,*" *Phil. Tr. Roy. Soc. London* (Ser. B), **203:**161–84 (5 plates).

22. Rogoff, William M., and Moxon, Alvin L., 1952. "Cable type back rubbers for horn fly control on cattle," *J. Econ. Entomol.,* **45:**329–34.

23. Rosenau, M. J., 1912. In "Society Proceedings," *J.A.M.A.,* **59**:1314. Report on poliomyelitis presented at meeting of International Congress on Hygiene and Demography, 1912.

24. Sawyer, W. A., and Herms, W. B., 1913. "Attempts to transmit poliomyelitis by means of the stable fly (*Stomoxys calcitrans*)," *J.A.M.A.,* **41:**461–66.

25. Smart, John, 1956. *A Handbook for the Identification of Insects of Medical Importance,* 3rd ed. London: British Museum (Natural History). xi + 303 pp. (13 plates).

26. Swynnerton, C. F. M., 1936. "The tsetse flies of East Africa," *Tr. Roy. Entomol. Soc. London,* vol. 84. xxxiv + 579 pp. (7 maps, 22 plates).

Chapter 17

MYIASIS

Myiasis is a term meaning an infestation of the organs and tissues of man or animals by fly maggots and the disturbances resulting therefrom. Such invasions may be benign in effect or may result in more or less violent disturbances, even in death. When the intestinal tract is invaded, it is called *intestinal myiasis;* when the stomach is concerned, it is *gastric myiasis;* invasion of the digestive tract in general is called *enteric myiasis,* a term which can be used to include both gastric and intestinal myiasis; invasion of the urinary tract is called *urinary myiasis;* invasion of the nasal passage, *nasal myiasis;* invasion of the ears, *auricular myiasis,* or *otomyiasis;* of the eyes, *ophthalmomyiasis;* when wounds or ulcerations of the skin are infested by maggots, the term *traumatic dermal myiasis* is applied; invasion of the skin is also known as *cutaneous myiasis.* etc. When maggot infestations are traceable to species which are normally scavengers, coprobionts, or saprobionts, the term *accidental myiasis* is usually employed; when the species of maggot is a necrobiont or facultative sarcobiont (involving fresh wounds), the term *semispecific* is used; and when the infestation is traceable to obligatory sacrobionts, such as the warble flies and bot flies, the term *obligate myiasis* is used.

ACCIDENTAL MYIASIS

Accidental myiasis may be caused by a considerable number of species of Diptera belonging to several families, such as the **Calliphoridae** (blow flies, comprising the bluebottle and greenbottle flies), **Sarcophagidae** (flesh flies), and **Muscidae** (house flies, and their relatives). The larvae of these flies normally feed on decomposing animals and vegetable matter, garbage, dead animals, and manures. Infestations in man are usually traceable to the ingestion of fly eggs or larvae with contaminated food or water.

Enteric Myiasis. Fifty species of fly larvae have been reported, either positively or questionably, from cases of enteric myiasis. These species are principally those members of the families Muscidae, Calliphoridae, and Sarcophagidae, which commonly deposit their eggs or larvae on cold meat, cheese, and other foods of man and are thus ingested. Also, flies may deposit their eggs on or near the anus, particularly in the use of old-fashioned privies, and the larvae on hatching may make their way into the intestine.

The reality of enteric myiasis as a pathologic condition in man has been questioned by many workers. The subject has been discussed in considerable detail by Riley,[27] James,[17] and West,[38] who come to the conclusion that, in spite of experimental evidence to the contrary (which these authors do not consider to be conclusive), "there seems no doubt that genuine enteric myiasis does occur from time to time, when chemical and physical conditions within the patient's alimentary tract are such as to favor survival of the parasites" (West). The evidence for the reality of enteric myiasis rests on the number of clinical cases described by competent entomologists and physicians. Nevertheless, great care should be used in diagnosing enteric myiasis. Contamination of stools or previous contamination of chamber vessels are possibilities that should not be overlooked; even a covered chamber vessel is not always maggotproof, particularly when the Sarcophagidae are involved.

The clinical symptoms of intestinal myiasis depend on the number as well as the species of fly larvae and on their location in the intestine. No doubt many instances occur in which living fly larvae are passed in the stool without having caused any intestinal disturbance. In severe infestations, there will be nausea, vertigo, and more or less violent pain in the abdomen; diarrhea with discharge of blood may occur as the result of injury of the intestinal mucosa by the larvae. Living and dead larvae are expelled with either the vomit or stool, or both.

An obstinate case of intestinal myiasis was reported by Herms and Gilbert.[15] The patient, female, age 38 years, was first seen April 26, 1930. Her chief complaints were attacks of nausea, vomiting and diarrhea, nervousness, and joint aches. There were recurring attacks of nervousness, vomiting, and diarrhea, and apparently rather frequent hemorrhages from the bowels. The patient was considerably depressed at times, and treatment was difficult because of lack of cooperation except after she had experienced an acute attack. Because of the difficulty of obtaining stool specimens, especially during the acute attacks, and in view of the fact that it was felt that there must be other reasons for her condition, early in the spring of 1931, during an attack of nausea with vomiting and diarrhea, the patient was kept for one entire day in the office under observation, and stool and vomit specimens were obtained, both containing the first larvae which were studied. During these attacks it was difficult for her to obtain relief with fairly large doses of opiates. Following observation, she was given santonin by mouth and colonic irrigations containing thymol. Many larvae were recovered after this, all of which were dead. Following the attacks of diarrhea the patient had a number of severe hemorrhages. Tetrachlorethylene capsules were given by mouth, but they caused gastric distress. In the hospital a duodenal tube was passed, and tetrachlorethylene was injected beyond the stomach. For a few weeks there was apparent improvement, but the attacks recurred, with the passage of larvae by vomiting and bowel discharge.

Three lots of fly larvae were studied in the laboratory, viz.: March 31, May 12, and July 28, 1931. Adult flies belonging to three genera, *Calliphora, Phaenicia* (*Lucilia*), and *Sarcophaga* were reared from these larvae.

The recurrence of violent symptoms with evacuation of larvae in vomit and stools can be interpreted as the result of repeated infestations. The patient's physical condition and apparent susceptibility to parasitism were undoubtedly contributing causes. The authors' suggestion that pedogenesis (reproduction by fly larvae) is involved cannot be substantiated.

Cheese Skippers as Agents. The larvae of the cheese fly, *Piophila casei* (Linnaeus) of the family Piophilidae, frequently cause myiasis, as they are able to pass through the digestive tract without injury. Simmons[29] cites a number of instances indicating the frequency of their occurrence in the digestive tract of man. The adult flies measure from 2.5 to 4 mm in length; superficially they appear shining black, with reddish-brown eyes and wings held flat over the dorsum when at rest. The eggs are deposited on cured meats, old cheese, dried bones, smoked fish, and many similar materials. The eggs hatch in from 30 to 48 hours at 65° F; the larval stage requires about 8 days, the pupal about 12 days. These stages are greatly influenced by temperatures. The larvae have the peculiar habit of curving the ends of the body together and then suddenly springing to a distance of from 3 to 6 in.

Soldier Fly. Several cases of intestinal myiasis caused by the larvae of a soldier fly, *Hermetia illucens* (Linnaeus), family Stratiomyidae, are on record. A typical one is reported by Meleney and Harwood.[24] This fly deposits eggs on decaying fruits, vegetables, and animal matter. The source of infestation according to the authors was apparently raw fruit and vegetables. The symptoms were local irritation in the stomach and rectum, and spells of fainting. The patient was a boy of 10 years. One patient in Houston, Texas, expelled these larvae for several months (M. A. Stewart, private communication).

Rat-tailed Larvae (Family Syrphidae). The frequency with which the "rat-tailed" larvae of the drone fly *Tubifera tenax* (Linnaeus) (= *Eristalis tenax*) occurs in liquid excrement must lead to extreme caution in accepting reports that these larvae have been evacuated with discharges from the bowels. The writer (Herms) has on several occasions received specimens of "rat-tailed" larvae which were said to have been evacuated by the "double handful," and the patient was said to have "steadily improved" thereafter.

There are, however, several recorded cases which seem to be incontrovertible, notably the case reported by Hall and Muir,[12] who also brought together all information then available relative to *Tubifera* and myiasis. The case referred to was that of a boy, aged 5 years:

> . . . who had been ailing for about ten weeks and who had been under medical treatment for indigestion and obstinate constipation for about five weeks at that time. The child was emaciated and anemic. Very striking symptoms were the constant and pronounced twitching of the eyelids and other nervous movements. He gritted his teeth in his sleep at times, and made convulsive movements of the limbs. When awake he complained of pain in the limbs and headache. The

emaciation seemed to be due to the fact that the boy had for some time vomited almost everything he ate. The breath was very bad, "worse than rotten eggs," according to his parents. On the basis of the nervous and digestive disturbance and the general debility, a diagnosis of worm infestation was made.

With this diagnosis in mind, the mother of the boy gave him a dose of proprietary worm remedy, resulting in the discharge of an object wriggling around vigorously in the feces and urine. The container into which the stool was passed was in regular use and had been previously rinsed with tap water and allowed to dry during the day. The specimen was identified by the authors as one of the "rat-tailed larvae" measuring 3.2 cm in length, including the long "tail." A second larvae was said to have been discharged the following day. The case is believed by the authors to be probably a genuine case of "gastric myiasis."

After the passage of the larvae, the child is said to have improved in health and become normal; the nervous symptoms and vomiting disappeared.

Three chances for infestation were pointed out; namely, first, the eating of "overripe" or probably decaying peaches in which "rat-tailed" larvae might have occurred; secondly, the drinking of "ditch" water polluted with kitchen refuse, etc.; lastly, stable manure in a neighbor's yard where the child played.

The authors offer the following comment relative to the gastric disturbances:

> A larva supplied with the stigmatic apparatus of *Eristalis* would apparently be fitted for life in a stomach with a small amount of food and plenty of the atmospheric air which is swallowed in eating and drinking and at other times. Such a condition would simulate the normal life conditions fairly closely. That the stomach would not fill to the point where it would drown the larva might be insured by the vomiting, perhaps automatically, the activity of the larva increasing as the stomach filled to where it threatened to cover the rising stigmatic tube, and so setting up an irritation leading to vomiting. The mother states that the child's stomach was extremely intolerant of milk and that drinking milk was promptly followed by vomiting. This suggests that milk, usually taken in long drinks and considerable quantities, quickly threatened the larva with drowning and set up such activity as promptly to cause vomiting.

Tubifera tenax (Linnaeus), the drone fly (Fig. 112), is a large insect, a little larger than a honey bee and resembling the drone bee very closely; indeed it is commonly referred to as its mimic. The fly deposits its eggs on liquid manure or excrement by-products in cans, slop jars, privies, septic tank effluent, etc. The larvae are known as "rat-tailed larvae" (Fig. 113); these also occur occasionally in heaps of horse manure.

Family Muscidae. Among other species that are involved in enteric myiasis are several muscids, including the lesser house fly, *Fannia canicularis*

(Linnaeus), the latrine fly, *Fannia scalaris* (Fabricius) and the false stable fly, *Muscina stabulans* (Fallén). West[37] states that perhaps 75 per cent of all gastrointestinal myiasis is caused by the *Fannia* species mentioned. The author (James) has on several occasions determined *Muscina stabulans* from larvae taken in human enteric myiasis. *Musca domestica* has also been reported as a causative agent.

Urinary Myiasis. As in intestinal myiasis, the symptoms of urinary myiasis depend on the number and kind of larvae, and their localization.

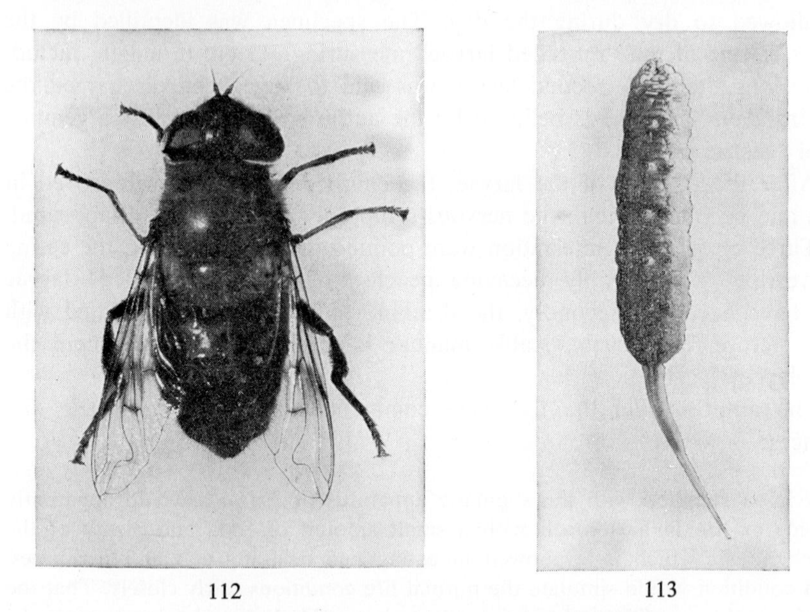

112 113

Fig. 112. The drone fly, *Tubifera tenax*. × 3.5.
Fig. 113. The "rat-tailed" larva of *Tubifera tenax*. × 2.

There may be obstruction and pain; pus, mucus, and blood in the urine; and a frequent desire to urinate. Larvae are expelled with the urine. Chevril[6] reports that *Fannia canicularis* (Linnaeus) (see Chapter 15) is most frequently found in urinary myiasis, although *Fannia scalaris* (Fabricius) and *Musca domestica* Linnaeus have been encountered. Hoeppli and Watt[16] believe that albumin and sugar in the urine may provide food, as may mucus and leucocytes; the lack of oxygen presents the chief difficulty, although very small amounts of oxygen are needed by the larvae.

Infestation is probably usually accomplished at night in warm weather when persons may sleep without covering. The flies deposit their eggs around the urethral opening; these hatch in a few hours, and the larvae enter the urethra.

SEMIOBLIGATE MYIASIS

Traumatic Myiasis. The invasion of wounds or ulcers by fly larvae is of relatively common occurrence in warm, humid climates. A large number of species of flesh flies (*Sarcophaga,* etc.) and blow flies (*Phaenicia sericata, P. cuprina, Calliphora* spp., etc.) are responsible for this type of myiasis. The following description of a case by *Phormia regina* (Meigen) reported by Stewart[30] will serve as an illustration:

The dermatitic area was not large at first but it continued to spread after hospitalization. An extremely offensive odor was given off, but aside from the dermatitis and irritation of the sores, the patient appeared to be feeling well; appetite, digestion and egestion were good. At first treatment was applied only to the area around the ears, but on the night of the patient's admission to the hospital the discovery was made that the scalp was a mass of pus and a supersaturated sulphur wash was applied. The hair was parted to allow the wash to penetrate freely to the scalp and a towel was tied about the head, coming below the ears. The supersaturated sulphur was applied every two hours.

After the second treatment was applied to the scalp the patient became very restless, working the fingers into the palms of her hands and alternately putting her hands to her ears. Soon she began to scream, acted frantic, and became nearly delirious. She was given a sedative without effect.

On taking the towel from the patient's head the nurse observed fly larvae, which had been forced into activity by the treatment, crawling over the towel, hair, and down the cheeks. The nurse estimated that she killed twenty-five or thirty larvae in the hour and a half she spent in removing them and still the hair and scalp remained full of them. Back of the ears the mass of living larvae was so great that they could almost have been spooned out. At this time the patient complained of a buzzing in the ears similar to that occurring when the ears are full of water, and said that she could not hear. The nurse then used toothpick swabs to remove the great quantity of larvae found in the pinnae of the ears; in so doing most of the larvae were killed, but some were kept alive and placed on raw beef in vials so that they might complete their larval growth and pupate.

As soon as pupation occurred the puparia were removed to fresh vials and covered with fine dry soil until they emerged as adults, when they were identified as *Phormia regina* Meig.

After the removal of all visible larvae had been completed the patient's hair was clipped, the supersaturated sulphur wash treatment was continued, and the scalp bandaged. To the original area of dermatitis around the ears was applied a paste consisting of salicylic acid, 2 gm.; zinc oxide, 24 gm.; starch, 24 gm.; petrolatum, sufficient to make 100 gm.

It is obvious that an adult female fly had been attracted to the suppurating scalp sores by the foul odor given off and had oviposited in one or more of these sores. The larvae were driven from the scalp to the pinnae of the ears by the application of the supersaturated sulphur wash.

Chrysomya megacephala (Fabricius) was responsible for much traumatic myiasis in the South Pacific during World War II. Stewart[31] describes a new treatment for traumatic dermal myiasis:

A new douche composed of 15 per cent chloroform in light vegetable oil, has been employed in the treatment of seventeen cases of traumatic dermal myiasis. In every case all the maggots were removed with a single treatment, extending over a period of thirty minutes.

The new douche has advantages over the commonly used chloroform-milk solution in that chloroform is entirely soluble in vegetable oil and only slightly soluble in milk; in that the chloroform-vegetable oil solution is very stable and can be kept indefinitely in closed containers, whereas, the chloroform-milk mixture has to be made up fresh for each application, and in that the vegetable oil is very soothing to the raw tissue of the infested wound.

Cutaneous Myiasis. The larvae of *Wohlfahrtia vigil* (Walker), a member of the Sarcophagidae in eastern North America, frequently cause cutaneous myiasis of a furuncular (boil-like) type. Walker[34] describes the cases of a five-month old boy thus:

Most of the lesions were clustered together on the left side of the neck under the angle of the jaw, one being on the left cheek. They had been first noticed by the mother 24 hours earlier, and when seen by the writer they were already secondarily infected with pus organisms, the child being in a poor general condition and suffering from an intestinal disorder. They were similar to the lesions observed in the previous cases, each being a boil-like sore with an external opening, and from these openings five or six larvae had already been expressed. Only three additional larvae were obtained, these measuring 5 to 7 mm. in length. Each was placed on raw beef in a separate test-tube, plugged with cotton wool. In 24 hours they reached a length of 12 to 13 mm., and in another 24 hours they were full-grown, each measuring about 17 mm. in length.

A male *Wohlfahrtia vigil* was reared from one of the maggots. As in previous cases studied by Walker, the child recovered rapidly after the removal of the larvae.

A closely related species, *Wohlfahrtia opaca* (Coquillett) (Fig. 114) occurs in the west. Biologically, the two species are very close, if not identical, and they may be merely forms of the same species. *Wohlfahrtia opaca* has been reported in furuncular (boil-like) dermal myiasis of human infants in many parts of the western United States and Canada, and it is there also a pest of mink and fox ranches, where it can kill the newly born or very young animals. The larvae penetrate the unbroken skin and usually infest dermal tissues and muscle, although in mink kits and fox pups they may enter the body cavity.

Wohlfahrtia opaca has been considered an obligate parasite; however, the work of Kraft[21] has shown at least its later stages can develop in carrion.

It apparently is a fly in a late stage of transition between a facultative and obligate parasitic larval existence. Several obligate myiasis-producing flies, such as *Cordylobia anthropophaga, Dermatobia hominis,* and, sometimes, *Callitroga hominivorax,* may produce a similar type of myiasis.

Wool Maggots (*Fleeceworms*). Flies of this group were undoubtedly at one time solely scavengers feeding in the maggot stage on carrion and animal wastes, but with the introduction of herds of domesticated animals, they have acquired the habit of attacking living animals. Froggatt[9] has pointed out that, prior to the introduction of cattle and sheep into Australia, blow flies existed on that continent as simple scavengers, ovipositing in animal matter that happened to be festering in the sun. The transition from wool

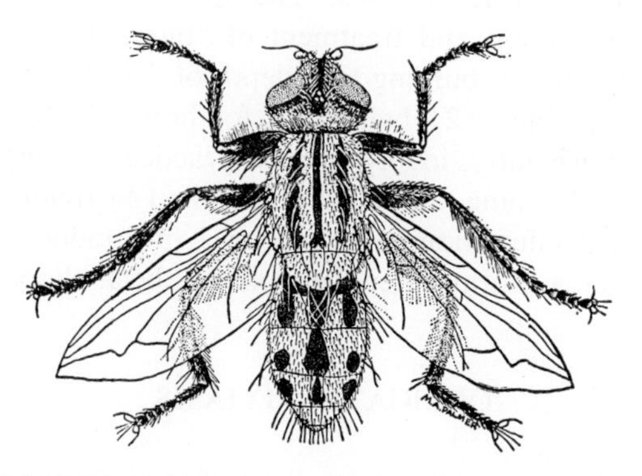

Fig. 114. *Wohlfahrtia opaca.* (Drawing by Miriam A. Palmer.)

of dead sheep to blowing damp or soiled wool of living animals was not a large one. The increase of rabbits aided in building the populations of the flies, the dead carcasses of slaughtered animals, of poisoned dingoes, hawks, and carrion crows, added great quantities of decaying flesh in which the scavenger flies could breed.

The next, and perhaps the most important, factor in the development of the sheep-maggot pest is the work of the sheep breeders themselves. Forty years ago there were many thousands of Merino sheep of the bare-belly, bare-legged type, which did not produce a third of the weight of wool of the modern, improved Merino. The ambition of every sheep-breeder has been to make every inch of the sheep's skin grow wool, and in the case of some classes of Merinos to produce a wrinkled skin, giving even more wool-bearing surface. A sheep clothed with such a mass of thick, close, fine wool, fitting closely over the rump and around the tail, is sure to get more or less stained and damp round the crutch, and to attract flies. This artificial increase in weight, quantity and fineness of wool is accompanied, too, by an increased secretion of yolk, which rising from the skin and spreading all through the wool fibre, forms an additional attraction for the flies, and supplies food for the maggots.[9]

The wool maggot problem is most severe in Australia, where it is considered one of major importance. The most important fly involved there, as well as in South Africa, is *Phaenicia cuprina* (Wiedemann). Several other species, including *Phaenicia sericata* (Meigen) and *Calliphora* (*Anastellorhina*) *augur* (Fabricius), are of lesser importance as Australian wool maggots. It is interesting to note that the relative roles of the two species of *Phaenicia* are reversed in the United States, *P. sericata* being, along with *Phormia regina* (Meigen) and *Callitroga macellaria* (Fabricius), the most important species, whereas *P. cuprina,* which occurs throughout the southern states, is of little or no importance in this respect. *Phaenicia sericata* is also important as a wool maggot in the British Isles and in New Zealand.

Control of Wool Maggot Flies. The following measures are recommended for the prevention and treatment of "blow fly strike": (1) carcass burning, or, if not feasible, burying to a depth of 4 feet or more after sprinkling the carcass with lime; (2) baiting, as for house fly control; (3) proper methods of sheep husbandry, involving such practices as tagging (crutching), bringing about early lambing, and ducking lambs; (4) treatment of wool with toxaphene to prevent infestation (effective for 1 or 2 months); (5) treatment of wounds as for screw-worm, after the wool has been clipped around the infested areas.

OBLIGATE MYIASIS

The Primary Screw-worm. The several changes in the name of the primary screw-worm fly since the discovery of its distinctness from the secondary screw-worm in 1930 have been confusing to the nontaxonomist. The name is now accepted as *Callitroga hominivorax* (Coquerell), and it is unlikely that any further changes will be made. Unlike the secondary screw-worm fly, *Callitroga* (= *Cochliomyia*) *macellara* (Fabricius), which is more particularly a scavenger fly, *C. hominivorax* is an obligate parasite and, according to Laake, Cushing, and Parish, initiates the great majority of cases of screw-worm infestations in man and animals in the United States and probably in the entire neotropical region. It is known to be a cause of nasopharyngeal myiasis in man. The following is a detailed description of a case which terminated fatally (from Osborn [1896] quoted by Richardson in the Peoria, Ill., *Medical Monthly* for February, 1883):

> While traveling in Kansas in the latter part of last August, a citizen of this place had the misfortune to receive while asleep a deposit of eggs from this fly. He had been troubled with catarrh, hence the attraction to the flies. He returned home a few days after the accident and shortly after began complaining of a bad cold. Growing rapidly worse, I was called to attend him. Monday, my first day, his appearance was that of a man laboring under a severe cold. Had slight congestion of the lungs, and moderate fever. His nose seemed greatly swollen and he

complained of a smarting, uneasy feeling in it, and general misery through the head. Gave him treatment to relieve the congestion and fever. Tuesday, saw him again. His nose and face were still swollen, and in addition to the other symptoms he was becoming slightly delirious and complained a great deal of the intense misery and annoyance in his nose and head. A few hours after, I was sent for in haste with the word that something was in the nose. I found on examination a mass of the larvae of this fly (or "screw worms" as they are commonly called in the South) completely blocking up one nostril. On touching them they would instantly retreat *en masse* up the nostril. Making a 20 per cent solution of chloroform in sweet milk I made a few injections up both nostrils, which immediately brought away a large number, so that in a few hours I had taken away some 125 of them. By Wednesday evening erysipelas had begun, implicating the nose and neighboring portions of the face. Another physician was called. By continual syringing with a strong antiseptic solution of salicylate of soda, bicarbonate of soda, and carbolic acid we hoped to drown out the remaining larvae. But they had by this time cut their way into so many recesses of the nose and were so firmly attached that we were unable to accomplish much. Finally we resorted to the chloroform injections, which immediately brought away a considerable number. Friday I was able to open up two or three canals that they had cut, extracting several more that had literally packed themselves, one after another, in these fistulous channels. His speech becoming suddenly much worse, I examined the interior of his mouth and found that a clear-cut opening had been made entirely through the soft palate into his mouth and large enough to insert the end of a common lead pencil. Saturday the few remaining larvae began changing color and one by one dropped away. On Sunday for the first time hemorrhage from both nostrils took place, which continued at intervals for three days, but was not at any time severe. On this day the patient began to improve, the delirium and erysipelas having subsided, leaving but little or no annoyance in his head. In a few days he became able to go about home, and even walk a distance of half a mile to visit a friend and return. But while there he began complaining of a pain in the neighborhood of his left ear, apparently where the eustachian tube connects with the middle ear. It proved to be an abscess. Being already so reduced by the first attack he was unable to withstand the second, and died after an illness of nearly three weeks, completely exhausted by his prolonged sufferings. Three days before his death the abscess discharged its contents by the left nostril. The quantity of pus formed was about 2 1/2 ounces (78 grams).

In all about 250 larvae were taken from him during the first attack, and as the visible results, not only had they cut the hole through the soft palate, but had also eaten the cartilage of the septum of the nose so nearly through as to give him the appearance of having a broken nose. The case occupied, from the first invasion of the fly to its final result, nearly two months. He doubtless would have recovered but for the formation of the abscess, which from all the symptoms, was caused by one or more of the larvae having found their way up the left eustachian tube.

Callitroga hominivorax (Fig. 115) is strongly attracted to the wounds and sores of animals; even a tick bite may be sufficiently attractive to produce an infestation. Laake[22] estimated that at the time of his writing (1936) the loss occasioned by this fly in the southwestern United States was $5,000,000. He found the following predisposing causes of attack: among sheep and lambs, wounds caused by needle grass take first rank; among goats and kids, shear cuts take first rank; among cattle, injuries by the horns of other cattle; among calves, exposed tissue at birth; and among horses and mules, wire cuts.

Laake points out that the more common causes of screw-worm attack are due to farm practices that can be corrected. He stresses particularly care in shearing, dehorning, removing and disposing of old barbed wire

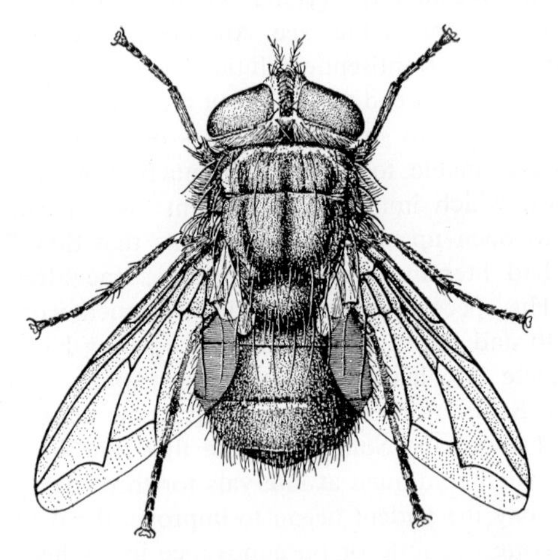

Fig. 115. *Callitroga hominivorax,* adult female. (Drawing by Arthur Cushman; U.S.D.A. photograph.)

from fences, also the timing of dehorning, castrating, and branding so as to expose the wounds as little as possible to flies during the season of abundance.

An epidemic of human myiasis caused by *C. hominivorax,* 81 cases in five provinces of Chile occurring during the months of December to April, 1945–46, is reported by Gajardo-Tobar and Honorato,[10] who also describe the biology of the fly concerned.

Life History of the Screw-worm Fly. The adult *Callitroga hominivorax* has a deep greenish-blue metallic color with yellow, orange, or reddish face, and three dark stripes on the dorsal surface of the thorax. It is difficult, unless one is experienced, to separate this species from *C. macellaria.* Females of *C. macellaria* may usually be distinguished from *C. hominivorax* by the fact that the basicostal scale (a small sclerite at the base of the wing) of the former is of a yellowish color, whereas in the latter it is black. Also, both sexes of *C. macellaria* have yellow hairs on the lower half of the parafrontals (just above the antennae, and to each side of the median frontal stripe), whereas in *C. hominivorax* these hairs are black (Fig. 116). The two species can be accurately separated from each other by the use of the characters exhibited by the male terminalia.

Individual females of *C. hominivorax,* according to Laake, Cushing, and Parish, may lay as many as 2853 eggs, the eggs being deposited in characteristic batches of 10 to 393 eggs each, and the laying of as many as 300 eggs may be completed in from 4 to 6 minutes. The incubation period of the eggs on wounds in animals ranges from 11 to 21.5 hours, under natural conditions. The larval feeding period ranges from 3.5 to 4.5 days or more;

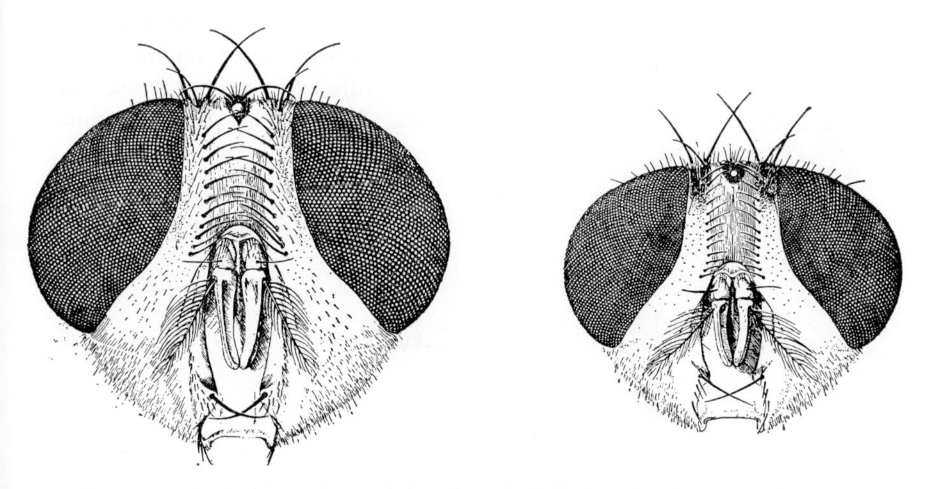

Fig. 116. Head, front view, of females of *Callitroga hominivorax* (*left*) and *C. macellaria* (*right*). Note small proclinate fronto-orbital bristles of *C. macellaria,* absent in *C. hominivorax.* The hairs of the lower parafrontalia are black in *C. hominivorax,* pale in *C. macellaria.* (Drawings by Arthur Cushman; U.S.D.A. photographs.)

the prepupal period from a few hours to about 3 days (7 hours to 76 hours); the pupal stage lasts about 7 days. The prepupal and pupal stages are greatly influenced by temperature and moisture. The life history from egg to egg under natural conditions requires about 24 days. In the United States, the screw-worm fly overwinters only in the South, particularly in Texas and Florida, but through migration they may fly as far north as Colorado, Missouri, and Virginia. North of that area, screw-worm infestations may assume local and temporary importance through introduction in stock cars or with parasitized animals.

Screw-worm Control. The screw-worm is a true parasite and lives only in the living flesh of warm-blooded animals; it is not found in snakes, lizards, or other cold-blooded animals, nor in carcasses, dead fish, decaying meats, or decaying vegetable matter. The maggots found in dead animals are not true screw-worms (Fig. 117). This fact was not realized until 1930, when Cushing and Patton first recognized the distinctness between the primary screw-worm fly, which they called *Cochliomyia americana,* new species, and the secondary screw-worm fly, *C. macellaria.*

In the light of this information, much serious damage by screw-worms may be prevented by good herd management, which involves such matters as controlled breeding and proper utilization of climate and natural growth of native grasses; having the calves dropped in the spring as the grasses become green; eliminating nonbreeders and shy breeders; separating the breeding herd from the steers; feeding bulls during the winter and having them in good condition in spring; castrating bull calves when they are young by the bloodless operation; nubbing the sharp points of horns; marking and branding during the winter seasons and using a repellent smear on these parts; using common sense in handling and driving cattle; eliminating the use of the whip and catch dogs; avoiding the jamming of cattle into pens and chutes;

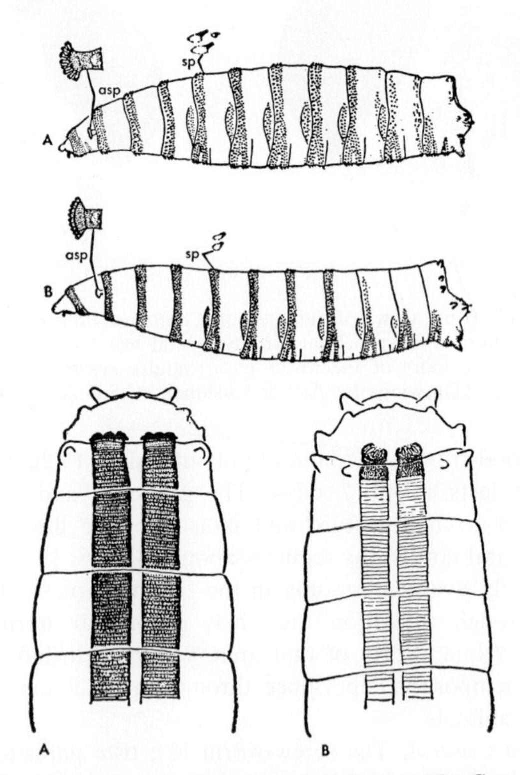

Fig. 117. Mature larva of (*A*) *Callitroga hominivorax,* (*B*) *C. macellaria.* (*Above*) Larva, side view. (*Below*) Dorsal view of posterior segments, showing pigmented tracheal trunks of *C. hominivorax* and unpigmented tracheal trunks of *C. macellaria.* (After Laake, Cushing, and Parish.)

eliminating unnecessary wounds and bruises of all kinds. Livestock should be examined frequently for wounds and injuries, and all cases of screw-worm should be treated promptly. In treating animals, one should avoid making wounds bleed. All wounds should be treated with a repellent smear. Smear EQ335, containing 3 per cent lindane and 35 per cent pine oil, is effective, but must be used as directed and in the minimum amount necessary, particularly on baby calves. Another effective smear is EQ62, containing 35 per cent diphenylamine.

An amazing new chapter in insect control has recently been written as a result of screw-worm control investigations. It was found that male screw-worm flies could be sterilized by irradiation in the pupal stage with X-rays or gamma rays, but that they mated normally, i.e., several times for each male to a single mating for the female. The result was that sterilized males liberated into a wild population of females produced a relatively large number of sterile matings (Baumhover *et al.*[3]). On Curaçao, an island with an area of about 170 square miles, 40 miles north of Venezuela, *Callitroga hominivorax* was apparently completely eradicated within a period of 8 weeks by the release of sterilized males. This unique method of control is being applied successfully in such areas as the southeastern United States, where the primary screw-worm is a relatively new arrival; it should also find application in several other types of problems in medical entomology.

Other Screw-worm Flies. In Africa and India, a calliphorid fly, *Chrysomya bezziana* Villeneuve, occupies a position similar to that of *Callitroga hominivorax* in America. Interestingly, a similarity exists between *C. bezziana* and the scavenger, *C. megacephala* (Fabricius) comparable to the similarity between the American *Callitroga hominivorax* and its scavenger relative *C. macellaria.* In eastern Europe and Siberia, a sarcophagid, *Wohlfahrtia magnifica* (Schiner), is important as a parasite of man and animals; its habits, unlike those of the American *Wohlfahrtia,* are those of a screw-worm.

The bot and warble flies, now segregated into four families, were heretofore placed in one family, the Oestridae. The larvae of all these flies are obligate parasites in the digestive tract or other parts of the body of many mammals. *Bots* are the larvae of members of the family Gasterophilidae, medium-sized, 9–18 mm long, stout, pollinose flies; the eyes are large; the antennae are depressed in facial grooves, the arista is bare; mouth parts are rudimentary; the thorax is pilose; the wings are large, the apical cross vein is absent, the squamae are small. *Warbles* are the larvae of the family Hypodermatidae, large, robust, hairy, beelike flies; with arista bare, palpi small or absent; mouth parts rudimentary; wings large, apical cell open. The term "warble" (also "bot") is also applied to the larvae of the family Cuterebridae, large hairy flies often black and white in color. As in the oestrids, the mouth parts of these flies are nonfunctional although there is a large oral orifice; the palpi are very small; the arista is naked or plumose;

wings and squamae are large. *Head bots* refer to the larvae of the Oestridae (in a restricted sense), beelike flies known as "nose flies"; with eyes naked and small, antennae depressed in sunken facial grooves, mouth parts vestigial, wings and squamae large; the females are larviparous.

The horse bot flies belong to the family Gasterophilidae with only one genus, *Gasterophilus,* and four North American species: (1) *Gasterophilus intestinalis* (De Geer), with cloudy patches near the center and apex of the wings and possessing a prominent spur on the third trochanter; (2) *G. inermis* (Brauer), which also has wings with cloudy patches, but the trochanter is without a spur; (3) *G. haemorrhoidalis* (Linnaeus), without cloudy patches on the wings, and with the anterior basal cell ending before the apex of the discal cell and the tip of the abdomen reddish; and (4) *G.*

Fig. 118. Eggs of the horse bot fly, attached to a hair of the host. × 20.

nasalis (Linnaeus), also with hyaline wings and with the anterior basal cell ending approximately at the same plane as the apex of the discal cell. The flies of this genus are somewhat smaller than honey bees; the ovipositor of the female is large and protuberant. They are strong fliers. The larvae live in the stomach and intestines of horses. A taxonomic review of the group has been presented by Zumpt and Paterson.[39]

Gasterophilus intestinalis (De Geer) [*Gasterophilus equi* (Clark)] is the common horse bot fly or nit fly, a widely distributed, nearly cosmopolitan, species commonly seen in the United States from June to September. The light yellow eggs (Fig. 118) are firmly attached to the hairs of the forelegs, belly, flanks, shoulders, and other parts of the body of the horse, but chiefly on the inside of the knees where they are accessible to the tongue, teeth and lips. The female fly (Fig. 119A) hovers from 2 to 3 feet away from the animal, darting swiftly and repeatedly at the horse, each time attaching an egg to a hair. Wells and Knipling[37] report one fly placing 905 eggs in 2 3/4 hours. The sudden increase in temperature arising from the warmth of the tongue (not friction and moisture, as was previously considered the case) provide the necessary stimulus for the hatching of the eggs. The incubation period is from 7 to 14 days, but may be greatly prolonged by cool weather so that viable eggs may be found unhatched on the hair of the horse until late autumn, long after the flies have disappeared. The larvae on hatching (Fig. 120) are provided with an armature which enables them to excavate galleries in the subepithelial layer of the mucous membrane. Wehr,[36] who has studied the behavior of the larvae, states, "Many very small, threadlike subepithelial burrows, ramifying in every direction, were visible on the anterior half of the tongue, while those on the posterior half of the tongue were larger in size. Larvae were visible at the terminations of many of these galleries." Wehr found that newly hatched larvae when placed on the tongue

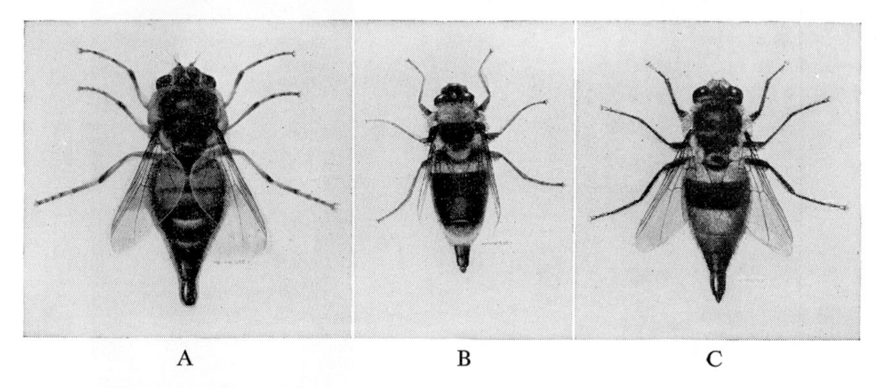

Fig. 119. Horse bot flies. (*A*) *Gasterophilus intestinalis;* (*B*) *G. haemorrhoidalis;* and (*C*) *G. nasalis.* (Adapted from Hearle.)

of a freshly killed rabbit almost immediately began burrowing and within 1 minute nearly all became entirely embedded in mucous membrane. From the mouth in the normal host, the larvae apparently pass rapidly to their preferred site in the alimentary canal, the left sac or esophageal portion of the stomach, where second and third stage larvae remain fixed with little or no change in position until the following spring and early summer, when they detach themselves and pass out of the intestine with the droppings. They are then from 1.5 to 2 cm in length (Fig. 121). Pupation takes place shortly thereafter in loose earth or in dry droppings. The pupal stage varies considerably, depending upon moisture and temperature, but the usual time is from 3 to 5 weeks when the winged bot fly emerges. Copulation soon takes place, and egg laying begins in early summer. The life history requires about 1 year.

Gasterophilus haemorrhoidalis (Linnaeus) (Fig. 119B) is a North American and European species. It is commonly known as the "nose fly," because the female fly forceably "strikes" the animal in the region of the nose, where it attaches its black eggs to the fine hairs of the lips. Because of the orange-red terminal segments, this fly is known as the "redtailed bot." The fully grown larvae have the habit of moving from the stomach during the early spring and attaching close to the anus before finally dropping to the ground.

Gasterophilus nasalis (Linnaeus) [*G. veterinus* (Clark)] (Fig. 119C) is the chin fly or throat bot fly, also a widely distributed species said to be especially abundant in the Rocky Mountain region. This fly is very annoying to horses, since its eggs are attached to hairs under the jaws, and when the fly darts at the throat, it causes the animals to throw their heads up as

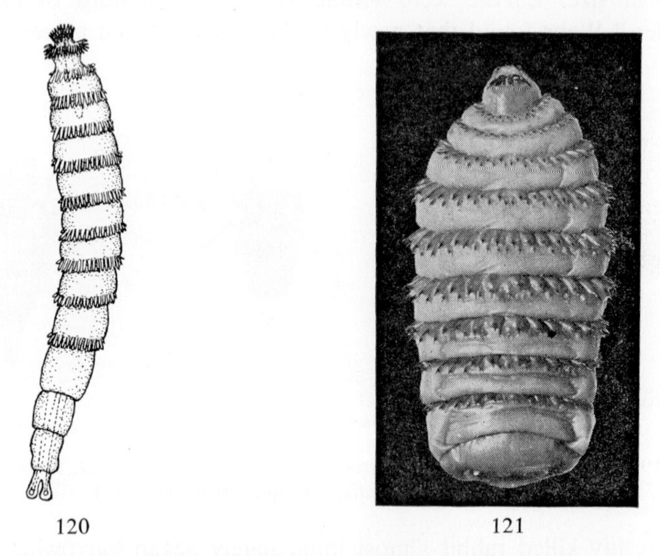

120 121

Fig. 120. Newly emerged larva of the horse bot fly. × 60.
Fig. 121. Mature larva of the horse bot fly, *Gasterophilus intestinalis*. × 4.

though struck under the chin. Egg deposition takes place during late spring and early summer. The larvae hatch without the need for heat, moisture, or friction in from 4 to 5 days. The newly hatched larvae travel along the jaw and enter the mouth between the lips. The larvae travel to their preferred site in the alimentary tract, the pyloric portion of the stomach and the anterior portion of the duodenum, where they are found in groups and remain for 10 to 11 months, i.e., until they are mature. Pupation takes place in a few hours after the larvae are voided with the manure during the early summer. The pupal stage requires about 3 weeks.

Gasterophilus inermis (Brauer) is a European species introduced at one time into the United States (Knipling[18]) but probably not established here. The eggs are deposited on the hairs of the cheeks of the host and, according to Knipling, when hatched the larvae penetrate the epidermis and work their way under it until the mouth is reached; thence, after molting in the epithelial layer of the cheek, they migrate to the rectum, where they remain until fully mature. *Gasterophilus pecorum* (Fabricius), a European and African species, is said to deposit its eggs on the food of the host and on nearby objects. The larvae burrow into the mucous membrane of the mouth, migrating soon to the stomach and rectum.

Pathogenesis. While a moderate infestation of bots will give no outward indications, a heavy infestation will be indicated by digestive disorders

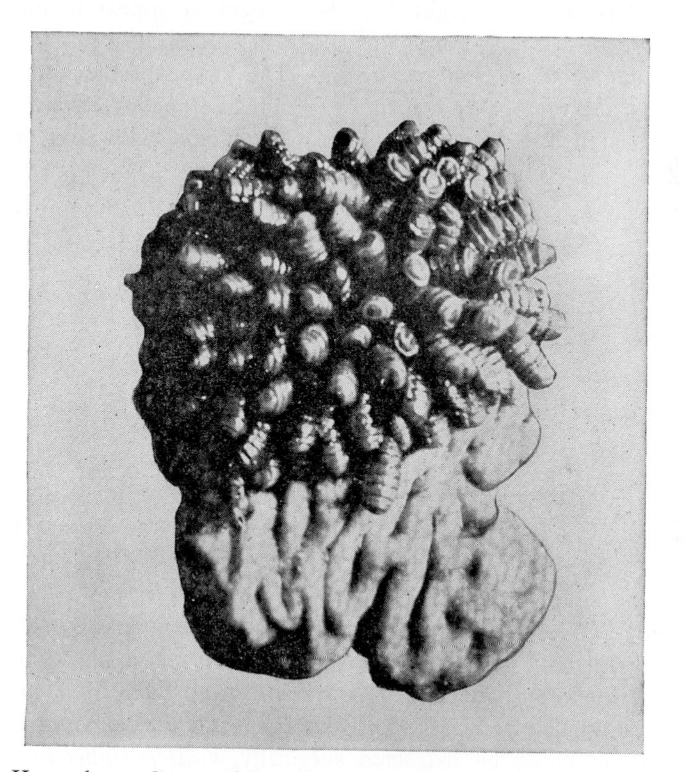

Fig. 122. Horse bots, *Gasterophilus intestinalis,* attached to mucous lining of the stomach of a horse. × 0.75. (Photograph by Wherry.)

(which may of course be traceable to other causes as well). The discovery of bots in the manure is sufficient evidence. A light infestation is probably of no consequence; there are indeed some individuals who erroneously maintain that a horse must have at least a few bots in order to be well.

The injury which bots produce is: (1) abstraction of nutriment, both from the stomach and its contents; (2) obstruction to the food passing from the stomach to the intestine, particularly when the larvae are in or near the pylorus; (3) irritation and injury to the mucous membrane of the stomach (Fig. 122) due to the penetration of the oral hooklets; (4) irritation of the intestine, rectum, and anus in passage.

Control. In northern climates, washing the animal with warm water (104° F or warmer) on days when air temperatures do not rise above 60° F will cause the eggs to hatch and the larvae to perish. This may be done effectively in the fall after oviposition has ceased. Carbon disulfide may then be used effectively, but it should be administered only by veterinarians. After preparation of the animal by fasting it for 18 hours (water may be allowed), the chemical is administered in gelatin capsules at the rate of 1.5 fluid drams for each 250 pounds of weight. The bots begin to appear in the animal's droppings in 5 or 6 hours. Purgatives should not be used in this treatment.

Gasterophilus as a Human Parasite. The larvae of the horse bot flies burrow freely and may cause a form of creeping cutaneous myiasis in human beings. Since man is a very unusual host, the larvae, with very rare excep-

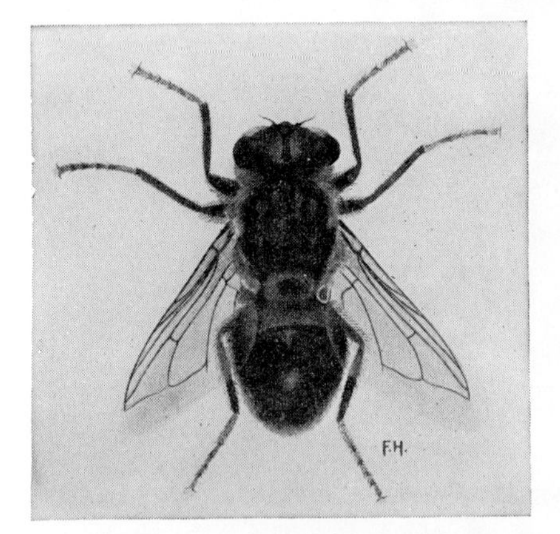

Fig. 123. The common cattle grub, *Hypoderma lineatum.* (Adapted from Hearle.)

tions, do not live beyond its first stage. The burrow made by the creeping larva is very tortuous and plainly visible. It may cause severe itching but never any serious consequences. The larvae, which measure 1 to 2 mm in length, are easily detected a short distance beyond the apparent end of the burrow and can easily be extracted surgically. *Gasterophilus intestinalis* is usually the species involved.

Cattle grubs (ox warbles) are the larvae of flies belonging to the family Hypodermatidae, genus *Hypoderma,* the heel flies. Although the normal host is cattle, horses and humans are occasionally parasitized. Persons dealing with cattle are familiar with the tumerous swellings on the backs of cattle during the late winter and early spring, and most stockmen have squeezed out the large grubs which inhabit these tumors. There are two well-known species: *Hypoderma lineatum* (de Villers), the common cattle grub, widely distributed in the United States, as well as in Europe and Asia; and *Hypoderma bovis* (De Geer), the northern cattle grub, less widely distributed but occurring over approximately the northern half of the United States.

Hypoderma bovis is the larger of the two species, measuring about

15 mm in length, while *H. lineatum* measures about 13 mm. The former has the thorax covered with dense yellow hairs in front, and black ones behind, with the terminal hairs on the abdomen yellow, while the latter, *H. lineatum* (Fig. 123), has a fairly uniform hairy covering of mixed brownish black and white with four prominent smooth and polished lines on the thorax, the hairs of the terminal segment of the abdomen being reddish orange. The full-grown larvae are easily distinguished by examination of the spiny armature, *H. bovis* having the last two segments entirely devoid of spines, while *H. lineatum* has only the last one smooth; the posterior spiracular plates, also, are different, that of *H. bovis* being deeply excavated, funnel-like, toward the button, whereas that of *H. lineatum* is more shallowly and broadly excavated (Fig. 124). The full-grown larva of the former measures from 27 to 28 mm in length and that of the latter about 25 mm (Fig. 125).

Life History and Habits. The eggs of both species are laid on the hairs of cattle, *H. lineatum* attaching as many as a dozen in a row to a single hair, while *H. bovis* is said to attach but a single egg to a hair. As many as 800

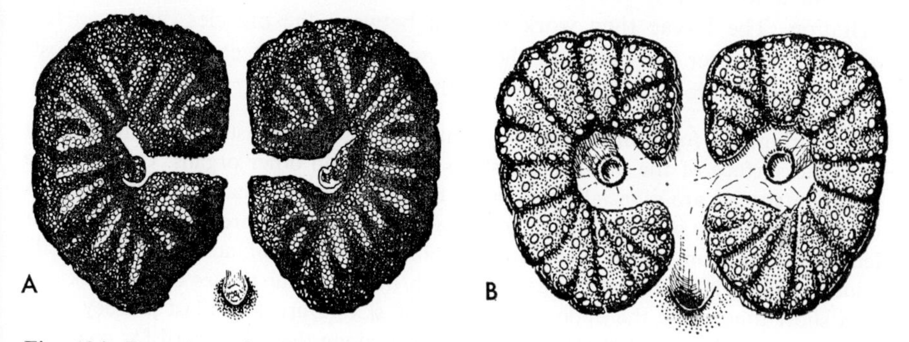

Fig. 124. Posterior spiracles of mature larva of (*A*) *Hypoderma bovis* and (*B*) *H. lineatum*. (Drawing by Arthur Cushman; U.S.D.A. photograph.)

Fig. 125. Larva of the common cattle grub, *Hypoderma lineatum*. × 1.3.

eggs may be laid by a female of either species (Warburton[35]). The eggs are evidently deposited by preference on the legs from the hock to the knee of the standing animal, but in recumbent animals the eggs may be attached to the hairs of other parts of the body close to the ground. Although no pain is inflicted at the time of oviposition, cattle become terror-stricken when the fly is discovered and gallop madly for water or shade in which to stand to escape the enemy. This is termed "gadding" and often spreads to the whole herd.

The eggs of both species hatch within a week, and the tiny armored larvae crawl down the hairs of the host and bore either directly into the skin or into the hair follicles. Knipling's[19] studies indicate that there are only three stages, instead of four or five as was previously thought.

Bishopp, Laake, and Wells[4] state that the eggs are ordinarily deposited only on sunny days, although *H. bovis* (De Geer) may continue to oviposit during cloudy periods. A stiff breeze apparently deters the flies, although egg deposition was observed at temperatures as low as 40° F. The eggs hatch in from 3 to 4 days, and the larvae penetrate the skin causing considerable irritation. The larvae then work upward between the muscles, and in a few months thereafter are found in the abdominal and chest cavities of the host. The above-mentioned authors state further:

> During the following seven or eight months they constantly burrow about over the surface of the paunch, intestines, spleen, and other organs. Grubs of the common species are especially numerous between the muscular and mucous layers of the esophagus or gullet. The grubs in these situations are slender, and their length ranges from about one-tenth to about two-thirds of an inch. In the fall, winter, and spring the grubs migrate through the muscular tissues of the back and in a short time reach the under surface of the skin. During this last journey some of them enter the spinal canal and may burrow along the spinal cord for considerable distances. Soon after the skin is reached the grub cuts a minute hole through to the surface. At this time it is still slender and white and about two-thirds of an inch long.

From 1 to 5 days later, the grub molts for the first time. Following this molt, the skin of the larva is closely set with spines. The body of the host now begins to isolate the invading parasite by forming a pocket or cyst around it. The growth of the grub from this time on is rather rapid, and a second molt occurs about 25 days after the first. In the last larval stage of its development, the color gradually darkens, first becoming yellow, then brown, and finally almost black. During this entire development beneath the skin, a breathing hole is kept open to the surface, and the grub lies with its two spiracles, which are located on the end, applied rather closely to the opening in the skin. As growth proceeds, the hole in the skin is gradually enlarged. In late spring and early summer "at the end of the period of development in the back, which requires from 35 to 89 days, growth is complete, and the repulsive, spiny grub works its way out and falls to the ground." There the larvae crawl away into the loose earth or debris, becoming rapidly dark brown to black in pupation, and in from 4 to 5 weeks emerge as warble flies. The complete life cycle requires about a year.

Injury Done. The injury done by the warbles is first that of *irritation* caused by their migrations in the body of the animal and later by their emergence from beneath the skin; secondly, the escape of the larva from the tumor leaves an open, running wound which persists for a long time and is attractive to screw-worm flies and other tormenting insects. The direct pathogenesis is of minor importance, however, in the face of the economic loss produced by this insect.

Economic Losses. The economic losses produced are: (1) Reduction in the milk secretion of cattle, which is estimated at from 10 to 20 per cent of the normal yield. (2) Loss of flesh due to the wild endeavor of the animals to escape from flies and the irritating larvae (which is pointed out by Holstein: "A cow quietly grazing will suddenly spring forward, throw up her tail and make for the nearest water at a head-long gait. Seemingly deprived at the moment of every instinct except the desire to escape, she will rush over a high bluff on the way, often being killed by the fall. This, with miring in water holes and the fact that cattle are prevented from feeding, causes the loss"). (3) Depreciation of the value of the carcass as flesh, which becomes greenish yellow, jellylike in appearance, and unfit for consumption at the points where the grubs are located. (4) Injury to the hide, which becomes "grubby," full of holes, where the grubs have emerged (Fig. 126).

It is difficult, in light of changing control and fluctuating dollar values, to estimate the cost of the damage sustained by cattle grubs, but losses as high as $35 per head due primarily to hide and carcass damage and totaling in the neighborhood of $100,000,000 a year in the United States are probable. It is signified that the warbles damage that part of the hide that is most valuable for leather and those areas of flesh that produce the most valuable steaks.

Control. Although hand extraction of the warbles is possible in cases where only one or a few animals are involved, the most effective method of control, up to 1957, was the use of rotenone applied after warbles had made their appearance in the animal's back. Both methods were, of course, aimed at breaking the life cycle in the late larval stage and prior to the transformation to pupa and adult. Effective control depended upon cooperation among neighboring ranchers, and even under such circumstances cattle driven from a winter range were often subjected to fly attacks as they passed through areas where effective control was not maintained. Another objection to the use of rotenone is its limited period of effectiveness after application; in areas where both the northern and the common cattle grub are present as pests, as many as five applications were necessary.

In 1957 a new systemic insecticide, ronnel, (Dow ET-57),[1] was tested by many experiment stations in the United States, Canada, and Europe, and was found to average better than 90 per cent effectiveness in control of *Hypoderma lineatum* and *H. bovis*. The chemical is best administered orally into the stomach in a bolus with a balled gun; it is equally effective as an oral drench in water, but the administration in this form is somewhat more difficult and more hazardous. Animals should have access to feed and water before and after the treatment, and treatment should not be administered to animals in poor health, in tired condition immediately following shipment, or within 60 days prior to slaughter. Directions for proper dosage and seasonal

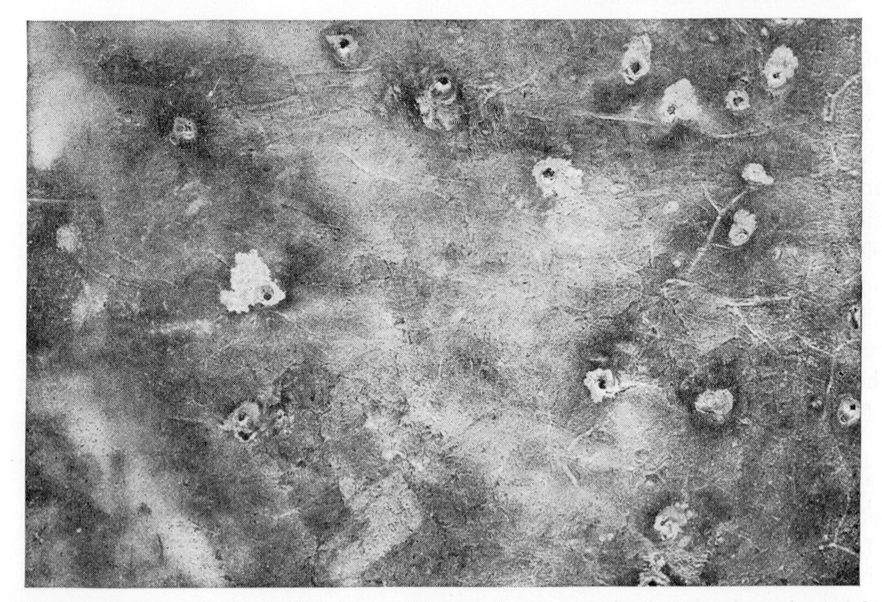

Fig. 126. A piece of sole leather 21 × 31.5 cm, showing work of the cattle grub. × 0.3.

application should be followed closely. Application too late in the season may produce illness caused by an anaphylactic reaction resulting from toxins produced by the dead grubs. If properly administered, ronnel appears to be quite safe to use. It does not kill older larvae within 2 weeks of the time that they will leave the warble. It also serves as an anthelmintic, and it has potentialities in the control of the screw-worm and bloodsucking flies.

Another systemic insecticide which shows great promise is Bayer 21/199. The advantage of this formulation is that it can be sprayed on the animal, the insecticide presumably being absorbed by the skin and translocated to the tissues in which the grubs are located. It should not be used on dairy animals. This insecticide is also known as Co-Ral.

Hypoderma as a Human Parasite. Numerous records of attacks on man by *H. lineatum, H. bovis,* and *H. diana* Brauer, a European parasite of deer, have been published. Most case histories reveal some association with cattle during the summer or fall preceding the attack. The incidence of attacks on children is proportionately higher than that on adults. A typical case history is described by Herms,[14] as follows:

Mr. C. is a ranch superintendent, spending much of his time on horseback. On a Sunday toward the end of July, 1924, he had ridden to a point known as Mission Ridge near San Jose, when feeling tired, he dismounted and lay down on the ground in the open and slept. He distinctly remembers that his shirt had rolled up above his belt, exposing his skin, but felt no irritation at the time. Whether this exposure was taken advantage of by the fly can only be a matter of conjecture. Several days later, exact time not remembered, soreness was experienced and a slight swelling in the region of the right groin appeared. In about a week the swelling had increased to the width of a hand with no discoloration. The swelling then crept downward toward the left side affecting the scrotum, thence downward along the left leg to the knee and calf, thence back up the left leg following about the same course to the left groin, thence across to the right groin and back again to the left and upward along the left side of the body, slightly anterior to the shoulder, thence downward to the upper right arm to near the elbow, when the arm could not be raised without great pain, thence the swelling traveled upward again to the neighborhood of the shoulder blade where a "hive-like" local swelling was formed without any itching sensation. Mr. C. stated that at this point he was "bothered" all night, and while rubbing his arm and manipulating his shoulder muscle a larva of some insect "popped" out. This emergence took place about the end of October (1924). The larva was placed in a vial for shipment but was lost in transit.

Relative to the second larva which was delivered to the writer in person on the day following its emergence, Mr. C. states that since October when the first larva emerged, no further swellings were observed, but soreness in the region of the thigh and lower abdomen, similar to severe strain, persisted. However, on January 28 (1925) he experienced a severe "soreness" in the region of his right thigh which gave much distress, particularly when walking. By that night a swelling had developed and the following day the muscular soreness continued to spread; by January 31 a hernia-like swelling had developed which enlarged upward and outward to the region of the belt-line, the lower hernia-like swelling gradually disappearing. Sunday night, February 1, a hive-like swelling as observed in the case of the first larva began to form, enlarging to an area of about four by eight inches. Tuesday evening, February 3, lymph exuded from a small opening near the middle of the swollen area. About a tablespoonful of lymph stained with blood was pressed out and in the process of manipulation a larva similar to the first "popped" out. This specimen was delivered to the writer February 4 in good condition and identified as a third-stage larva of *Hypoderma bovis* DeG. The larva was milky white in color, about 12 mm. in length by 2 mm. in width at the middle, tapering bluntly at both ends. Very little swelling and practically no discoloration were visible on examination, although the point of emergence was clearly seen.

As in cattle, ingress is probably through the skin. The wanderings of the larva may cause severe discomfort, itching, pains, and cramps, and may be associated with stomach disorders. When the larva is reaching the end of its wandering stage, it moves upward, as in cattle, but, because of man's upright position, it usually forms its warble in the upper part of the chest, the neck, or the head. The pain and discomfort accompanying parasitism may be severe. An apparently increased nighttime activity of the larva may interfere with sleep. Local paralysis may occur; in one case, a boy parasitized by seven larvae of *H. lineatum* suffered almost complete paralysis of the lower extremities for about a year. Such paralysis may be due to invasion of the spinal canal. There are cases on record of an eye being invaded and destroyed; in another case, a small boy died after a larva had produced a fetid ulcer around the back teeth of the lower jaw. Surgical removal of the larva may often be accomplished.

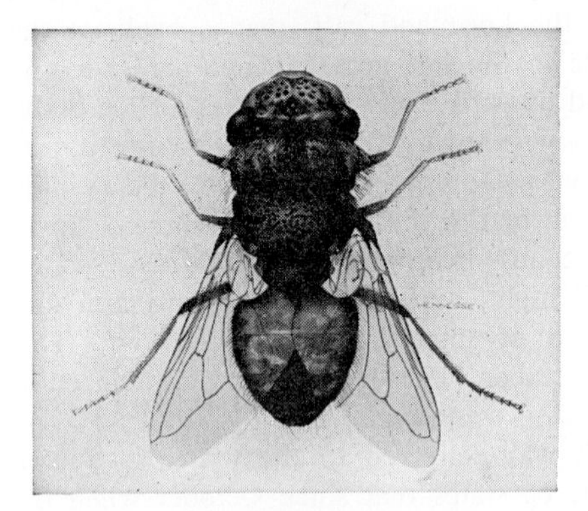

Fig. 127. The sheep bot fly, *Oestrus ovis*. (Adapted from Hearle.)

The Caribou warble fly, *Oedemagena tarandi* (Linnaeus), is widely distributed over the range of its host both in northern Europe and northern North America. Hearle[13] states that the fly is yellowish orange in color and has a beelike appearance. The life history resembles that of the warble fly of cattle.

Sheep bot flies (head maggots, grub-in-the-head), are the larvae of *Oestrus ovis* Linnaeus, a very widely distributed species belonging to the family *Oestridae*. The fly (Fig. 127) is about 12 to 14 mm in length, smaller than a honey bee, which it somewhat resembles; it is yellow to brownish gray in color, and hairy. The abdomen is variegated with brown and straw-yellow; the legs are brown. It is further described by Osborn as follows:

The under side of the head is puffed out and white. The antennae are extremely small and spring from two lobes which are sunk into a cavity at the anterior and under part of the head. The eyes are purplish brown, and three small eyelets are distinctly visible on the top of the head. It has no mouth and cannot, therefore, take any nourishment. The wings are transparent and extend beyond the body, and the winglets (calypteres) which are quite large and white, cover entirely the poisers. It is quite lazy and, except when attempting to deposit its eggs, the wings are seldom used.

Life History. The sheep bot fly deposits living young during early summer to autumn in the nostrils of sheep and goats and may also attack human beings. One female fly may deposit as many as 60 larvae in an hour. The larvae at once begin to move up the nasal passages, working their way into the nasal and frontal sinuses often as far as the base of the horns in rams and attach themselves to the mucous membranes. Here numbers of these whitish grubs may be found wedged in closely in various conditions of development. The posterior of the larvae present conspicuous spiracles. The grubs reach full growth with a length of from 25 to 30 mm by the following spring, a larval period of from 8 to 10 months. At the end of this time they work their way out of the nostrils (they are usually sneezed out), fall to the ground, bury themselves in the earth, and pupate in a few hours. The pupal period lasts from 3 to 6 weeks and over, 19 to 34 days according to Fallis,[8] who found that reared flies lived on an average of 16 days, one surviving as long as 28 days. Fallis also found that the complete development of the parasite stage in spring lambs in Texas and New Mexico required from 2 1/2 to 3 1/2 months.

Symptoms. In the presence of the fly, the sheep (or goats) are very much excited, shake the head, rush with their noses into the dust, snort and otherwise indicate that they are trying to escape something that persists in entering the nostrils. In parasitized animals, there is a purulent discharge from the nostrils, vigorous shaking of the head, and perhaps the occasional discharge of a maggot, loss of appetite, grating of the teeth; and, when the animals walk, the forefeet are lifted in a pawing movement. The great majority of the cases do not result fatally, but death often comes in a week or less after the appearance of aggravated symptoms.

Treatment. Materials such as snuff, pepper, etc., may be introduced into the nostrils or sprinkled among the flock, to induce violent sneezing, which causes the expulsion of many of the larger grubs. Law recommends the injection of benzene, lifting the sheep's nose somewhat and pouring a teaspoon of the remedy into each nostril. The lower nostril into which the benzene is poured is held shut for 30 sec; the other side is then turned and the treatment repeated. The application is repeated daily or more often until the maggots are all expelled.

The larvae of *Oestrus ovis* at times invade the nasal cavities of man as is normally the case with sheep. Severe frontal headaches result.

Head Maggot of Horses. An important species of head maggot attacking horses in Russia and parts of Europe, Asia, and Africa, is *Rhinoestrus purpureus* (Brauer). Its habits are said to be similar to those of *Oestrus ovis*.

Ophthalmomyiasis of man is commonly traceable to the larvae of *Oestrus ovis* and *Rhinoestrus purpureus*. Since man is not a normal host, the larva is unable to progress beyond its first stage, and the infestation is, consequently, short-lived. In the typical case history, the patient, who usually has had a close association with sheep or goats, will report being struck in the eye by an insect or small foreign object, with pain and inflammation developing a few hours later. The condition is similar to acute catarrhal conjunctivitis, and may be diagnosed as such. It is never serious. This type of myiasis is most common among nomadic shepherds whose food consists to a large extent of goat's milk and cheese.

Family Cuterebridae. This family includes the genus *Cuterebra,* the larvae which are commonly parasitic on rodents and on wild and domestic

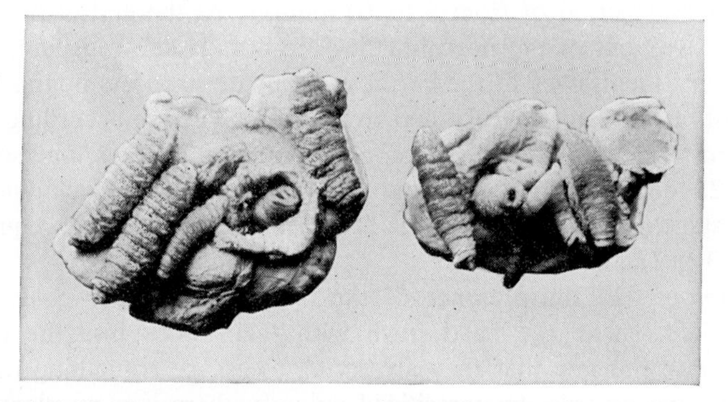

Fig. 128. Head maggots of deer, attached to tissues in the nasal sinuses.

rabbits. These animals may be severely infested with dermal tumors in which the large grubs lie. The adults are bumble-bee-like, although they are much less hairy, as a rule, and may be predominantly shining black or blue. The taxonomy of the group is in a confused state.

Occasionally animals other than rodents or rabbits, including dogs, cats, and man, are parasitized by *Cuterebra* larvae. Human cases are very rare, the larva forming a boil-like lesion in the dermal and subdermal tissues. The larvae are easily removed.

Head Maggot of Deer. Deer, caribou, elk, and other related wild animals are commonly infested with head maggots (Fig. 128); among these are the European species *Cephenemyia stimulator* Clark in the roe deer, *C. rufibarbis* Meigen in the red deer, *C. ulrichii* Brauer in elk, and *C. trompe* Linnaeus in caribou. Among the known species in the United States besides *C. trompe* are *C. phobiger* Clark from the white-tailed deer (*Odocoileus virginianus*), eastern United States; *C. pratti* Hunter from mule deer (*Odocoileus hemionus*) in the western United States, often at high elevations; *C. jellisoni* Townsend from the Pacific coast black-tailed deer (*Odocoileus hemionus columbianus*).

Dermatobia hominis (Linnaeus), the human bot or neotropical bot (Fig. 129), is commonly found in Central and South America and Mexico. The larva is known by several names, including *ver macaque, torcel, tórsalo,* and *berne.* The fly measures from 12 to 16 mm in length and is entirely brown in color. This fly parasitizes a large number of species of mammals and even birds. It has been found in cattle, swine, cats, horses, mules, sheep, goats, monkeys, man, and various wild animals. It is a serious pest of cattle in parts of Brazil and Central America. In man the larva has been reported from various regions of the body, mainly head, arm, back, abdomen, scrotum, buttocks, thigh, and axilla.

The life history of this fly is extremely interesting. The adult is a forest-inhabiting insect; the female does not deposit eggs directly on human skin

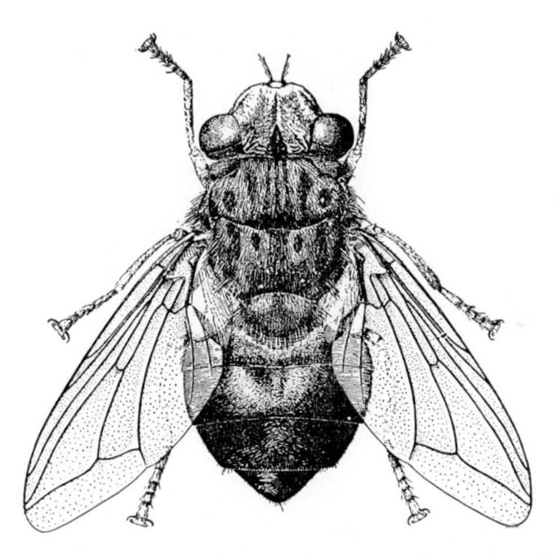

Fig. 129. The human bot fly, *Dermatobia hominis.* (Drawing by Arthur Cushman; U.S.D.A. photograph.)

but, rather, on the bodies of flies, rarely ticks, which will transport them to the host. *Stomoxys* and other bloodsucking flies, nonbloodsuckers such as *Fannia* and *Sarcopromusca,* day-flying mosquitoes such as *Psorophora* (*Janthinosoma*) *lutzii* (Theobald), and possibly other insects act as carriers of the eggs (Fig. 130). The female *Dermatobia* oviposits on the undersides of the bodies of the mosquitoes; when the latter suck blood, it is possible for the eggs to come in contact with the warm-blooded host where either contact or warmth stimulates the larvae; rapid emergence results, and entrance to the skin of the host is effected. The larval period in the body of the host requires about 6 weeks when, like *Hypoderma,* the larvae leave the tumorous swellings they have produced, drop to the earth, and enter the soil to pupate. Unlike *Hypoderma,* the larva of *Dermatobia* (Fig. 131) remains for the full period of its development in the lesion which it makes upon entering the skin; there is no wandering period prior to the warble formation. The entire life cycle requires 3 to 4 months.

Dunn[7] has described the life history of the human bot fly most accurately as the result of an infestation which he permitted himself to suffer in the Canal Zone. In his case the fly *Limnophora,* not a bloodsucker, was the vehicle for the eggs. Two larvae were observed to enter the skin of his arm, requiring 42 minutes for the first and 1 hour and 35 minutes for the second. Dunn experienced "absolutely no sensation caused by the entrance

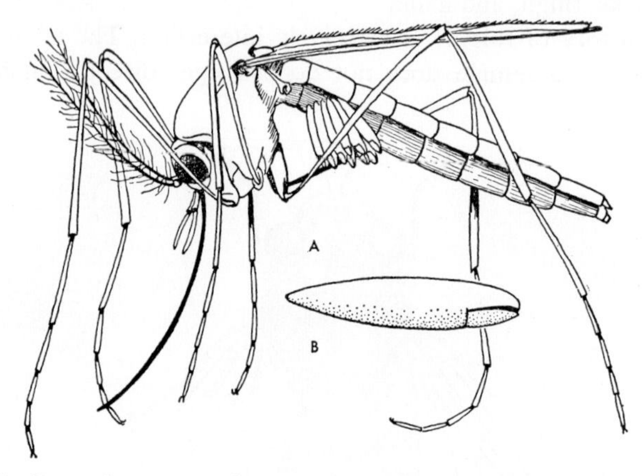

Fig. 130. (*A*) *Psorophora* mosquito carrying a load of Dermatobia eggs; (*B*) egg, enlarged. (Drawing by Arthur Cushman; U.S.D.A. photograph.)

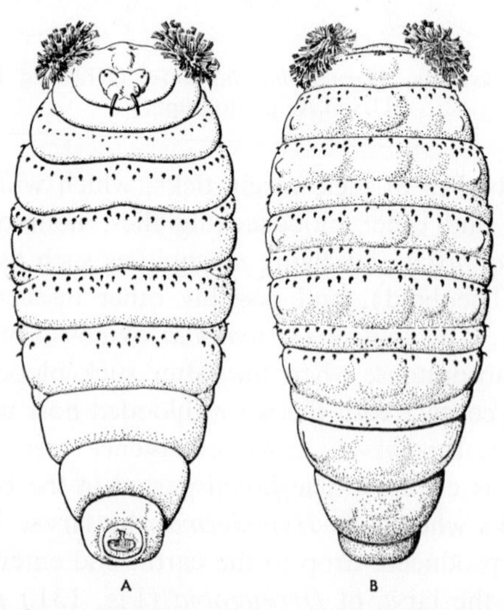

Fig. 131. *Dermatobia hominis,* mature larva: (*A*) ventral view; (*B*) dorsal view. (Drawing by Arthur Cushman; U.S.D.A. photograph.)

of the (first) larva until after the first 30 minutes. Then, as the posterior end was being drawn inside, a sharp pricking, which lasted for about two minutes, was experienced." He states that there was at first a sharp itching at night, and by the end of 2 weeks the lesions had the appearance of small boils, and by the end of 3 weeks these were excruciatingly painful. At the end of 46 days and 15 hours, and 50 days and 15 1/2 hours, respectively, the larvae emerged from the skin, causing "absolutely no pain or sensation." The pupal periods were from 22 to 24 days.

Control of the tórsalo is being actively investigated in Central America, where the economic problem in respect to cattle is severe; consult, for example, the studies of Morales[25] in Costa Rica and Koone and Banegas[20] in Honduras. A spray using toxaphene, lindane, or a mixture of BHC and DDT as its active ingredients has given good results, after several applications, in reducing the larval incidence to a low level. The chemical is effective not only against newly hatched larvae but has an effect also in repelling the egg vectors to the tórsalo. The use of systemic insecticides, either as a spray or an oral drench, is even more promising.[20] To obtain effective control, pastures and grazing lands should be kept free of tall weeds and brush growing in damp locations. Dry soil is favorable to the development of the pupae.

SUNDRY MAGGOT INFESTATIONS

Tumbu Fly. An African calliphorine fly which causes a boil-like (furuncular) type of myiasis is *Cordylobia anthropophaga* (E. Blanchard), the "tumbu fly." Austen describes it as being a "thickset, compactly built fly, of an average length of about 9 1/2 mm. . . . Head, body, and legs are straw yellow." According to Blacklock and Thomson,[5] the eggs are deposited in excrement-polluted sand and soil. The incubation period may be as short as 24 hours. If contact is made with the skin of man or other animals, the larvae penetrate the unbroken skin, forming furuncular swellings, or where multiple and contiguous infection occurs, extensive "sloughing and gangrenous" conditions result. In 8 to 10 days the full-grown larvae, measuring 13 to 15 mm in length, leave the host and pupate in a few days. Wild rats are looked upon as the main reservoir of the infection in nature.

Congo Floor Maggot. An African calliphorine fly which is commonly referred to in the literature of myiasis is *Auchmeromyia luteola* (Fabricius), the larva of which is a bloodsucker and is known as the "Congo floor maggot" (Fig. 132). The fly is commonly found in and about human habitations. The eggs are deposited in small clusters in various situations, such as on sleeping mats spread on the ground in huts, in dusty crevices, in dry sand—situations where the larvae may readily find suitable food. According to Roubaud,[28] whose treatise on this insect should be read by all interested in this subject, the eggs hatch in 36 to 40 hours. The larvae are remarkably resistant to extreme dryness and lack of food. They are nocturnal in their feeding habits, sucking the blood of sleeping persons, producing a wound by means of powerful buccal hooklets. They feed for 15 to 20 minutes, detach, and hide in the crevices of mats, etc., during the day, repeating the attack almost nightly if hosts are available. They attack persons sleeping on the ground or in low beds; they cannot reach beds of ordinary height. The larval period may be as short as 2 weeks or, in the absence of food, perhaps as long as 3 months when the larvae pupate in protected situations. The pupal stage lasts from 11 to 12 days.

Toxic Effect of Ingested Fly Larvae. Botulism, known as "limberneck" in chickens, is traceable at least in part to the ingestion of large numbers of fly larvae such as those of *Lucillia caesar, Phaenicia sericata,* and no doubt other species of flies, or of meat containing type C *Clostridium botulinum*

Fig. 132. Congo floor maggot, *Auchmeromyia luteola.* (After Blacklock, in Martini's *Zoönosen der Haut in wärmeren Ländern.*)

(Van Ermengen) Holland. The organism multiplies in the unburied bodies of dead animals, as flesh is a favorable medium for growth, and the flesh flies developing in the carcasses acquire the toxin produced by the organism, which they in turn pass on to the chickens that eat the maggots. This is another good reason why dead animals should be speedily and safely disposed of, preferably by incineration.

Bloodsucking Maggots of Birds. In a study of bloodsucking fly larvae in birds' nests, Plath[26] found an average of 61 per cent of a total of 63 nests examined to be infested with an average of 47 maggots per nest. The species of birds were the Nuttall's white-crowned sparrow, California purple finch, greenbacked goldfinch, willow goldfinch, and California brown towhee. The parasite involved was a species of *Protocalliphora.* Hall[11] has listed more than 50 species of birds, mostly passerines but including several species of hawks and other nonpasserines which are parasitized by maggots of various species of *Protocalliphora* (= *Apaulina*).

The effect of parasitism on the host is a matter on which there is some disagreement. Plath concludes that from 5 to 10 per cent of the parasitized nestlings die from loss of blood, and some of those that become full-fledged are so weakened by the loss of blood that they fall an easy prey to rapacious animals. The presence of the maggots may at times lead to desertion of the nest by the mother bird.

Surgical Maggots. Although now largely discontinued in favor of other treatments, the use of sterile maggots, maggot therapy, in the disinfection of osteomyelitis and other infected wounds was introduced into professional medical practice by Baer shortly after the end of World War I. Baer[2] had noticed that when men wounded in battle had been lying out on the ground for some time before being carried into dressing stations, their wounds were infested with maggots. He noticed particularly that these men whose wounds were crawling with maggots did not develop infections, as did the men whose wounds had received early treatment. It was discovered that the maggots were eating the dead tissue in which the bacterial infection throve; the maggots actually served as a "viable antiseptic." Baer's work attracted a great deal of attention, and much experimentation followed, resulting in numerous publications by many investigators.

In 1932 Livingston and Prince[23] reported that filtered, uncontaminated products derived from the bodies of larvae in culture, when brought into contact with pyogenic organisms in petri dishes, destroyed the cultures.

The fly larvae used in earlier osteomyelitis treatment apparently belonged indiscriminately to the species *Phaenicia sericata, Lucilla caesar,* and *Phormia regina.* It was assumed that all these species fed only on dead tissues. Stewart[32] has shown that even *Phaenicia sericata* larvae, which have been most commonly used in practice, will establish themselves in and feed upon normal healthy tissue, although they prefer necrotic tissue. He warns that they, and probably the larvae of *Phormia regina, Lucilia caesar,* and *Wohlfahrtia nuba* (Wiedemann), are potentially dangerous to normal tissue and must be utilized with care by an experienced person.

Stewart[33] also came to the conclusion that not only do the scavenging activities of the maggots play an important role in the successful results obtained, but the calcium carbonate, which was found to be constantly exuded by the larvae, is also of importance because of its property of alkalinizing the wound and of markedly increasing phagocytosis. Robinson in his later investigations discovered that allantoin and urea are present in maggot excretions, and that both have good effect in the treatment of osteomyelitis; however, because of its low cost and high solubility urea is now generally used, thus largely disposing of the use of maggots.

REFERENCES

1. Anonymous, 1958. *Trolene (Dow ET-57) for Cattle Grub Control. A Summary of 1957–58 Results with This New Synthetic Animal Insecticide and Suggestions for Further Research.* Midland, Michigan: The Dow Chemical Company, ACD Information Bull. 108. 23 pp.

2. Baer, W. S., 1931. "The treatment of chronic osteomyelitis with the maggot (larva of the blowfly)," *J. Bone & Joint Surg.*, **13**:438–75.

3. Baumhover, A. H.; Graham, A. J.; Bitter, B. A.; Hopkins, W. D.; New, W. D.; Dudley, F. H.; and Bushland, R. C.; 1955. "Screw-worm control through release of sterilized flies," *J. Econ. Entomol.*, **48**:462–66.

4. Bishopp, F. C.; Laake, E. W.; and Wells, R. W.; 1936. *Cattle Grubs or Heel Flies with Suggestions for Their Control.* Washington, D. C.: Dept. Agric., in Farmers' Bull., no. 1596. 22 pp. (Revised).

5. Blacklock, B., and Thompson, M. G., 1923. "A study of the tumbufly, *Cordylobia anthropophaga* Grünberg, in Sierra Leone," *Ann. Trop. Med.*, **17**:443–501 (4 plates).

6. Chevril, R., 1909. "Sur la myiase des voies urinaires," *Arch. de Parasitol.*, **12**:369–450.

7. Dunn, L. H., 1930. "Rearing the larvae of *Dermatobia hominis* Linn., in man," *Psyche*, **37**:327–42 (1 plate).

8. Fallis, A. Murray, 1940. "Studies on *Oestrus ovis* L.," *Canad. J. Research*, **18**:442–46.

9. Frogatt, W. W., 1922. *Sheep-Maggot Flies.* Dept. Agric., New South Wales, Farmers' Bull., no. 144. 32 pp.

10. Gajardo-Tobar, R., and Honorato, Armando, 1947. "Anotaciones acerca de una epidemia de miasis humana," *Hospital de Viña del Mar*, Chile, **3**:5–14.

11. Hall, David G., 1948. *The Blowflies of North America.* Thomas Say Foundation. 477 pp. (5 color and 46 black-and-white plates).

12. Hall, M. C., and Muir, J. T., 1913. "A critical study of a case of myiasis due to *Eristalis*." *Arch. Int. Med.*, **2**:193–203.

13. Hearle, Eric, 1938. *Insects and Allied Parasites Injurious to Livestock and Poultry in Canada.* Dominion of Canada, Dept. Agric., in Publ., no. 604. 108 pp.

14. Herms, W. B., 1925. "A case of human myiasis caused by the ox-warble, *Hypoderma bovis* DeG.," *J. Parasitol.*, **11**:149–50.

15. Herms, W. B., and Gilbert, Q. O., 1933. "An obstinate case of intestinal myiasis," *Ann. Int. Med.*, **6**:941–45.

16. Hoeppli, R., and Watt, John Y. C., 1933. "Experiments on resistance of dipterous larvae in connection with the problem of intestinal and urinary myiasis," *Chinese M. J.*, **47**:1298–1306.

17. James, Maurice T., 1948. *The Flies That Cause Myiasis in Man.* Washington, D. C.: Dept. Agric., in Misc. Publ., no. 631. 175 pp. (1947).

18. Knipling, E. F., 1935. "*Gastrophilus inermis* Brauer, a species of horse bot not previously recorded from North America," *Entomolog. News*, **46**:105–7.

19. Knipling, E. F., 1935. "The larval stages of *Hypoderma lineatum* de Villers and *Hypoderma bovis* DeGeer," *J. Parasitol.*, **21**:70–82.

20. Koone, Harold D., and Banegas, Alberto D., 1959. "Biology and control of *Dermatobia hominis* (L. Jr.) in Honduras. (Diptera: Cuterebridae)," *J. Kansas Entomol. Soc.*, **32**:100–108.

21. Kraft, Gerald Frederick, 1956. *The Bionomics of Wohlfahrtia opaca* (Coq.). Pullman, Wash.: State College of Washington, M. S. thesis. 59 pp.

22. Laake, E. W., 1936. "Economic studies of screwworm flies, *Cochliomyia* species (Diptera, Calliphorinae), with special reference to the prevention of myiasis of domestic animals," *Iowa State Coll. J. Sc.,* **10:**345–59.

23. Livingston, S. K., and Prince, L. H., 1932. "The treatment of chronic osteomyelitis; with special reference to the use of the maggot active principle," *J.A.M.A.,* **98:**1143.

24. Meleney, H. E., and Harwood, P. D., 1935. "Human intestinal myiasis due to the larvae of the soldier fly, Hermetia illucens Linné (Diptera, Stratiomyidae)," *Am. J. Trop. Med.,* **15:**45–49.

25. Morales M., Evaristo, 1958. "Algunas observaciones sobre el control del torsalo," *Proc. 10th Internat. Cong. Entomol.,* **3:**751–56.

26. Plath, O. E., 1919. "A muscid larva of the San Francisco Bay region which sucks the blood of nestling birds," *Univ. Calif. Pub. in Zool.,* **19:**191–200.

27. Riley, W. A., 1939. "The possibility of intestinal myiasis in man," *J. Econ. Entomol.,* **32:**875–76.

28. Roubaud, E., 1913. "Recherches sur les Auchmeromyies," *Bull. scient. France et Belgique,* **47:**105–202.

29. Simmons, Perez, 1927. *The Cheese Skipper as a Pest in Cured Meats.* Washington, D. C.: Dept. Agric., in Dept. Bull., no. 1453. 55 pp.

30. Stewart, M. A., 1929. "A case of dermal myiasis caused by *Phormia regina* Meig.," *J.A.M.A.,* **92:**798–99.

31. Stewart, M. A., 1934. "A new treatment of traumatic dermal myiasis," *J.A.M.A.,* **103:**402.

32. Stewart, M. A., 1934. "The rôle of *Lucilia sericata* Meig. larvae in osteomyelitis wounds, "*Ann. Trop. Med.,* **28:**445–60.

33. Stewart, M. A., 1934. "A new treatment of osteomyelitis: Preliminary report," *Surg. Gynec. & Obst.,* **58:**155–65.

34. Walker, E. M., 1922. "Some cases of cutaneous myiasis, with notes on the larvae of *Wohlfahrtia vigil* (Walker)," *J. Parasitol.,* **9:**1–5 (3 plates).

35. Warburton, Cecil, 1922. "The warble flies of cattle," *Parasitology,* **14:**322–41.

36. Wehr, Everett E., 1933. "The life history of *Gastrophilus* larvae of the horse and lesions produced by the larvae," *Cornell Veterinarian,* **23:**254–71.

37. Wells, K. W., and Knipling, E. F., 1938. "A report on some recent studies on species of *Gastrophilus* occurring in horses in the United States," *Iowa State Coll. J. Sc.,* **12:**181–203.

38. West, Luther S., 1951. *The Housefly.* Ithaca, New York: Comstock Publ. Co. 584 pp.

39. Zumpt, F., and Paterson, H. E., 1953. "Studies on the family Gasterophilidae with keys to the adults and maggots," *J. Entomol. Soc. South Africa,* **16:**59–72.

Chapter 18

FLEAS

Order Siphonaptera

Structural Characteristics. "No part of the external anatomy of an adult flea could possibly be mistaken for that of any other insect. The head, the mouth parts, the thorax, the legs, the abdomen, the external genitalia, all present features that are not elsewhere duplicated among the hexapods." Snodgrass[52] continues to marvel, as well he may, "there are numerous peculiarities that strain the imagination for a plausible explanation, and the complexity of the male intromittent apparatus is almost beyond belief." Yet internally, except for the array of spines in the proventriculus, the flea is a fairly generalized insect.

Fleas constitute the order Siphonaptera (Suctoria or Aphaniptera of some authors); they are laterally compressed, highly sclerotized, totally wingless,* minute bloodsucking ectoparasites of warm-blooded vertebrate animals. The commoner species vary from 1.5 to 4 mm in length. The males are, as a rule, smaller, often considerably smaller, than the females; both sexes are bloodsuckers. The posterior pair of legs is strikingly adapted for leaping; some species, such as the chigoe fleas, are able to burrow partly into the skin of the host and are practically sessile.

The head is a highly specialized cranial capsule; it is set closely against the pronotum with a very short neck which precludes much movement of the head, but does allow some. On the sides of the head are depressions (grooves) that contain the tiny knobbed antennae (the knobs are segmented), and in front of these are the simple eyes, when these are present. The presence of a conspicuous bristle (ocular bristle) in certain position in front of or below the eye may be useful in classifying fleas; also useful in classification is the presence in some species of a conspicuous comb of bold spines, *ctinidium,* located just above the mouth parts—the oral or *genal ctenidium* (Fig. 133). The head is sometimes divided into an anterior and a posterior part by the interantennal suture and associated ridge, known collectively as the *falx.*

The mouth parts of the adult flea include a minute *labrum,* a long slender, unpaired *epipharyngeal stylet,* a pair of maxillae with paired *maxillary stylets*, a small *hypopharynx*, and a simple *labium.* Mandibles are lacking in the adult flea, although present in the larva in the form of toothed jaws.

The thorax of the flea is compact, consisting of the pro-, meso-, and

* Sharif,[50] studying the pupae of *Xenopsylla cheopis, Ceratophyllus gallinae,* and *Nosopsyllus fasciatus,* has demonstrated the presence of wing buds in these species.

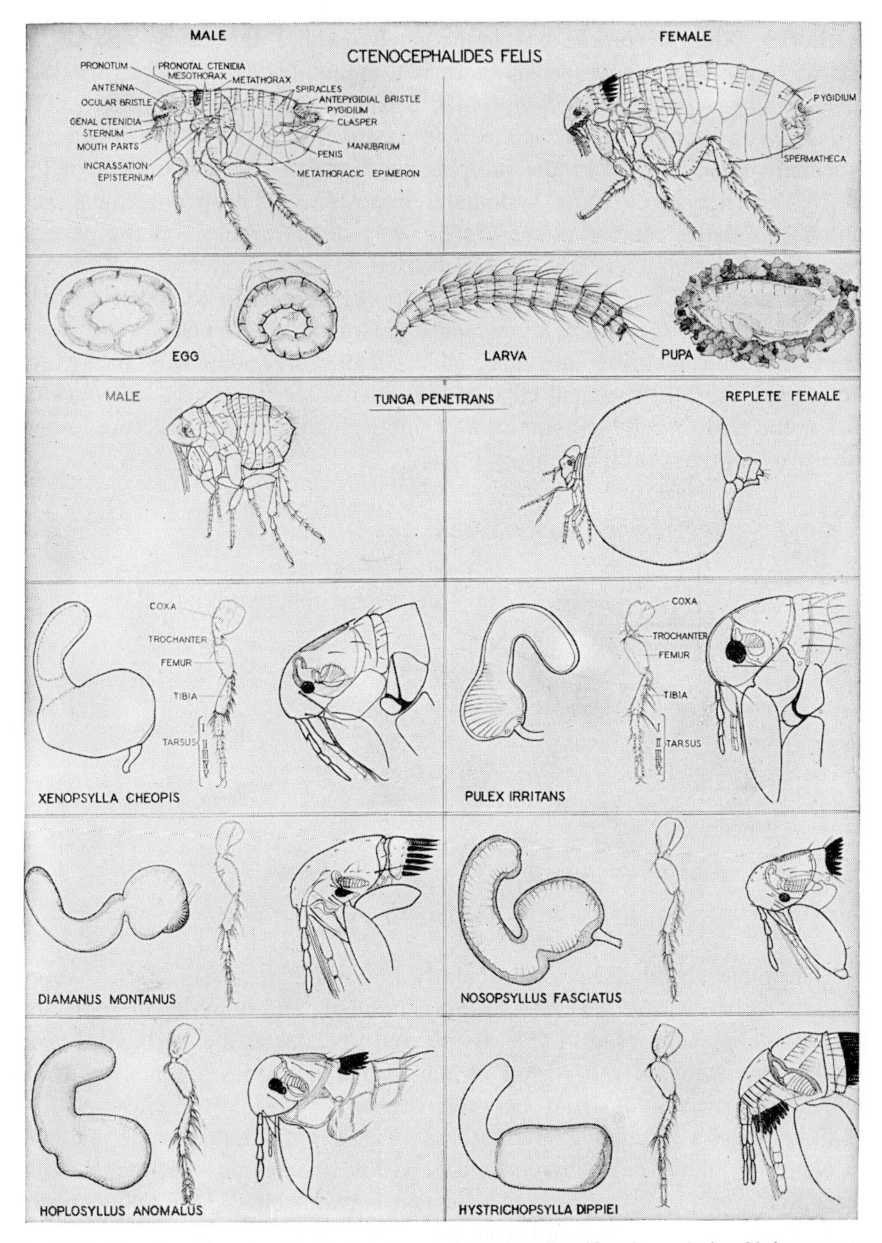

Fig. 133. Showing the structural details used in the classification of the Siphonaptera; also, the life history.

metathorax. The *pronotum* lies immediately behind the head, and at its posterior margin in many species there is a ctenidium of spinelike processes known as the *pronotal ctenidium*, which is useful in rough classification. The *mesonotum* is a simple arched plate. The *metathorax* is highly developed and is specially fitted to sustain the jumping mechanism. The chaetotaxy of the thoracic sclerites is of some systematic importance. The arrangement and number of bristles on the tarsus are likewise of importance on the generic level; other leg characters are not much used.

The abdomen consists of 10 (actually 11 according to Kessel[29]) segments, which like the thoracic segments are made up of plates (sclerites), except that the pleurites are concealed. There are numerous backward-pointing spines. On the apical edge of the seventh tergite are the *antepygidial bristles;* the ninth tergite consists of a peculiar pincushionlike structure known as the *pygidium,* probably a sensory organ.

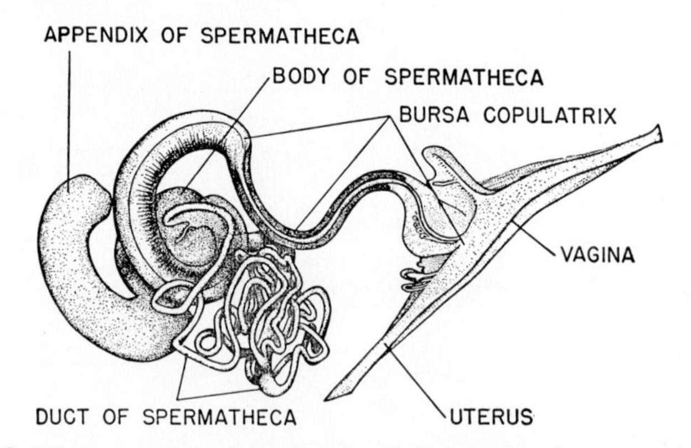

Fig. 134. Copulatory organs of the female of *Nosopsyllus fasciatus.* (After Fox.)

The male terminalia are particularly important in classification. Among the parts to be observed are the *claspers,* movable and nonmovable portions, and the manubrium (Fig. 133). In cleared specimens the springlike *penis* may be seen lying in the region of the fifth and sixth segments, which in copulation projects out from between the upper and lower claspers. The females possess a sacculated spermatheca (Fig. 134), situated in the region of the eighth or ninth segment and easily visible in cleared specimens. Some species have two spermathecae. This organ is characteristic for many species and is, therefore, an important taxonomic character (Fig. 133).

Digestive Tract. As soon as blood begins to flow from the wound made by the protraction and retraction of the maxillary laciniae, it is drawn up into the *pharynx* by the action of both the cibarial and the pharyngeal pumps. By means of powerful muscles the blood is aspirated from the wound, and on relaxation it is carried to the long narrow *esophagus,* which begins in the region of the brain and passes through the circumesophageal ring. The esophagus opens into the stomach through the bulbous *proventriculus*, which is provided internally with radially arranged (seven rows), hairlike, sclerotized processes (Fig. 135) which, when the encircling bands of muscle contract, cause them to meet and form a valve, thus preventing regurgitation from the stomach. The *stomach* is a capacious distensible organ nearly as long as the abdomen, emptying into the short *intestine,* which in turn empties into the wide *rectum* with its six rectal glands. Where the stomach joins the intestine, four filamentous *Malpighian tubules* arise.

Fig. 135. Spinelike epithelial cells in the proventriculus of *Xenopsylla cheopis:* (*A*) at rest; (*B*) showing opening into stomach closed.

Life History. The eggs of a flea (Fig. 136) are comparatively large (5 mm long), glistening white, and rounded at both ends. Relatively few, from 3 to 18, are deposited at one laying; however, during the entire lifetime of a female the number may be quite considerable. Bacot[1] records a total of 448 eggs over a period of 196 days deposited by a single female *Pulex irritans*. Most species deposit dry eggs which do not become attached to the hairs of the host even though oviposition takes place on the host. Fleas seldom oviposit among the hairs of the host, preferring the nest of the host where flea excrement occurs. Captured fleas will readily oviposit in glass vials or other receptacles in which they are trapped. If deposited on a dog or cat, the eggs fall off readily when the animal stretches and shakes itself; thus, great numbers of eggs may be found on the sleeping-mat of a flea-infested animal.

Temperatures of 65° to 80° F when combined with a fairly high humidity, 70 per cent and over, appear to favor egg laying. High mean temperatures, 95° to 100° F (close to the normal body temperature of most mammals), inhibits development, which may account for the fact that the eggs do not hatch well on the host. Low temperatures also inhibit the developmental stages. The incubation period normally varies from 2 to 12 days. The sensitivity of both adult and developing fleas to conditions of temperatures and humidity is probably the principal reason why fleas tend to occur in larger numbers on animals which live in burrows or where nests and beds are protected from storms or weather; for example, cottontails, *Sylvilagus* spp. which inhabit burrows, harbor many more fleas than do hares and jack rabbits, *Lepus* spp., which live and rear their young in the open.[19]

The embryo is provided with a sharp spine (egg burster or "can opener") on the head by means of which the eggshell is cut into shreds by a tumbling motion of its inhabitant, which is thus liberated.[29] The larvae (Fig. 136) are very active, slender, thirteen-segmented, and yellowish-white, with segmentally arranged bristles. The mouth parts are of the biting type, and the newly hatched larvae of some species, e.g., *Nospsyllus fasciatus* (Bosc), may subsist wholly on the feces of the adult flea. Very little food seems to be necessary for their development, although excrementitious matter, e.g., feces from rabbits, rats, squirrels, and other rodents, and also dry blood may be used as food. Excessive moisture is certainly detrimental to the life of the larvae, although a high percentage of moisture in the air is needed. The larvae are frequently found in houses in the crevices of the floor under carpet or matting, also in stables, coops, kennels, nests of rodents, pig pens, etc.

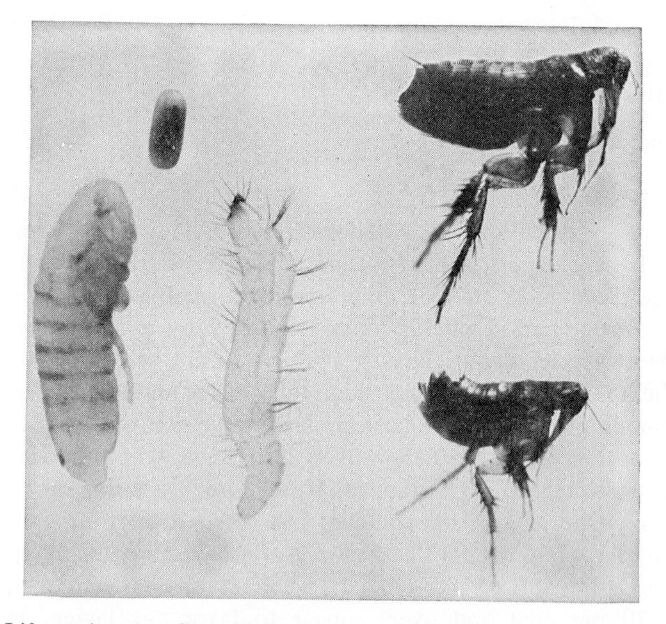

Fig. 136. Life cycle of a flea: (*upper left*) egg; (*center*) larva; (*lower left*) pupa; (*upper right*) female; (*lower right*) male.

When conditions are favorable, the time required for the larval period may be but 9 to 15 days; if they are unfavorable, it may extend over 200 days. At the end of the active feeding period when full growth has been achieved, the larva enters a quiescent stage, spins a cocoon, and pupates. The cocoon is whitish in appearance and so loosely spun that one may see the pupa within it.

The pupal period (Fig. 136) is influenced by temperature and varies greatly, from as short a time as 7 days to nearly a year. The life cycle (egg to adult) accordingly may vary from as short a time as 18 days to 20 months or more. Under laboratory conditions at a temperature of 24° C, Kerr[28] reports the life cycle of *Ctenocephalides felis* to be 20 to 24 days (larval stage 11 to 12 days). His cultures were from fleas fed on a cat.

Figures obtained by different workers have varied greatly even within a species, but most fleas seem to require 30 to 75 days for a complete life cycle. For *Nosopsyllus fasciatus*, according to Bishopp, extremes of 20 and 467 days have been recorded.

Longevity of Fleas. Bacot[1] states that with nearly saturated air at 45° to 50° F, fleas can live for many days unfed. He reports that *Pulex irritans* survived for 125 days, *Nosopsyllus fasciatus* for 95 days, *Xenopsylla cheopis* for 38 days, *Ctenocephalides canis* for 58 days, and *Ceratophyllus gallinae* for 127 days. If fed on their natural host, *P. irritans* may live upward of 513 days, *N. fasciatus* for 106 days, and *X. cheopis,* fed on man, 100 days. *Ctenocephalides canis* and *Ceratophyllus gallinae* have lived for periods of 234 and 345 days, respectively, when fed on man. Thus, Bacot indicates that the maximum possible length of life of the various species mentioned is 966 days for *Pulex irritans,* 738 days for *Ctenocephalides canis,* 680 days for *Nosopsyllus fasciatus,* 481 days for *Ceratophyllus gallinae,* and 376 days for *Xenopsylla cheopis.* In a moist medium, such as sprouting wheat grains and sawdust, Mayne (Mitzmain)[40] has kept squirrel fleas alive for 38 days in one case and 65 days in another, the former a male, and the latter a female. Male rat fleas fed on human blood alone averaged 2 1/2 days (maximum 17) of life, and the females 34 4/5 days (maximum 160).

Hosts and Occurrence of Species. As will be seen later in this chapter, the rodent fleas are important from the public health standpoint, and ready transfer of fleas from host to host of different species adds much to the potential of disease transmission.

While it is apparent that ordinarily a certain species of flea predominates on a given species of host, e.g., *Ctenocephalides* canis on the dog, *Nosopsyllus fasciatus* on the rat in Europe and the United States, *Xenopsylla cheopis* on the rat in Asia, *Leptopsylla segnis* on the domestic mouse, and *Pulex irritans* on the human, etc., host specificity in fleas is not strongly marked in many species.

Of the fleas recovered from rats during the San Francisco plague epidemic of 1907,[30] a great preponderance were *Nosopsyllus fasciatus.* Percentages based on 10,972 specimens were as follows:

	PER CENT
Nosopsyllus fasciatus (Bosc)	68.07
Xenopsylla cheopis (Rothschild)	21.36
Pulex irritans Linnaeus	5.57
Leptopsylla segnis (Schönherr)	4.48
Ctenocephalides canis (Curtis)	0.52

Certain fleas, particularly those of medical or sanitary importance, will readily pass from one host to another. *Pulex irritans* attacks not only man, but hogs, dogs, cats, goats, domestic rats, and such wild animals as skunks, coyotes, and badgers; it has even been recorded from the echidna (*Tachy-*

glossus aculeatus), mallard duck (*Anas platurhynchos*), and short-eared owl (*Asio flammeus*).[20] It may breed in the litter in hog houses. *Ctenocephalides canis* and *C. felis* freely attack both dogs and cats; they may readily bite man. Rodent fleas may divide their attention among various rodent species.

An extended study on host relationships of fleas has been made by Hubbard and incorporated in his book on the fleas of western North America.[21] From several sources, Hubbard lists the following fleas as being reported to attack man in the United States: *Tunga penetrans* Linnaeus, *Echidnophaga gallinacea* (Westwood), *Pulex irritans* Linnaeus, *Ctenocephalides canis* (Curtis), *C. felis* (Bouché), *Diamanus montanus* (Baker), *Xenopsylla cheopis* (Rothschild), *Hoplopsyllus affinis* (Baker), *Cediopsylla simplex* (Baker), *Nosopsyllus fasciatus* (Bosc), *Orchopeas howardii* (Baker), *Ceratophyllus niger* C. Fox, *C. gallinae* (Schrank), and *Dasypsyllus gallinulae perpinnatus* (Baker). Holland lists the following additional species: *Ceratophyllus garei* (Rothschild), *Hystrichopsylla* sp., *Monopsyllus ciliatus protinus* (Jordan), *M. eumolpi eumolpi* (Rothschild), *M. vison* (Baker), *M. wagneri wagneri* (Baker), and *Oropsylla arctomys* (Baker). *Hoplopsyllus amomalus* (Baker), a common parasite of ground squirrels in California and a proven vector of plague, is also known to bite man.[46]

THE COMMONER SPECIES OF FLEAS

Systematics. About 1500 described species and subspecies of fleas had been catalogued up to 1956, according to Hopkins and Rothschild (Volume II);[20] for America north of Mexico (including Greenland), Jellison *et al.*[24] list 72 genera containing 243 species and 55 subspecies. The matter of family classification of the Siphonaptera is a difficult one, upon which specialists in this order do not agree. The problem is discussed briefly by Holland.[19] The family classification used here follows that used by Jellison and by Holland. Also, instead of presenting a key to the families, which would be difficult for the student to use, because of the complex combination of characters that would necessarily be involved, we are presenting a key, based largely upon that of Holland, that should separate the genera most likely to be encountered in studies in North America that involve problems in medical entomology. This selection of genera includes: (1) those known to attack man; (2) those commonly found on the Norway rat; (3) rodent fleas that are known to be involved to transmission of plague.

For a more intensive study of North American fleas, the student is referred to the works of Fox,[14] Ewing and Fox,[11] Hubbard,[21] and Holland.[19] The chapter by Jordan in Smart's *Insects of Medical Importance*[27] will be useful in helping to recognize Old World fleas, and the very important work of Hopkins and Rothschild[20] covers the world fauna, as represented in the rich

Rothschild and other collections of the British Museum (Natural History). For a valuable bibliography on North American fleas, see Jellison and Good.[23]

KEY TO THE MEDICALLY MORE IMPORTANT GENERA OF FLEAS OF TEMPERATE NORTH AMERICA*

1. Pronotal ctenidium absent; genal ctenidium absent or represented by a single inconspicuous tooth 2
   Pronotal ctenidium present; genal ctenidium present or absent 6
2. The three thoracic tergites together shorter than the first abdominal tergite. 3
   The three thoracic tergites together as long or longer than the first abdominal tergite 4
3. Hind coxa with a patch of spinelike bristles on its inner apical surface .... *Echidnophaga*
   Hind coxa with only scattered bristles on its inner surface .... *Tunga*
4. Two rows of bristles on a typical abdominal segment ...... *Rhopalopsyllus*
   One row of bristles on a typical segment 5
5. Mesopleuron divided by a pleural ridge or rod that runs upward from the base of the middle coxa .... *Xenopsylla*
   Mesopleuron without such a pleural ridge or rod .... *Pulex*
6. Genal ctenidium present 7
   Genal ctenidium absent 12
7. Anterior abdominal terga each with one row of setae; eyes well developed 8
   Anterior abdominal terga each with two or more rows of setae; eyes absent or vestigial 9
8. Genal ctenidium more or less horizontal, with sharp, slightly curved spines .... *Ctenocephalides*
   Genal ctenidium oblique, with blunt spines .... *Cediopsylla*
9. Genal ctenidium of two spines only, overlapping each other .... *Epitedia, Neopsylla*
   Genal ctenidium of three or more spines 10
10. Genal ctenidium of three spines; apical segment of labial palpus with a hooklike seta .... *Ctenophthalmus*
    Genal ctenidium of more than three spines; labial palpus not as above .. 11
11. Genal ctenidium of four spines, arranged vertically .... *Leptopsylla*
    Genal ctenidium of four or more, long, slender spines, arranged in an oblique row .... *Hystricopsylla*
12. First abdominal tergite with a ctenidium which is as prominent as that of the gena .... *Stenoponia*
    First abdominal tergite without a ctenidium 13
13. Anterior abdominal terga each with but one row of setae .... *Hoplopsyllus*
    Anterior abdominal terga each with two or more rows of setae 14
14. One or no lateral setae on fore femur .... *Orchopeas*
    A number of lateral setae on each fore femur 15

* Modified from Holland[19] and other sources.

15. Anterior inner surface of mid and hind coxae with long thin setae from base to apex, aside from those fringing the anterior margin of coxa .. 16
Basal part of mid and hind coxae with no setae except those along the anterior margin 17
16. Basal abdominal sternum with a patch of lateral setae ....*Opisocrostis*
Basal abdominal sternum without a patch of lateral setae............
.... *Thrassis, Oropsylla, Diamanus*
17. Total of 24 or more spines in pronotal ctenidium. Usually on birds....
.... *Ceratophyllus*
Less than 24 spines in pronotal ctenidium. On mammals 18
18. Eye somewhat reduced, its longest diameter shorter or barely as long as distance from eye to heavily incrassated portion of genal lobe ..*Malaraeus*
Longest diameter of eye greater than this distance. *Monopsyllus, Nosopsyllus*

Family Tungidae. *Tunga penetrans* Linnaeus, the chigoe, is also known as the "jigger," "chigger," "chique," or "sand flea." The head of this flea is definitely angular and is usually larger proportionately than the head of other fleas; there are no ctenidia on the head or pronotum; the mouth parts are conspicuous; the palpi are four-segmented.

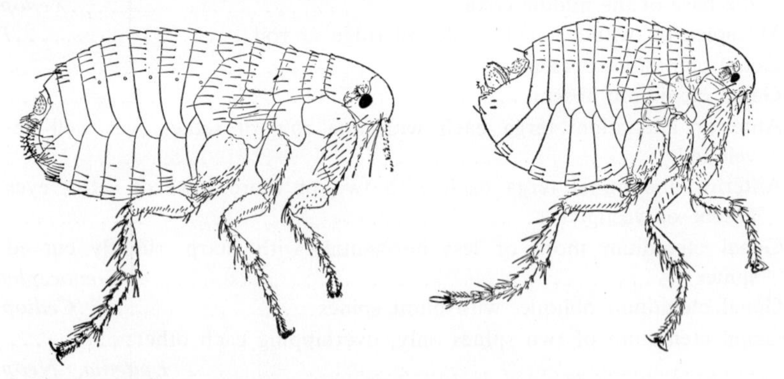

Fig. 137. *Pulex irritans,* the human flea; (*right*) male; (*left*) female. × 17.

Family Pulicidae. *Pulex irritans* Linnaeus (Fig. 137) is commonly known as the human flea. It is cosmopolitan in distribution and occurs on a surprisingly wide range of hosts, including domesticated animals, particularly swine. This species has neither oral nor pronotal ctenidia. The metacoxae have a row or patch of short spinelets on the inner side; the mesosternite has an internal rodlike incrassation extending dorsoanteriorly. The maxillary laciniae extend about halfway down on the fore coxae, which distinguishes this species from *Pulex simulans* Baker (mandibles extending at least three-fourths the length of the fore coxae), also known as a human flea but restricted to the New World (northwestern United States to the northern half of South America).

Pulex simulans has until recently[51] been confused with *P. irritans,* and undoubtedly some of the published information relative to the latter belongs properly to the former. *Pulex irritans* transmits plague under laboratory conditions and may be the chief vector of two unusual types of plague, e.g., *viruola pestosa* (a vesicular form) and *angina pestosa* (a tonsillar form) found in Ecuador.

Echidnophaga gallinacea (Westwood)* the sticktight flea of poultry, resembles *Tunga penetrans* in the great reduction of the thoracic segments; it differs in having the angles of the head acutely produced, while in *T. penetrans* the head is obtuse instead of rounded and the eyes and antennae are in the posterior half of the head. It is from 1 to 1 1/2 mm in length.

Ctenocephalides canis (Curtis) and *Ctenocephalides felis* (Bouché) are the dog flea and cat flea, respectively. Both species attack cats and dogs as well as man. Both have the genal ctenidium consisting of 7 or 8 sharp black teeth, a character which distinguishes them from all other fleas;[21] the frontal ctenidium consists of 16 teeth. They may be separated as follows:

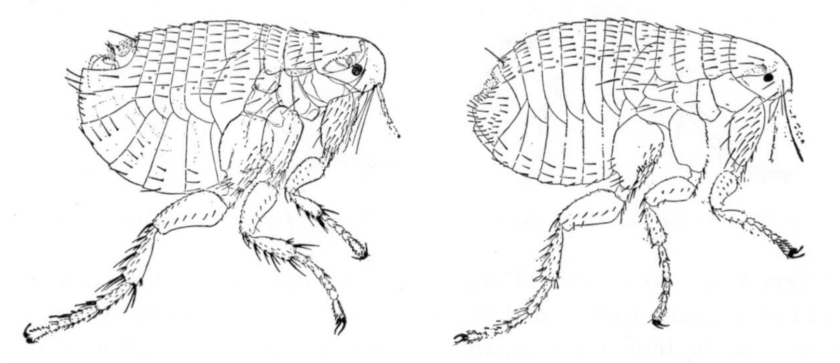

Fig. 138. *Xenopsylla cheopis*, the Oriental rat flea; (*left*) male; (*right*) female. × 17.

In the female the head is fully twice as long as high (seen from side) and pointed; the first and second genal spines are of approximately equal length; two or three bristles on metathoracic episternum; bristles on metathoracic epimeron, first row, four to eight, second row, five to seven; seven to ten bristles on inner side of hind femur . . . . *felis*

In the female the head is less than twice as long as high (seen from the side) and rounded; the first spine of the genal comb is shorter than the second; three or four bristles on metathoracic episternum; bristles on metathoracic epimeron, first row, seven to eleven, second row, seven to nine; ten to thirteen bristles on inner side of hind femur . . . . *canis*

Xenopsylla cheopis (Rothschild) (Fig. 138) is the Oriental rat flea. It habitually inhabits buildings and bites man freely. It resembles *Pulex irritans* in that both the oral and pronotal ctenidia are absent. The ocular bristle is in front of and just above the middle of the eye; there are two bristles on the gena; oral bristles placed low down just above the base of the maxillae; each abdominal tergite has but one row of bristles; the hind femur

* Hopkins and Rothschild place *Echidnophaga* in the Pulicidae. Some authorities disagree with this family reference.

has a row of about eight bristles. The mandibles reach nearly to the end of the anterior coxae.

Mellanby[34] has performed experiments proving that *X. cheopis* can complete its life history between 18° and 35° C in moist air. Between 18° and 29° C, air with a relative humidity of 40 per cent is unfavorable, while with 60 per cent relative humidity pupation takes place successfully. Pupation at 18° C required 8 days; at 22° C, it required 6 days; and at 29° to 35° C, it required 4 days. The developmental zero for pupation is about 15° C.

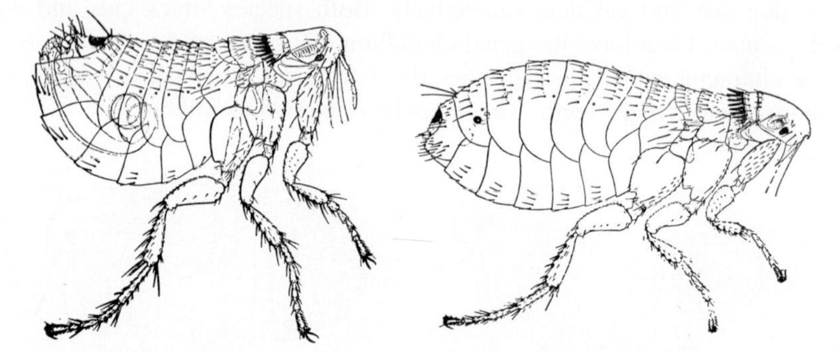

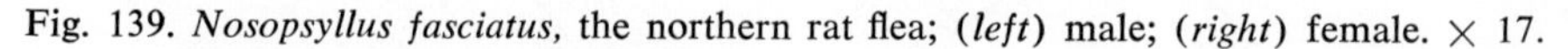

Fig. 139. *Nosopsyllus fasciatus,* the northern rat flea; (*left*) male; (*right*) female. × 17.

Xenopsylla brasiliensis (Baker) is an African species, the predominant rat flea in Uganda, Kenya, and Nigeria. It has spread to South America and certain areas in India. It is regarded as a more important vector of plague than *X. cheopis* in Kenya and Uganda, since it is "the flea of the hut," while the latter infests rats of stone and brick buildings.

Xenopsylla astia Rothschild has a restricted distribution:

. . . being found mostly along the low-lying coast of Ceylon, the east coast of India, and along the opposite coast of Bengal . . . while *X. astia* may be the responsible vector [of plague] in certain circumscribed and isolated outbreaks, the available evidence . . . points to its inferior position in the epidemiological picture. . . . Moreover, *astia* outbreaks, if and when they do occur, are not known to carry over from one season to another.

Xenopsylla vexabilis hawaiiensis Jordan is a common flea of the Hawaiian rat, *Rattus hawaiiensis*. According to Eskey reported by Jordan,[26] this species has a very peculiar distribution.

It has not been found in Honolulu or vicinity, while it is quite common on rats caught about nine miles away on the opposite side of the island. It is essentially a flea of field rats and rarely found on rats caught in buildings.

Family Ceratophyllidae. *Nosopsyllus fasciatus* (Bosc) is the northern rat flea (Fig. 139). It is widespread over Europe and America, being less common in other parts of the world. It has been recorded on rats, house mice, pocket gophers, skunk, man, and many other host animals. It has but one ctenidium, the pronotal, which has 18 or 20 spines. There are three bristles in front of the eye; and in the female two bristles, and in the male four in front of these. There are three or four hairs on the inner surface of the hind femur. *N. fasciatus* (Bosc) is regarded as a negligible factor in the causation of natural outbreaks of plague.

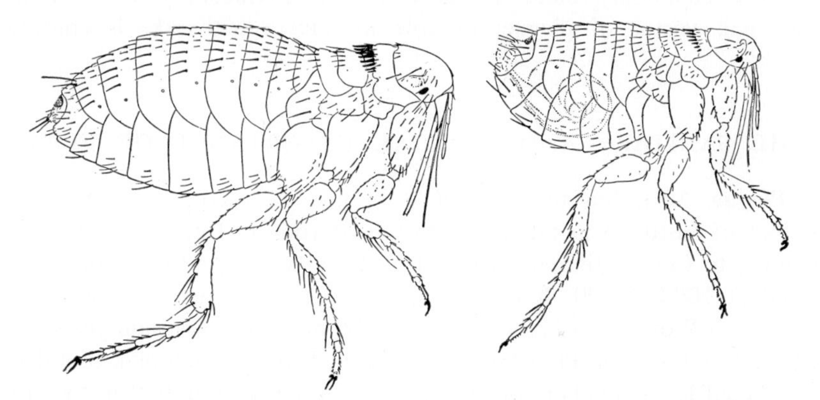

Fig. 140. *Diamanus montanus,* the squirrel flea; (*right*) male; (*left*) female. × 17.

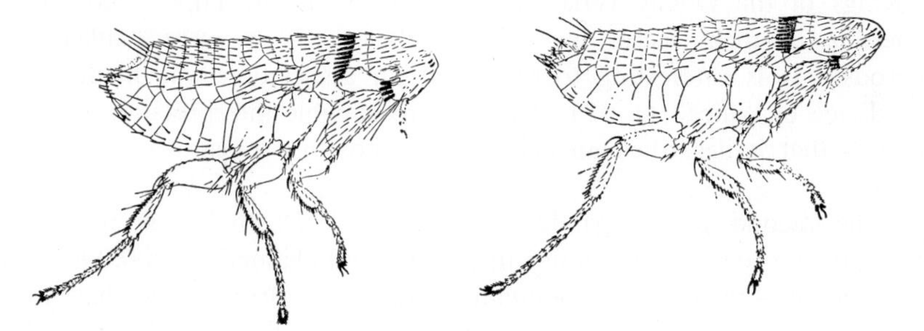

Fig. 141. *Leptopsylla segnis,* a mouse flea; (*right*) male; (*left*) female. × 17.

The genus *Nosopsyllus* may be distinguished from the genus *Diamanus* by the fact that in *Diamanus* there are long, thin bristles on the inside of the mid and hind coxae from the base of the apex, while in *Nosopsyllus* such bristles occur at most in the apical half.

Diamanus montanus (Baker) (Fig. 140) is a common species of squirrel flea described from California. This species may be recognized by a spine at the tip of the second joint of the hind tarsus longer than the third joint and reaching over on to the fourth joint; the abdominal tergites have each two rows of bristles; the male claspers are very large and long, and sickle-shaped.

Ceratophyllus niger C. Fox, the western chicken flea, was originally described from specimens taken from man and from *Rattus r. norvegicus* in California. *Ceratophyllus gallinae* Schrank is commonly known as the European chicken flea, although it has a wide range of hosts. The large number of spines on the pronotal ctenidium furnishes a striking characteristic for distinguishing these fleas from the others discussed here.

Leptopsylla segnis (Schonherr) is the cosmopolitan mouse flea (Fig. 141). It is commonly found on rats. It bites man reluctantly, and is regarded as a weak vector of plague; its role in human outbreaks is considered negligible.

THE SANITARY AND MEDICAL IMPORTANCE OF FLEAS

Plague. According to Wu *et al.*,[59] the first recorded pandemic of plague was that of Justinian in the sixth century, starting in Egypt in 542 A.D. and spreading to Constantinople. It lasted 50 to 60 years, and its victims are estimated at 100,000,000. It is certain, however, that plague was rampant in the Western World long before that time. More than a thousand years before the time of Christ, the Philistines were afflicted with an outbreak of a disease which killed large numbers of their people (more than 50,000 in the city of Bethsames, or Bethshemesh, alone), according to the writer of I Samuel (I Kings of the Douay version), Chapters 5 and 6. Those who died had "emerods in their secret parts," and the survivors were "afflicted with emerods." It is interesting to note that an association was made with an abundance of "mice" (rats?). The only reasonable interpretation of this account is that it described an epidemic, or possibly a pandemic, of bubonic plague.

The second plague pandemic, the "Black Death," took place in the middle of the fourteenth century in Europe and claimed 25,000,000 victims, or about one-fourth of the population. In Great Britain from half to two-thirds of the people perished. The great plague epidemic of London, 1664–1666, is said to have killed 70,000 persons out of a total population of 450,000. Plague disappeared from England in about 1680, having been almost continuously present for nearly 140 years, with five epidemics.

Gradually this infection receded from Europe and the Near East, and as Wu *et al.* point out, the existence of endemic foci:

> . . . comparable to stagnant pools left behind by the lowering tide, was recognized . . . we now know a whole series of endemic plague foci, usually with epizootics among the wild rodents situated near or even contiguous with Central Asia . . . the whole of this vast territory with its hosts of wild rodents might be compared with a heap of embers where plague smoulders continuously and from which sparks of infection may dart out now and then in various directions.

The present pandemic is believed to have originated in a wild hibernating rodent, the tarabagan (*Manmota bobak sibirica* Radde) in the interior of China, and began as an epidemic in Hongkong in 1894 and was transported along world trade routes to many parts of the globe. The rat, as transported in commerce, constitutes the chief means of spreading the disease, the infection being carried from rat to rat by means of rat fleas. For this reason, plague may appear in a city far removed from the original focus of infection.

The first recorded appearance of plague on the North American continent[16] occurred in San Francisco, California, on March 6, 1900, when the body of a Chinese who had died of plague was discovered in the Chinese quarter. Rat infection was not demonstrated until 1902. Human cases of plague continued to appear in San Francisco, and 121 cases with 118 deaths were reported up to February, 1904, when the last case in the first outbreak was recorded. In May, 1907, plague was again discovered in San Francisco, and the last of this series with 167 deaths occurred in July 1908. In 1907 a small outbreak at Seattle, Washington, numbered 7 cases, all fatal.

The next outbreak of plague in the United States occurred in New Orleans in 1914 with 30 cases and 10 deaths reported from June 21 to September 8. A second outbreak in New Orleans in 1919 and 1920 accounted for 20 more cases, 8 of which were fatal. In 1920, other Gulf Coast cities in Florida and Texas experienced small outbreaks which totaled 41 cases and 25 deaths. The Los Angeles outbreak of plague—chiefly pneumonic, November 1, 1924, to January 5, 1925—resulted in 41 cases with 36 deaths. The outbreaks traceable to plague-infected rats and their fleas were quickly stamped out. Link, who has reviewed at some length the history of plague in the United States,[30] states that from 1900 through 1951, 523 cases of plague have occurred in the continental United States with 340 deaths.

The answer to the question, "Is the disease in man and rodents identical?" was not forthcoming until 1894 with the work of Yersin and Kitasato in Hongkong. The former found the organism in the corpses of dead rats and gave the first detailed and accurate description of *Pasteurella pestis,* Yersin[60] calling it "bacille de la peste." To Kitasato, we owe the earliest account of the organism, as he found the plague bacilli in the "finger blood of a patient with axillary bubo."

The Disease in Man. In addition to the work of Wu *et al.*,[59] two valuable general references are the well-documented monograph of Pollitzer[46] and Hirst's interestingly written book, *The Conquest of Plague.*[18] Wu *et al.* give the period of incubation from 2 to 10 days; the onset usually occurs within a period of 3 to 4 days. Fox in *Insects and Disease of Man,*[12] page

294 (P. Blakiston's Son & Co., by permission), describes the disease as follows:

It develops suddenly with a rapid rise of temperature, reaching 103° or 104° F. in two or three days, after which it is more or less irregular. There is headache, the eyes are injected and the facies are characteristic of extreme illness. Prostration is profound and comes on early. Delirium also appears early. The characteristic lesion of the disease, the bubo, usually is sufficiently pronounced by the second day to be readily detected. The most common site for the bubo is the femoral or inguino-femoral region, then the axillary region, cervical, iliac and popliteal. Over the enlarged glands oedema appears and pressure elicits great tenderness. The individual lymph nodes cannot be palpated. This swelling forms the primary bubo. Secondary buboes may appear in other parts of the body. In these, the glands are not matted together as in the primary bubo. Four forms of skin eruption may be described—a petechial eruption, ecchymoses, a subcuticular mottling, and thc so-called plague pustule . . . a bulbous-like formation containing thin, turbid material teeming with plague bacilli. It is believed to indicate the original point of inoculation, the flea bite. Extending from this to the nearest lymphatic glands faint red lines indicating lymphangitis may be observed. A secondary pneumonia due to the deposit of plague bacilli in the pulmonary tissues may occur. In about a week if the patient survives, the bubo breaks down leaving an ulcer which heals slowly.

Plague is an acute infectious disease caused by *Pasteurella pestis* (Lehmann and Newmann) Holland. It is essentially a disease of rodents, usually transmitted by rodent fleas, but it may under certain conditions cause serious epidemics among human beings. The term *bubonic plague* is applied when inflammation of lymph glands results from the infection, and buboes are formed; these are the first foci and may remain so localized and cause little discomfort. The buboes vary from 2 cm to 10 cm in diameter, and are usually located in the groin (femoral glands) and axilla (axillary glands). The pathogenesis of plague infection follows a standard course: from the lymphatics and lymph nodes, to the blood streams, to the liver and spleen. When, because of the rapidity of the multiplication of the bacteria or for other reasons, the liver and spleen cannot cope with the invaders, the infection enters the blood stream and becomes *septicemic* plague. As Meyer[38] points out, septicemic plague is really plague in which the buboes are inconspicuous; it is better to distinguish only two forms of human plague: the *primary bubonic,* or zootic form, and the *primary pneumonic* (pulmonary), or demic form. The latter is not transmitted by fleas; it is transmitted from human to human by infective droplets coming from the lung of a plague patient.

Fleas as Vectors. Ogata[43] in 1897 came to the conclusion on epidemiologic grounds that fleas were the agents of transmission, pointing out that fleas leave the rat as it becomes cold after death, and so may transmit the virus direct to man. He pointed out that the flea can ingest plague bacilli while feeding, having produced plague in mice by injecting an emulsion of crushed flea taken from plague rats.

Simond[49] in 1898 was the first to succeed in transmitting plague from a sick rat to a healthy rat through the agency of infected fleas. Simond's work was discredited for several years, but was successfully repeated by Verjbitski[55] in 1903.

Liston[31] in 1904, working in Bombay, came to the following conclusions: (1) There was one flea infesting rats in India far more commonly than did any other, viz., *Xenopsylla cheopis;* (2) that these fleas when feeding on a plague rat harbored the plague bacilli in their bodies and that these multiplied therein; (3) that where fatal plague occurred, many of these infected fleas were at large; and (4) that after a local epizootic of rat plague, man was also found to harbor these rat fleas, and might become infected as had the guinea pigs used in the experiment.

The following is a very brief summary of experiments conducted by the Indian Plague Commission.

In the first instance healthy rats were confined in close proximity to rats which, inoculated with plague, were beginning to succumb to that disease and were artificially infested with rat fleas (*X. cheopis*). The separate confinement of the rats in each case was so arranged that both contact with and access to all excreta were excluded, although it was provided that the fleas could pass from the inoculated to the healthy rats; thus, transfer actually did take place, and in many cases these fleas contained virulent plague bacilli. When healthy nonimmune rats were thus infected, they died of plague to the extent of 79 per cent. This extent of infection fell to 38 per cent when partly immune rats of local origin were employed.

That the plague had originated in the healthy rats through the intermediary of rat fleas was further demonstrated when these were actually transferred from artificially plague-infected to healthy English rats, and the disease developed in 61 per cent of the latter.

Further, on constructing a series of miniature houses so as to reproduce the conditions pertaining to ordinary domiciles, it was found that whenever these were so constructed as to admit rats to their roofs, but not to their interiors, guinea pigs confined therein became successively infested with rat fleas and infected by plague, but that in those houses to which rats could not gain access, plague originated in guinea pigs living therein, either by transferring rat fleas to them, derived from plague-infected guinea pigs, or by an accidental admission of rat fleas from other sources. Also, when so confined, guinea pigs had under these conditions died of plague; healthy flea-free guinea pigs, subsequently introduced, became infected, and the infection remained in the place in proportion as the test animals were accessible to, and were found to be infested with, fleas; in other words, that "if the fleas be present, the rate of progress is in direct proportion to the number of fleas present." Further, when healthy guinea pigs were confined in one of the houses, to the interior of whose roof fleas could not gain access, they became flea-infested and infected when running on the ground, but to a less extent when the cage was placed 2 in. therefrom, and not at all when it was suspended 2 ft above it. The fact that infection took place where guinea pigs were located 2 in. above the ground indicates that contact with infected soil is not necessary for plague to originate, and that "an epizootic of plague might start without direct contact of healthy with infected animals."

To demonstrate that this communication of plague from guinea pig to guinea pig was through the intermediary of fleas, rat fleas were taken from a morbid guinea pig and allowed to feed through muslin on healthy animals. The results were positive.

The state of affairs that existed in actual domiciles in which plague occurred or had existed was next inquired into, advantage being taken of the fact that plague-susceptible guinea pigs would serve as hosts for fleas as well as for the collection of fleas.

Guinea pigs free from fleas were introduced into rooms in which persons had died of plague, or from which plague-infected rats had been taken. They were allowed to be at large in these rooms for periods of from 18 to 24 hours. These guinea pigs not only collected the fleas on their bodies, most of which were rat fleas, but 29 per cent of them also contracted plague and died of plague within a few days after being restored to ordinary confinement. As before, many of the fleas which they yielded harbored plague bacilli in their stomachs and were capable of infecting additional animals.

Further, after first washing the floors and walls of the rooms with mercuric chloride and so adequately disinfecting them for plague, but not for fleas, and then introducing guinea pigs, these became plague-infected when rat fleas were present.

That the infection was actually due to fleas was also shown by the positive results when fleas collected from rats occurring in plague-infected houses were transferred to healthy rats or guinea pigs in the laboratory. These in due course became infected and died of plague.

Similarly, fleas taken from the clean guinea pigs, then allowed to run in plague-infected houses, and transferred to fresh animals, communicated plague to the fresh animals in 8 out of 40 tests.

Subsequently, plague-free white rats, guinea pigs, and monkeys were placed in enclosures, which precluded contact as well as soil infection, in plague-infected rooms; pairs of one animal or another were used in each of the 42 experiments conducted of this class, one individual being confined to a fleaproof receptacle, and the other to an adjacent one accessible to the fleas (one animal being thus a control). In the latter case, plague resulted in four instances, i.e., 10 per cent gave positive results.

As a variation of the same experiments, the enclosures for individual animals, while protected from soil or contact infection, were either surrounded by 2 1/2 in. of sticky flypaper as a screen to fleas, or were denied this protection, the flypaper being replaced by sand (20 experiments were conducted). In the latter case, the animals became infested with fleas, one having as many as 20 fleas; seven animals became fatally infected with plague. In the former, individual fleas were found on only three of the rats, and no animals became plague-infected.

Examining the fleas entrapped, 247 in number, it was found that 147 were human fleas, 84 were rat fleas, and 16 were cat fleas. Moreover, a large proportion of each kind was examined for infection. No plague bacilli were found in the cat fleas, one only in 85 of the human fleas was infected, and no less than 23 out of 77 of the rat fleas harbored plague organisms.

It was also shown that, when rats in the course of an epizootic died of plague, the pathological features manifested in their bodies corresponded to those exhibited by artificially rat-flea–infested animals; hence, it was inferred that in nature and under experimental conditions the animals had succumbed to a single agency. This similarity in pathological features was concerned with the site in which buboes arose, since in both instances where the place of inoculation could be observed, the site was the same.

Further Observations. Blue[4] reports a number of observations made in San Francisco during 1906: Two small boys found the body of a dead rat in an unused cellar; the rat was buried with unusual funeral honors and in 48 hours both were taken ill with bubonic plague. Again, a laborer picked up a dead rat with the naked hand and threw it into the bay. He was taken ill with plague 3 days later. The case of a physician's family is also cited in which foul odors pervaded their second-story apartment over a grocery store. On removing the wainscotting around the plumbing to ascertain the cause of the odor, 2 rat cadavers were found in the hollow wall. In 2 or 3 days thereafter, the two members of the family who used the room sickened, one dying on the fifth day of cervical bubonic plague. Blue believes that the removal of the wainscoting set free infected rat fleas.

The following instance is reported in the *Public Health Reports* (November 7, 1913, p. 2356): A fatal case of plague occurred in Manila (P.I.) in the person of an American, editor of the *Manila Daily Bulletin.* A plague rat had been found on September 6 in the block adjacent to the one in which the newspaper offices were located. The editor was admitted to the hospital September 19, and died at the Plague Hospital 3 days later. A mummified rat was found in the desk of the late editor, together with live fleas, *Xenopsylla cheopis.* The fleas revealed bipolar staining organisms, and inoculations made from the dead rat into healthy laboratory rats produced typical cases of plague terminating fatally.

That the mummified rat must have been dead at least 2 weeks and that the live fleas contained plague bacilli suggests "strong proof that plague might be introduced into a country without either the importation of human or rat cases of plague and that fleas might be alone concerned."

Role of the Flea in Plague Transmission. The Indian Plague Commission showed that the average capacity of a flea's stomach (*Xenopsylla cheopis*) was 0.5 cubic millimeter, and that it might receive as many as 5000 *Pasteurella pestis* while imbibing blood from a plague rat. The Commission found that the bacillus multiplies in the stomach of the flea and that the percentage of fleas with bacilli in the stomach varied with the season of the year. In the epidemic season the percentage was greatest for the first 4 days, and on one occasion the stomach was found filled with the organisms on the twentieth day. In the nonepidemic season, no plague bacilli were found in the stomach after the seventh day. They also found that in the epidemic season fleas might remain infective up to 15 days, while in the nonepidemic season but 7 days, and in the latter case the percentage of infection in animals was much less than in the epidemic season. They showed that while one flea was occasionally able to carry the infection, this was not usual. It was found that both males and females were capable of transmitting the disease. As to the manner of dissemination the Commission found bacilli in the stomach and rectum only, never in the salivary glands or body cavity, and but rarely in the esophagus, and then only when the flea was killed immediately after feeding. After digestion, the blood in the stomach passes into the rectum and is ejected as a dark-red or tarry droplet, containing virulent plague bacilli, which if rubbed into recent flea bites resulted in infection of the animal. The actual inoculation therefore, it was believed, was accomplished indirectly by the flea-bitten person's scratching or rubbing the site of the bite after the infected flea had discharged fecal material upon the skin. That there is a great deal of difference in the consistency and other characteristics of the fecal deposits of the various species of fleas is easily observable, e.g., the human flea, *Pulex irritans,* defecates freely while feeding but is not a ready vector of bubonic plague, while the Oriental rat flea, *Xenopsylla cheopis* seldom defecates while feeding and is a potent vector.

Bacot and Martin[3] (1914) demonstrated a mechanism of infection which is based on observations made by Swellengrebel[54] (1913) in Java that *Xenopsylla cheopis* seldom defecates when feeding and showed that infection resulted when the flea's only contact with the experimental animal was by means of the proboscis, i.e., the infection is introduced with the bite directly. That this mode of infection was in the manner of regurgitation due to a temporary obstruction at the entrance to the stomach was discovered by Bacot and Martin,[3] who state that on:

> . . . examining the contents of the stomach of a flea a day or two after it has fed upon infected blood, clusters of minute brown specks darker in colour and firmer in consistency than the rest of the contents are visible. . . . Later the stomach

and proventriculus show jelly-like masses of a brown colour. These masses are possessed of considerable cohesion and are with difficulty teased out so as to make a film suitable for microscopical examination. The plague-culture grows in the proventriculus as well as in the stomach. Owing to its gelatinous consistency, it not infrequently leads to incompetence and even complete blocking of the proventricular valve. . . . Although with the proventriculus obstructed in this manner fresh blood cannot find its way into the stomach, this does not prevent the insect sucking, as the pump which aspirates blood up the sucking tube and propels it into the stomach is situated in the pharynx. On the contrary, the flea suffers from thirst and is persistent in its efforts to satisfy this appetite, but only succeeds in distending the oesophagus. The blood in the distended oesophagus may flow out again on cessation of the sucking act, and we have seen drops of blood escape from the mouth parts of "blocked" fleas when the insect withdrew its proboscis. . . . Given the opportunity, the insects suck blood again and again and if the pharyngeal pump ceases for a moment, some of the blood will by the elastic recoil of the oesophageal wall be driven back into the wound and carry with it plague bacilli.

Bacot and Martin found that infected fleas lived as long as 50 days at from 10° to 15° C and 23 days at 27° C, and died infected. Working with two species of rat fleas, *Xenopsylla cheopis* and *Nosopsyllus fasciatus,* fed on septicemic blood, Bacot and Martin conclude that they "can transmit plague during the act of sucking and that certain individuals suffering from a temporary obstruction at the entrance to the stomach were responsible for most of the infections obtained, and probably for all." In the course of time the plague culture forming the proventricular plug undergoes autolysis and the normal passage of blood is re-established.

Figure 135A shows the position of the spinelike epithelial cells in the proventriculus when at rest, the opening into the stomach being free for the passage of blood. Figure 135B shows the opening into the stomach closed against the outward passage of blood on contraction of the muscular bands. Bacot[2] points out that it is the lodgment and growth of the bacilli among the spines that constitute the initial stage of the blockage.

In describing the mechanism of plague transmission by fleas, Eskey and Haas[10] show numerous photomicrographs of blood-distended stomachs of fleas after feeding. The elapsed interval between an infective blood meal and an infective bite (transmission) for *Xenopsylla cheopis* averaged about 21 days (shortest interval, 5 days; longest, 31 days); for *Diamanus montanus* the average was 53 days; the longest interval in the series for any species was 130 days. The average length of life of fleas after being plague infected was 17 days (maximum 44 days) for *X. cheopis,* and 47 days (maximum of 85 days) for *D. montanus.*

Eskey[9] has shown that virulent plague organisms are more constantly present in the feces of some species of fleas than in others. He reports that plague followed every inoculation of feces deposited by infected *Diamanus montanus,* while less than one-third of the fecal inoculations of *Nosopsyllus fasciatus* gave positive reactions. He also reports that the feces of *Xenopsylla cheopis* gave positive reactions, but these fleas did not survive long enough to determine whether or not the results would be constant for any length of time. Eskey points out that there seems to be danger of infection from virulent plague organisms present in the feces of all plague-infected fleas.

Still another possible mode of transmission has been suggested by various workers, namely, that of crushing infected fleas with the teeth, with infection through the mucosa of the buccal cavity resulting in lymph node involvement in the region of the neck. This mode of transmission usually applies only to rodents, though tonsillar plague among the Indians of Ecuador seems to be transmitted in this manner.[46]

Plague in Field Rodents. The existence of a plague epizootic in wild rodents in California was suspected as early as 1903, but plague was demonstrated in ground squirrels, *Citellus beecheyi beecheyi* (Richardson), under natural conditions in 1908 by McCoy. According to that author at the time of his writing a report on this finding (1910),[33] about a dozen persons had contracted the disease under circumstances that pointed conclusively to squirrels as the cause. The two species of fleas commonly infesting the ground squirrel in California are *Diamanus montanus* (Baker) and *Hoplopsyllus anomalus* Baker, of which the former is far more numerous. McCoy proved the first-named species a carrier as follows: He inoculated a ground squirrel subcutaneously with a broth culture of *P. pestis* derived from a human case of plague. This squirrel died on the fifth day, but 3 days before its death, 100 fleas, *D. montanus,* were put in the cage with it. The dead animal was removed from the cage while warm, and 27 live fleas taken from its body. Smears of the crushed bodies of 2 of these fleas showed an abundance of pestlike bacilli in each. The remaining 25 fleas were put into a clean cage with a healthy squirrel. This animal died of subacute plague 10 days later, the buboes being in the region of the median, posterior inguinal, and pelvic glands. A pure culture of *P. pestis* was obtained from the liver. McCoy states that the experiment is conclusive in showing that *D. montanus* may convey plague from a sick to a healthy squirrel. The squirrels used in the experiment were kept in quarantine for at least a month prior to their being used, which was necessary to exclude any naturally infected ones. McCoy found the bacilli in squirrel flea feces 4 days after removal of the fleas from the host.

The designation sylvatic (selvatic) plague was proposed by Ricardo Jorge (1928) (see p. 6) for the plague of field rodents. The designation *campestral plague* (wild-rodent or feral plague) is more apt, since the term "sylvatic" implies woodland, which is not typical plague territory. Fleas play an important role in transmission from rodent to rodent and consequently in the endemicity of the disease. It is now known that under certain ecologic conditions in vacated squirrel burrows fleas may continue to harbor virulent *P. pestis* for many months, thus providing a virtual insectan reservoir for the infection under campestral conditions. Fleas have been known to survive although starved for more than 6 months (196 days).

Aside from the matter of flea transmission, it is important to bear in mind that the great epidemic of plague in Manchuria resulting in 60,000 deaths in 1910–1911 was of the pneumonic type and sprang from the wild tarabagan, *Marmota bobak sibirica* Raddle (Siberian marmot), which was hunted for its valuable reddish-brown fur by numerous Chinese hunters unfamiliar with its dangers. The mountainous portions of Central Asia, i.e., portions of Siberia, Mongolia, Tibet, and Manchuria, are regarded as the original home of plague, and the tarabagan, as well as its flea parasites, plays an important role as reservoir of the infection in this area. These large rodents are about half a meter in length with a bushy tail about 15 cm long. It is pointed out that the low body temperature of the tarabagan during hibernation enables the animal to survive and thus to carry over the infection from one season to the next, and the flea, *Oropsylla silantiewi* (Wagner), as well as perhaps other bloodsucking ectoparasites, transmits the infection from animal to animal.

Comparable endemic foci of campestral plague occur in South Africa where the gerbilles (Muridae, Gerbillinae) belonging to three genera, particularly *Tatera,* e.g., *Tatera lobengulae* (De Winton), the multimammate mouse, *Mastomys coucha* (A. Smith) (Muridae, Murinae), and their flea parasites play the leading role.[47] In the Russian steppes, the susliks, e.g., *Citellus rufescens* Keyserling and Blasius (Sciuridae), and their flea parasites, *Citellophilus tesquorum* (Wagner) and *Neopsylla setosa* Wagner, play a similar role. In North America, as already explained, ground squirrels (*Citellus* spp.) (Sciuridae) and their fleas, e.g., *Diamanus montanus,* may be important reservoirs of campestral plague. In South America, the cavy, *Cavia asperea* Pallas, and its fleas, e.g., *Rhopalopsyllus cavicola* (Weyenbergh), play a similar role. Burroughs[5] gives further consideration to the matter of animals (other than rats) naturally infected with plague.

Campestral plague remains localized or at best spreads slowly, and in each endemic region a particular native animal or group of animals (rodents) maintains the infection, and when other small house-invading rodents such as mice and rats come in contact with such a focus, the infection may be carried to human habitations, and human cases may result; or likewise if humans invade the territory of campestral plague, infection may occur. The importance of the threat from these sylvatic foci is illustrated by a chain of cases occurring in Oakland, California, in 1919. A squirrel hunter became ill and died of "influenza," and subsequently several who had had contact with him died of "pneumonia." A total of 14 cases occurred, 13 of which were fatal. Finally a diagnosis of pneumonic plague was made; it is probable that all fatal cases were this form of the disease.

In the United States, campestral plague has spread gradually throughout the states west of the Great Plains and into Canada. Meyer[37] lists 38 species of wild rodents and rabbits which have been found plague-infected in 14 states of the western United States. Three groups of rodents constitute the primary natural reservoirs of plague in that part of the country: (1) ground squirrels (*Citellus*), Pacific coast and northern intermountain area; (2) wood rats (*Neotoma*), southwest desert areas; (3) prairie dogs (*Cynomys*), plateau regions of Arizona and New Mexico.

Meyer[36] points out that many of the unknown factors in campestral plague are intimately related to the influence of the climatic conditions on the life and longevity of the insects involved (fleas and lice). Too little attention has been given to the host-parasite relationships of this as well as other diseases involving arthropod vectors. The factors influencing the low transmissibility of campestral plague are as yet little understood. In the meantime, Meyer urges the maintenance of so-called "rodent free" belts around towns and "research and more research into the ecology of sylvatic plague."

Wild Rodent Fleas. Dunn and Parker[7] investigated the flea population of a variety of species of wild animals in the Bitter Root Valley of Montana. *Thrassus petiolatus* (Baker), misidentified as *Ceratophyllus idahoensis* (Baker), was found infesting a large percentage of the 94 ground squirrels, *Citellus columbianus* (Ord), examined, the average per animal being 3.86. Much additional information concerning the fleas of wild rodents in Montana can be obtained from the work of Dunn and Parker, although the student must make allowance for misidentification. Hubbard[21] also gives many valuable records of the wild rodent fleas.

Macchiavello[32] has brought together a large amount of information relating to fleas as vectors of plague. The student is referred to his work for a listing of fleas, both those of cosmopolitan and of local occurrence, which have been proven to be vectors of the disease, as well as those unproven vectors which have been found naturally infected or which have been infected experimentally.

Infected and Infective Fleas. In relation to the spread of campestral plague, Meyer[35] calls attention to certain paradoxical observations: (1) that despite active reservoirs with hundreds of infected rodents, very few cases of human plague were diagnosed on the North American continent; (2) that plague-infected fleas are taken from animals which had anatomically been declared noninfected; (3) squirrel hunters and plague-survey crews are commonly "covered" by fleas and are bitten by squirrel fleas yet are not infected. The danger represented by individual fleas appears therefore more limited than was originally believed. Wild rodent fleas serve as "preservers" of plague infections in suitable rodent burrows for many months, and under such natural conditions, while infected, harbor bacilli which are presumably of low virulence or avirulent. These "preserver" fleas are believed to be "nonblocked."

Meyer continues,

> Rodents with latent infections will hibernate only to develop acute plague early in spring (March and April). Since the flea population is as a rule simultaneously very high, a great reservoir of infected vectors is thus created. The cadavers of the dead rodents are rapidly and effectively removed by the larvae of the *Lucilia* flies, while the fleas persist in the nests. With the migration of the young squirrels and chipmunks into the empty abandoned burrows and nests, highly susceptible hosts are thus brought in contact with infected and infective fleas. They may bring the vectors to the surface and some may thus contribute to the intensity and the expansion of the virus. These events are probably accompanied by a variable degree of subclinical immunization favored by factors of age and reduced metabolism due to the approaching hibernation. Again latent infections and infected fleas in the burrows furnish the chain which connects the epidemic of one year with that of the next. Thus sylvatic plague smoulders for years and is everlasting. Suppressive measures against sylvatic plague in order to be effective must by necessity be directed against the hosts, the rodents, and the vectors, the various species of fleas. In selecting the procedures to reduce the rodent populations chemicals, preferably gases which are also insecticidal, must be chosen.

Laboratory tests indicate that many species of Siphonaptera (more than 30) can be infected experimentally, but the work which has been done on *vector efficiency* by Wheeler and Douglas[56] and subsequent investigators is significant. These investigators point out that the vector efficiency of a species of arthropod incriminated in the transmission of an infectious agent must necessarily take into consideration the following factors: (1) the *infection potential;* (2) the *vector potential;* and (3) the *transmission potential.* The first is based upon the percentage of a given species in which the infection becomes established; the second, upon the percentage of infected individuals which become infective, and the third is the mean number of transmissions effected by a group of infective individuals. The vector efficiency is the product of the three factors (1), (2), and (3). Thus, these workers demonstrated that *Diamanus montanus* has an infection potential of 0.85, a vector potential of 0.54, and a transmission potential of 2.58 with a *vector efficiency* of 1.14 (that is, $0.85 \times 0.52 \times 2.58$), compared with an infection potential of 0.98, a vector potential of 0.29, a transmission potential of 1.44 and a vector efficiency of 0.39 for *Xenopsylla cheopis.*

Reporting on the results of his vector efficiency studies in relation to campestral plague, Burroughs[5] states that experimental evidence was obtained that different strains of a species of flea taken in different geographic areas may differ markedly in their biological vector capacity. This observation was based primarily on experiments with *Diamanus montanus,* which proved much less efficient than *Xenopsylla cheopis,* in striking contrast to the results obtained by Wheeler and Douglas,[56] whose *D. montanus* came from a widely separated area.

Eskey and Haas[10] conducted transmission experiments with individual fleas collected from wild rodents in areas known to be campestral plague foci. Many of the infective fleas (proved on guinea pigs) transmitted plague to more than one experimental animal (guinea pigs). Both male and female fleas transmitted the infection, although males proved to be much less efficient on the whole; however, one *Xenopsylla cheopis* female infected 10 guinea pigs, and one male ground squirrel flea, *Opisocrostis labis,* infected 11 guinea pigs.

Rat Fleas on Ships and at Seaports. The United States Public Health Service has conducted a number of rat-flea surveys at various seaports. Williams[57] reports that on a 2-year survey of ships at the port of New York, 1913 ships produced 18,265 rats, an average of 9.6 rats per ship. The ship rat is almost exclusively the black rat, *Rattus r. rattus,* and the roof rat, *Rattus r. alexandrinus.* Because of the climbing habits of these rats, they are more likely to get into cargo and aboard ships than the Norway rat. The report indicates that the majority of ships carry few rats, and about only 50 per cent of arriving ships constitute about 90 per cent of the potential plague menace.

The dead rats collected after ship fumigations (hydrocyanic acid) were examined for fleas. A total of 7886 fleas was taken from 18,265 rats, an average of 0.43 per rat, which was about 30 per cent of the expectation of fleas from live rats. Of the total number of fleas, 6992 (88.68 per cent) were *Xenopsylla cheopis* and 786 (9.97 per cent), *Nosopsyllus fasciatus.* Except for 63 *Leptopsylla segnis,* other species were represented by negligible numbers.

The rat-flea survey at Norfolk, Virginia[17] resulted in the capture of 1561 rats, of which 883 harbored fleas; 4898 fleas were taken. Of these fleas, 81.6 per cent were *Xenopsylla cheopis,* and 17.7 per cent were *Nosopsyllus fasciatus.* The Norfolk survey was based on caged, trapped rats taken under favorable conditions for harborage and propagation. Consequently, the number of fleas per rat (the living rats were chloroformed) was much higher than the average per ship rat on fumigated vessels, i.e., 5.5 against 0.43; also *Rattus r. norvegicus* (Erxleben) constituted all but four of the total number of rats taken at Norfolk.

At the port of New Orleans, Fox and Sullivan[13] report that from 3839 live rats 17,559 fleas were taken, of which 6566 were *Xenopsylla cheopis,* 10,269 were *Leptopsylla segnis,* and 724 were *Nosopsyllus fasciatus*—an average of 4.83 per rat. These authors state that it is quite significant that at the port of New Orleans, where plague has actually existed, *Xenopsylla cheopis* is the predominant rat flea present during every month of the year.

Inspection of vessels for rat infestation has two principal objects according to Williams:[58] first, to establish the presence or absence of rats so as to determine whether or not a vessel shall be fumigated or otherwise treated to kill fleas and rats; and second, to determine the location of rats when present so as to apply fumigation effectively and to maintain proper ratproofing.

Murine (Endemic) Typhus. In 1898 Brill reported mild typhus for the first time in the United States. This disease entity has been confused with murine typhus, but various workers have shown that Brill's disease is a recrudescence of Old World typhus, found chiefly in larger cities and among recent immigrants from Europe. Epidemic typhus had existed in the eastern United States and Canada, but apparently had died out before 1900. In 1913 Paullin, in Georgia, recognized a clinical typhus fever that had a low mortality.[22] This disease has also been shown to be distinct from Brill's disease and is called murine or endemic typhus.

The causal organism of murine typhus is *Rickettsia typhi* (Wolbach and Todd) Philip, according to Philip,[45] though some authors insist that the correct name is *Rickettsia mooseri* Monteiro. The infection was long believed to be of murine origin. In 1931 Mooser, Castañeda, and Zinsser[41] reported rats as carriers in Mexico. In 1932 Dyer *et al.*[6] reported transmission of endemic typhus by rubbing crushed infected fleas or infected flea feces into wounds. Several species of rat and mouse fleas, including *Xenopsylla cheopis, Nosopsyllus fasciatus,* and *Leptopsylla segnis,* have been incriminated. Other fleas known to harbor the parasite, either experimentally or naturally, are *Echidnophaga gallinacea, Ctenocephalides felis,* and *C. canis.* Dyer and associates report that the incubation period in one experimental animal, a guinea pig, after inoculation of a flea emulsion, was 10 days; also the virus remained viable in the flea for at least 52 days, showing the importance of the flea as a reservoir under natural conditions.

Endemic typhus, as it occurs in North America, is a disease of rats, genus *Rattus,* and mice, *Mus musculus.* Fleas may spread it from rodent to rodent, but lice such as the spined rat louse *Polyplax spinulosa* (Burmeister), or mites such as the tropical rat mite *Ornithonyssus bacoti* (Hirst), may also be involved. The method of transmission is uncertain; it may be by the bite of the flea or mite, by passage of the infection through skin abraded by scratching, by inhalation or ingestion of rickettsia-laden flea feces or rickettsia-laden rodent urine in the dust of buildings, or by a combination of these methods.[22] The most likely method of transmission from rodent to man is through the infective feces of *Xenopsylla cheopis* being scratched into the skin in an attempt to alleviate the itching.

Zinsser[61] held to the belief that both types of typhus may be either endemic or epidemic. He states:

> Although the murine disease reaches man first from infected rats by flea vectors, this virus can also, like the European, pass from man to man by the louse . . . capable of epidemic dissemination of the murine as well as of the classical typhus. . . . Brill's disease is an imported classical typhus, endemically established in cities with large immigrant populations.

Castañeda,[6] reporting on flea-borne and louse-borne typhus in Mexico, states that the geographic distribution of both types of typhus in Mexico follows the climate of each zone. Pure murine typhus is found in warm regions and is flea-borne. Classic typhus occurs in cold and mild zones, where louse-borne infection is frequent. In these zones *murine typhus* also occurs and *may become louse-borne* and cause important epidemics of high mortality. In Mexico City Castañeda reports that from 1927 to 1931 it was demonstrated that murine typhus was the prevalent type, while in 1938 most of the isolated strains from typhus patients were classic. He continues, " . . . during the last seven years murine strains have been found only on rare occasions; complement fixation tests have corroborated the prevalence of classic typhus in the cold and temperate zones where typhus is endemic." Castañeda states that rat campaigns are advisable in zones where there is danger of louse-borne murine typhus.

Fleas as Vectors of Other Diseases. Jellison[22] has given a concise summary of the role of fleas as vectors of diseases of domestic animals and wild animals. Myxomatosis of rabbits, a viral disease, may be transmitted by mosquitoes or fleas, according to present evidence; in Europe, where the disease is considered detrimental because of its effect on game and domestic rabbits, fleas are considered at least the most important vectors. Fleas are known to transmit the protozoon *Trypanosoma lewisi* (Kent), a nonpathogenic parasite of the rats, but there is no evidence that they can transmit the related *T. cruzi,* the pathogen of Chagas' disease.

Fleas, as well as mosquitoes, have for some time been known to be involved in the transmission of heart worm of dogs, a filariid nematode. Newton and Wright[42] have shown that two types of microfilariae are involved in this disease, one of which, *Dirofilaria immitis* (Leidy), is mosquito-borne and the other, an undetermined species of *Dipetalonema* but probably *D. reconditum* (Grassi), is flea-borne. The latter will develop to the infective stage in the body cavity of *Ctenocephalides felis* and *C. canis.*

Fleas as Intermediate Hosts of Cestodes. Although Melnikoff in 1867 showed that the biting louse of the dog, *Trichodectes canis* De Geer, serves as an intermediate host of the double-pored dog tapeworm, *Dipylidium caninum* (Linnaeus), it has since been shown by other workers that fleas play a more important role in the transmission of this tapeworm, particularly the cat and the dog flea, *Ctenocephalides felix* and *C. canis*. Although *Dipylidium caninum* is a tapeworm of dogs, cats, and certain wild carnivores, it also occurs in man, particularly in young children. The embryonated eggs of the tapeworm are discharged in the fecal material of the host and are ingested by the larval flea, and develop into cysticercoids in the body cavity of the insect. Thus the mature flea, which would not be able to ingest the tapeworm eggs itself, is infected, and when ingested by a cat or dog or human, the cysticercoids are liberated and develop into tapeworms in the animal's digestive tract.

A common tapeworm of rats and mice, *Hymenolepis diminuta* (Rudolphi), has numerous intermediate arthropod hosts, among them *Nosopsyllus fasciatus* and *Xenopsylla cheopis*. A related rodent tapeworm, *H. nana* Siebold, has, among its intermediate hosts, the fleas *X. cheopis, Ctenocephalides canis,* and *Pulex irritans*. Both cestodes frequently infest children.

Fig. 142. The chigoe flea, *Tunga penetrans*.

Tunga penetrans is a tiny burrowing flea found in the tropical and subtropical regions of North and South America, also in the West Indies and Africa (Fig. 142). Its introduction into Africa is said to have occurred as late as 1872. The chigoe (not to be confused with the chigger mite) is reddish brown and measures about 1 mm in length except that the impregnated female may become as large as a small pea. The adult fleas are intermittent feeders but adhere closely to the host. The female when impregnated proceeds to "burrow" into the skin of the host, frequently between the toes and into the soles of the feet, causing nodular swellings which ulcerate. Actually, as Jellison[22] has pointed out, the insect cannot burrow; "somehow the skin envelops the flea except for a small sinus with an external opening through which eggs and dejecta are passed." The larvae which emerge in a few days from the eggs are typical flea larvae. Some hatch within the sinus; these usually drop to the ground to develop under conditions similar to those having hatched on the ground. Faust and Maxwell[15] report a case in which the eggs had hatched in or on the body around the sites of the burrows of the gravid females, and the larvae had thrived and grown there. The larval period under favorable conditions probably requires not more than 10 to 14 days, and the cocoon or pupal period about a like number of days.

Pathogenesis. The chigoes commonly attack the bare feet, these being nearest the ground, infesting the skin between the toes and soles, but no part of the body is exempt from attack. The "burrowing" female flea causes extreme irritation; the area surrounding it becomes charged with pus, producing a distinct elevation. The ulcerations due to the presence of numerous chigoes become confluent. Wellman (personal communication to Herms) attributes the commonly observed autoamputation of toes of natives in Angola to the work of the chigoe. Tetanus and gangrene frequently result.

Where the chigoe flea occurs, walking in bare feet should be avoided. Parts of the body attacked by the fleas should receive immediate attention. Repeated bathing of the infested part with dilute Lysol solution gives good results. The insect can be removed quite easily by means of a sterile needle or very fine-pointed knife blade. The wounds caused by this treatment must be carefully dressed to heal.

The Sticktight Flea. *Echidnophaga gallinacea,* also known as the "sticktight," is a serious poultry pest in many parts of subtropical America. It commonly attacks poultry of all kinds, also cats, dogs, rabbits, horses, and man.

Before copulation, both sexes are active, hopping about much as do other species of fleas. Shortly after feeding, the females attach themselves firmly to the skin of the host. At this time the sexes are in copulation. The females deposit their eggs in the ulcers which have been produced by the infestation. The usual incubation period according to Parman[44] is from 6 to 8 days at a temperature average of 76° F. If the eggs are deposited in the ulcer, the larvae crawl out and drop to the ground, where they grow rapidly under favorable conditions, feeding on nitrogenous matter, dry droppings, etc. The full-grown larva, which is not unlike other flea larvae, is about 4 mm in length, reaching this stage in about 2 weeks. The larva then spins a cocoon, pupates, and in about 2 weeks (9 to 19 days) emerges as a fully developed flea. The life history requires from 30 to 60 days. Eggs are also deposited in the dust or dry droppings of poultry or in old nests, etc.

The fleas are most likely to attack the skin around the eyes, the wattles and comb, and the anus or other bare spots. The ulceration and wartlike elevations around the eyes often become so aggravated that blindness occurs, the host is unable to find its food, and death results. Since this flea also lives on dogs, cats, rats, quail, blackbirds, and sparrows, suitable precautions should be taken to exclude these from chicken pens.

The western chicken flea, *Ceratophyllus niger* Fox, is considerably larger than the sticktight and does not attach except when feeding and then only for a brief period. It readily attacks man, cats, and dogs. It breeds primarily in fowl droppings. The European chicken flea, *Ceratophyllus gallinae* Schrank, which has habits similar to *C. niger* Fox, is also at times a serious pest of poultry.[53]

Fleas in the Household. Very few species of fleas are annoying to household pets. Among these are particularly the dog and cat fleas, *Ctenocephalides canis* and *felis* (Fig. 143), and the human flea, *Pulex irritans*. While the common name might imply that there is a specified host relationship, this is not the case, since interchange of host species is quite usual. Cat and dog fleas readily attack humans, and the human flea is often remarkably abundant on swine.

Fleas in the house generally indicate that cats or dogs are present or have been present fairly recently. Fleas may be carried on clothing into the

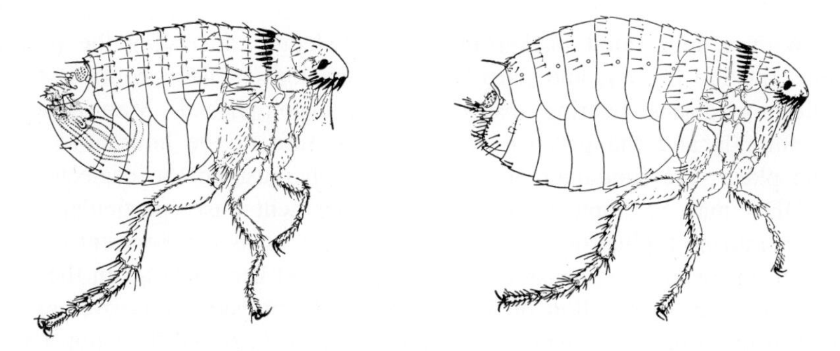

Fig. 143. *Ctenocephalides felis,* the cat flea; (*left*) male; (*right*) female. × 17.

house from pig pens or from flea-infested public meeting places. The exclusion of cats and dogs or their proper management is necessary to prevent flea infestations. Cats and dogs (unless properly bedded), as well as rats, must be excluded from the basement and from beneath the house.

No home that is infested with fleas can be considered satisfactory from the standpoint of either the human beings or the pets that occupy it. Flea bites can be very annoying to both. Wholly aside from their disease-transmitting potentialities, and from strictly the pest standpoint, fleas should not be tolerated any more than mosquitoes, flies, and other household annoyers.

Ordinarily, fleas lay their eggs on the infested animal, but because the eggs are dry, they drop off when the host shakes itself. For this reason, mats should be provided upon which the animals may sleep at night, and these should be shaken off every day or two over fires or into kerosene (see flea control). The eggs are minute glistening white objects. The incubation period varies considerably, but they usually hatch in from 5 to 6 days, sometimes less, and the wormlike sparsely haired larvae emerge. The larvae feed on particles of dry blood, fecal matter, and various organic substances collected in corners and crevices. The larvae are quite active and in 2 to 4 weeks reach a length of about 1/4 inch, and then spin a crude cocoon in which they pupate. The flea emerges from the cocoon in about a week; thus 3 to 4 weeks are required for the entire life history of a common house flea under favorable conditions. Undisturbed mats, rags, and carpets favor the development of fleas. All carpets or matting tacked down and covering the floor should be dispensed with and smaller rugs substituted. Houses that have been vacant for several weeks may be badly infested with fleas, because these insects are able to live without food for several weeks.

FLEA AND RODENT CONTROL

Flea Control

With a substantial background of knowledge concerning the parasitic habits, the life history, and particularly the ecology of fleas, control of these pestiferous, disease-bearing insects can be accomplished. Management of host animals and the practice of good sanitation in the household and in public places are fundamental principles which must not be neglected.

DDT may be applied either as a 10 per cent dust (particularly when used in murine typhus fever control operations) or as a 5 per cent emulsion or solution for application as a spray to floors and beneath rugs in the house, basements, etc. One gallon of 5 per cent DDT sprayed lightly over areas of about 1000 square feet will completely eradicate fleas. DDT is not a repellent, and it kills slowly. It retains its killing effect against fleas for about 2 months.

In homes, rooms and upholstered furniture should first be cleaned with a vacuum cleaner; the insecticide should then be applied to floors, with special care taken to see that it gets into cracks and dark recesses, and to baseboards to a height above a foot. A light mist should be applied to rugs and upholstered furniture. After a day or two, excess powder may be removed with a vacuum cleaner.

Wherever pets sleep or are accustomed to lie down, DDT dust (10 per cent recommended) is applied where fleas will come in contact with it. The dust should be forced into cracks and crevices and in all places where fleas may breed. Excess powder if objectionable after a few days can be wiped up with a cloth or removed with a vacuum cleaner. Flea-infested basements as well as yards and other outdoor areas should be similarly dusted.

Dogs, except pups under 2 months of age, may be safely dusted with DDT; one tablespoonful of powder (for an average-size, short-haired dog) applied particularly to the neck, back, and top of head and rubbed thoroughly into the hair is sufficient to kill all the fleas and to prevent reinfestation for several weeks. Since DDT agitates fleas before killing, this activity causes the dog to scratch and bite vigorously until the insects cease crawling about.

Although DDT dust is not absorbed through the skin of mammals, cats should not be treated with DDT because of their cleaning habits; however, treating the cat's bed is usually sufficient. Flea powders containing rotenone, pyrethum, malathion, or methoxychlor are safe to use on cats. The addition of a synergist to the pyrethrum permits its effective use at a much lower concentration. However, since the pyrethrum may merely stun the fleas, the animal should be brushed over a paper, and the collected fleas and paper then should be burned.

Fleas, including *Pulex irritans, Ctenocephalides canis, C. felis,* and *Xenopsylla cheopis,* have shown some resistance to DDT and, in some cases, dieldrin and chlordane. Malathion and methoxychlor may be used on cats or dogs, and chlordane or lindane on dogs (except young pups), where DDT-resistance has been encountered.

In the use of DDT dust (10 per cent DDT) in murine typhus control, the United States Public Health Service points out that this is aimed at the flea link in the typhus chain. Proper dusting of rat runs and harborages with DDT combats fleas both on and off their rodent hosts.

With regard to the use of DDT for the control of murine typhus fever, the United States Public Health Service points out that rats in passing over the dusted places, pick up a considerable amount of dust on their feet, bellies, and tails, and fleas on the rats come in contact with the DDT dust and, if exposed to it for a sufficient length of time, are killed. Thorough residual dusting (not too heavy) of rat runways, both inside of buildings and in outside areaways, is essential not only to ensure killing fleas on the rats but also to kill the fleas (off the animals) in or near rat runs, nests, or harborages. Treatment of premises and buildings should be repeated at intervals of 2 or 3 months throughout the flea breeding season. Success depends upon a good knowledge of the habits of rats and careful inspection.

Personal Protection from Fleas. Diethyltoluamide appears to be a very satisfactory repellent for fleas; it is particularly effective against the dangerous rat fleas. Benzyl benzoate, dimethyl phthalate, and undecenoic acid (2 per cent) plus pyrethrum (1 per cent) have also been used as repellents. Clothing impregnated with benzyl benzoate shows some repellence, even after two or three launderings, to fleas, chiggers, and other annoyers.

There is evidence that persons who are hypersensitive to flea bites may obtain some relief through the use of desensitizing antigens. According to Jellison a major program for the study of this subject is now under way at the Kaiser Foundation in cooperation with the United States Public Health Service Laboratory at San Francisco.

Rodent Control

The fact that rats and other rodents harbor fleas that may readily attack man implies that elimination of the rodent host will lead to a decrease in the number of man's annoyers. Also, where flea-borne typhus or plague is a consideration, the elimination of the reservoir, as well as the vector, becomes a major consideration.

Together with the house mouse, *Mus musculus* Linnaeus, the cosmopolitan species of rats belong to the rodent family Muridae. *Rattus norvegicus* (Erxleben), the brown rat or sewer rat, better known as the Norway rat, is the largest of the common house rats. *Rattus rattus* (Linnaeus) is the black rat, which is almost solidly blue-black in color; it is smaller and more slender than the Norway rat. *Rattus alexandrinus* (Geoffroy-Saint Hilaire and Andouin) is called the Alexandrine or roof rat, and also the tree rat. Both the black rat and the roof rat can climb readily and may nest in trees, palms, and attics of houses.

Methods of Rat Control. One should aim at permanent control as the only satisfactory solution of the rat problem. There should be good sanitation the year round. Good housekeeping is good insurance against rats; cleanliness is the rat's worst enemy. The United States Fish and Wildlife Service (Circular 13, 1948) points out that food and shelter are the two most important factors in a rat's existence. Any program of rat control to be successful must incorporate these four major phases: (1) elimination of rat harborages; (2) elimination of food supply for rats; (3) ratproofing of buildings; and (4) destruction of rats.

Silver, Crouch, and Betts[48] state that the rat problem will have been largely solved when ratproofing becomes the regular practice. However, ratproofing (exclusion) is not enough; such construction must be frequently inspected and kept in good repair. Also, rats may be introduced into "ratproof" granaries, where, provided that they have a source of water, they may breed in great numbers.[18] Ratproofing can be done at the time of construction at slight extra cost, but when applied to old buildings it is usually an expensive procedure. However, exterior ratproofing, i.e., *rat stoppage* can be done inexpensively. In addition, measures should be taken to cut off the rat's water supply in granaries, by such methods as mending leaks in the roof; also, one should bring about sanitary disposal of refuse from the household, garbage, slaughterhouse refuse, feed refuse in connection with piggeries, poultry houses, barns, feeding lots, etc. Cleanliness, neatness, good housekeeping in general, and efficient farm management will aid materially in the control of rats and other rodents.

In the use of rat poisons, a system of prebaiting and baiting is employed. Since the rat poison is usually mixed with rat food, one should have some knowledge of the food habits of these rodents. Rolled oats and other cereals, corn meal, bread crumbs, diced bread, raw meat (horse meat is acceptable to rats), and raw fish are the commonest baits used. Prebaiting is a practice based on the fact that rats are suspicious and avoid new objects, even a new food. If a clean prebait is offered, they will overcome their fear in a few nights (two or more) and will accept the new food. Small piles of clean unpoisoned baits are placed at selected sites or in special containers for 4 or 5 nights, replenishing the supply whenever the bait is eaten. On the fifth or sixth day the unpoisoned prebait is replaced with poisoned bait. If the poisoning is successful, the above-described routine may not need to be repeated for several months; otherwise, a follow-up campaign may be undertaken in a couple of weeks.

Of the rodenticides in current use, *warfarin* (a blood anticoagulant), which was introduced in 1950, has very wide usage; it is relatively very safe to use and highly effective. It may be used in cereal baits, or in water-soluble form, in water placed alongside food batch baits. Other anticoagulants, such as *Pival* and *Fumarin,* are also used. Continued baiting for a period of 7 days or more is required in order for these poisons to take effect, but the rat does not develop any antagonism to them. These poisons are effective against all domestic rats and mice and have largely replaced the formerly used rodenticides such as: fortified *red squill,* which is safe to use though far less effective; *ANTU,* which is effective against only the Norway rat, and which, after repeated use, is avoided by that rodent; and *sodium fluoroacetate* (1080), which is highly effective but at the same time highly toxic to man and his pets, with no known antidote, and consequently very hazardous to use.

Rodenticides, even the safest to use, are poisons and should be treated as such. Children and pets particularly should be protected from the poisoned baits. In using rodenticides, one should take care to follow instructions on the label or printed directly in special bulletins on rodent control.

In trapping rats the proper placement of the trap is far more important than the selection of a bait. Bacon strips, a piece of fresh fish, or bacon-scented oatmeal is better than cheese as a bait according to the "Fish and Wildlife Service." Such baits should be tied firmly to the trigger of the trap.

Dead rats resulting from poisoning, gassing, trapping, or any other cause should be treated copiously with kerosene, boiling water, or an insecticide before disposal, to destroy any fleas still present on the body. Incineration or deep burial of dead rats is good practice. *Deodorants* such as powdered activated charcoal may be used where rats have died within walls.

Wild Rodents. It would seem that the threat of campestral plague could be eliminated or greatly reduced in a given area through the destruction of the rodents and rabbits which constitute its reservoir. The problem is not that simple, however; our knowledge of the ecology of the small mammals is insufficient. For example, *Citellus beecheyi beecheyi* (Richardson) has been considered the chief reservoir in California, but evidence is at hand that would indicate that it is only an accidental host, that the true reservoirs are such rodents as *Microtus* and *Peromyscus*.[25,39]

Meyer points out that total destruction of wild rodents is beset with several disadvantages: (1) it is almost impossible and exceedingly costly; (2) the ectoparasites of the rodents, some of them undoubtedly infected, will transfer to new hosts, thus including new rodents in the plague cycle, unless a simultaneous campaign has been directed at the ectoparasites; and (3) the extermination of species may upset ecologic balance with unpredictable consequences.

Wild rodent control must be part of a well-organized plan under the direction of specialists. In most instances, our knowledge of rodent ecology is not such that successful planning can be done. Particularly in the presence of epizootics of plague or murine typhus, the use of insecticides to destroy the ectoparasites should accompany any poisoning, shooting, trapping, or other methods directed at the rodents.

REFERENCES

1. Bacot, A., 1914. "A study of the bionomics of the common rat fleas and other species associated with human habitations, with special reference to the influence of temperature and humidity at various periods of the life history of the insect," *J. Hyg.*, **13** (Plague Supp.):447–654 (8 plates).

2. Bacot, A. W., 1915. "Further studies on the mechanism of the transmission of plague by fleas," *J. Hyg.*, **14** (Plague Supp. 4):774–76.

3. Bacot, A. W., and Martin, C. J., 1914. "Observations on the mechanism of the transmission of plague by fleas," *J. Hyg.*, **13** (Plague Supp. 3):423–39.

4. Blue, Surgeon Rupert, 1910. *Rodents in Relation to the Transmission of Bubonic Plague. The Rat and Its Relation to the Public Health.* Washington, D. C.: U. S. Public Health and Marine Hospital Service. 254 pp.

5. Burroughs, Albert Lawrence, 1947. "Sylvatic plague studies—the vector efficiency of nine species of fleas compared with *Xenopsylla cheopis*," *J. Hyg.*, **45:**371–96.

6. Castañeda, M. Ruiz, 1948. "Flea-borne and louse-borne typhus in Mexico," *Proc. 4th Internat. Cong. Trop. Med. & Malaria,* Washington, D. C., **1:**408–13.

7. Dunn, L. H., and Parker, R. R., 1923. "Fleas found on wild animals in the Bitterroot Valley, Montana," U. S. Public Health Service, *Pub. Health Rep.*, **38:**2763–75.

8. Dyer, R. E.; Ceder, E. T.; Workman, W. G.; Rumreich, A.; and Badger, L. F.; 1932. "Transmission of endemic typhus by rubbing either crushed infected fleas or infected flea feces into wounds," U. S. Public Health Service, *Pub. Health Rep.*, **47:**131–33.

9. Eskey, C. R., 1938. "Recent developments in our knowledge of plague transmission," U. S. Public Health Service, *Pub. Health Rep.*, **53:**49–57.

10. Eskey, C. R., and Haas, V. H., 1940. *Plague in the Western Part of the United States*. Washington, D. C.: Govt. Print. Office, in Pub. Health Bull., no. 254. 83 pp.

11. Ewing, H. E., and Fox, Irving, 1943. *The Fleas of North America: Classification, Identification, and Geographic Distribution of These Injurious and Disease-spreading Insects*. Washington, D. C.: Dept. Agric., in Misc. Publ., no. 500. 142 pp.

12. Fox, Carroll, 1925. *Insects and Disease of Man*. Philadelphia: P. Blakiston's Son & Co. xii + 349 pp.

13. Fox, Carroll, and Sullivan, E. C., 1925. "A comparative study of rat-flea data for several seaports of the United States," U. S. Public Health Service, *Pub. Health Rep.,* **40:**1909–34.

14. Fox, Irving, 1940. *Fleas of Eastern United States*. Ames, Iowa: Iowa State College Press. vii + 191 pp. (3 plates).

15. Faust, E. C., and Maxwell, J. A., 1930. "The finding of the larvae of the chigoe, *Tunga penetrans,* in scrapings from human skin," *Arch. Dermat. & Syph.,* **22:**94–97.

16. Hampton, Brock C., 1940. "Plague in the United States," U. S. Public Health Service, *Pub. Health Rep.,* **55:**1143–58.

17. Hasseltine, H. E., 1929. "Rat-flea survey of the port of Norfolk, Va.," U. S. Public Health Service, *Pub. Health Rep.,* **44:**579–89.

18. Hirst, L. Fabian, 1953. *The Conquest of Plague*. Oxford: The Clarendon Press. xvi + 478 pp.

19. Holland, George P., 1949. *The Siphonaptera of Canada*. Ottawa: Canada Dept. Agric., in Tech Bull., 70. 306 pp. (42 plates).

20. Hopkins, G. H. E., and Rothschild, Miriam, 1953–56. *An Illustrated Catalogue of the Rothschild Collection of Fleas (Siphonaptera) in the British Museum (Natural History)*. London: British Museum (Natural History). Vol. I, 361 pp. (45 plates); Vol. II, 445 pp. (32 plates). A third volume is in preparation.

21. Hubbard, C. Andresen, 1947. *Fleas of Western North America*. Ames, Iowa: Iowa State College Press. 533 pp.

22. Jellison, William L., 1959. "Fleas and disease," *Ann. Rev. Entomol.,* **4:**389–414.

23. Jellison, William L., and Good, Newell E., 1942. *Index to the Literature of Siphonaptera of North America*. Washington, D. C.: U. S. Public Health Service, in Nat. Inst. Health Bull., no. 178. 193 pp.

24. Jellison, William L.; Locker, Betty; and Bacon, Roma; 1953. "A synopsis of North American fleas, north of Mexico, and notice of a supplementary index," *J. Parasitol.,* **39:**610–18.

25. Jones, Robert W., III, 1956. "The public health significance of rodents in California," *Calif. Vector Views,* **3:**31, 33–34.

26. Jordan, Karl, 1932. "A new *Xenopsylla* from Hawaii," *Novitates Zoologicae,* **38:**264–66.

27. Jordan, Karl, 1956. "Suctoria," in Smart, John, *A Handbook for the Identification of Insects of Medical Importance,* 3rd ed. London: British Museum (Natural History). pp. 211–45.

28. Kerr, R. W., 1946. "Control of fleas: Laboratory experiments with DDT and certain other insecticides," *J. Council Sci. & Indust. Research,* **19:**233–40.

29. Kessel, Edward L., 1939. *The Embryology of Fleas.* Smithsonian Misc. Coll., vol. 98, no. 3. Washington, D. C.: Smithsonian Inst. Publ. no. 3527. 69 pp. (12 plates).

30. Link, Vernon B., 1955. *A History of Plague in the United States.* U. S. Public Health Service, in Pub. Health Monograph no. 26. 120 pp.

31. Liston, W. G., 1905. "Plague rats and fleas," *J. Bombay Nat. Hist. Soc.,* **16:**253–73.

32. Macchiavello, A., 1954. "Reservoirs and vectors of plague," *J. Trop. Med. & Hyg.,* **57:**3–8, 45–48, 65–69, 87–94, 116–21, 139–46, 158–71, 191–97, 220–24, 238–43, 275–79, 294–98.

33. McCoy, George W., 1910. "Bubonic plague in ground squirrels," *N. Y. Med. J.,* **92:**652–65.

34. Mellanby, Kenneth, 1933. "The influence of temperature and humidity on the pupation of *Xenopsylla cheopis,*" *Bull. Entomol. Research,* **24:**197–202.

35. Meyer, K. F., 1938. "The role of the infected and the infective flea in the spread of sylvatic plague," *Am. J. Pub. Health,* **28:**1153–64.

36. Meyer, K. F., 1942. "The ecology of plague," *Medicine,* **21:**143–74.

37. Meyer, K. F., 1947. "The prevention of plague in the light of newer knowledge," *Ann. New York Acad. Sci.,* **48** (art. 6):429–67.

38. Meyer, K. F., 1955. "The modern outlook on plague in California," *Calif. Vector Views,* **2:**41, 43.

39. Meyer, K. F., 1957. "The natural history of plague and psittacosis," U. S. Public Health Service, *Pub. Health Rep.,* **72:**705–19.

40. Mitzmain, M. B., 1910. "Some new facts on the bionomics of the California rodent fleas," *Ann. Entomol. Soc. Amer.,* **3:**61–82.

41. Mooser, H.; Castañeda, M. R.; and Zinsser, H.; 1931. "Rats as carriers of Mexican typhus fever," *J.A.M.A.,* **97:**231–32.

42. Newton, Walter L., and Wright, Willard H., 1956. "The occurrence of a dog filariid other than *Dirofilaria immitis* in the United States," *J. Parasitol.,* **42:**246–58.

43. Ogata, M., 1897. "Ueber die Pestepidemie in Formosa," *Centralbl. f. Bakt.,* **21:**769–77.

44. Parman, D. C., 1923. "Biological notes on the hen flea, *Echidnophaga gallinacea,*" *J. Agric. Research,* **23:**1007–09.

45. Philip, Cornelius B., 1953. "Nomenclature of the Rickettsiaceae pathogenic to vertebrates," *Ann. New York Acad. Sci.,* **56:**484–94.

46. Pollitzer, R., 1954. *Plague.* Geneva, Switzerland: World Health Org., in Monograph series, no. 22. 698 pp.

47. Roberts, Austin, 1935. "Mammals concerned in the bubonic plague and rabies problems in South Africa," *South African J. Med. Sc.* **22:**414–60.

48. Silver, James; Crouch, W. E.; and Betts, M. C.; 1942. *Ratproofing Buildings and Premises.* U. S. Fish and Wild Life Service, Washington, D. C.: Conservation Bull. no. 19. 26 pp.

49. Simond, P. L., 1898. "La propagation de la peste," *Ann. Inst. Pasteur,* **12:**625–87.

50. Sharif, M., 1935. "On the presence of wing buds in the pupa of Aphaniptera," *Parasitol.,* **27:**461–64.

51. Smit, F. G. A. M., 1958. "A preliminary note on the occurrence of *Pulex irritans* L. and *Pulex simulans* Baker in North America," *J. Parasitol.,* **44:**523–26.

52. Snodgrass, R. E., 1946. *The Skeletal Anatomy of Fleas (Siphonaptera).* Smithsonian Misc. Coll., vol. 104, no. 18, Washington, D. C.: Smithsonian Inst. (Publ. no. 3815). 89 pp. (21 plates).

53. Stewart, M. A., 1927. "A means of control of the European hen flea, *Ceratophyllus gallinae* Schrank," *J. Econ. Entomol.,* **20:**132–34.

54. Swellengrebel, N. H., and Otten, L., 1914. "Experimentelle Beiträge zur Kenntnis der Uebertragung der Pest durch Flöhe und Läuse," *Centralbl. f. Bakt.,* **74:**592–603.

55. Verjbitski, D. T., 1908. "The part played by insects in the epidemiology of plague," *J. Hyg.,* **8:**162.

56. Wheeler, C. M., and Douglas, J. R., 1941. "Transmission studies of sylvatic plague," *Proc. Soc. Exp. Biol. & Med.,* **47:**65–66.

57. Williams, C. L., 1929. "A rat and rat-flea survey of ships at the port of New York," U. S. Public Health Service, *Pub. Health Rep.,* **44:**443–76.

58. Williams, C. L., 1932. "Rat infestation inspection of vessels," U. S. Public Health Service, *Pub. Health Rep.,* **47:**765–800.

59. Wu, Lien-Teh; Chun, J. W. H.; Pollitzer, R.; and Wu, C. Y.; 1936. *Plague, a Manual for Medical and Public Health Workers.* Shanghai: Weishengshu National Quar. Service. xxxiii + 547 pp.

60. Yersin, 1894. "La peste bubonique a Hong-Kong," *Ann. Inst. Pasteur,* **8:**862–67.

61. Zinsser, Hans, 1937. "The Rickettsia diseases, varieties, epidemiology, and geographical distribution," *Am. J. Hyg.,* **25:**430–63.

Chapter 19

TICKS AND TICK-BORNE DISEASES
Class Arachnida, Order Acarina, Superfamily Ixodoidea

Introduction. Probably all species of vertebrate animals higher than fishes are subject to attack by ticks, but particularly mammals, whose warm blood is highly attractive to these parasites. The food of ticks consists of blood and lymph, and as a rule adult ticks, both males and females, are bloodsuckers, as are usually all immature stages. Hunters have long observed tremendous infestations on the bodies of wild animals. Stockmen suffer enormous losses due to ticks on cattle, horses, and other stock; poultry is often severely parasitized. Hunter and Hooker,[53] United States Bureau of Entomology, reported that as many as 200 pounds of blood may be withdrawn from a large host animal by ticks in a single season.

Woodward and Turner,[102] using the common cattle tick, *Boophilus annulatus* (Say), found that tick-infested cows under experimental conditions gave only 65.8 per cent as much milk as tick-free cows. Furthermore, the tick-free cows gained 6.1 per cent in body weight during the time of the experiment, while the tick-infested animals gained 3.6 per cent. Death due to exsanguination by ticks is believed to be possible. Jellison and Kohls[54] found that an adult female *Dermacentor andersoni* Stiles withdrew from 1.7 to 2 gm of blood in the act of engorgement, and they concluded that "tick-host anemia is not only an experimental disease but occurs with some frequency in nature, and may be the immediate cause of death in animals." During the months of October to March, 1935–1936, one riding academy in Alameda County, California, lost 83 horses, whose deaths were reported to be due to loss of blood (exsanguination) through huge infestations of *Dermacentor albipictus* (Packard). Autopsies, blood examinations, and inoculation of blood into other horses produced no symptoms not attributable to simple secondary anemia.

There are many disorders and diseases of man and animals traceable to ticks; among these are: (1) *dermatosis,* inflammation, itching, swelling, and ulcerations at the site of the bite, also skin ulceration and lesions resulting from improper or partial removal of tick mouth parts: (2) *envenomization,* inoculation of toxic salivary fluids at the site of the bite often resulting in severe systemic disturbances; (3) *exsanguination,* a serious matter when an animal is badly infested with ticks, resulting in a secondary anemia and possibly death; (4) *tick paralysis,* an acute ascending, flaccid type of paralysis, often fatal, caused directly by the bite of certain species of ticks, affecting children and young animals such as lambs, calves, colts, pigs, and dogs;

(5) *otoacariasis,* invasion of the auditory canal by ticks; (6) *predisposition* to myiasis and secondary bacterial infections through tick-bite injuries. *Infections* transmitted by ticks include *piroplasmoses* (*babesioses*), e.g., Texas cattle fever; *rickettsioses,* e.g., Rocky Mountain spotted fever; *viroses,* e.g., Colorado tick fever; and *spirochetoses,* e.g., tick-borne relapsing fevers; ticks may also assist in the spread of *tularemia* and certain helminthic infections.

High Vector Potential of Ticks. Some of the factors which account for the potency of ticks in the spread of disease of man and animals are the following: they are first of all *persistent bloodsuckers*—they *attach firmly* while feeding and cannot be dislodged easily; the later stages (nymphs and adults) are *highly sclerotized,* hence very resistant to environmental stresses; they are relatively *free from natural enemies;* most species have a *wide host range,* thus ensuring a relatively certain source of blood; very few species of ticks are dependent upon a single host species; usually many species are available. Cooley[14] reported 28 species of hosts for the adult of *Dermacentor andersoni* Stiles, and 32 for the immature stages. Other factors adding to the vector potential of ticks are: (1) *longevity*—the life span of some species may be 5 years or more (see p. 440); (2) *the long duration of the life cycle* in many species, due to the longevity of the several developmental stages, is an important factor in that, for example, the tick vector of relapsing fever may be a dangerous carrier of the infection for several years, having received the infection through the egg from the previous generation; (3) the *reproductive potential* of ticks is quite great, as some species may deposit as many as 18,000 eggs, and parthenogenesis sometimes occurs. Moreover, ticks apparently have the power to regenerate lost parts, such as amputated legs, and the ability to repair mutilated mouth parts.

Man Not a Natural Host for Ticks. Ticks are in general parasites of animals in nature; they parasitize man and his domesticated mammals fortuitously. However, man has set the stage for enormous infestations of his herds of cattle, horses, and other animals. Certain tick-borne infections in wild animals have persisted for many centuries, and a host-parasite relationship has developed resulting in a benign (nonpathogenic) condition of infection rendering the wild animal a true reservoir. Thus, rabbits (several species) harbor rickettsiae of Rocky Mountain spotted fever, and that infection is transmitted from rabbit to rabbit by a relatively host-specific tick. There is thus maintained in nature a continuous reservoir of infection; man is not an essential factor. Other species of ticks, more particularly *Dermacenter andersoni* Stiles, which bite other animals as well as man, pick up infection from an infected rabbit, and if man intervenes (a fortuitous host), he will suffer a rickettsial infection often of great severity, probably because he is an *inappropriate* host. Spirochetal infections are described later in this chapter. No doubt, other infections not yet described will be revealed.

Diseases limited to animals, i.e., not transmissible to man, also possess similar tick-host relationships. Thus, the causal agent of bovine anaplasmosis is harbored by wild deer without causing apparent symptoms, but when it is transmitted to domestic cattle by ticks a severe disease results.

Historical. Although ticks were referred to as "disgusting parasitic animals" by Aristotle in the fourth century B.C., the orderly classification of these parasites dates from the publications of Linnaeus in 1746 (Fauna Suecica). Linnaeus placed them among the Acari in the genus *Acarus* specifically, according to Nuttall (Monograph of the Ixodoidae, Cambridge University Press, May, 1911). Pliny is said to have used the word *ricinus* to signify a "tick" because the fully engorged female resembles the seed of the caster oil plant (*Ricinus*). The scientific nomenclature of ticks began with Latreille in 1804 when he set up 11 genera, among them *Ixodes;* therefore, the species of Linnaeus became as we have it today, namely *Ixodes ricinus* (Linnaeus). It was not until 1844 that Koch separated the ticks from the Acari, which included both ticks and mites. In 1896 Neumann placed the ticks in the order Acarina and divided them into two subfamilies, namely, (1) Argasinae and (2) Ixodinae. Finally, in 1901, Salmon and Stiles raised the two subfamilies of Neumann to family rank and placed them in the superfamily Ixodoidea established by Banks in 1894. Thus, systematic knowledge of the ticks grew slowly, and knowledge of their biology was exceedingly scant. Nevertheless, when Nuttall and associates published their bibliography on ticks in 1911 there were already 2004 titles.

Theobald Smith (see p. 4) was the first (1893) experimentally to incriminate ticks as vectors of disease. He had previously (1889) discovered that Texas cattle fever was caused, like malaria, by a blood corpuscle–invading protozoon, *Babesia bigemina.* Earlier discoveries pertaining to malaria were, no doubt, helpful. Smith and his associates, of course, also knew well the habits of the tick, *Boophilus annulatus,* which abundantly parasitized the diseased as well as healthy cattle. They knew that this species is host-specific and needs but one host for its complete development. The astonishing fact was revealed by Theobald Smith that the etiologic agent of Texas cattle fever was carried from the infected female tick to her offspring (generation to generation) through the eggs. This discovery gave the answer to the puzzling question as to how this tick could infect other cattle when it was well known that once it had dropped off its host (the female deposits her eggs on the ground and then dies) it never again resumes its parasitic position on another host animal. Transovarian (generation to generation) transmission explained this readily—the newly hatched ticks were already infected, hence infectious, when feeding began.

In 1903, Marchoux and Salimbeni proved fowl spirochetosis, caused by *Borrelia anserina* (= *Spirochaeta gallinarum* Blanchard), to be tick-borne. They showed the common fowl tick, *Argas persicus* (Oken), to be a vector. This was apparently the first demonstration that a tick can transmit spirochetosis. In the meantime, the puzzling so called "tick-bite" fever of man in the African Congo was nearing a solution. This fever was long associated with the bite of certain ticks by the natives. David Livingstone, the explorer, in 1857, was the first to report upon the evil effects following the bite of a tick. Murray in 1877 named this tick *Argas moubata.*

It was not until 1904 that Ross and Milne,[83] reporting from Uganda, proved that this tick, *Ornithodoros moubata* (Murray), was a vector of the causal organism, a spirochete. This discovery was confirmed in 1905 by Dutton and Todd,[29] working in the Belgian Congo, and by Robert Koch in (German) East Africa. The "tick-bite fever" of the natives, therefore, was shown to be a tick-borne relapsing fever. Transovarian transmission was also demonstrated. These were epoch-making discoveries and quickened the interest of workers in the fields of parasitology and epidemiology everywhere. In the brief period of a dozen years, both families of ticks, the Ixodidae, hard ticks, and the Argasidae, soft ticks, had been incriminated as disease vectors involving both man and his domesticated animals.

Characteristics of Ticks. Ticks are easily distinguished from insects, in that the body is not definitely divided, i.e., there is a strong fusion of the thorax and abdomen producing a saclike leathery appearance. A discrete head is lacking, but the mouth parts, together with the *basis capituli* in many species, form a structure known as the *capitulum.* Like most other Arachnida the mature ticks and nymphs bear four pairs of legs; the larvae are hexapod. Ticks should not be confused with ticklike wingless insects such as the saclike Pupipara, particularly the sheep ked (sometimes called the "sheep tick").

All adult and nymphal ticks bear a pair of spiracles, situated lateroventrally on the abdomen, one on each side near the third and fourth coxae. In the ixodid ticks, the dorsum of the adult male is largely or wholly covered by a plate called the *scutum.* In immature ticks and females, the scutum is restricted to the anterior part of the dorsum, behind the capitulum. The scutum may be *ornate,* i.e., with a pattern of gray or white imposed upon a dark background, or *inornate,* i.e., without such a pattern. A pair of simple eyes located on the lateral margins or submargins of the scutum in the hard ticks, or along the submargins in certain soft ticks, may be present. Many species of ticks are eyeless. In certain hard ticks, there is a row of more or less rectangular areas, separated from adjacent ones by grooves, along the posterior submarginal area of the dorsum. These are known as *festoons.* Festoons may be present in both sexes, although they may not be evident in engorged females. Ventrally (Fig. 144), an *anal* groove may set off a plate or area on which the anus is located; the anal groove may be evident only in front of the anus, or it may occur only beside and behind the anus. Other plates of the ventral surface may be of some taxonomic significance, such as the *adanal plates* (to each side of the anal plate) and the *accessory plates* (anterior to the adanal plates).

Ticks vary considerably in size according to species but in fully engorged females rarely exceed 20 mm in length. The females are capable of great distention and, when fully engorged, are beanlike in form.

Tick Mouth Parts and Feeding Habits. The capitulum bears the mouth parts and palps (Fig. 20). The basal portion is known as the *basis capituli,* from which projects a pair of protrusible chelicerae. The distal portions (digits) of the chelicerae are divergent, and are provided with recurved teeth. Situated ventrally and medianly and projecting forward from the *basis capituli* is the *hypostome,* bearing many recurved teeth. Laterally are located the *palpi* (one pair) consisting of four segments, of which three are commonly visible.

For sucking blood, both the hypostome and the chelicerae are inserted into the skin of the host. The impression that the mouth parts are formed like

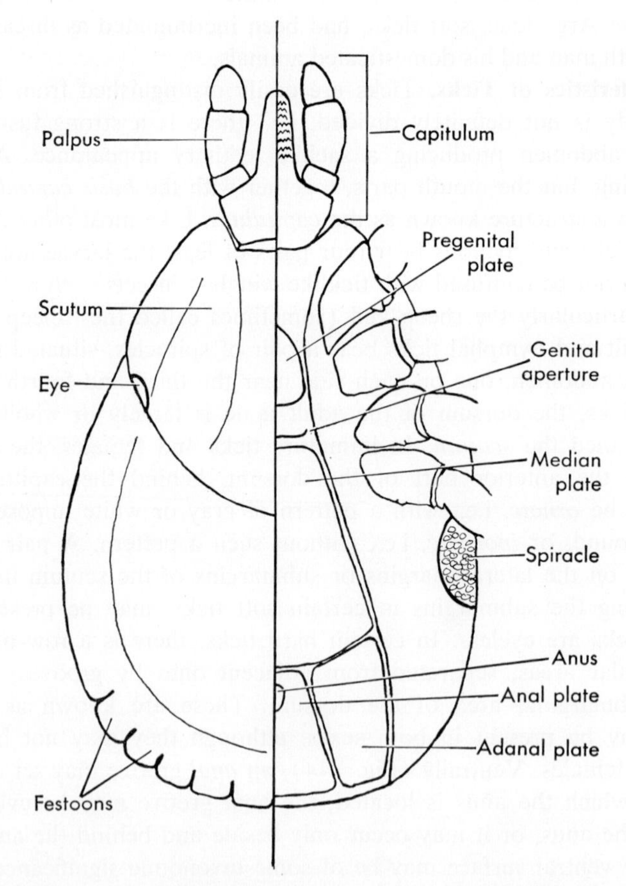

Fig. 144. Diagrammatic illustration of the anatomy of an ixodid tick. (*Left*) Dorsal view; (*right*) ventral view. (Redrawn and adapted as a composite of two illustrations from Gregson, 1956.)

a corkscrew and may be removed by "unscrewing" is of course erroneous. By "unscrewing" one is more likely to leave the mouth parts in the flesh. Because of the recurved teeth and a quick hardening "cement" that it may secrete about them,[41] the tick is enabled to hold so fast to the host that it is difficult to remove it without tearing the capitulum from the body of the tick. The tick itself, however, is apparently able to detatch itself quickly and with little effort, at will, after it has fed to repletion.

One does not usually feel the tick when it is biting. As Cooley[14] has so well said, "a person is always completely surprised when he finds a tick attached." For removal of ticks which have become attached, see page 470.

The length of time that a tick remains attached in the act of uninterrupted feeding depends on the species and the stage of development. The larval ticks commonly feed for a number of days. The nymphs and adults differ greatly in this respect; thus, the common poultry tick, *Argas persicus,* feeds nightly and intermittently, while the nymphs and adults of the cattle tick, *Boophilus annulatus* (Say), feed from 6 to 8 days before becoming fully engorged. Nymphs of *Otobius megnini* are known to feed for months. Other species of ticks, notably the relapsing fever tick, *Ornithodoros hermsi,* are able to engorge fully in from 15 to 20 minutes. Both male and female ticks suck blood; in the case of the Ixodidae, only the females become greatly distended when engorged, while both sexes become distended in the Argasidae.

Life History. Under natural conditions a few species of ticks show a rather marked host specificity, e.g., *Boophilus annulatus* on cattle, and *Dermacentor parumapertus* on jack rabbits. However, most species have a fairly wide range of hosts, e.g., *Dermacentor occidentalis.* The life histories of ticks vary considerably for the several species; hence, it is quite impossible to generalize, except that it may be said that all species of ticks pass through four stages (*egg, larva, nymph,* and *adult*) in from 6 weeks to 2 years, e.g., the Rocky Mountain wood tick, *Dermacentor andersoni* Stiles, requires normally about 2 years to complete its life history. The fully engorged female ticks usually deposit their eggs on the ground, the number varying from 100 in some species to 18,000 in others. The larvae are hexapod (six-legged) and remain in this condition until the first molt is completed. The nymph emerges from the first molt with its fourth pair of legs present and remains in this stage until the time that it transforms to the sexually mature form, or adult. Ixodid ticks have only one nymphal stage, but there may be as many as five nymphal molts in argasid ticks. Copulation takes place after the last molt when the females engorge and then deposit eggs. In the majority of species the ticks drop off the host animal to molt, but in several species, notably *Dermacentor albipictus* and those of the genus *Boophilus,* the molting takes place on the host. In *Boophilus* there may be two or possibly three generations of ticks in 1 year under very favorable climatic conditions.

The larval ticks emerging from the eggs on the ground commonly climb up grasses and other low vegetation in order to come within easy reach of grazing or passing animals. The nymphs and adults of many species have similar habits. Wild lilac (*Ceanothus*) is a favorable shrub for that purpose, in fact in some localities in California it is known as a "tick bush."

The larvae having reached the body of the host, there follows a sequence of feeding and molting until maturity is reached. When this sequence is completed on one animal, as for example in the case of the cattle fever tick, the species is said to be a *one-host tick*. When the sequence is completed on two host animals, as with the African red tick, *Rhipicephalus evertsi* Neumann, the species is said to be a *two-host tick*. The larva of this two-host species hatches on the ground like other ticks, then proceeds to attach itself to the inner surface of the ear of the host animal where it becomes fully engorged and molts. The nymph then engorges and drops off to molt, after which the adult tick emerges and must now find a second host upon which it engorges and then drops to the ground, where the female lays her eggs.

When the tick species requires three different hosts to complete its cycle, it is called a *three-host tick,* as for example, *Dermacentor andersoni,* the Rocky Mountain wood tick. In this species the larva selects smaller mammals, such as ground squirrels upon which engorgement is achieved after which the larva drops to the ground to molt and reaches the nymphal stage. In this stage the second host is also one of the smaller mammals. After engorging, the nymph drops to the ground, molts, and reaches the adult stage. It once more finds a host animal (usually one of the larger animals or sometimes man) upon which it feeds and then drops to the ground, where the female lays her eggs.

In such species of ticks as *Ornithodoros hermsi,* a vector of the relapsing fever in California and other western states, several individual host animals are required; such species are known as *many-host ticks*. There are usually five molts in this species, each of which is completed off the host; hence, at least five host animals are needed to complete the cycle. Moreover, the adult may feed intermittently, and consequently additional hosts may be attacked by this stage of the tick.

Longevity. The longevity and hardiness of ticks are truly remarkable, a matter not to be overlooked in applying control measures. Furthermore, chemicals which kill most insects in a few minutes may act very slowly on these arachnids.

Unfed larvae of *Argas persicus* remain alive quite readily for more than a month; nymphs survive a longer time, and the adults even longer than the nymphs. Nuttall and Warburton[60] cite cases in which nymphs of this species survived 2 months, and adults (unfed) "a little over two years." Graybill[37] reports considerable variation in the longevity of *Boophilus annulatus,* depending on the season of the year; unfed larvae survived from 7 to 85 days (average 38.6) for July, and 30 to 234 days (average 167.4) for October. Nuttall and Warburton mention cases in which the unfed larvae of *Ixodes ricinus* survived 19 months; unfed nymphs, 18 months; and unfed adults, 15 to 27 months. Unfed adult *Dermacentor andersoni* survived 413 days. Herms kept a female *Otobius megnini* alive without food in a pill box for 2 years and 7 months. A specimen of *Ornithodoros coriaceus* remained alive similarly over 6 years with an average of 2 blood meals annually.

Gregson[38] has recorded an adult life span of 7 years for *Ixodes texanus* Banks and some soft ticks, and a total life cycle of more than 21 years for

TABLE II
DIFFERENCES BY WHICH THE TWO FAMILIES OF THE IXODOIDAE MAY BE SEPARATED (ADAPTED FROM NUTTALL)

	ARGASIDAE	IXODIDAE
Sexual dimorphism	Slight	Marked
Capitulum	Ventral	Anterior
Base	No porose areas	Porose areas in females
Palpi	Leglike, with subequal segments	Relatively rigid, of very varied form
Body		
Scutum	Absent	Present
Festoons	Absent	Generally present
Eyes (when present)	Lateral on supracoxal folds	Dorsal on the sides of the scutum
Legs		
Coxae	Unarmed	Generally armed with spurs
Tarsi	Without ventral spurs	Generally armed with 1 or 2 ventral spurs
Pulvilli	Absent or rudimentary	Always present

I. texanus. (On the other hand, *I. pacificus* apparently can live only a few months under the best of conditions.) Anastos has mentioned a Russian record of adult ticks being kept alive 40 years, with five-year feedings (personal communication, Gregson to James).

Classification. The ticks are considered by some authors to form a separate suborder of Acarina, the Ixodides; and by others to form, along with a number of mite families, the suborder Mesostigmata. They constitute the superfamily Ixodoidea, which includes well over 500 species, and which is divided into two* families, namely: (1) *Ixodidae,* also known as the hard-bodied ticks, comprises scutate ticks with a terminal capitulum; sexual

* A third family, Nuttalliellidae, contains a single rare African species, *Nuttalliella namaqua* Bedford, which is morphologically intermediate between the Ixodidae and the Argasidae.

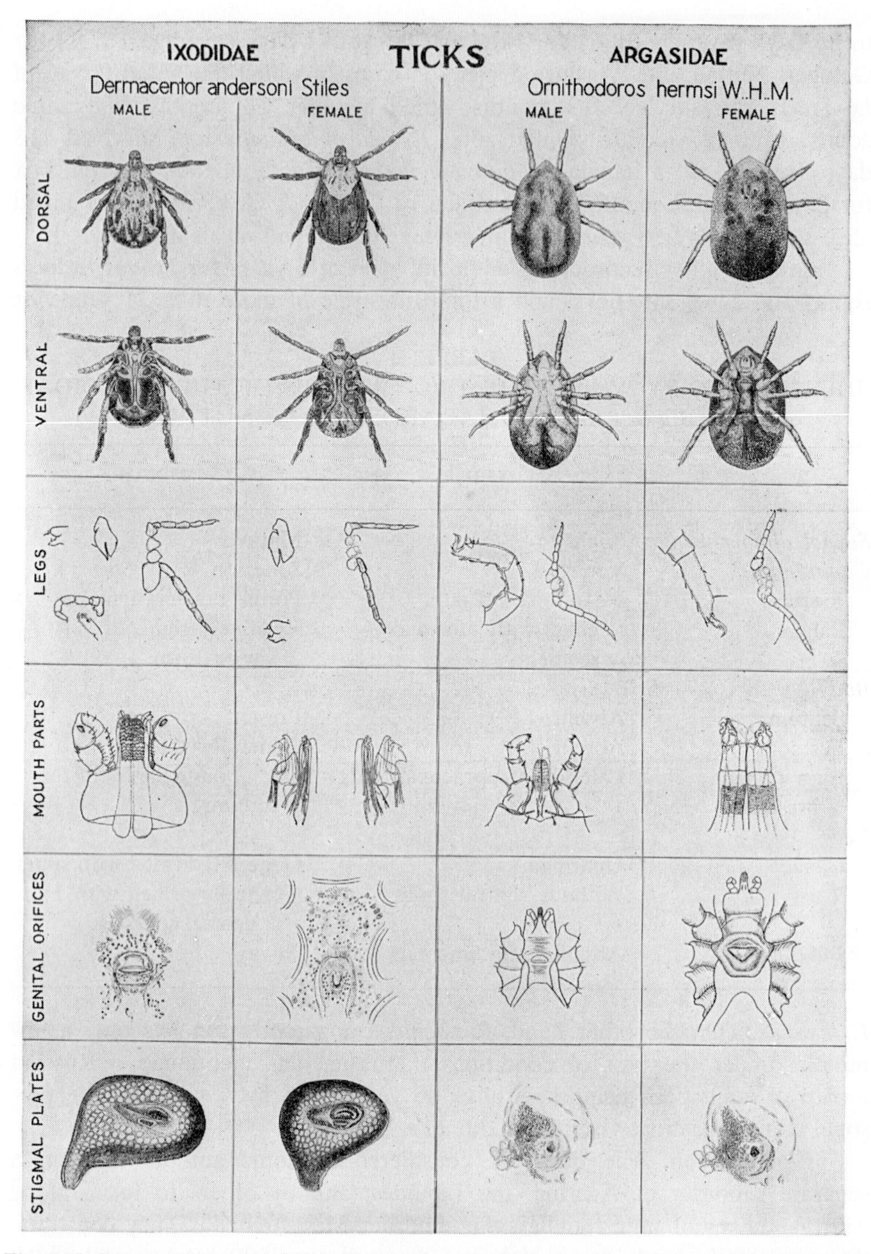

Fig. 145. Structural details of the two common families of ticks, Ixodidae and Argasidae.

dimorphism is marked; the males have a scutum which also covers the dorsum, and are incapable of great distention; in the females the scutum is a small shield immediately behind the capitulum; the females are capable of enormous distention. (2) *Argasidae,* also known as the soft-bodied ticks, includes ticks without a scutum (nonscutate); sexual dimorphism is not marked; the capitulum is ventral and the palpi are leglike; the eyes when present are lateral and situated on the supracoxal folds; the spiracles are very small. The student will find the papers by Bequaert,[5] Cooley,[15,16] and Cooley and Kohls[17,18,19] very useful in the taxonomy of ticks. A more recent publication by Gregson[39] will aid further in the study of the ixodid ticks of Canada and the northern United States.

The two families may be readily separated by means of Table II (p. 441) and Figure 145.

FAMILY IXODIDAE (HARD-BODIED TICKS)

The Family Ixodidae. Nuttall and Warburton[60] include nine genera in the family Ixodidae, namely, *Ixodes, Haemaphysalis, Dermacentor, Rhipicentor, Rhipicephalus, Margaropus, Boophilus, Hyalomma,* and *Amblyomma.* Two other genera of some importance that are now recognized are *Aponomma* and *Anocentor* (= *Otocentor*). Other genera have been proposed in recent years, but either they are of no medical or veterinary importance or else they have not been generally accepted. The following key (see also Fig. 146) will separate the above-mentioned genera.

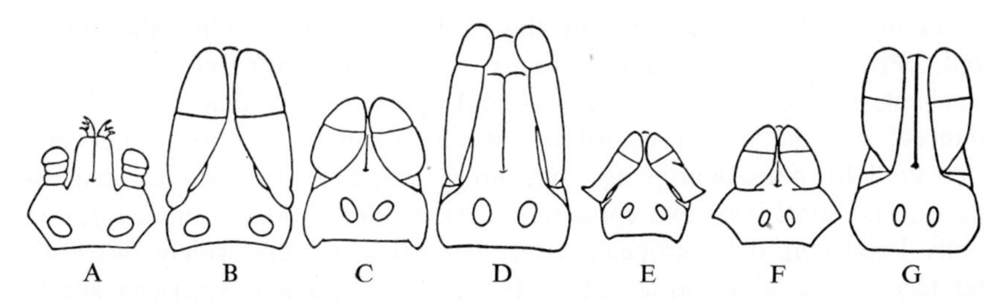

Fig. 146. Characteristic capituli of several genera of ixodid ticks: (*A*) *Boophilus;* (*B*) *Ixodes;* (*C*) *Dermacentor;* (*D*) *Amblyomma;* (*E*) *Haemaphysalis;* (*F*) *Rhipicephalus;* and (*G*) *Hyalomma.* (Adapted after Cooley.)

KEY TO THE GENERA OF IXODID TICKS OF MEDICAL IMPORTANCE

1. Eyes absent.. 2
   Eyes present 4
2. Anal groove surrounding the anus in front; festoons absent; inornate. .*Ixodes*
   Anal groove not surrounding the anus in front; festoons present; ornate or inornate 3

3. Ornate or inornate tropical or subtropical ticks, occurring mostly on reptiles; second palpal segment much longer than wide........*Aponomma*
   Inornate ticks; second palpal segment about as long as wide...*Haemaphysalis*
4. Mouth parts much longer than the basis capituli; second palpal segment much longer than wide.. 5
   Mouth parts about as long as the basis capituli; second palpal segment as long as wide.. 6
5. Eyes submarginal; adanal plates present in the males; scutum inornate ....*Hyalomma*
   Eyes marginal; adanal plates absent in the male (though small, ventral sclerotized plates may occur close to the festoons); scutum usually ornate ....*Amblyomma*
6. Festoons absent.. 7
   Festoons present 8
7. Male with a preanal plate which is continued backward as two prongs, one on each side of the anus; no adanal or accessory plates; segments of fourth leg greatly swollen..........................*Margaropus*
   Male without preanal plate but with adanal and accessory plates; segments of fourth leg not greatly swollen.........................*Boophilus*
8. Usually ornate; ventral plates absent in both sexes...........*Dermacentor*
   Usually inornate; ventral plates present or absent.................. 9
9. Ventral plates present in the male......................*Rhipicephalus*
   Ventral plates absent in both sexes............................. 10
10. Basis capituli hexagonal dorsally; spurs on coxa IV of male very long ....*Rhipicentor*
    Basis capituli rectangular dorsally; spur on coxa IV short........*Anocentor*

Genus Ixodes. This genus is world-wide in its distribution. About 40 North American species are recognized. It is clearly separated from all other genera of the family Ixodidae by the anal groove surrounding the anus in front (Prostriata). Eyes and festoons are absent; coxae either unarmed, trenchant, spurred, or bifid; tarsi without spurs; sexual dimorphism is pronounced, especially with regard to the capitulum; in the male the venter is covered by nonsalient plates; one pregenital, one median, one anal, two adanal, and sometimes two epimeral plates. *Ixodes ricinus* (Linnaeus), commonly known as the European castor bean tick, is very widely distributed and feeds on a wide variety of hosts. A closely related American species, *Ixodes scapularis* Say, the black-legged tick, is widespread in the southeastern United States and along the East Coast. It congregates along paths, trails, and roadways and may inflict a painful bite on man. *Ixodes pacificus* Cooley and Kohls (Fig. 147) is a common deer tick in California but flourishes on cattle as well. It bites human beings freely and often causes severe disturbances.

Genus Dermacentor. These are ornate ticks with eyes; festoons, 11 in number; palpi short, broad, or moderate; basis capituli, rectangular dorsally. In some species coxae from I to IV of the male increase progressively in size; in all species coxa IV is much the largest; the male shows no ventral plates or shield. Coxa I is bifid in both sexes. The spiracles are suboval or comma-shaped. The genus includes about 20 species.

Dermacentor variabilis (Say) the American dog tick, is the principal, if not the only, vector of Rocky Mountain spotted fever in the central and eastern portion of the United States. It is also an important vector of tularemia. It may cause canine paralysis and is a common pest of dogs, which are the preferred hosts of adult ticks of this species. It also freely attacks horses and many other animals, including man. The immature stages feed almost exclusively on small rodents, very largely on meadow mice [*Microtus pennsylvanicus pennsylvanicus* (Ord) in the Atlantic states]. It is widely distributed North American species. It is commonly referred to as the "American dog tick" (Smith, Cole, and Gouck[85]). It commonly congregates along trails, paths, and roadways where man is apt to be attacked.

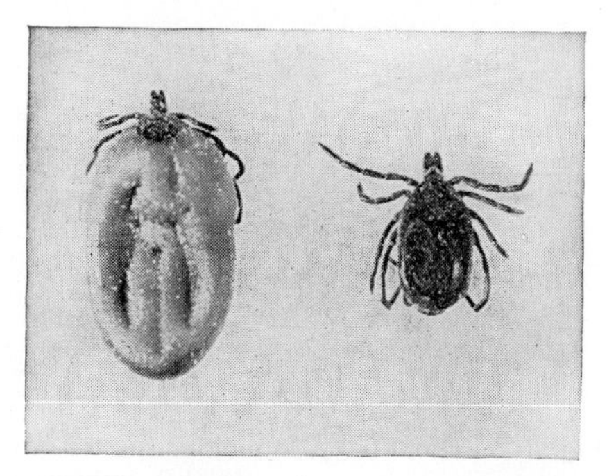

Fig. 147. A common deer and cattle tick of the Pacific coast, *Ixodes pacificus;* (*left*) female; (*right*) male. × 3.5.

The fully engorged females drop from the host and in 4 to 10 days lay their eggs (4000 to 6500) on the ground. The incubation period during the summer months is about 35 days; however, temperature influences this stage greatly. The larvae remain on the ground or on low-growing vegetation while awaiting a host, usually a field mouse. The period of larval engorgement varies from 3 to 12 days (average about 4 days), after which the larvae drop to the ground and molt in about a week, although this period is often greatly prolonged. The nymphs having reached a host, again usually a field mouse, engorge in from 3 to 11 days (average about 6 days) and once more drop to the ground and molt in from 3 weeks to several months. The unfed adults may live for more than 2 years; however, having reached the adult stage the ticks usually attack dogs and other large host animals including man. Engorgement of the females requires from 6 to 13 days. Mating takes place on the host. Like the unengorged adults, the immature stages have a remarkable longevity in the absence of suitable hosts, which may prolong the life history 2 or more years, although under favorable conditions the life cycle from egg to adult may not require more than 3 months.

Dermacentor andersoni Stiles, the Rocky Mountain wood tick, (Fig. 148) is a widely distributed and very common species throughout western North America from British Columbia, Saskatchewan and North Dakota southward to New Mexico, Arizona, and California. "It is most abundant in regions or localities where the predominating vegetation is low, brushy, and more or less open, i.e., in areas where there is good protection for the small mammalian hosts of the larvae and nymphs with sufficient forage to attract the large hosts (either wild or domestic) of the adult ticks. It is relatively scarce in heavily timbered areas or country of a strictly grassland prairie type" (Parker *et al.*[71]).

This species may be recognized by comparison with Figure 148. The adult ticks feed mostly on large animals, such as horses, cattle, sheep, and

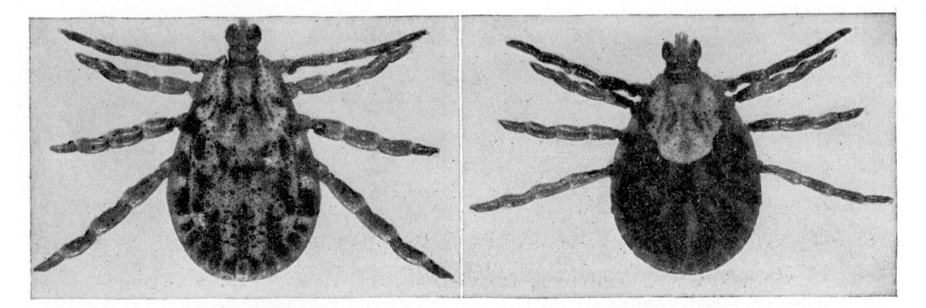

Fig. 148. The Rocky Mountain spotted fever tick, *Dermacentor andersoni;* (*left*) male; (*right*) unengorged female. × 3.5.

also deer, bear, and coyote; the larvae and nymphs feed on small mammals such as rabbits, ground squirrels, pine squirrels, woodchucks, and chipmunks; all three stages may feed on animals of intermediate size such as jack rabbits and porcupines.

The life cycle of the Rocky Mountain wood tick is fully described by Cooley,[14] and from his description the following summary is largely taken. Copulation takes place on the host, and, when fully fed, the greatly distended female drops to the ground. The preoviposition period is about a week, after which egg-laying begins, continuing over a period of about 3 weeks. If undisturbed, the eggs pile up ahead of the female in one large mass, averaging some 6400 eggs. The incubation period of the eggs requires about 35 days, when the larvae emerge and find suitable hosts, feed for 3 to 5 days, drop off and molt in from 6 to 21 days, emerging as nymphs with four pairs of legs.

These nymphs, the progeny of overwintered adults, go into hibernation to come up for feeding the next spring when they seek hosts, to which they attach for feeding over a period of from 4 to 9 days. When fully engorged, the nymphs drop to the ground and in 12 to 16 days or more molt, emerging as adults. Some of these adults may find hosts in the same summer in which they have emerged as adults, but by the time they have emerged, Cooley explains, the season has generally become hot and dry, making it necessary for them to seek protection under waste vegetation. The "normal cycle" is therefore 2 years. The larvae are found feeding through the summer months, and while the adults commonly disappear by about July 1, the nymphs continue in diminishing numbers until late summer. Since man is usually bitten only by adult ticks, danger from this source exists from early spring to about July 1, although the danger period may extend well into August at high elevations.

Like other species of ticks *Dermacentor andersoni* is remarkably resistant to starvation. Hunter and Bishopp[52] report that all unfed larval ticks hatching from a mass of eggs usually die within 1 month after the first eggs hatch if food is not available. However, in one instance a period of 117 days elapsed between the beginning of hatching of the eggs and the death of the last larvae. (A later record noted by these investigators exceeded 317 days.) Unfed nymphs have been found to survive 1 year and 11 days, and adults collected on vegetation during the spring months may survive for 413 days without feed. Students concerned with anatomy of this important species of tick will need to consult the work of Douglas.[27]

The very important role of *D. andersoni* in connection with Rocky Mountain spotted fever, Colorado tick fever, tick paralysis, etc., will be discussed in connection with these diseases.

Dermacentor albipictus (Packard), the winter tick (also sometimes called the elk tick or horse tick), is a widely distributed North American species. It is a one-host tick and does not occur on the host during the summer months. The eggs are laid during the spring months and hatch in from 3 to 6 weeks. The larvae then bunch tightly together, remaining in a torpid condition until the first cold weather in autumn, when they become very active and seek host animals. Molting takes place on the original host animal. The females reach maturity with the final molt and engorge usually in about 6 weeks after the seed ticks have become attached. Although the females drop off the host after final engorgement as do other ticks, egg-laying is delayed until spring, often after an interval of several months.

Heavy infestations of horses, moose, elk, and deer may result in death due to the drain on the vitality of the infested host.[44] Cattle are seldom attacked.[39] A disease of moose *Alces alces* (Linnaeus) is described by Thomas and Cahn[92] as occurring in northeastern Minnesota and the adjacent region. Man may be attacked through transfer of the tick by direct contact, as while he is skinning and dressing elk or deer. At least one case of Rocky Mountain spotted fever seems to have been transmitted by winter ticks under such circumstances, although the question as to how the tick acquired the infection is unsettled.[75]

Dermacentor occidentalis Marx has a narrow westerly distribution in Oregon and California. Adults of this species have been taken from cow, horse, mule, ass, deer, rabbit, sheep, dog, man, and the immature stages from many species of smaller animals, such as ground squirrel, rabbit, skunk, and field mouse. *Dermacentor andersoni* and *D. occidentalis,* although distinct species, are closely related and have been hybridized experimentally.

KEY TO THE ADULTS OF THE GENUS DERMACENTOR IN THE UNITED STATES (AFTER COOLEY)

1. Spurs on coxa I widely divergent.................................. 2
   Spurs on coxa I with proximal edges parallel or only a little divergent.... 3
2. Scutum with deep large punctations................*parumapertus* Neumann
   Scutum with large punctations shallow and moderate in size (known from peccary in southern Texas)............................*halli* McIntosh
3. Spiracular plate oval, without dorsal prolongation and with goblets few and large...*albipictus* (Packard)
   Spiracular plate oval, with dorsal prolongations, and with goblets many or of moderate number... 4
4. Cornua (projections extending backward from the lateral posterior dorsal angles of the basis capituli) long.....................*occidentalis* Marx
   Cornua short or of moderate length (cf. Fig. 146C).................. 5
5. Spiracular plate with goblets very numerous and small.......*variabilis* (Say)
   Spiracular plate with goblets moderate in size and number (Fig. 145).... 6
6. The larger punctations of the scutum very large and deep.....*andersoni* Stiles
   The larger punctations of the scutum moderate in size and depth (known from Rocky Mountain sheep in southern Arizona)........*hunteri* Bishop

Genus Anacentor (= *Otocentor*). Inornate ticks, with eyes present but obsolescent and with seven festoons. Basis capituli rectangular dorsally. No ventral plates present. Coxa I bifid in both sexes. Palpi short, the first and second segments fused. Spiracles oval, without dorsal prolongations. The only known species, *Anacentor nitens* (Newmann), attacks chiefly horses; it is known from extreme southern Texas to Brazil.

Genus Haemaphysalis. The members of this genus, numbering about 90 species, of which 2 are North American, are usually small, and the sexes are very similar. They are inornate and eyeless, but have festoons; the second segment of the usually short conical palpus projects laterally beyond the basis capituli forming an acute angle. The spiracles of the males are ovoid or comma-shaped; in the female rounder or ovoid. Most of the species parasitize mammals, but some are restricted to birds.

Haemaphysalis leporis-palustris (Packard) is widely distributed in the New World from Alaska and Canada to Argentina. Although it is commonly known as the rabbit tick, it has been taken on a number of species of birds and rarely on domestic animals such as the horse, cat, and dog. It rarely bites man but is important in the spread of Rocky Mountain spotted fever and tularemia among wild animal reservoir hosts.

Haemaphysalis leachii (Audouin), the yellow dog tick of Africa, is common in parts of Asia and Africa. It is usually found on wild and domestic carnivores, frequently on small rodents and rarely on cattle. This tick is a vector of malignant jaundice in dogs. *Haemaphysalis chordeilis* (Packard) occurs commonly on upland game birds in North America; it is of economic importance as a parasite of turkeys and a vector of diseases of wildlife.

Genus Rhipicentor. This small and relatively unimportant genus of ticks is inornate, with eyes and festoons present; the palpi are short with basis capituli hexagonal dorsally and having very prominent lateral angles. Coxa I is bifid in both sexes; coxa IV is much the largest; there are no ventral plates or shields; spiracles subtriangular in the female or comma-shaped in the male. The genus is exemplified by *Rhipicentor bicornis* Nuttall and Warburton.

Genus Rhipicephalus. This genus comprises about 50 species and subspecies, all Old World except for the cosmopolitan brown dog tick and possibly one other introduced species. They are usually inornate and possess eyes and festoons; the palpi are short, and the basis capituli is usually hexagonal dorsally. Coxa I is bifid. The male possesses a pair of adanal shields and usually a pair of accessory shields; some males when replete show a caudal protrusion. The spiracles are bluntly or elongatedly comma-shaped.

Rhipicephalus sanguineus (Latreille) is the brown dog tick; its principal host is undoubtedly the dog, although it is known to attack numerous other animals. Man is only uncommonly attacked by it. It is probably the most widely distributed of all ticks, inhabiting practically all countries between 50° N and 35° S, including most of the United States and parts of southeastern Canada. It is widely known as a vector of malignant jaundice of dogs and in some areas is considered to be the principal vector of boutonneuse virus. It is a vector of Rocky Mountain spotted fever in parts of Mexico. The adult ticks are most often found in the ears and between the toes of dogs, and the larvae and nymphs in the long hair at the back of the neck. The eggs are deposited in such places as cracks and crevices of the kennel or other quarters frequented by the dog. The ticks have a strong tendency to crawl upward, hence are often found hidden in cracks in the roofs of kennels or in the ceilings of porches. It may become a very great nuisance. The eggs hatch in from 20 to 30 days and over, depending upon temperature. The life cycle corresponds to that of ixodine three-host ticks.

Genus Margaropus. This genus has an obsolete anal groove and no ornamentations or festoons; the palpi are short, and the capitulum is highly sclerotized and similar in shape to that of *Boophilus*. The coxae are conical and unarmed except for a small spine posteriorly on coxa I. The male has a median plate prolonged into two long spines projecting beyond the anus on both sides; when replete it shows a caudal protrusion. It may be separated from *Boophilus,* which it closely resembles, by the presence of greatly enlarged posterior legs and by the prolonged median plate.

Margaropus winthemi Karsch, the South American winter horse tick, is restricted to a few South American highland areas. Cattle and sheep are uncommonly attacked. When engorged the females may easily be mistaken for *Boophilus decoloratus* (Koch) but may be distinguished by the dark bands at the joints of the legs. This is a one-host tick, usually appearing only during the winter months.

Genus Hyalomma. Size is usually large; ornamentation, if present, is confined to pale bands on legs; eyes, convex; festoons are more or less coalesced. Palpi are long, segment 2 less than twice as long as segment 3. Males have anal shields and usually also subanal shields. The coxae are bifid, and spiracles are usually comma-shaped.

The genus, consisting of approximately 20 species, is distributed from the Indian subcontinent, through much of U.S.S.R., the Middle East,

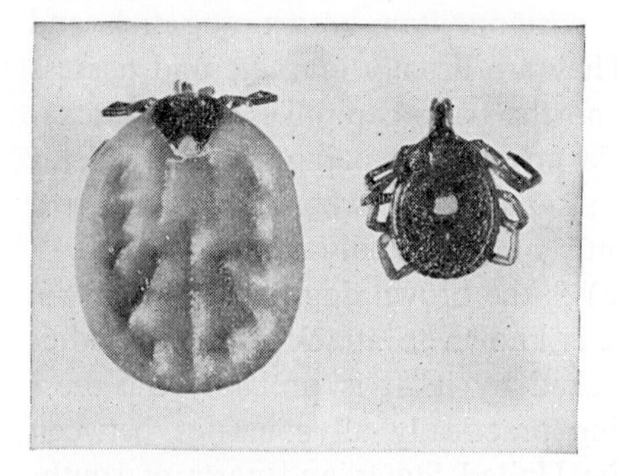

Fig. 149. The lone star tick, *Amblyomma americanum.* × 3.5.

Arabia, and North Africa, into southern Europe and southern Africa. Adults parasitize all domestic and some wild animals; those of *H. aegypitum* (Linnaeus) infest tortoises. Larvae and nymphs of some species also attack domestic animals; others parasitize small wild mammals, birds, and/or reptiles. Life cycles are of the one-, two-, or three-host type, although often variable within a single species.

These are among the hardiest of ticks; many species exist under extreme conditions of cold, heat, and aridity; they are therefore variable in appearance and often difficult to identify. The number and variety of mechanical injuries they cause and of human and animal pathogens they harbor and transmit are exceptionally great.

Genus Amblyomma. These are generally ornate ticks, with eyes and festoons; the palpi are long, segment 2 especially so; the basis capituli is of variable form. The male is without adanal shields, but small ventral plaques are occasionally present close to the festoons. Spiracles are subtriangular or comma-shaped. There are about 90 species in this genus. *Amblyomma americanum* (Linnaeus) is the "lone star" tick (Fig. 149) of the southern United States, particularly Oklahoma, Missouri, Arkansas, Texas, and

Louisiana. Its range appears to extend considerably northward, and southerly into Mexico. This species has a wide variety of hosts, including wild and domestic animals, birds, and man.[17] Unlike the common species of *Dermacentor,* this tick will attack man in the larval and nymphal, as well as the adult stages. It takes high rank as a pest and is a vector of Rocky Mountain spotted fever and tularemia. It is a three-host tick.

Amblyomma cajennense (Fabricius) occurs in Texas, Mexico, Central America, and the West Indies, and South America. Larvae, nymphs, and adults commonly attack man, horses, cattle, sheep, dogs, pigs, and many other animals. This species is abundant in a few counties in Texas.[17] It is considered to be a vector of Rocky Mountain spotted fever in Mexico, Panama, Colombia, and Brazil.

Genus Boophilus. Members of this genus have neither festoons nor ornamentations, but eyes are present. The palpi and hypostome are short,

Fig. 150. The cattle tick, *Boophilus annulatus;* (*left*) female; (*right*) male. × 3.5.

compressed, and dorsally and laterally ridged. The basis capituli is hexagonal dorsally and slightly sclerotized. Coxa I is bifid; the anal groove is obsolete in the female and faintly indicated in the male. Unfed adults are small; the scutum of the females is quite small, and spiracles are circular or oval in both sexes. There are only a few species known, and some of these are still of uncertain taxonomic validity.

The cattle tick, *Boophilus annulatus* (Say) (Fig. 150), in the western hemisphere is normally restricted to the southern United States and Mexico. A similar if not identical species, *B. calcaratus* (Birula), occurs in the Mediterranean basin and the Near East. Populations apparently referable to *B. annulatus* also occur in central Africa and certain other parts of the world. Although typically a cattle tick, the species occurs at times on deer, horses, donkeys, sheep, goats, and other animals. This species and the tropical cattle tick, *B. microplus* (Canestrini),[90] of similar habits and economic importance, have now been eradicated from the United States. The latter species still occurs abundantly in the West Indies, and Mexico and in countries southward to Argentina and Chile. It is also widely distributed in many other parts of the world.

Fully engorged females range in length from 10 to 12 mm, while the males range from 3 to 4 mm. The body of the female is about equally rounded both posteriorly and anteriorly, with a slight median incurving. The anterior pair of legs is set well out on the shoulders away from the capitulum (in *Dermacentor* close to the capitulum). The palpi are short, and the capitulum is inconspicuous. The relatively small (about 1 mm long) scutum is solid chestnut brown in color.

Economic Importance. In 1906 it was estimated that the annual losses to southern United States occasioned by the cattle tick directly and indirectly amounted to $130,500,000.[1] This sum included: (1) death, from Texas fever, of pure-bred cattle imported from the North for breeding purposes; (2) death, from Texas fever, when cattle reared in isolated tick-free areas were unintentionally or accidentally placed with ticky cattle, or on tick-infested areas; (3) death of native cattle from excessive parasitism and fever, occasioned by the ticks; (4) universal loss of weight by all tick-infested cattle, and their failure to gain flesh at a rate great enough to make beef production profitable; (5) the lower price which "southern" cattle brought upon the market, regardless of how perfect their condition; (6) sterility induced in high-grade cattle by tick infestation; (7) the expense of maintaining the federal quarantine for the protection of the North against invasion by the tick, and the added expense of maintaining quarantine pens for southern cattle shipped North for slaughter; (8) the discouraging effect on the breeding of pure-bred cattle in the South by reason of southern breeders not being allowed to exhibit in northern show rings; (9) by no means least, the potential loss in fertility of southern farm lands due to a one-crop system, which, with the tick eradicated, would quickly give way to a diversified agriculture, thus tending to conserve and increase fertility of soils; (10) shrinkage in milk production of tick-infested cattle.

From 1906, when cooperative tick-eradication work was undertaken between the United States Bureau of Animal Industry and state authorities, to December, 1918, a total of 456,529 square miles of territory was released from quarantine against Texas cattle fever, which speaks well for methods employed. The tick has subsequently been eradicated from the United States.

Life History of the Cattle Tick. Boophilus annulatus is a one-host tick. The life history may be divided into two phases: (1) the parasitic phase during which the tick is attached to the host and which terminates when the mature tick drops to the ground after fertilization; (2) the *nonparasitic* phase when the tick is on the ground. After the mature female tick drops to the ground, there is a preoviposition period of 3 or 4 days to perhaps a month. Oviposition usually begins about 72 hours after the tick drops and continues usually for 8 or 9 days but may be greatly prolonged if the temperature is adverse.

The maximum number of eggs deposited by a female tick according to Graybill[37] was 5105, the minimum 357, with an average ranging from 1811 to 4089. The incubation period, also dependent on temperature, ranged from 19 days in summer to 180 days in early autumn, with the average of 43.6 days for April, 26.3 days for May, 24.5 days for June, 20.5 days for July, 21.2 days for August, and 35.9 days for September. The hatching period depends on the time when the eggs are laid, the eggs first deposited ordinarily hatching first. The larvae on hatching are very active; they climb onto blades of grass or other objects which they ascend to the top, remaining clustered there until a suitable host animal brushes against them to which they can attach themselves. The time during which the larvae

TABLE III

COMPARISON OF THE LIFE CYCLE OF A WOOD TICK AND THE TEXAS CATTLE FEVER TICK

WOOD TICK (*Dermacentor variabilis* or *D. andersoni*)	TEXAS CATTLE FEVER TICK (*Boophilus annulatus*)
I. Adult tick becomes engorged on host animal and drops to ground	Adult tick becomes engorged on host animal and drops to ground
II. Adult tick begins egg laying after 3–5 days	Adult tick begins egg laying after 3–5 days
III. Larvae hatch from eggs in about 30 days	Larvae hatch from eggs in about 30 days
IV. Larvae ascend grass and await coming of host animal, from 1 day to several weeks	Larvae ascend grass and await coming of host animal from 1 day to several weeks
V. After feeding 3–12 days, larvae drop to ground and molt	After 7–12 days, seed ticks molt *on* host animal
VI. Nymphs crawl up on grass and await coming of second host animal from 1 day to several weeks	
VII. Ticks get on second host animal and feed 3–11 days, then *drop to ground* and molt second time	Nymphs feed 5–10 days, then molt second time *on* host animal, and the newly emerged mature ticks mate
VIII. Mature unengorged ticks crawl up on grass and await coming of third host animal from 1 day to several weeks	
IX. Adult ticks mate and feed 7–14 days to engorgement, then drop to the ground and lay eggs	Adult ticks feed 4–14 days to engorgement, then drop to the ground and lay eggs

remain alive, i.e., longevity of the newly hatched ticks, again varies considerably depending on temperature; the longevity for April ticks was found to be 65.1 days; May ticks, 62.3 days; June ticks, 65.1 days; July ticks, 38.6 days; August ticks, 84.9 days; October ticks, 167.4 days.

The three stages considered in the parasitic period of the ticks are larval (seed ticks), nymphal, and adult. As Graybill has well said, "The duration of each of these stages and the duration of a single infestation upon cattle during different portions of the year are of great practical importance. Upon the duration of an infestation depends the time animals must be kept on the tick-free fields in order to become free from ticks." After the seed tick has attached itself to the host, the larval period ranges from 5 to 10 days, the nymphal period from 5 to 20 days, and the life of the adult female from 5 to 35 days, with a total period of infestation, including the time for molting twice, which is accomplished on the host, from 20 to 65 days. The entire life cycle may be completed in about 40 days under most favorable conditions, usually nearer 60 days under natural conditions.

DISEASES CAUSED BY IXODID TICKS

Texas Cattle Fever. Bovine piroplasmosis or babesiosis, splenic fever, bloody murrain, Mexican fever, red water, etc., are names given to a widely distributed disease of cattle, being endemic in southern Europe, Central and South America, parts of Africa, the Philippines, Mexico, and formerly in the southern United States, where it has been known for more than a century, having been introduced into this country probably from Europe. Eradication of the tick vectors of the causal organism, *Babesia bigemina* (Smith and Kilbourne), a protozoon (Fig. 151), has eliminated the disease from the United States, but constant vigilance is required to prevent its introduction again from countries where it is still prevalent. There has been no bovine babesiosis in the United States since 1939.

The name Texas fever became attached to the disease in the United States because of the large herds of cattle which were driven northward from Texas, giving a certain disease in some mysterious manner to northern cattle that crossed the trail of the southern cattle. The first account of the disease was given by James Mease in 1814 before the Philadelphia Society for Promoting Agriculture. In 1879 Salmon began an investigation of the disease; and in 1889 Smith made his epoch-making discovery of the intracorpuscular protozoon parasite inhabiting the blood of the diseased cattle. Immediately thereupon followed the experiments of Smith and Kilbourne, on suggestion of Salmon, which proved the disease to be tick-borne, a suspicion held as early as 1869 according to Smith and Kilbourne. Until that time (1889) infection was variously attributed to saliva, urine, or feces. The

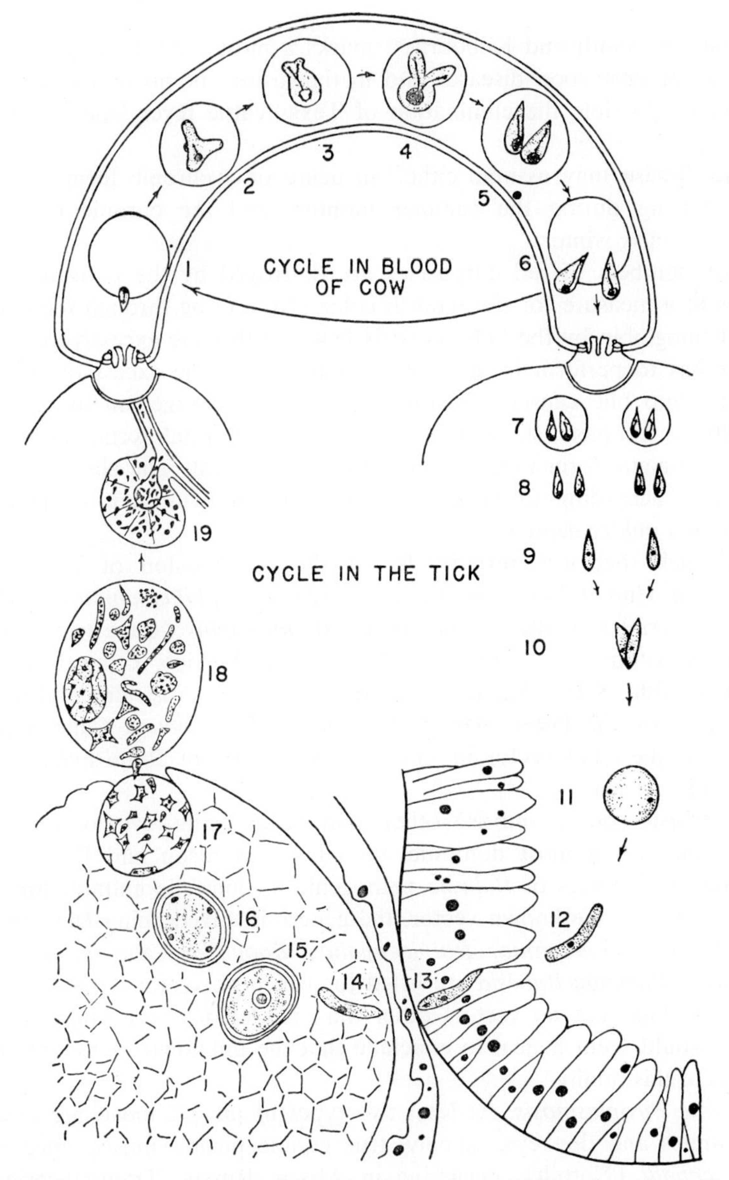

Fig. 151. A schematic diagram of the life cycle of *Babesia bigemina*. (*1–6*) The cycle in the bovine host, showing binary fission; (*7*) parasite just taken into the gut of the tick; (*8*) freed trophozoites in the gut of the tick; (*9*) vermicule-like isogametes; (*10*) beginning of syngamy, association of the gametes in pairs; (*11*) completion of syngamy; (*12*) motile zoite or ookinete; (*13–14*) ookinete passing through wall of gut of tick, through the oviduct, and entering the ovum; (*15*) sporont formed by the rounding-up and growth of the ookinete; (*16–17*) formation of sporoblasts; (*18*) sporokinetes in one of the large cells which are destined to form part of a salivary acinus; (*19*) sporozoites in a salivary gland (a single acinus shown) of the larva of the tick, whence they are transferred into the blood of a new host. (After Dennis.)

work done by Smith and Kilbourne[86] marks a most important epoch in our knowledge of protozoon diseases and in the history of preventive medicine. It has made possible the elimination of Texas cattle fever from the United States.

The disease may assume either an acute or a chronic form, the acute form occurring during the summer months, and the chronic during the autumn and early winter.

Vast numbers of red corpuscles are destroyed by the parasites, which accounts in a measure for the reddish color of the urine through the elimination of hemoglobin by the kidneys. It is believed that the excessive work that the liver has to perform in attempting to transform the excess of destroyed corpuscles into bile causes this organ to become deranged in function, and eventually a complete stagnation may result with fatal termination. Mortality in the acute form ranges from 50 to 75 per cent. The chronic form of the disease, according to Mohler,[58] shows all the symptoms of the acute type, but in a milder degree.

The tick that was responsible for the transmission of Texas cattle fever in the United States is the cattle tick, *Boophilus annulatus* (Say). Other tick carriers of the protozoon are *B. microplus* (Canestrini) and *B. decoloratus* within their range—for the former, Mexico, Central America, southern Florida, South America, the Oriental region, Australia, and parts of Africa; and for the latter, Africa. *Haemaphysalis punctata* Canestrini and Fanzango is the chief vector in Europe, and species of *Rhipicephalus* serve as vectors in Africa.[77]

Babesiosis (piroplasmosis) other than Texas cattle fever occurs in one form or another in most domestic animals. Richardson and Kendall[77] list nine additional species of *Babesia* pathogenic to domestic animals for which ticks are listed as the known vector, the genera involved being *Dermacentor, Haemaphysalis, Hyalomma, Rhipicephalus, Boophilus,* and *Ixodes*. Four additional pathogenic *Babesia* are listed for which no vector is known, but in view of the fact that no vectors other than ixodid ticks are known for this genus, it would seem logical to conclude that the unknown vectors are probably ticks of this family.

Equine Piroplasmosis. At least two types of piroplasmosis are found in horses, mules and donkeys, namely, true equine piroplasmosis, traceable to *Babesia caballi* (Nuttall), occurring in Africa, Russia, Transcaucasia, and probably Siberia, and secondly a similar though distinct disease traceable to *Babesia equi* Laveran, occurring in Transcaucasia, Italy, Africa, India, and South America (Brazil). *Babesia caballi* is transmitted by three species of *Dermacentor,* four of *Hyalomma,* and two of *Rhipicephalus,* and *Babesia equi* is transmitted by two species of *Dermacentor,* four of *Hyalomma,* and three of *Rhipicephalus*.

Canine babesiosis (*piroplasmosis*), also known as "malignant jaundice" of dogs, is prevalent in southern Europe, Asia, South Africa, and more recently in the United States (Florida). The causal organism is *Babesia canis* (Piana and Galli-Valerio). *Rhipicephalus sanguineus* is a carrier in many parts of the world; *Hyalomma marginatum* Koch is a vector in Russia; *Haemaphysalis leachii* (Audouin) is a South African vector; *Dermacentor reticulatus* (Fabricius) and *Ixodes ricinus* (Linnaeus) transmit the infection in southern Europe. Brumpt and Larousse[10] have shown that *Dermacentor andersoni* can carry the disease. The infection is transovarian in the tick, but transmission to the dog is effected by the bite of the adults, not by the bite of larvae or nymphs, according to Brumpt.[9] The incubation period varies from 10 to 20 days. Sanders[84] reported that *R. sanguineus* is by far the most common species encountered in kennels and on animals affected with canine babesiosis in Florida.

East Coast fever is a highly fatal disease of cattle in eastern, central, and southern Africa. The mortality, it is said, may run over 90 per cent and may, in endemic areas, take 80 per cent of the cattle crop annually. The disease is caused by the protozoon, *Theileria parva* (Theiler), family Theileridae. Unlike red water, it is not readily transmitted by means of blood inoculations, nor is it accompanied by jaundice or hemoglobinuria. A very characteristic symptom is swelling of the superficial lymphatic glands.

The disease is transmitted by several species of ticks as reported by Lounsbury as early as 1906. The adult brown tick, *Rhipicephalus appendiculatus* Neumann, is the most important vector, but the disease may also be transmitted by the Cape brown tick, *R. capensis* Koch, and the red tick, *R. evertsi* Neumann.

Henning[45] states that, unlike red water, East Coast fever is not transmitted from the adult female tick to the larvae through the egg, but only by an adult tick which became infected during its nymphal stage or by a nymph that became infected during the larval stage. A single tick can transmit the infection only once, and that during the stage following the one in which it had the infectious meal. While *Rhipicephalus appendiculatus* and *R. capensis* are three-host ticks, *R. evertsi* is a two-host tick; hence, since the tick remains on the same host during both its larval and nymphal stages, transmission of the infection is possible only during the adult stage.

Bovine Anaplasmosis. Anaplasmosis is an important and practically world-wide infection of cattle caused by minute punctiform blood parasites described by Theiler in 1910 as *Anaplasma marginale* with the organism at or near the periphery of the red cells and *A. centrale,* a somewhat smaller body, located approximately in the center of the infected corpuscle. The latter species is relatively benign.

Anaplasmosis is an acute, subacute, or chronic, febrile, infectious, protozoan disease. The average mortality ranges from 30 to 50 per cent in the animals affected. Mechanical transmission of the infection by several species of tabanid flies has been reported, and Stiles[89] records a total of 17 species of ticks which have been incriminated by various investigators in transmission, among them *Boophilus annulatus* (Say), *B. decoloratus* (Koch), *B. microplus* (Canestrini), *Rhipicephalus simus* Koch, *R. bursa* Canestrini and Fanzango, *Ixodes ricinus* (Linnaeus), *Hyalomma lusitanicum* (Koch), *Rhipicephalus sanguineus* (Latreille), *Dermacentor variabilis* (Say), *D. andersoni* Stiles, and *D. occidentalis* Neumann. Transovarian transmission has been demonstrated.

That deer, namely the southern black-tailed deer, *Odocoileus hemionus columbianus* (Richardson), and the Rocky Mountain mule deer, *Odocoileus hemionus hemionus* (Rafinesque), may serve as reservoirs for anaplasmosis was proved by Boynton and Woods in 1933.[7]

Rocky Mountain spotted fever has been known in the Bitter Root Valley of Montana since 1872.[88] It is also known as "tick fever," "black fever," "blue disease," and "black measles." The most characteristic and constant symptom is the rash which appears about the second to the fifth day on the wrists, ankles, and less commonly on the back, later spreading to all parts of the body. Parker[67] states that the rash is sometimes preceded by a mottled appearance of the skin. The symptoms most often complained of at the outset are frontal and occipital headaches, intense aching in the lumbar region, and marked malaise. The incubation period is from 2 to 5 days in the more severe infections and from 3 to 14 days in the milder ones. The fever rises rapidly in the more virulent infections to 104° and 106° F. In fatal infections, death usually occurs between the ninth and fifteenth day. Strains of spotted fever of different virulence occur in the same locality.

Because errors in diagnosis are easily made, laboratory tests are advised. One of the common tests consists of the intraperitoneal injection of blood (1 cc whole blood) into guinea pigs. In positive tests the guinea pigs show scrotal swelling, reddening, and sloughing of the skin, the virulence of the strain being indicated by the strength of the reaction. The causal agent was discovered by Wolbach[101] in 1919; he named it *Dermacentroxenus rickettsii* in honor of Dr. Howard T. Ricketts, who made great contributions to our knowledge of both Rocky Mountain spotted fever and typhus fever, and who lost his life in the conduct of investigations in Mexico. The several rickettsioses transmitted by lice, fleas, mites, and ticks are caused by infectious agents known as rickettsiae; hence, the causal agent of Rocky Mountain spotted fever is generally referred to as *Rickettsia rickettsi* (Wolbach).

Rocky Mountain spotted fever is endemic in the United States, in some parts of Canada, in Mexico, and in some parts of South America where it is known as São Paulo fever and by other names. The greatest number of cases occur in populations engaged in outdoor occupations, principally agriculture. Both sexes and all ages are subject to the disease. In the western part of the United States, most of the cases occur in men, while in the eastern part of the United States more women and children contract the disease. Parker suggests that this is probably due to the fact that the eastern vector is a tick, *Dermacentor variabilis,* which infests the dog, a household animal. The Rocky Mountain wood tick, *Dermacentor andersoni,* is found far less frequently on dogs.

Tick Transmission of Spotted Fever. In 1902, after a preliminary investigation, Wilson and Chowning[100] advanced for the first time the theory that a tick ("wood tick") acts as the natural vector of the disease. According to Ricketts (in the 48th Biennial Report of the Montana State Board of Health, p. 106) as recorded by Hunter and Bishopp:[52]

> . . . the first experiments which resulted in the proof of the transmission of spotted fever by a tick were conducted by Drs. McCalla and Brereton of Boise, Idaho, in 1905. In these experiments a tick which was found attached to a spotted fever patient was removed and allowed to bite a healthy person. In 8 days this person developed a typical case of spotted fever. The experiment was continued by allowing the same tick to bite a second person. In this case again a typical case of spotted fever resulted.

The famous experiments of Ricketts[78] were begun in April 1906. The more important published work of this lamented investigator has been brought together in a memorial volume[80] from which the following summary is made of his reports on spotted fever. First of all it was shown that the disease could be transmitted to guinea pigs by direct inoculation and that the duration of the fever and cutaneous phenomena resembles very closely the conditions as observed in humans. Hence, the susceptibility of this species being proven, the guinea pig was used for further experimentation.

On June 19, 1906, a small female tick was placed at the base of the ear of a guinea pig inoculated intraperitoneally June 11 with 3 cc of defibrinated blood of a patient with spotted fever. The tick fed for 2 days on this animal and was then removed and kept for 2 days in a pillbox and on June 23 placed at the base of the ear of a healthy guinea pig, the former animal dying on the same day with characteristic symptoms. On June 28, the second guinea pig showed decided rise in temperature, which continued high until July 5 and became normal on July 7. Proper controls were conducted, and two guinea pigs which were in the same cage with tick-bitten guinea pigs for 2 weeks did not become infected, indicating that mere association did not result in contracting the disease. It will be noticed that Ricketts called the wood tick which he used *Dermacentor occidentalis.* Evidently the species was actually *Dermacentor andersoni.*

In addition to many other successful experiments, during the following year Ricketts found that the disease can be transmitted by the male[79] as well as by the female tick and that "one attack of the disease establishes a rather high degree of immunity to subsequent inoculations." Furthermore, a collection of ticks taken in the field transmitted the disease to a guinea pig in the laboratory, indicating the fact that infective ticks occur in nature in small numbers.

It was also ascertained that:

> . . . the disease may be acquired and transmitted . . . by the tick during any of the active stages . . . and that the larvae of an infected female are in some instances infective . . . The disease probably is transferred through the salivary secretion of the tick, since the salivary glands of the infected adult contain the virus."

The transmission is believed to be "biological rather than purely mechanical."

Experiments conducted by Moore (Ricketts,[80] pp. 428–36) show that the "minimum duration of feeding necessary for a tick to infect a guinea pig was one hour and forty-five minutes. The average time necessary seems to be about ten hours, while twenty hours were almost constantly infective." Maver (see Ricketts, pp. 440–44), in a series of experiments with other species of ticks, found that spotted fever can be transmitted from infected to normal guinea pigs by nymphal *Dermacentor variabilis* infected as larvae, by adult *Dermacentor parumapertus* and nymphs of *Amblyomma americanum.* Ricketts showed transmission by adult *Dermacentor albipictus* infected as nymphs.

The Infection in Nature. Parker points out that field observations made in eastern Montana in 1916 and 1917 suggested that under the "epizootilogic" conditions concerned, some agent other than *Dermacentor andersoni* was likely involved in the natural maintenance of the virus. In 1923 Parker[62] established the fact that the rabbit tick, *Haemaphysalis leporis-palustris,* is capable of transmitting the infection from rabbit to rabbit and also that infected rabbit ticks occur in nature. A third important fact was established, namely that the infection is transmitted by infected female ticks to the egg as in the case of *Dermacentor andersoni.* While the rabbit tick only rarely bites man, it is important indirectly in that it is a potent vector under natural conditions and is furthermore the only known vector which occurs in all parts of the United States. The infection carried by this tick is reported by Parker to be extremely mild. Rabbits of all species studied are hosts of both wood ticks and rabbit ticks. Rabbits are natural reservoirs of the infection in western North America, field mice in other parts. Dogs are believed to be important reservoirs of the infection in the closely related disease, boutonneuse fever of Europe.

The American dog tick, *Dermacentor variabilis* was proved to be a carrier of the eastern type of Rocky Mountain spotted fever in 1931 by Dyer, Badger and Rumreich,[30] who used larvae bred from eggs. The larvae were fed on a guinea pig infected with eastern spotted fever and after engorgement were allowed to molt. The nymphs were fed to engorgement on a noninfected guinea pig and were then ground up and injected into fresh guinea pigs, thus establishing a strain of pathogens in guinea pigs. The results of these investigators confirmed the early work of Ricketts and Maver (1911). They also proved that transmission is transovarian. Parker,[66] 1937, reports successful stage-to-stage and generation-to-generation transmission with *Dermacentor occidentalis* and *Rhipicephalus sanguineus.* In the latter species, continuity of the rickettsia was shown from larval ticks of one generation through six successive stages to adults of the next. In *Amblyomma americanum,* Maver (1911) had already reported larva-to-adult continuity, and transmission from female to larva was accomplished by Parker. With *Amblyomma cajennense,* the Cayenne tick, transmission from larvae to adults has been shown, and for *Dermacentor parumapterus,* a rabbit tick, transmission from nymphs to adults was shown by Maver (1911), and continuity from larvae to nymphs as well as survival of the pathogens in adults was shown by Parker.[66] Parker states that these data are considered sufficient to indicate that each of these six additional species is a possible natural carrier of spotted fever organisms and that four of these, *D. occidentalis, R. sanguineus, A. americanum,* and *A. cajennense* are possible present or future agents of transmission to man. Actually, *Amblyomma americanum* is now known to be a vector of spotted fever in Oklahoma and Texas (Parker, Kohls, and Steinhaus[70]); and *Amblyomma cajennense* is a vector of the São Paulo fever (spotted fever) of Brazil and of Tobia petechical fever (spotted fever) of Columbia.

Transmission of the Rocky Mountain spotted fever by other ticks is a distinct possibility. Philip and Kohls[75] have shown that *D. albipictus* may, under certain circumstances, transmit the disease to man. *Anocentor nitens,* species of *Amblyomma* other than *cajennense* and *americanum,* and even species of the argasid genera, *Ornithodoros* and *Otobius,* may at times be involved. Since Philip *et al.*[74] have demonstrated the presence of the rickettsia in *Dermacentor parumapertus* feeding on native rabbits, that species must also be considered as having some importance in maintaining the natural reservoir.

Mechanism of Infection. The infection is acquired from the reservoir animal by a feeding tick in any stage of its life history and is passed on from stage to stage; e.g., infected blood is ingested by the larva, the infection is passed on to the nymph (which may infect), and thence to the adult, which in turn may infect; then at least some infected female ticks will pass the pathogen on through their eggs to the larvae of the next generation.

When normal adult ticks are first fed on an infected host, just long enough to ensure ingestion of the pathogen, and are then transferred directly to a normal host (the tick-feeding thus being interrupted but essentially continuous), Parker's[64] tests showed a period of from 9 to 12 days between the ingestion and the transmission of the pathogens. Except under experimental conditions, infection is not transmitted by the same stage of the tick that acquires it, but by the next and subsequent stages. The infection is transmitted by the *bite* of the tick. The great majority of persons with cases of Rocky Mountain spotted fever give a definite history of "tick" bite from 2 to 10 or 12 days before onset." The percentage of ticks that contain the infectious agent is reported to be very small; it may be less than 1 per cent and is rarely as high as 5 per cent.

Parker[64] states that a minority of perhaps 5 per cent of infected persons deny the possibility of having been infected by the tick bite. The reason for this can perhaps be understood in the light of Parker's studies. In an "exceptionally clear-cut series of tests," it was shown that the rickettsia from tick tissues: "would infect if merely dropped among the hairs on the unabraded skin of guinea pigs, also if dropped into the eye. In another series of tests it was demonstrated, contrary to previously accepted ideas, that tick excrement is frequently infectious." Crushed tick tissues and feces might easily produce infection through abrasion, but not through the unbroken skin. Crushing ticks with the fingernails can consequently be a dangerous practice.

The rickettsia survives the winter in infected nymphal or adult ticks. At the end of the winter the rickettsia in these ticks is present according to Parker[65] as a nonsymptom-producing and frequently immunizing form, and does not produce symptomatically recognizable infections until its level of virulence is raised, either by heat or by the ingestion of blood. This phenomenon of *reactivation* has direct bearing on the fact that the bites of hibernated ticks in nature very early in the spring do not result in frank infection. It also explains why tick bites grow more dangerous as the season advances. Parker states, "In the early spring when the . . . [rickettsia] in the recently emerged tick is at its lowest ebb of infectiousness, and while the days and nights are still cool, it takes so long for the . . . [rickettsia] to become reactivated after the tick has become attached that it is usually detected and removed before the . . . [rickettsia] has become virulent." It may be a matter of some hours and not frequently a day or more after the tick attaches itself before reactivating occurs. The shortest recorded interval is 1 3/4 hours (Ricketts). If a tick which has become attached is removed within a few hours, the danger of infection is materially minimized.

A significant factor in the epidemiology of Rocky Mountain spotted fever is the interference phenomenon demonstrated by Price.[76] When guinea pigs were infected intraperitoneally with a strain of *Rickettsia rickettsii* of low virulence, the animals were protected from the highly virulent strain, provided that the concentration of the former was 10 to 30 times that of the latter. Infection with the rickettsiae of Q fever, scrub typhus, endemic typhus, and epidemic typhus gave the same type of protection under the same conditions. The interference phenomenon may help to explain certain aspects of the epidemiology of Rocky Mountain spotted fever, e.g., the contention that in certain limited localities strains having low and high virulence persist year after year.

Other Tick-borne Rickettsioses. *Tick-borne typhus* (Boutonneuse fever, Kenya typhus, South African tick bite, etc.) is a typhuslike disease characterized by general body macular rash, the presence of a black spot (*tache-noire*) at the site of the tick bite, and swelling of the corresponding lymph nodes. Its causative agent is *Rickettsia conorii* Brumpt. Its onset, after an incubation period of usually 5 to 7 (sometimes up to 18) days, is sudden and accompanied by chills and high fever. Except in aged or physically deficient persons, the disease is usually mild. The disease has been known since 1910. It occurs throughout southern Europe, the Mediterranean areas of Asia Minor, and Africa. Excellent accounts of it have been given by Olmer and Olmer[61] and by Gear.[36]

The chief vector in the Mediterranean area is *Rhipicephalus sanguineus,* but in Africa other species of *Rhipicephalus,* as well as *Amblyomma, Haemaphysalis, Hyalomma,* and perhaps other genera are involved. Gear says, "It seems probable that most species of ixodid ticks are capable of transmitting the disease."

Queensland tick typhus, first described in 1946, is caused by *Rickettsia australis* Philip. It is very similar to the tick-borne typhus of the Mediterranean region. On epidemiologic evidence, *Ixodes holocyclus* Neumann appears to be the vector.

Several other tick-borne or presumably tick-borne diseases of the spotted fever group have been described. *Indian tick typhus,* widespread in southern Asia, is a mild disease closely related to the Mediterranean disease; a group of similar, relatively mild, acutely febrile diseases occurs in widespread areas in Siberia. A rickettsiosis with inflammation of the kidneys, which may be tick-borne or mite-borne, was reported by O. S. Korshunova, from Siberia, in 1954. For a detailed summary of these rickettsioses, the student is referred to Rivers and Horsfall.[81]

Q fever was first reported from Queensland, Australia, in 1937,[26] where most of the infected persons were abattoir workers. The same year the finding of a rickettsial infection was reported in the tissues of animals injected with *Dermacentor andersoni* ticks collected in western Montana;[21,68] the disease was called "Nine Mile fever," Nine Mile Creek being the locality at which the ticks were collected. The causal organism, *Coxiella burnetii* (Derrick) (= *Rickettsia diaporica* Cox), is now known to be the same for both described disease entities, which are consequently identical.[87] The rickettsia is now known to be present in 51 countries on five continents.[81]

Q fever is a mild to severe illness which can be debilitating and which can develop into a chronic disease. It is characterized by an acute onset with chills, prostration, and a continuous fever which lasts from a few days to as long as 3 months. The symptoms are similar to those of brucellosis, influenza, virus pneumonia, and atypical pneumonia. Because of the lack of specificity of the symptoms, diagnosis is difficult, often requiring confirmation either by isolation of the rickettsia or by rise in the specific serum antibody.[56] Death seldom results.

In light of the history of the discovery of the infection in Montana, it was natural to suspect and seek tick vectors. In 1943 Parker and Kohls[69] reported the rickettsia in the lone star tick, *Amblyomma americanum,* and in 1948 Philip[73] reported that the feces from infected *Dermacentor andersoni* were very rich in rickettsiae, which remain viable in storage as long as 586 days. At least 22 species of ixodid and argasid ticks, representing 8 genera, have been found infected, an indication that ticks play an important part in maintaining the natural reservoir of the infection.[81] In Australia *Haemophysalis humerosa* Warburton and Nuttall, which does not bite man, is considered an important vector in bandicoots (*Isodon* spp.), serving as an important factor in maintaining endemicity of the disease. *Ixodes holocyclus* Neumann, which bites man and a variety of other hosts, may be a factor where the disease exists in marsupials, in that the infection may be deposited on the skin with the tick feces or may be otherwise transmitted.

Actual transmission to man by the bite of the tick has not been satisfactorily demonstrated. In fact, the vast majority of human patients deny any history of tick bite preceding the onset of the disease. Raw milk has been shown to be one source of human infection.[50] Other human cases are attributable largely to occupational exposure to livestock (cattle, sheep, goats) or to residence near infected premises.[56] The rickettsia very easily becomes air-borne and is very resistant to destruction. Pasteurization of milk at 145° F will kill it, however. The disease is prevalent in Europe, according to Luoto, and is a serious public health problem there, perhaps because of infection in more animals, or because people live in closer proximity to infected animals.

Colorado Tick Fever. Medical reports of army physicians stationed at forts and camps in the Rocky Mountain region, as early as 1850, included descriptions of fevers occurring early in the spring, sometimes accompanied by a body rash and sometimes not so. The latter was not described as a separate clinical entity until 1930, however, when D. E. Becker called it Colorado tick fever and suggested that it was tick-borne. Parker, in 1937, reported it as a febrile disease of frequent occurrence in many parts of the Rocky Mountain region following the bite of *Dermacentor andersoni.* In 1950, Florio, Miller, and Mugrage[34] isolated the virus from ticks collected in nature and succeeded in infecting other ticks experimentally by feeding them on hamsters, which had been found to be susceptible to the virus. In 1958, Eklund, Kohls, and Jellison[32] reported isolation of the virus from the golden-mantled ground squirrel, *Citellus lateralis lateralis* (Say), and from the porcupine, *Erethizon dorsatum epixanthum* Brandt, in nature, in western Colorado, and serologic evidence of the occurrence of natural infections in the Columbian ground squirrel, *Citellus columbianus* (Ord), in western Montana. Thus, it was established that Colorado tick fever was a viral disease, transmitted to man through the bite of the tick, *Dermacentor andersoni,* with wild rodents serving as the reservoir in nature.

The disease usually starts, 4 or 5 days after the bite of the tick, with a sudden onset, with a fever, chilly sensations, headache, deep ocular pains, and severe aching of the muscles of the back. Anorexia is common, and there may be nausea, vomiting, and photophobia. *There is no rash.* Malaise is usually intense. After about 2 days, the fever is remitted, followed by a relapse of 2 to 3 days. The two febrile periods, together with a lowered leucocyte count (2000–3000 per cmm) is highly indicative, especially when there is a history of *D. andersoni* bite about 4 days prior to the onset of the fever. The disease seems to be more common in its area than Rocky Mountain spotted fever and is probably much more prevalent than records would indicate. It is a relatively mild disease, although in children symptoms of encephalitis or meningitis, coma, or mental disorientation may occur;[31] one fatal case in a child has been recorded.[81]

Colorado tick fever is the only viral disease of man in the Western Hemisphere known to be tick-transmitted. *Dermacentor andersoni* is the only proven vector, although the virus has been isolated from *D. parumapertus* and other tick species. The known distribution of the disease corresponds remarkably well with that of *D. andersoni.*[81] Rodents form the natural reservoir; the virus has been isolated in nature from the porcupine, *Erithizon dorsatum epixanthum;* the golden-mantled ground squirrels, *Citellus lateralis lateralis* and *C. l. tescorum* (Hollister); the Columbian ground squirrel, *C. columbianus columbianus;* the chipmunk, *Eutamias amoenus* (Allen); the pine squirrel, *Tamiasciurus hudsonicus richardsoni* (Bachman); and the deer mouse, *Peromyscus maniculatus* (Wagner). Burgdorfer and Eklund[11] have shown that in Montana, in spite of the presence of other reservoir hosts, Colorado tick fever appears to be characterized by sharp localization of infection correlated with the presence of the golden-mantled ground squirrel, *C. lateralis tescorum.*

Old World Viral Diseases. In the Old World, ticks are known to transmit viral diseases of two groups: the hemorrhagic fevers and the tick-borne encephalitides.

Tick-borne Hemorrhagic Fevers. In the 1940's, several disease entities were described from the Soviet Union and nearby areas and given the collective name "hemorrhagic fevers," the descriptive name referring to the bleeding (nasal, uterine, gastrointestinal, renal) accompanying the febrile periods. Chumakov[12] has grouped these diseases into three types based on their antigenic relationships: (1) hemorrhagic nephrosonephritis; (2) Crimean hemorrhagic fever; and (3) Omsk hemorrhagic fever. Hemorrhagic nephrosonephritis is thought to be mite-borne; but ticks are involved as vectors in the other two diseases.

Crimean hemorrhagic fever is an acute, systemic infection of man, occurring particularly in the late spring and summer, and widespread in the steppes of southeastern Europe and nearby Asia. The mortality rate is 2 to 8 per cent. *Hyalomma* ticks are considered to be the vectors, the virus having been isolated from *H. plumbeum* (Panzer) and *H. anatolicum* Koch.

Omsk hemorrhagic fever, which has its main foci in the Great Barabin steps of the Omsk and Novosibirsk regions, Siberia, is a milder disease than the Crimean type, although it is highly pathogenic for mice, field mice, monkeys, and many other animals. The virus is antigenically related to those of the tick-borne encephalitides rather than to that of Crimean hemorrhagic fever. Ticks of the genus *Dermacentor,* particularly *D. pictus* and *D. marginatus,* are, according to Chumakov, both reservoirs and vectors.

Other tick-borne hemorrhagic fevers may exist. For example, North Bukhovinian hemorrhagic fever, found in the wooded Carpathian foothills of Northern Bukhovinia, appears to be a viral disease, and there is evidence that *Ixodes ricinus* may be the vector. Further investigation is needed to answer the question as to the status of this disease.

The Tick-borne Encephalitides. A group of tick-borne neurotropic viral diseases occurs over widespread areas in Europe and Asia. Clinical pictures vary considerably, but fully developed cases consist of two phases, an influenzalike one and a second febrile phase with involvement of the central nervous system. Apparently many cases are subclinical, and in clinical cases only the first phase may occur. During recent years, evidence indicates that the several types of tick-borne encephalitis are due to different strains of a single virus.

The form that occurs in the British Isles, louping ill, is predominantly a disease of sheep; man, though sometimes seriously affected, appears to acquire the virus in a decreased pathogenicity. Several forms occur from central Europe to eastern Siberia; in certain of these, clinical pictures, which may vary from one form to another, may be associated with similar characteristics and epidemiologic features. Russian tick-borne or spring-summer encephalitis, under at least two forms, is widespread throughout much of eastern Europe and Siberia. A Far Eastern form appears to be much more serious, with high fatality and permanent neurologic or psychotic sequelae, and with omission of the influenzalike phase. *Ixodes ricinus,* chiefly in the west, and *I. persulcatus,* chiefly farther east, are the vectors. Other species of *Ixodes* and species of *Dermacentor* and *Haemaphysalis* may also be involved in the transmission of the virus.

Kyasanur Forest disease is the name that has been given to a tick-borne viral infection[103] discovered in Mysore State, India, in 1957. Man, monkeys, and probably other animals are affected, sometimes fatally. The virus, which is closely related to those of the tick-borne encephalitides and hemorrhagic fevers, has been repeatedly isolated from ticks, most frequently from *Haemaphysalis spinigera* Neumann.

Tick Transmission of Tularemia. Parker[63] states that tularemia infection in ticks was suspected in numerous instances during the seasons of 1922 and 1923 on account of the gross lesions at death in guinea pigs into which such ticks had been injected. Confirmation was made by cultivation of *Pasteurella tularensis* from guinea pigs in which the tick strain had been propagated. *Dermacentor andersoni* collected from nature proved infective; also experimentally, infection acquired by immature ticks was passed on to subsequent stages of the same generation. Later, Parker and Spencer[72] (1926) demonstrated transovarian transmission. This is believed to be the first record of transovarian transmission of a known bacterial infection. Several species of ticks are able to transmit the infection; among them are *Dermacentor andersoni, D. occidentalis, D. variabilis, Rhipicephalus sanguineus, Amblyomma americanum,* and *Haemaphysalis leporis-palustris.* These ticks are largely responsible for the maintenance of the infection in nature. *Pasteurella tularensis* has been recovered both from infected sage hens in Montana and from the tick, *Haemaphysalis chordeilis* (Packard), taken from the same birds. Davis and Kohls[25] discovered evidence indicating that *Ixodes pacificus* Cooley and Kohls may also be a carrier of tularemia to human beings.

Tick Paralysis. A paralysis of sheep and calves attributable to ticks has been known in Australia according to Henning[45] since 1843. Paralysis reported as "acute ascending paralysis" associated with tick bite was described in 1912 by Temple[91] in Oregon. The case reported was that of a child in which there was a complete paralysis of the motor and sensory nerves extending to the knees, causing inability to stand in the morning after retirement in apparently good health. On the third day the paralysis had involved the nerves of the throat and the child was unable to swallow or speak. Upon removal of two fully engorged ticks from the occipital region, recovery was rapid and complete within a week. The ticks were not positively identified, though they were presumably *Dermacentor andersoni.* In 1913 Hadwen[42] reported cases of paralysis in sheep following the bite of *Dermacentor andersoni* (*D. venustus* Banks). He also cites excerpts from letters (*Canad. M.A.J.,* 1912) from physicians in British Columbia indicating frequent occurrence of paralysis in children following tick bites. The ticks were commonly removed from the nape of the neck.

In 1913 Hadwen and Nuttall[43] reported having produced paralysis experimentally in the dog by means of *D. andersoni.* The paralysis was the same as in sheep.

Tick paralysis occurs in a number of mammals, including man; in fact, weight for weight, man appears to be more sensitive than any other species (Gregson[40]). Gregson has shown that, among North American wild mammals, none of the larger species, except the bison, *Bison b. bison* (Linnaeus), is known to be susceptible; deer, moose, bighorn sheep, Rocky Mountain goats, and bears do not seem to be susceptible to paralysis, although deer and moose are frequently killed of exsanguination as the result of heavy infestations. On the other hand, domestic cattle, horses, domestic sheep, and dogs may be paralyzed or killed by one or a small number of ticks. Smaller wild mammals may be highly susceptible. Gregson has shown that the yellow-bellied marmot, *Marmota flaviventris avara* (Bangs), and the Columbian ground squirrel, *Citellus c. columbianus* (Ord), are readily susceptible to paralysis, a fact which has been confirmed by Hughes and Philip[51] for these animals, as well as for the hamster and for the bushy-tailed packrat *Neotoma cinerea* (Ord). The hamster furnishes a very desirable experimental animal for a study of the transmission of the disease.

Livestock are at times seriously involved. Herds of cattle in Montana have been known to succumb to paralysis and ultimately death, either from the paralysis itself or from predators taking advantage of the helpless animals, if the ticks were not removed in time. Hearle,[44] speaking of conditions in Canada, states:

> Cases in sheep have been particularly numerous, and many deaths have resulted. Cattle are usually less susceptible, but trouble from tick paralysis has been noted from time to time, and in the spring of 1930 a serious outbreak in steers was investigated; over 100 paralysis cases, sixty of them fatal, being noted in one herd. We know of only one equine case. In sheep districts where this trouble is prevalent, flock masters are obliged to examine their animals frequently for the purpose of removing the offending ticks from sheep showing symptoms of weakness or staggers.

In man, tick paralysis is an acute disease characterized by a flaccid ascending paralysis which, in fatal cases, causes death by involvement of the cranial nerves with resulting respiratory paralysis. Unlike poliomyelitis, with which it may be confused, in its early stages it is painless and without fever, or relatively so. It is most frequently observed in children under 2 years of age. In North America, it occurs chiefly in the Pacific Northwest,[82] but it is becoming more common in the eastern United States.[20]

The disease is not caused by a pathogenic organism, but rather is produced by the bite of the feeding female tick. The nature of the toxin is not yet understood; but it produces a blockage of the neuromuscular junctions and probably some of the synapses of the spinal cord,[59] and there is evidence that other specific types of neuromuscular activity may be interfered with. The toxin apparently is produced, in sufficient quantities to cause paralysis, only by the female tick, 5 to 9 days after attachment. The toxin either decomposes or is excreted rapidly, since removal of the tick before the paralysis has proceeded too far leads to rapid and complete recovery. The reason why some ticks may produce paralysis, and others of the same sex and species do not is not known; a hereditary factor may be involved.[51]

A very valuable account of the disease, its etiology, diagnosis and treatment, and a detailed description of a typical case history, has been given by Costa.[20] Although the disease is rare, accurate diagnosis is essential to save human lives. Rose[82] lists 332 cases from the Pacific Northwest, 11.7 per cent of which were fatal. Those 39 lives could almost certainly all have been saved, had the ticks been discovered and removed in time.

In the eastern and southern United States, *Dermacentor variabilis, Amblyomma americanum,* and *A. maculatum* Koch are known to produce tick paralysis in man and dogs. Most tick paralysis in the United States, however, has been associated with *Dermacentor andersoni. Ixodes holocyclus* Neumann causes paralysis in calves, sheep, and dogs in Australia, and *I. rubicundus* Neumann causes the disease in sheep, goats, and calves in South Africa.

COMBATING AND AVOIDING IXODINE TICKS

Control and Prevention. The control of Rocky Mountain spotted fever over a wide area by the control of the tick vectors has been discouraging. According to Parker[65] definite local good has been accomplished by dipping, grazing control, and the control of rodents, but lack of permanence of results and lack of knowledge as to the relative importance of the various factors of the local complex have all militated against gains.

Control of ticks by the use of two species of parasites, *Ixodiphagus texanus* Howard and *Hunterellus hookeri* Howard, has been attempted, but neither proved successful. The latter species was introduced from France by Larousse to Naushon Island, off the coast of Massachusetts, but subsequent attempts to establish it as a successful parasite in Massachusetts, Montana,[13] and South Carolina failed: either the parasite failed to become established, or else, if established, it did not seem to affect the tick population. It appears as though there is not much hope for tick control by this means, at least in the United States.

The avoidance of tick bites is urged by keeping out of known tick-infested areas during spring and early summer, or by wearing suitable clothing, such as high boots, leggings, puttees, or socks *outside* the trousers legs. Before retiring at night, or after leaving a tick-infested area, one should bathe, if possible, and carefully search his body and clothing for presence of ticks. The advantage of early removal of ticks that may have escaped attention and have become attached has already been pointed out.

Diethyltoluamide applied to the socks and trousers is an effective repellent against ticks. Dimethyl phthalate and ethylhexanediol have also been widely used as repellents.

For removal of attached ticks, Circular 10 (revised, 1956) of the Rocky Mountain Laboratory, Hamilton, Montana, gives the following recommendations:

If a tick is found attached to the body it is best to remove it immediately. This is desirable because every added moment of attachment increases the danger of spotted fever or other tick-borne infection. Many practices have been employed for removal. However, the desired result is most easily and quickly accomplished by gently pulling the tick off with the fingers. So far as the ticks that transmit spotted fever are concerned, there is little ground for the idea that the mouth parts will thus be left in the wound, in spite of popular opinion to the contrary. Better the mouth parts, however, than spotted fever, tularemia, or some other equally unattractive infection. However, there is a definite danger of breaking off the mouth parts of ticks which have a longer hypostome, such as, for example, *Ixodes pacificus,* which is prevalent in parts of the West Coast of the United States and Canada, and *Amblyomma americanum,* common in parts of the South Central and South Atlantic States.

When sterile instruments are at hand, ticks of any species may be removed easily by pulling the tick gently so as to make a tent of the skin surrounding the site of attachment and then slipping the point of a hypodermic needle or scalpel under the mouth parts. The instrument is then raised, thus removing the mouth parts with a minimum of tissue. However the tick is removed, iodine or some other agent for asepsis should be applied to the site of the bite. A silver nitrate pencil, which can be purchased at any drug store, is convenient for outdoor use.

Ticks on Livestock. Tick control on domestic animals is necessary, not only from the standpoint of good livestock management, but also in reducing the threat to man. Dogs particularly need to be treated, since they commonly bring the American and the brown dog ticks into premises. To free dogs of ticks, a thorough application of derris powder or wash is recommended by Bishopp and Smith.[6] Derris when used as a powder should have a rotenone content of at least 3 per cent and should be applied lightly next to the skin at intervals of 2 or 3 days. A dip or wash can be made by dissolving 1 oz of neutral soap in a gallon of tepid water and mixing 2 oz of derris powder of which the rotenone content is 3 per cent. The dip should be applied at intervals of 5 or 6 days. The dog may be put in a tub or a brush may be used. The dip is allowed to dry on, or if necessary surplus liquid may be removed with a towel. Do not permit the dip or powder to get into the eyes of the animal.

Dog ticks can also be controlled by a wash containing 1 per cent of DDT, as a wettable powder, or 0.01 per cent of lindane, as an emulsified concentrate. DDT may also be used as 10 per cent dust, but it is less thorough and effective in this form.

For cattle, sheep, or goats, lindane, toxophene, malathion, and Bayer 21/199 are effective and safe, if used according to directions and under the proper circumstances. Special precautions should be taken in respect to treating animals that are under 3 months of age or that are sick, emaciated, or lactating. Treatments may need to be repeated after an interval of 2 or 3 weeks.

Control of Ticks on Vegetation. As has already been explained, when ixodine (hard) ticks reach maturity on the host they drop to the ground where the eggs are deposited and the larvae emerge, climbing up low shrubbery, weeds, and grass, ready to cling to any suitable passing animal. Enormous numbers of larvae may thus be encountered, particularly along cattle and deer paths in more or less wooded areas and on well-marked trails of meadow mice and other rodents in less wooded situations. As has also been explained, in the commoner species of hard ticks the nymphs likewise drop to the ground to molt. In some areas large numbers of nymphs and young adult ticks (before engorgement) climb up the branches and twigs of low shrubbery, where they are in an excellent position to attach themselves to larger animals, including man, as these brush against vegetation.

Manifestly much good could be accomplished if an economical insecticidal treatment were available both for use on the ground and on vegetation along such pathways. Outdoor areas[2] may be treated with DDT as a 10 per cent dust at the rate of 20 to 25 pounds per acre; in woody or brushy areas this should be increased to 40 pounds per acre. Chlordane, toxaphene, or dieldrin as a 5 to 10 per cent dust may be used instead of DDT. Lindane gives initial results but does not have the lasting value; it may be applied at the rate of 0.02 to 0.4 pound (actual lindane) to the area. Sprays using 1 or 2 pounds of DDT, toxaphene, chlordane, or dieldrin (actual insecticides) or 0.1 to 0.2 pound of lindane, may be used. A spray may be more difficult to apply than a dust.

Before the insecticide is applied, a quick survey of the area may be made by dragging a white flannel cloth over the ground and vegetation. The cloth should be examined frequently for ticks. The presence and abundance of ticks on the cloth will serve as an index to what areas should be treated and when and how often applications of the insecticides should be made. One application may suffice for the season unless indications are otherwise.

FAMILY ARGASIDAE (SOFT-BODIED TICKS)

The family Argasidae includes the so-called soft-bodied or nonscutate ticks in which sexual dimorphism is slight. The integument of all stages except larvae is leathery, wrinkled, granulated, mammillated, or with tubercles. The capitulum is either subterminal or distant from the anterior margin and in adults and nymphs lies in a more or less marked depression, the camerostome. The articulations of the palpi of all stages are free; the porose areas are absent in both sexes. There are about 85 species. Cooley and Kohls[18] provide us with an excellent account of this family. They recognize four genera, namely, *Argas, Ornithodoros, Otobius,* and *Antricola,* and give the following key for the separation of the genera:

1. With a definite sutural line separating dorsal and ventral surfaces...... *Argas*
   Lacking a definite sutural line separating dorsal and ventral surfaces..... 2
2. Nymphs with integument beset with spines, hypostome well developed; adults with integument granular, hypostome vestigial............ *Otobius*
   Integument of adults and nymphs essentially alike, mammillated or tuberculated, and lacking spines; hypostome of various forms in nymphs and adults but not vestigial.................................... 3
3. Hypostome broad at the base and scooplike (associated with bats)... *Antricola*
   Hypostome of various forms but not scooplike (associated with various classes of animals and including bats).................... *Ornithodoros*

The Genus Ornithodoros. In this genus the capitulum is either subterminal or distant from the anterior margin; the hypostome is well developed. In the integument, discs and mammillae commingle in a variety of patterns; hood, camerostome,* checks, and eyes are present or absent; dorsal humps and subapical dorsal protuberances on legs are progressively more prominent in the successive nymphal stages. The body is more or less flattened but strongly convex dorsally when distended. The integument pattern is continuous over the sides from dorsal to ventral surfaces.[18] The genus includes about 60 species, some 20 of which occur in North America, Central America, and Cuba.

Ornithodoros moubata (Murray) is widespread in central and southern Africa, where it is the only known vector of relapsing fever. It is known as the eyeless tampan, the hut tampan, or African relapsing fever tick (Fig. 152). It occurs in native huts, hiding in dust and thatch. It feeds chiefly at night and engorges rapidly. It is an eyeless species with a specific arrangement of the "humps" on the protarsus of the first pair of legs, being "subequal and toothlike." The adults measure from 8 to 11 mm in length and about 7 mm in breadth. The color varies from dusty brown to greenish brown in living specimens. Eggs are deposited in batches of from 35 to 340 at intervals after blood meals during the lifetime of the female. The maximum number of eggs laid by one female was 1217, according to Jobling.[55] The incubation period lasts from 7 to 11 days and over, depending on temperature. Davis[22] calls attention to the fact that the larvae are completely

* The *camerostome* is the depression or cavity in which the capitulum lies; it is usually less definite in engorged specimens. The *hood* is the anterior portion of the integument, extending above the capitulum and forming in part the wall of the camerostome.

quiescent, with legs closely applied to the body, and within a few hours molt in the split eggshell to the first nymphal stage.

The form that many authors refer to as the newly hatched larva is actually the first nymphal stage, which attaches itself to its first host animal and feeds for about half an hour, then disengages itself and molts for the second time. There then follow several other feeding periods and molts, about five in all before sexual maturity. This species feeds on man, chickens, pigs, and on certain wild animals including warthogs (*Phacohoerus*) and porcupines (*Hystrix*), as well as on rabbits, mice, rats, monkeys and fowls in the laboratory. It appears to be essentially a parasite of man, however, and is a man-to-tick-to-man vector of relapsing fever. Much of the information on this important species has been summarized by Hoogstraal.[49] Walton[93,94] has recently reported that the species consists of four biological variants; he discusses their relationship to relapsing fever.

Fig. 152. African relapsing fever tick, *Ornithodoros moubata*. × 3.

Ornithodoros talaje (Guérin-Méneville) is a South and Central American (south to Argentina) and Mexican species, occurring also in Florida, Texas, Arizona, Nevada, Kansas, and California. It feeds on wild rodents, also swine, cattle, horses, man, and other animals. It inflicts a very painful bite. It is a vector of relapsing fever in Guatemala, Panama, and Colombia. Bates, Dunn, and St. John[3] reported this tick a vector of relapsing fever in Panama by human experimentation in 1921; in one instance the bites of a naturally infected tick resulted in infection. However, Davis[23] has pointed out that for the most part the ticks under study were not *O. talaje* but *O. rudis,* which is now considered to be the important vector in that region.

Ornithodoros rudis Karsch (= *venzuelensis* Brumpt) is a Central and South American species. It is considered the most important vector of relapsing fever in Panama, Colombia, Venezuela, and Ecuador. Dunn[28] collected 4880 ticks of this species in 68 homes in 20 villages, towns, and cities in various parts of Colombia. Ticks infested with relapsing fever spirochetes were present in nearly 28 per cent of the homes in which collections were made. The altitude mentioned for one of the localities, a barracks at Muzo, was 2700 feet. Like *O. moubata,* this species appears to be essentially a parasite of man, although it is known to feed on other animals.

Ornithodoros erraticus Lucas (possibly a complex of two species) occurs in Spain, Portugal, and northern Africa. It is an important vector of relapsing fever in northern Africa. *Ornithodoros tholozani* (Laboulbène and Mégnin) is a vector in central Asia.[48] Several other species in Asia, Africa, and Europe are proven or suspected vectors.

Three species of *Ornithodoros* have been associated with relapsing fevers in the United States. *Ornithodoros turicata* (Dugès), the relapsing fever tick widespread throughout the southern United States and into Mexico, readily attacks man in all its stages. Its bite may be highly irritating or painful. *Ornithodoros parkeri* Cooley, primarily a parasite of rabbits and rodents, and *O. hermsi* Wheeler, Herms, and Meyer, a rodent parasite, are proven vectors of relapsing fever. These two species are widespread in the Rocky Mountain and Pacific Coast states.

Tick-borne Relapsing Fever. Although we are told that the natives in many parts of Africa dreaded tick bites for many generations, David Livingstone, the explorer, was first to report (1857) upon evil effects following the bite of a tick which was later named *Ornithodoros moubata* (Murray, 1877). It was not, however, until 1904 that Ross and Milne[83] and in 1905 Dutton and Todd[29] reporting from Uganda and the Congo, and almost simultaneously Robert Koch reporting from German East Africa, gave us a knowledge that these evil effects were due to relapsing fever, a spirochetosis, and that the tick so dreaded by the natives, was actually the vector.

The symptoms of the disease are described by Nuttall and Warburton:[60]

> Headache (especially at the back of the head), vomiting, abdominal pains and purging, with severe fever, a pulse of 90 to 120, dry hot skin, congested eyes and shortness of breath. After a period of fever lasting about two days, there is a fall of temperature, but a fresh attack soon follows. These relapses occur more frequently than in European (louse-borne) relapsing fever, being usually 5 or 6 in number, but there may be more. The attacks leave the patient in a weak condition for a long time after recovery, which usually follows, but death occurs in about 6 per cent of the cases.

How Infection Is Transmitted. Dutton and Todd[29] proved that the infection is not only introduced with the bite of the tick, but it also is transmitted to the offspring of the female tick through the egg. The newly hatched ticks were proved to be infective. Once infected, the tick remains so, and the infection may be transmitted from generation to generation without renewal for at least three generations. The infection is transmitted by the bite of either the male or female tick during all its active stages. The coxal fluids play an important role since they contain spirochetes which may be introduced into the bite wound or even penetrate the unbroken skin. The attack of fever takes place in the human in from 5 to 10 days after the tick has bitten. Feng and Chung[33] report that:

. . . shortly after the spirochaetes are ingested by the ticks they penetrate the stomach wall and reach the body cavity as evidenced by finding spirochaetes in the legs six hours after the infective feed. . . . The spirochaetes gradually disappear from the stomach and reach the body cavity with the result that from the twelfth day on no more spirochaetes could be found in the stomach contents. . . . From the body cavity the spirochaetes invade the salivary glands, the coxal glands. . . . The constant presence of numerous spirochaetes in the acini of the salivary glands and the finding on several occasions of spirochaetes actually inside the small salivary ducts suggests that besides the coxal fluid the bite alone may also be infective. . . . [The spirochaetes] multiply by transverse division after they have penetrated the stomach wall and reached the body cavity and other organs of the tick. . . . Mice inoculated . . . with feces remained sterile.

Tick-borne Relapsing Fever in the United States. The earliest known focus of endemic (tick-borne) relapsing fever in the United States is believed to have been in Colorado, where cases were reported by Meador[57] in 1915; this focus was in the mountains near Denver. In 1921 Briggs[8] reported two cases of relapsing fever in which the infection had been acquired at Polaris, Nevada County, California, at an elevation of 5750 feet. It would seem that Briggs suspected lice since he remarks, "Many tramps, put off trains at Truckee, find a day or so of employment here, only to move on. It is quite evident, therefore, that there are great opportunities for the dissemination of vermin by a nomadic population." However, ticks collected some years previously by Mark F. Boyd in the vicinity of Lake Tahoe (vicinity of Briggs' cases) identified as *Ornithodoros talaje,* a species reported to be a vector of relapsing fever in Panama, were later shown to be the species described by Wheeler, *et al.*[99] as *O. hermsi.* It is of interest to note that prospectors and others who worked in the Sierra Nevada at altitudes of 5000 feet and over frequently reported suffering from a malarialike disease which they called "squirrel fever." In the light of our present knowledge and particularly the experience of C. M. Wheeler, it is obvious that this infection was relapsing fever, infection having been due to contact with blood of spirochete-infected squirrels or due to tick bites not suspected.

In 1930 and 1931, cases of relapsing fever were contracted at elevations above 5000 feet in San Bernardino, Eldorado, and Sierra counties in California. An undescribed *Ornithodoros* was collected in several areas in the Sierra Nevada, and in 1935 Wheeler, who had an attack of the disease in 1930, described this as *O. hermsi.*[96] The name had, however, been published 1 month earlier by Wheeler, Herms, and Meyer,[99] who reported transmission of relapsing fever to a monkey and white mice by the bite of this tick. Proof that this species is capable of transmitting the infection to human beings was secured by Wheeler,[98] in May 1937, when an experimental infection resulted in a series of tests made on human subjects. From 1921 to 1944 inclusive, 283 cases of relapsing fever were reported in California, with epidemiologic evidence pointing to their origin in the Sierra Nevada at elevations of 5000 to 10,000 ft. *Ornithodoros hermsi* has since been taken in all endemic areas of California as high as 10,000-ft elevation, and as far north as Kamloops, British Columbia.

Weller and Graham[95] reported infected *O. turicata* in central Texas in 1930; they found a cave in the Colorado River Valley of central Texas

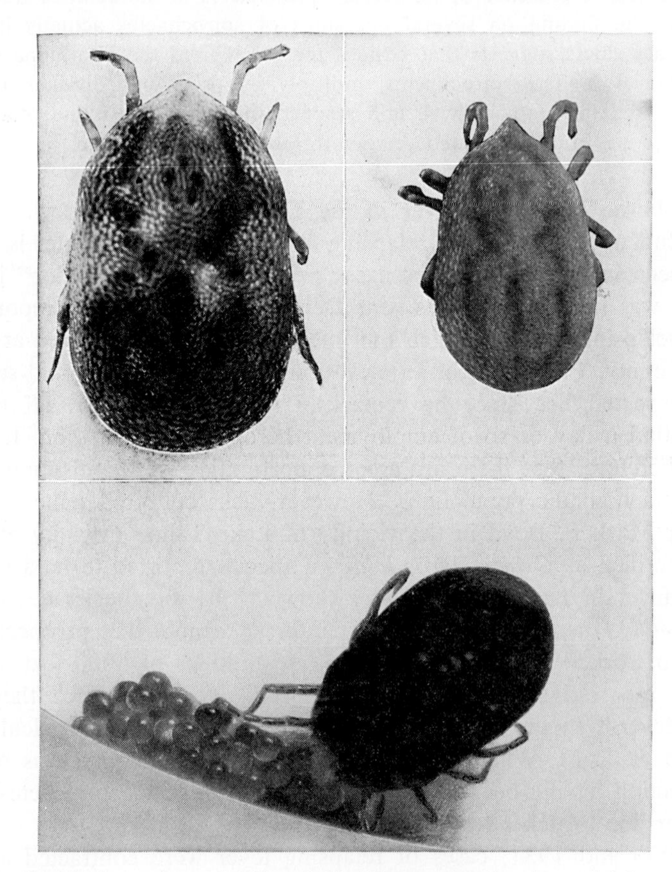

Fig. 153. *Ornithodoros hermsi.* (*Top left*) Mature female; (*top right*) mature male; (*bottom*) female depositing eggs.

which was "literally alive with ticks, a handful of sand yielding thirty or forty of different sizes." The cave, it was reported, is "frequented by goats and sheep, also probably wild animals such as bats, foxes, skunks, and rabbits." Some of the ticks were applied to 3 rabbits, allowed to feed for 15 minutes, and then crushed and rubbed into abrasions. Spirochetes were later observed in the blood of the rabbits.

Ornithodoros hermsi (Fig. 153) transmits the infection by the *bite* of both male and female ticks and in all stages of development. The proportion of infective larvae in hereditary transmission appears not to exceed 1 per cent. Wheeler[97] reports that from 35 per cent to 48 per cent of noninfective ticks, when allowed to feed as larvae on infected laboratory white mice, were able to acquire the spirochetes and transmit them to normal animals in some 1 or all of the subsequent developmental stages. One female tick has caused 4 infections in white mice during a period of about 4 months. Larvae from a presumably noninfective female tick produced infections; conversely, the larvae of an infective female may not be infective, although occasionally an infection may result from bites of later stages. The spirochetes are usually present in the blood of white mice about 5 days after the animals have been bitten by an infective tick. The time elapsing before infected ticks transmitted the infection depended, of course, on the time when the ticks were to

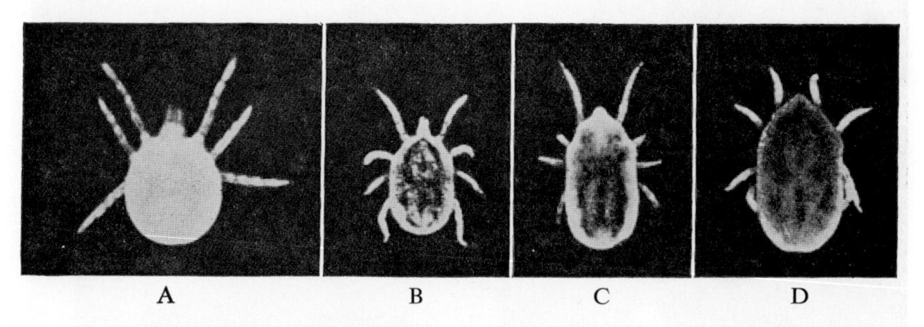

Fig. 154. Immature stages of *Ornithodoros hermsi:* (*A*) larva; (*B*) first nymphal stage; (*C*) second nymphal stage; and (*D*) third nymphal stage.

feed again with molts intervening; this elapsed period was 15 to 20 days at the shortest.

The life history of *Ornithodoros hermsi* (Fig. 154) as described by Herms and Wheeler[47] is as follows: The very tiny amber-colored eggs are deposited at intervals in batches of 12 to 140 from May to October, and range well over a total number of 200 per female. Under natural conditions, the eggs are deposited in the hiding places of the ticks; in summer cabins (Fig. 155), the eggs are laid in such corners and crevices as afford protection to the ticks.

The incubation period at a temperature of 75° F and 90 per cent humidity ranges from 15 to 21 days. The number of eggs and the percentage of larvae hatching seem to grow less in the later egg-layings, decreasing from as high as 95 per cent for the first batches to less than 50 per cent in the last. After several days the larvae are ready to feed, remaining attached to the host for only about 12 to 15 minutes, as in the case in later stages, although this attachment in the latter may be for from 1/2 to 1 hour in many cases. The larvae when fully engorged increase as much as three times in size and acquire a bright red color due to the imbibed blood. In this condition these

Fig. 155. (*Top*) A summer cabin in the Sierra Nevada of California in which relapsing fever was contracted. (*Bottom*) Interior view of the cottage.

tiny ticks have been referred to as a "strawberry seed insect" by persons living in relapsing fever areas.

Molting takes place in about 15 days after feeding. With this molt the fourth pair of legs appears, and this stage is termed the first nymphal instar. Ticks in the first nymphal stage may feed within a few days after molting, and again a period of 11 to 15 days elapses before the third molt and the appearance of the second nymphal instar. Then follow the third feeding and again an elapsed period, in this case about 10 to 32 days, before the fourth molt and the appearance of the third nymphal instar, or even the adult may appear with this molt. Usually a fifth feeding and a fifth molt are necessary before sexual maturity is reached. Egg-laying may begin in about 30 days after the last molt, fecundation taking place within a few days after maturity is reached. The cycle from egg to egg under laboratory conditions required about 4 months—e.g., from April 29, when the eggs were laid, to August 24, when eggs were laid by a female from the April-29 hatch of eggs.

The life cycle may be greatly prolonged in the absence of food because of the ability of these ticks to withstand starvation; thus, larvae may live as long as 95 days without food; unfed first-stage nymphs may live as long as 154 days; unfed second-stage nymphs may live as long as 79 days; third-stage, as long as 109 days, and adults well over 7 months. Adult ticks have been kept alive in pillboxes with occasional feedings for a period of 4 years.

The mature female tick (Fig. 153) measures from 5 to 6 mm in length by 3 to 4 mm in width. The male resembles the female closely in general appearance but is slightly smaller. This species is described as ovoid, conically pointed anteriorly, broadly rounded posteriorly. The anterior dorsal portion of the hood is visible from above. Unengorged individuals are of a light sandy color with the black of the intestinal diverticular visible through the integument of the dorsal surface; freshly engorged ticks are of a dull, deep garnet shade with grayish sheen over the body. The anterior conicle point is whitish. The color changes to a grayish blue a few days after feeding. Legs and hood are pale yellow. In newly molted forms, the body and legs are lighter but gradually assume the light sandy appearance and darken correspondingly.

Spirochetes of Endemic Relapsing Fever. The causal organism of tick-borne Central African relapsing fever was named *Spirochaeta duttoni* by Novy and Knapp in 1906. The South American strain was called *Spirochaeta venezuelense* by Brumpt in 1921, and the Texas strain was called *Spirochaeta turicatae* by Brumpt in 1933. Davis, in 1942, proposed the names *S. hermsii* and *S. parkerii* for the strains transmitted by *Ornithodoros hermsi* and *O. parkeri,* respectively. Other strains, such as *S. kochi* Novy, 1907; *S. hispanica* Sadi de Buen, 1926; *S. persica* Dschunkowsky, 1912; and *S. neotropicalis* Bates and St. John, Central and South America, have been recognized. Although these have been treated as separate "species" of *Borrelia,* some authors believe that they are probably strains of local varieties of one widely distributed species, *Borrelia recurruntis* (Lebert) (Fig. 156). These "species" or strains, however, show a high degree of host specificity. The various studies of G. E. Davis have shown that *Ornithodoros talaje, O. turicata, O. hermsi,* and *O. parkeri* each transmits its own species or strain of *Borrelia* and that one species of tick cannot transmit the spirochetes of the other species (cf. Fuller[35]).

Rodents have been considered vectors of tick-borne[4] (but not of louse-borne—see Chapter 8) relapsing fever, but the evidence now is that the tick is both the vector and the reservoir of the *Borrelia* which it transmits (Fuller[35]). According to Davis,[24] Nicolle proposed the theory that the infection was maintained by ticks and spread by lice; thus, tick-borne relapsing fever could, for a time, become louse-borne. Subsequent experimental evidence, by several workers over a period of time, lends strength to this hypothesis. The implications are interesting; they would materially affect some earlier concepts as to the origin of epidemics.

Prophylaxis and Control. In tick-infested areas (particularly where there is a history of relapsing fever), infested caves, camp sites, shacks, and ground areas should be avoided. If it is necessary or desirable to go into such areas,

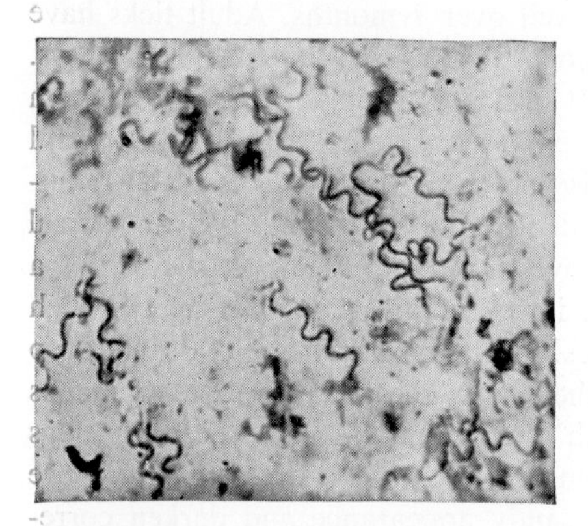

Fig. 156. Spirochetes of relapsing fever in a blood smear.

a repellent should be applied to the socks and trousers. Diethyltoluamide is very effective for this purpose. The feeding habits of *Ornithodoros* ticks should be kept in mind; these ticks attack rapidly, feed to repletion, and promptly leave the host; also, they are extremely hardy and may go without food for many months and continue to harbor the causal organisms (spirochetes) of relapsing fever. Consequently, a long vacancy of a cottage, cabin, or shack does not ensure freedom from ticks; they do not starve easily.

In areas of recreational importance, area-wide programs of tick and rodent control may be necessary. The latter without the former is useless and even dangerous, since ticks deprived of their usual hosts will turn avidly to human occupants of cottages for blood.

Some of the measures useful in the control of ticks and of chipmunks and other small animals infesting summer cottages are the following: (1) existing cottages should be tick- and rodentproofed; if this cannot be done, they should be replaced; (2) all crevices, knotholes and other points of ingress should be closed; all doors should be tight fitting, and the chimney should be covered with wire netting to keep out bats and rodents; (3) yards, woodpiles, etc., should be cleaned up and be kept in order to prevent chipmunks and rodents from concealing themselves and building their nests; (4) rodent reproduction should not be encouraged by feeding and making pets of these animals; the rodent population should be kept at a low level; (5) old tree snags in the vicinity which may harbor nesting squirrels and chipmunks should be destroyed; nests in such snags have been found to harbor numerous relapsing fever ticks in all stages of development; (6) firewood covered with loose bark beneath which ticks may be concealed should not be brought into the house or woodshed; (7) before or at the beginning of the occupancy for the season, lindane, as a dust, wettable powder, or emulsifiable concentrate, should be applied to the inner surfaces of beds, mattresses, rugs, and furnishings, with the usual precaution *not to contaminate food and dishes;* (8) in an area-wide program of relapsing fever control, the elimination of breeding niches for chipmunks (and other rodents) by complete

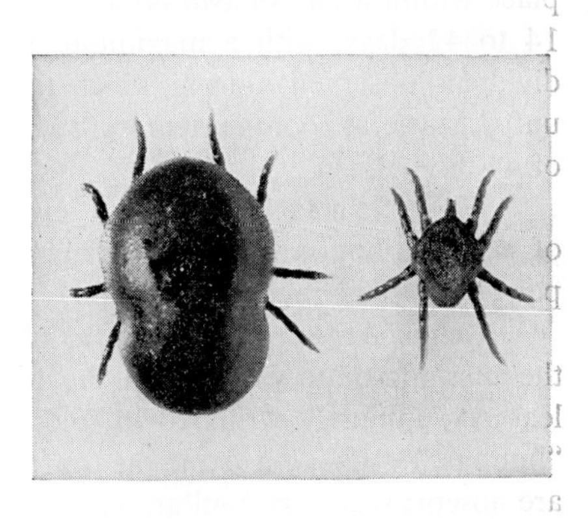

Fig. 157. Spinose ear tick, *Otobius megnini.* × 3.5.

destruction by fire (or other means) of "snags," partly dead trees is strongly urged—this is an important aspect of forest sanitation in recreation areas.

Genus Otobius. In adults the integument is granulated; nymphs have spines. The sexes are similar. The capitulum is distant from the anterior margin in adults and near the margin in nymphs. The hood and eyes are absent; the hypostome is vestigial in adults but well developed in nymphs. Cooley and Kohls recognize two species, *O. megnini* (Dugès) and *O. lagophilus* Cooley and Kohls,[18] the latter a parasite on the face of rabbits in western United States and Canada.

The spinose ear tick, *Otobius megnini* (Dugès), is a widely distributed species, being found in warmer parts of the United States, British Columbia, South America, South Africa, India, and no doubt other parts of the world. It receives its name from the fact that the nymph is covered with spines (Fig. 157) and that the larvae and nymph invade the ears of cattle, horses, mules, sheep, cats, dogs, and other domesticated animals, as well as deer, coyotes, rabbits, and other wild animals. There are several records of the occurrence of nymphs in the ears of man. Rather large dark eggs are deposited by this species on the ground; under laboratory conditions at a temperature of about 21° C, the incubation period is from 18 to 23 days. In the field newly emerged larvae crawl up weeds and other vegetation like the larvae of other ticks, coming in contact with suitable host animals, such as cattle, and gradually working their way to the shoulders, neck, and head, and thence to the deeper inner folds of the outer ear of the host, where they engorge and assume a peculiar saclike form.

After molting in the ear, the nymphs attach themselves and remain attached for long periods of time; this, the second nymphal stage, is the stage in which this species is most easily distinguished from other ticks. Individual ticks may remain in the ear as long as 121 days, as observed in our tests. On detaching, they crawl out of the ear, drop to the ground and molt again (there are three molts), after which maturity is reached. Copulation takes place within a day or two after the final molt, and oviposition occurs in from 14 to 42 days, with a maximum oviposition period of 155 days in the individuals observed, during which time 562 eggs were laid. The longevity of unfed larvae at room temperature ranged from 19 to 63 days, with an average of 44 days.[46]

The tick may be killed by introducing into the infested ears, by means of a spring-bottom oiler or syringe, 1/2 oz of a mixture consisting of 0.75 per cent lindane in xylene-pine oil.

Genus Argas. The members of this genus are distinctly flattened, with the margins quite even when the tick is fully engorged. The integument is leathery, minutely wrinkled in folds, often intermingled with small, rounded "buttons," each with a pit on top and often bearing a hair in the pit. Eyes are absent; sexes are similar. There are only two species in North America.

Argas persicus (Oken), a cosmopolitan *fowl tick,* is one of the most important poultry parasites in existence (Fig. 158). In addition to "fowl tick," this pest is commonly called "adobe-tick," "tampan," or "blue bug." In color it varies from light reddish-brown to a dark brown, depending on the stage of engorgement. In size the obovate, flattened adults average about 8.5 mm long by 5.5 mm wide in the female, and 6.5 mm long by 4.5 mm wide in the male. When unengorged their thickness is about 0.75 mm, and when fully engorged may be nearly 3 mm at the thickest part. The margin of the body is composed of irregular quadrangular plates or cells which often have one or more circular pits. The genital orifice of the male is "half-moon–shaped," while in the female it is "slitlike" and situated farther forward, i.e., immediately behind the capitulum as in other argasines. The capitulum has four long hairs, two hypostomal, and one near the articulation of each palpi, all directed forward. The palpi are about twice as long as the hypostome, second article longest, the others equal in length. The hypostome, apically rounded, has 6 or 7 fine denticles on each half distally, followed by stout teeth 2/2, the numbers increasing to 3/3, 4/4, 5/5 basally, the teeth decreasing in size, neither attaining the external border nor extending beyond half the length of the hypostome (Nuttall).

The nymphs and adults of *Argas persicus* are strikingly active at night, migrating long distances to find their host, and hiding in an inactive condition during the day. At night if one observes somewhat closely, one may see hordes of these ticks climbing up the sides of the chicken coop to the roosts and upon fowls, filling up leisurely with blood and before daybreak departing for their hiding places. The females deposit their large reddish-brown eggs in crevices occupied during the day. The eggs are laid in masses of from 25 to 100 and over, and there are usually several layings, each preceded by a

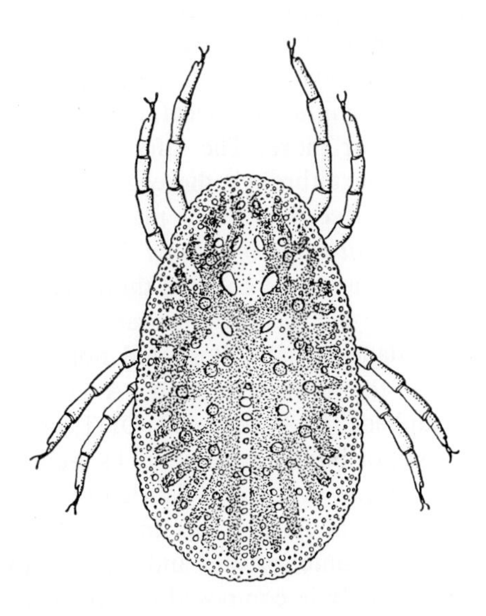

Fig. 158. The fowl tick, *Argas persicus*, dorsal view.

meal of blood, with a total of 700 eggs per female. Hatching takes place in from 10 days to 3 or 4 weeks. The larvae are hexapod and very active, attacking a host apparently as readily by day as by night.

Once attached, the larvae feed for about 5 days, occasionally longer, remaining firmly attached during this time. When fully engorged they appear like little reddish globules. At the end of this feeding period, the larvae detach themselves, having become flattened in the meantime, and then crawl away from the host, hiding in some convenient crevice near by. The larvae molt in about a week, when the fourth pair of legs appears; they are now in the first nymphal stage, looking like miniature adults. Nocturnal feeding now takes place, and in 10 to 12 days another molt occurs, and the second nymphal stage is reached. Again the tick attaches itself, being able to engorge itself in about an hour; again, after the expiration of something over a week, a third molt takes place (there may even be a fourth molt), and then the adult stage is reached. The adults are able to engorge themselves in from 20 to 45 minutes. Under favorable conditions the adult stage is reached in about 30 days. Absence of hosts to feed upon may greatly prolong the life history.

The species will bite man. Instances are recorded in which transient laborers occupying long-vacated but renovated poultry houses have been badly bitten by the poultry tick. It might perhaps under certain circumstances become involved in the transmission of human spirochetosis.

Avian spirochetosis. A very dangerous disease, known as "fowl spirochetosis" is traceable to *Borrelia anserina* (Sakharoff) Bergey *et al.* (= *gallinarum* Blanchard), occurring in India, Australia, Brazil, Egypt, and Persia, and is no doubt very widely distributed. The disease attacks chickens, geese, turkeys, guinea fowls, and other birds.

Argas persicus was proved to be a vector of this spirochete infection by Marchoux and Salimbeni, Balfour, Nuttall, and others. The spirochetes are transmitted by fecal contamination; the tick is said to be infective 6 months or more. The infection is carried over from one generation of ticks to the next through the egg. The incubation period in the fowl is from 4 to 9 days. Recovery from the disease is followed by immunity.

Combating the Fowl Tick. Walls, ceilings, floors, and roosts of hen houses should be covered thoroughly with a spray containing 3 per cent malathion or 0.5 per cent lindane. One-half gallon will treat 1000 square feet. If lindane is used, it should not be applied to the birds or to the henhouse while the birds are in it. A spray containing 0.5 per cent chlordane or toxaphene or 5 per cent DDT may be applied *outside only* on trees, old roosts, or buildings where ticks are numerous.

Argas reflexus (Fabricius), commonly known as the "pigeon tick," differs from *A. persicus* in that the body often narrows rather suddenly toward the anterior end and that the thin margin is flexed upward; the margin of the body is composed of irregular striations. The capitulum has "two long post-hypostomal hairs ventrally, directed forwards. Palps with articles subequal, the third the shortest, denticulated hairs dorsally. . . . Hypostome apically notched, some small denticles at the tip followed by 2/2 stout teeth merging into 3/3 to 6/6 progressively smaller teeth" (Nuttall).

Other species of Argas are the following: *A. brumpti* Neumann, the largest known species of the genus, measuring 15–20 mm in length by 10 mm in width. It feeds on a variety of hosts in Africa and is known to attack man. *Argas vespertilionis* (Latreille), a bat-infesting tick of wide distribution in the Old World, occasionally attacks man. Several other species are known from bats and other hosts in various parts of the world.

Genus Antricola. The dorsal walls are flattened and marginated; below the flattened dorsum the body is convex and deep; the integument is semi-translucent, and the surface smooth, shining, and with tubercles; the mouth parts are adapted for quick feeding and not for clinging to the host.

Antricola coprophilus (McIntosh) feeds on bats in Arizona and Mexico; *A. mexicanus* Hoffmann is known from a bat cave in Mexico; *A. marginatus* (Banks) is found in bat caves in Cuba and other parts of the West Indies.

REFERENCES

1. Anonymous, 1906. *The Cattle Tick.* State Crop Pest Commission of Louisiana, in Circ. no. 10.

2. Anonymous, 1955. *Wood Ticks, How to Control Them in Infested Places.* Washington, D. C.: Dept. Agric., in Leaflet no. 387. 8 pp.

3. Bates, L. B.; Dunn, L. H.; and St. John, J. H.; 1921. "Relapsing fever in Panama," *Am. J. Trop. Med.,* **1:**183–210.

4. Beck, M. Dorothy, 1937. "California field and laboratory studies on relapsing fever," *J. Infect. Diseases,* **60:**64–80.

5. Bequaert, J. C., 1946. "The ticks, or Ixodoidea, of the northeastern United States and eastern Canada," *Entomologia Amer.,* **25:**73–120.

6. Bishopp, F. C., and Smith, C. N., 1938. *The American Dog Tick, Eastern Carrier of Rocky Mountain Spotted Fever.* Washington, D. C.: Dept. Agric., in Circ., no. 468. 26 pp.

7. Boynton, W. H., and Woods, Gladys M., 1933. "Deer as carriers of anaplasmosis," *Science,* **78:**559–60.

8. Briggs, L. H., 1922. "Relapsing fever in California," *J.A.M.A.,* **79:**941–44.

9. Brumpt, E., 1919. "Transmission de la piroplasmose canine tunisienne par le *Rhipicephalus sanguineus,*" *Bull. Soc. path. exot.,* **12:**757–64.

10. Brumpt, E., and Larousse, F., 1922. "Transmission de la piroplasmose canine française par le *Dermacentor venustus,*" *Bull. Soc. path. exot.,* **15:**540–45.

11. Burgdorfer, Willy, and Eklund, Carl M., 1959. "Studies on the ecology of Colorado tick fever virus in western Montana," *Am. J. Hyg.,* **69:**127–37.

12. Chumakov, M. P., 1957. "Etiology, epidemiology, and prophylaxis of hemorrhagic fevers," Public Health Service: Public Health Monograph no. **50:**19–25.

13. Cooley, R. A., 1928. "Preliminary report on the tick parasite, *Ixodiphagus caucertei* du Buysson," Montana State Board of Entomol., *Biennial Rep.,* **7:**17–31.

14. Cooley, R. A., 1932. *The Rocky Mountain Wood Tick.* Bozeman: Montana State Coll., in Agric. Exp. Sta. Bull., no. 268. 58 pp.

15. Cooley, R. A., 1938. *The genera Dermacentor and Otocentor (Ixodidae) in the United States with Studies in Variation.* Washington, D. C.: U. S. Public Health Service, in Nat. Inst. Health Bull., no. 171. v + 89 pp. (30 plates).

16. Cooley, R. A., 1946. *The genera Boophilus, Rhipicephalus, and Haemaphysalis (Ixodidae) of the New World.* Washington, D. C.: U. S. Public Health Service, in Nat. Inst. Health Bull., no. 187. 54 pp.

17. Cooley, R. A., and Kohls, Glen M., 1944. "The genus *Amblyomma* (Ixodidae) in the United States," *J. Parasitol.,* **30:**77–111.

18. Cooley, R. A., and Kohls, Glen M., 1944. *The Argasidae of North America, Central America, and Cuba.* Notre Dame, Indiana: The University Press. American Midland Naturalist Monograph, no. 1. 152 pp.

19. Cooley, R. A., and Kohls, Glen M., 1945. *The Genus Ixodes in North America.* Washington, D. C.: U. S. Public Health Service, in Nat. Inst. Health Bull., no. 184. 246 pp.

20. Costa, Joseph A., 1952. "Tick paralysis on the Atlantic Seaboard," *Amer. J. Dis. Children,* **83:**336–47.

21. Cox, H. R., 1939. "A filter-passing infectious agent isolated from the tick. III. Description of organism and cultivation experiments," U. S. Public Health Service, *Pub. Health Rep.,* **53:**2270–76.

22. Davis, Gordon E., 1947. "A note on the larval stage of the argasid tick, *Ornithodoros moubata* (Murray) 1877," *J. Parasitol.,* **33:**495–96.

23. Davis, Gordon E., 1955. "Letters to the Editor," *Am. J. Trop. Med.,* **4:**961–62.

24. Davis, Gordon E., 1955. "The endemic relapsing fevers," in Hull, Thomas G., *Diseases Transmitted from Animals to Man,* 4th ed. Springfield, Ill.: Charles C Thomas. 717 pp.

25. Davis, Gordon E., and Kohls, G. M., 1937. *"Ixodes ricinus californicus* (Banks) a possible vector of *Bacterium tularense,"* U. S. Public Health Service, *Pub. Health Rep.,* **52:**281–82.

26. Derrick, E. H., 1937. " 'Q' fever. A new fever entity. Clinical features and laboratory investigation," *M. J. Australia,* **24:**281–99.

27. Douglas, J. R., 1943. "The internal anatomy of *Dermacentor andersoni* Stiles," *Univ. Calif. Pub. Entomol.,* **7:**207–72, plates 8–26.

28. Dunn, L. H., 1937. "Studies on the South American tick, *Ornithodoros venezuelensis* Brumpt in Colombia," *J. Parasitol.,* **13:**249–59.

29. Dutton, J. E., and Todd, J. L., 1905. *The Nature of Human Tick Fever in the Eastern Part of the Congo Free State, with Notes on the Distribution and Bionomics of the Tick.* Liverpool: School Trop. Med. Memoir no. 17. 18 pp.

30. Dyer, R. E.; Badger, L. F.; and Rumreich, A.; 1931. "Rocky Mountain spotted fever (eastern type) transmission by the American dog tick (*Dermacentor variabilis*)," U. S. Public Health Service, *Pub. Health Rep.,* **46:**1403–13.

31. Eklund, C. M.; Kohls, G. M.; and Brennan, J. M.; 1955. "Distribution of Colorado tick fever and virus-carrying ticks," *J.A.M.A.,* **157:**335–37.

32. Eklund, Carl M.; Kohls, G. M.; and Jellison, W. L.; 1958. "Isolation of Colorado tick fever virus from rodents in Colorado," *Science,* **128:**413.

33. Feng, Lan-Chou, and Chung, Huei-Lan, 1936. "Studies on the development of *Spirochaeta duttoni* in *Ornithodoros moubata,"* *Chinese M. J.,* **50:** 1185–90.

34. Florio, L.; Miller, M. S.; and Mugrage, E. R.; 1950. "Colorado tick fever. Isolation of the virus from *Dermacentor andersoni* in nature and a laboratory study of the transmission of the virus in the tick," *J. Immunol.,* **64:**257–63.

35. Fuller, H. S., 1956. "Medical and veterinary acarology," *Ann. Rev. Entomol.,* **1:**347–366.

36. Gear, J., 1954. "The rickettsial diseases of South Africa. A review of recent studies," *South African J. Clin. Sc.,* **23:**507–08.

37. Graybill, H. W., 1911. *Studies on the Biology of the Texas Fever Tick.* Washington, D. C., Dept. Agric., in Bur. Animal Indust., Bull. no. 130. 42 pp.

38. Gregson, J. D., 1949. "Note on the longevity of certain ticks (Ixodoidea)," *Proc. Entomol. Soc. British Columbia,* **45:**14.

39. Gregson, J. D., 1956. *The Ixodoidea of Canada.* Ottawa: Canada Dept. Agric., Science Service, Entomol. Division; in Publ. 930. 92 pp.

40. Gregson, J. D., 1958. "Host susceptibility to paralysis by the tick *Dermacentor andersoni* Stiles (Acarina: Ixodidae)," *Canad. Entomol.,* **90:**421–24.

41. Gregson, J. D., 1960. "Morphology and functioning of the mouthparts of *Dermacentor andersoni* Stiles." *Acta Tropica,* **17:**48–79.

42. Hadwen, S., 1913. "On 'tick paralysis' in sheep and man following bites of *Dermacentor venustus," Parasitology,* **6:**283–97 (2 plates).

43. Hadwen, S., and Nuttall, G. H. F., 1913. "Experimental 'tick paralysis' in the dog," *Parasitology,* **6:**298–301.

44. Hearle, Eric, 1938. *Insects and Allied Parasites Injurious to Livestock and Poultry in Canada.* Ottawa: Dept. Agric., in Publ., no. 604. 108 pp.

45. Henning, M. W., 1932. *Animal Diseases of South Africa.* South African Agriculture Series, **11:**298–329.

46. Herms, W. B., 1917. "Contribution to the life history and habits of *Ornithodoros megnini," J. Econ. Entomol.,* **10:**407–11.

47. Herms, W. B., and Wheeler, C. M., 1936. *"Ornithodoros hermsi* Wheeler as a vector of relapsing fever in California," *J. Parasitol.,* **22:**276–82.

48. Hindle, E., 1935. "Relapsing fever: some recent advances," *Trop. Dis. Bull.,* **32:**309–27.

49. Hoogstraal, Harry, 1956. *African Ixodoidea. I. Ticks of the Sudan.* Washington, D. C.: Dept. of the Navy. 1101 pp. (103 plates).

50. Huebner, R. J.; Jellison, W. L.; Beck, M. D.; Parker, R. R.; and Shepard, C. C.; 1948. "Q fever studies in southern California," U. S. Public Health Service, *Pub. Health Rep.,* **63:**214–22.

51. Hughes, L. E., and Philip, B. B., 1958. "Experimental tick paralysis in laboratory animals and native mountain rodents," *Proc. Soc. Exper. Biol. & Med.,* **99:**316–19.

52. Hunter, W. D., and Bishopp, F. C., 1911. *The Rocky Mountain Spotted Fever Tick.* Washington, D. C.: Dept. Agric., in Bur. Entomol., Bull., no. 105. 47 pp.

53. Hunter, W. D., and Hooker, W. A., 1907. *Information Concerning the North American Fever Tick.* Washington, D. C.: Dept. Agric., in Bur. Entomol., Bull., no. 72. 87 pp.

54. Jellison, W. L., and Kohls, G. M., 1938. "Tick-host anemia: a secondary anemia induced by *Dermacentor andersoni* Stiles," *J. Parasitol.,* **24:**143–54.

55. Jobling, B., 1925. "A contribution to the biology of *Ornithodoros moubata* Murray," *Bull. Entomol. Research,* **15:**271–79. (1 plate).

56. Luoto, L., 1959. "The epidemiology of Q fever in the United States," *Am. J. Pub. Health,* **49:**334–38.

57. Meador, Charles N., 1915. "Five cases of relapsing fever originating in Colorado, with positive blood findings in two," *Colorado Med.,* **12:**365–68.

58. Mohler, John R., 1930. *Tick Fever.* Washington, D. C.: Dept. Agric., in Farmers' Bull., no. 1625.

59. Murnaghan, Maurice F., 1958. "Tick paralysis in the dog: a neurophysiological study," *Proc. 10th Internat. Cong. Entomol.,* **3:**841–47.

60. Nuttall, G. H. F., and Warburton, Cecil, 1908. *Ticks, a Monograph of the Ixodoidea. Part I, Argasidae.* 104 + 35 pp. *Part II, Ixodidae.* xix + 105 + 348 pp. London: Cambridge Univ. Press.

61. Olmer, D., and Olmer, J., 1956. "Epidème des rickettsioses sur le littoral Mediterranéen; la fièvre boutonneuse," *Rev. Pathol. Gen.,* **56:**80–92.

62. Parker, R. R., 1923. "Transmission of Rocky Mountain spotted fever by the rabbit tick, *Haemaphysalis leporis-palustris* Packard," *Am. J. Trop. Med.,* **3:**39–45.

63. Parker, R. R., 1924. "Tularaemia. XI. Tularaemia infection in ticks of the species *Dermacentor andersoni* Stiles in the Bitter Root Valley, Montana," U. S. Public Health Service, *Pub. Health Rep.,* **39:**1057–73.

64. Parker, R. R., 1928. "Rocky Mountain spotted fever," Montana State Board of Entomol., *Biennial Rep.,* **7:**39–62.

65. Parker, R. R., 1933. "Certain phases of the problem of Rocky Mountain spotted fever," *Arch. Path.,* **15:**398–429.

66. Parker, R. R., 1937. "Recent studies of tick-borne diseases made at the United States Public Health Service Laboratory at Hamilton, Montana," *Proc. Fifth Pacific Sci. Cong.,* pp. 3367–74.

67. Parker, R. R., 1938. "Rocky Mountain spotted fever," *J.A.M.A.,* **110:**1185–88, 1273–78.

68. Parker, R. R., and Davis, Gordon E., 1938. "A filter-passing infectious agent isolated from ticks. II. Transmission by *Dermacentor andersoni,*" U. S. Public Health Service, *Pub. Health Rep.,* **53:**2267–70.

69. Parker, R. R., and Kohls, Glen M., 1943. "American Q fever: the occurrence of *Rickettsia diaporica* in *Amblyomma americanum* in eastern Texas," U. S. Public Health Service, *Pub. Health Rep.,* **54:**1510–11.

70. Parker, R. R.; Kohls, Glen M.; and Steinhaus, Edward A.; 1943. "Rocky Mountain spotted fever; spontaneous infection in the tick, *Amblyomma americanum,*" U. S. Public Health Service, *Pub. Health Rep.,* **58:**721–29.

71. Parker, R. R.; Philip, C. B.; Davis, G. E.; and Cooley, R. A.; 1937. "Ticks of the United States in relation to disease in man," *J. Econ. Entomol.,* **30:**51–69.

72. Parker, R. R., and Spencer, R. R., 1926. "Hereditary transmission of tularaemia infection by the wood tick, *Dermacentor andersoni* Stiles," U. S. Public Health Service, *Pub. Health Rep.,* **41:**1403–07.

73. Philip, Cornelius B., 1948. "Observations on experimental Q fever," *J. Parasitol.,* **34:**457–64.

74. Philip, Cornelius B.; Bell, J. Frederick; and Larson, Carl L.; 1955. "Evidence of infectious diseases and parasites in a peak population of black-tailed jack rabbits in Nevada," *J. Wildlife Management,* **19:**225–33.

75. Philip, Cornelius B., and Kohls, Glen M., 1952. "Elk, winter ticks, and Rocky Mountain spotted fever; a query," U. S. Public Health Service, *Pub. Health Rep.,* **66:**1672–75.

76. Price, Winston H., 1953. "Interference phenomenon in animal infections with rickettsiae of Rocky Mountain spotted fever," *Proc. Soc. Exper. Biol. & Med.*, **82:**180–84.

77. Richardson, V. F., and Kendall, S. B., 1957. *Veterinary Protozoology*. Edinburgh and London: Oliver and Boyd. xii + 260 pp.

78. Ricketts, H. T., 1906. "The transmission of Rocky Mountain spotted fever by the bite of the wood tick (*Dermacentor occidentalis*)," *J.A.M.A.*, **47:**358.

79. Ricketts, H. T., 1906. Observations on the virus and means of transmission of Rocky Mountain spotted fever," *J. Inf. Dis.*, **4:**141–53.

80. Ricketts, H. T., 1911. *Contributions to Medical Science*. Chicago: University of Chicago Press. 497 pp. (See pp. 278–450.)

81. Rivers, Thomas M., and Horsfall, Frank L., Jr., 1959. *Viral and Rickettsial Infections of Man*. Philadelphia: J. B. Lippincott Co. xviii + 976 pp.

82. Rose, Ian, 1954. "A review of tick paralysis," *J. Canad. Med. Assn.*, **70:**175–76.

83. Ross, P. H., and Milne, A. D., 1904. "Tick fever," *Brit. M. J.*, **2:**1453–54.

84. Sanders, D. A., 1937. "Observations on canine babesiasis (piroplasmosis)," *J. Am. Vet. M. A.*, **90,** n.s., **43:**27–40.

85. Smith, Carroll N.; Cole, Moses M.; and Gouck, Harry K.; 1946. *Biology and Control of the American Dog Tick*. Washington, D. C.: Dept. Agric., in Tech. Bull., no. 905. 74 pp.

86. Smith, T., and Kilbourne, F. L., 1893. *Investigations into the Nature, Causation, and Prevention of Texas or Southern Cattle Fever*. Washington, D. C.: Dept. Agric., in Bur. Animal Indust., Bull., no. 1. 301 pp.

87. Steinhaus, Edward A., 1946. *Insect Microbiology*. Ithaca: Comstock Publ. Co., Inc. x + 763 pp.

88. Stiles, C. Wardell, 1905. *A Zoological Investigation into the Cause, Transmission, and Source of Rocky Mountain "Spotted Fever."* Washington, D. C.: Public Health and Marine Hospital Service of the United States, in Hygienic Bull., no. 20. 121 pp.

89. Stiles, G. W., 1939. *Anaplasmosis in Cattle*. Washington, D. C.: Dept. Agric., in Circ., no. 154 (revised). 10 pp.

90. Tate, H. Douglas, 1941. "The biology of the tropical cattle tick and other species of ticks in Puerto Rico, with notes on the effects on ticks of arsenical dips," Univ. Puerto Rico, *J. Agric.*, **25:**1–24.

91. Temple, J. U., 1912. "Acute ascending paralysis, or tick paralysis," *Med. Sentinel*, **20:**507–14.

92. Thomas, L. J., and Cahn, A. R., 1932. "A new disease of moose. I," *J. Parasitol.*, **18:**219–31.

93. Walton, G. A., 1957. "Observations on biological variation in *Ornithodoros moubata* (Murr.) (Argasidae) in East Africa," *Bull. Entomol. Research*, **48:**669–710.

94. Walton, G. A., 1958. "Studies on *Ornithodoros moubata* Murray (Argasidae) in East Africa. Part I," *East African Med. J.*, **35:**57–84. Part II, **35:**107–36.

95. Weller, B., and Graham, G. M., 1930. "Relapsing fever in central Texas," *J.A.M.A.*, **95:**1834–35.

96. Wheeler, C. M., 1935. "A new species of tick which is a vector of relapsing fever in California," *Am. J. Trop. Med.*, **15:**435–38.

97. Wheeler, C. M., 1938. "Progress of spirochaete infection in the developmental stages of the host tick, *Ornithodoros hermsi* Wheeler," *Am. J. Trop. Med.*, **18:**413–19.

98. Wheeler, C. M., 1938. "Relapsing fever in California—attempts to transmit spirochaetes of relapsing fever to human subjects by means of the bite of the vector, *Ornithodoros hermsi* Wheeler," *Am. J. Trop. Med.*, **18:**641–59.

99. Wheeler, C. M.; Herms, W. B.; and Meyer, K. F.; 1935. "A new tick vector of relapsing fever in California," *Proc. Soc. Exper. Biol. & Med.*, **32:**1290–92.

100. Wilson, Louis B., and Chowning, William M., 1902. "The so-called 'spotted fever' of the Rocky Mountains. A preliminary report to the Montana State Board of Health," *J.A.M.A.*, **39:**131–36.

101. Wolbach, S. B., 1919. "Studies on Rocky Mountain spotted fever," *J. Med. Research*, **41:**1–197.

102. Woodward, T. E., and Turner, W. F., 1915. *The Effect of the Cattle Tick upon the Milk Production of Dairy Cows.* Washington, D. C.: Dept. Agric., in Bur. Animal Industry, Bull., no. 147. 22 pp.

103. Work, T. H., 1958. *Russian Spring-Summer Encephalitis Virus in India. Kyasanur Forest Disease.* In *Progress in Medical Virology*, pp. 248–79. New York: Hafner Publ. Co.

Chapter 20

MITES AND PENTASTOMIDS

Characteristics. In the mites, as in the ticks, the unsegmented abdomen is broadly jointed to the cephalothorax with little or no evidence of segmentation. All but a few species are minute, i.e., barely visible to the naked eye. Mites, like other arachnids, have, with a few exceptions such as the plant-feeding family Eriophyidae, four pairs of legs as adults but only three pairs in the larval stage. The mouth parts are quite varied but follow the general pattern of the ticks. The chelicerae of the parasitic species are rasping or piercing structures. Eyes are absent, or one or more pairs of simple eyes may be present. The respiratory system is in most species similar to that of the ticks, i.e., tracheal, while others absorb oxygen through the general body surface, which in these is quite soft. Nearly all species deposit eggs; however, there are a few which are ovoviviparous, e.g., *Pyemotes ventricosus* (Newport). From the egg there emerges the hexapod larva, which usually soon molts and then presents its fourth pair of legs. The life history of many species requires less than 4 weeks; in some it is as short as 8 days.

Mites may be of medical or veterinary importance in any of three ways: (1) through transmission of pathogenic agencies either as vectors or as intermediate hosts; (2) by causing dermatitis or other tissue damage directly; (3) through loss of blood. An infestation of mites is called *acariasis.* Although mites are commonly thought of as external parasites, some mites may cause damage internally, e.g., in the inner and middle ear, the respiratory passages and lungs, and in the nasal passages.

Although Baker and Wharton[7] recognize more than 200 families of mites, actually only a few of these contain species that affect man and his domestic animals. The identification of mites, even the few species of medical importance, is difficult, but the student is referred to Baker and Wharton's *An Introduction to Acarology;* to Baker, Camin, Cunliffe, Woolley, and Yunker's *Guide to the Families of Mites,*[5] to Baker, Evans, Gould, Hull, and Keegan's *A Manual of Parasitic Mites,*[6] to Strandtmann and Wharton's *Manual of Mesostigmatid Mites Parasitic on Vertebrates,*[50] to Wharton and Fuller's *A Manual of the Chiggers,*[57] and to Brennan and Jones' key to the chiggers of North America.[12] Radford[47] has published a very helpful list of "Genera and species of parasitic mites," which gives the authority, year of validity, and where possible the original host. Oudemans'[42] monumental work is a standard reference source for acarologists; see also Vitzthum[55] for an important foundation work.

Taxonomy. Mites, along with the ticks, constitute the order Acarina of the Arachinda, but acarologists are not in agreement as to where the divisions into suborders should be made. Baker and Wharton divide the order into five suborders: Onychopalpida, Mesostigmata, Ixodides, Trombidiiformes, and Sarcoptiformes. The only variation from this classification that need concern us is that many specialists prefer to unite, on morphologic groups, the Mesostigmata and Ixodides into a single suborder, the Parasitiformes. However, for the sake of simplicity, it seems better for the purpose of this work to accept the Baker and Wharton classification, even though this will not show the phylogenetic relationships between the ticks and the mesostigmatid mites.

The following key will aid in separating the suborders of mites. One must remember, however, that some structures, particularly the spiracles and associated peritremes, are difficult or impossible to see unless the specimen has been properly cleaned and mounted.

KEY TO THE SUBORDERS OF MITES

1. Stigmata present laterad to the legs and usually ventrally located; peritreme (a sclerotized tube or depression extending forward from the spiracle) usually present; no rodlike sensory setae on tarsi I 2
   Stigmata absent, or, if present, not lateral in position; peritremes sometimes present; rodlike sensory setae usually present on tarsi I 3
2. Two pairs of stigmata present; coxae of pedipalp not fused dorsally....... .... Onychopalpida
   One pair of stigmata present, located usually behind and laterad of the third coxa; coxae of pedipalpi fused dorsally so that the base of the gnathosoma* forms a tube which encloses the mouth parts ... Mesostigmata
3. Stigmata usually present and located on or near the gnathosoma; chelicerae usually modified into stylets for piercing; pedipalpi usually free and highly developed; anal suckers never present .... Trombidiiformes
   Stigmata absent, or if present not on or near the gnathosoma; chelicerae pincerlike, for chewing; pedipalpi simple; anal suckers frequently present .... Sarcoptiformes

THE MESOSTIGMATID MITES

Most mesostigmatid mites of recognized medical and veterinary importance belong to the family Dermanyssidae. There are, however, a few others that deserve mention.

The Haemogamasidae are medium-sized, oval mites, heavily clothed with setae that give the body, both dorsally and ventrally, a furry appearance. They are parasitic on small mammals all over the world. *Haemogamasus pontiger* (Berlese) was suspected of causing dermatitis to soldiers who slept

* The term *gnathosoma* is applied to the fused ventral parts of the three segments that enclose the mouth and bear the chelicerae and the pedipalps.

on straw-filled mattresses in England during World War II.[6] *Haemogamsus ambulans* (Thorell) (= *nidi* Michael), the lelaptid *Haemolaelaps glasgowi* (Ewing), and the dermanyssid *Hirstionyssus isabellinus* (Oudemans) (= *arvicolae* Zemska), taken from small mammal nests and burrows (*Microtus, Apodemus, Sorex*), were shown to harbor the virus of the hemorrhagic nephrosonephritis (epidemic hemorrhagic fever) of the Far East.[17] The close association of haemogamasid mites with small mammals suggests that they may have some bearing on the transmission of plague, typhus, tularemia, and perhaps other diseases.[7]

Several mesostigmatid mites are internal parasites on domestic animals. The canary lung mite, *Sternostoma tracheacolum* Lawrence (Family Rhinonyssidae), which invades the trachea, air sacs, bronchi, and parenchyma of the lungs of canaries, may cause illness and even death. *Pneumonyssoides caninum* (Chandler and Ruhe) (Family Halarachnidae) attacks the sinuses and nasal passages of dogs, usually with a benign effect, and a related species, *Pneumonyssus simicola* Banks, inhabits the lungs of monkeys. Human pulmonary acariasis, which during World War II produced a syndrome known as *tropical eosinophilia,* is apparently due not to halarachnids but rather to free-living species.[7]

The house fly mite, *Macrocheles muscaedomesticae* (Scopoli) (Family Macrochelidae), is of interest because the nymph and adult prey upon the eggs and, perhaps, the first-stage larvae of the house fly.

Family Dermanyssidae. This important group of mesostigmatid mites includes: the tropical rat mite, *Ornithonyssus bacoti* (Hirst); the northern fowl mite, *O. sylviarum* (Canestrini and Fanzago); the tropical fowl mite, *O. bursa* (Berlese); the chicken mite, *Dermanyssus gallinae* (De Geer); the house mouse mite, *Allodermanyssus sanguineus* (Hirst); and others.

The nomenclature involving the family and its members is somewhat confusing. The generic names *Liponyssus* and *Bdellonyssus,* which occur frequently in the literature for the tropical rat mite and its relatives, cannot be used for reasons of nomenclature; neither can the family name Liponyssidae, based on *Liponyssus.* Some authorities have advocated dividing the group into two families, the Macronyssidae for *Ornithonyssus* and its relatives, and the Dermanyssidae for *Dermanyssus* and *Allodermanyssus,* but we are following Baker and his co-workers in grouping all of these into a single family.

Baker and Wharton[7] give the following diagnosis of the family:

> Dermanyssids are medium-sized mites. The dorsal plate is either undivided in the female or is divided so that the anterior plate is large and the posterior one extremely small. The ventral plates of the female are typical of the suborder except that they are somewhat reduced. The sternal plate has three pairs of setae, while the metasternal plates are reduced and lateral to the genital plate. The genito-ventral plate is drop-shaped posteriorly. The anal plate has three character-

istic setae. In the Dermanyssidae the chelicerae may be extremely elongated and terminate in a minute shear so that they appear to be a pair of needle-like structures, or they may be more normal with merely reduced chelae. Tritosternum is present. All legs have pretarsi, caruncles, and claws.

The genus *Ornithonyssus* (= *Liponyssus* of Authors, *Bdellonyssus* Fonseca) includes a homogeneous group of mostly tropical species in which, according to the diagnosis of Strandtmann and Wharton,[50] the dorsal plate tapers posteriorly in the female, but is broadly rounded in the male; the female epigynial plate is narrow and pointed posteriorly; the male holoventral plate is undivided and not expanded behind coxa IV; the trochanter of the female pedipalp is with or without a palpal spur; the femur of the male pedipalp usually possesses a prominent seta on a noticeable elevation; and all coxae lack ventral spurs or spines.

The tropical rat mite (Fig. 159) was first recorded from rats (*Rattus norvegicus*) in Egypt by Hirst[30] and described as *Leiognathus bacoti.* This

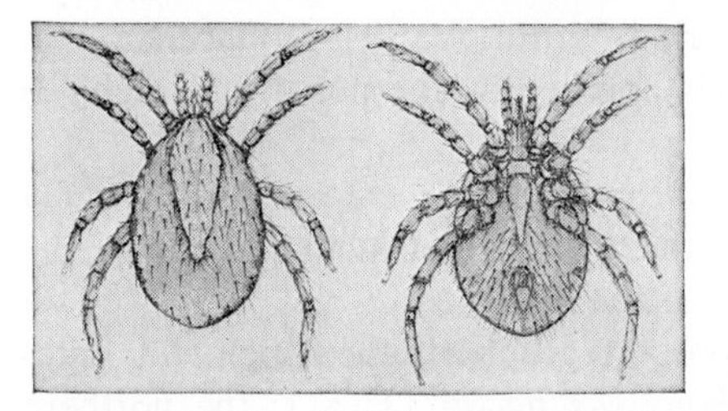

Fig. 159. The tropical rat mite, *Ornithonyssus bacoti;* (*left*) dorsal view; (*right*) ventral view. (After Dove and Shelmire.)

mite is now reported from many parts of the world as irritating to man; it occurs on all continents and in temperate as well as tropical regions. Bishopp[9] states: "The bite is distinctly painful at the time the mouth parts are inserted. A sharp itching pain is usually experienced. Usually there is more or less irritation and itching at the site of the bite for several hours along with the development of a small haemorrhagic area." The resulting dermatitis may be more or less severe, depending on the sensitivity of the host.

The tropical rat mite has not been incriminated in the natural transmission of any disease, but its potentialities along this line have not been sufficiently investigated. Dove and Shelmire[18] reported having experimentally transmitted the Texas strain of endemic typhus through the bite of this mite from guinea pig to guinea pig. Hopla[31] found that infections of the tularemia bacillus acquired by immature mites during feeding can be passed to subsequent stages and their progeny. Mites failed to produce infection by biting, but infection resulted when the mites were crushed orally by the experimental mice. Philip and Hughes[45] found it an experimental vector of rickettsial pox. Williams and Brown[59] have demonstrated that *O. bacoti* acts as an intermediate host of a filariid worm, *Litomosoides carinii* (Trav.), a parasite of the cotton rat, *Sigmodon hispidus* Say and Ord. Bertram, Unsworth, and Gordon[8] also demonstrated this relationship.

Life Cycle. Strandtman and Wharton[50] have summarized the life cycle of the tropical rat mite, based upon the studies of various investigators. *Ornithonyssus bacoti* has five developmental stages: the adult male and female, the egg, the nonfeeding larva, the bloodsucking protonymph, and the nonfeeding deutonymph. Two engorgements, one by the protonymph and one by the adult, are required to complete the life cycle. Unfertilized females reproduce parthenogenetically, the resulting offspring being males. The life cycle from egg to adult requires 7 to 16 days at room temperatures, provided that food is available for the protonymph. Unfed protonymphs have been known to survive 43 days. A minimum of 13 days seems to be necessary for development from egg to egg. Adult females live an average of 61 days and produce eggs in several batches, after subsequent feedings, which average about 100 per female.

The nymphs and adults are very active and readily leave the nests and harborages of the host and travel freely for some distance to attack persons in restaurants, warehouses, offices, the home, and other situations where rats abound or have been recently.

Control of the tropical rat mites is essentially rat control. In the absence of food the mites usually perish in about 2 weeks, although starved mites have been known to survive more than a month; therefore, if no other measures are taken, the pest will abate itself in about that time. However, with the elimination of the appropriate murine hosts, they may become more annoying because of their enforced search for a blood meal. Along with rat control, desks, chairs, cabinets, and woodwork may be treated with a spray containing DDT, chlordane, or lindane. These materials, or pyrethrum, may also be used as a spray for rat harbors, floors, or other surfaces on which these mites crawl.

Poultry Mites. *The tropical fowl mite, Ornithonyssus bursa* (Berlese), is a widely distributed poultry pest in tropical and subtropical areas on all continents, including the warmer parts of the United States. It appears to be a widespread parasite of the English sparrow, *Passer domesticus,* as well as of the domestic fowl. Other bird species may be attacked. Although man is frequently bitten by this mite, no symptoms are reported other than a slight irritation. Since the mite can not exist for more than 10 days apart from its avian host, annoyance to man is only temporary.

The northern fowl mite, Ornithonyssus sylviarum (Canestrini and Fanzago), closely resembles the tropical fowl mite. It is a widespread parasite of poultry in the north temperate region and has been recorded from Australia. In the absence of bird hosts, it will at times attack man and may cause itching both by its bite and by crawling over the skin.

The chicken mite, Dermanyssus gallinae (De Geer) (Fig. 160), also known as the red chicken mite or the roost mite, appears to be a pest of chickens throughout the world. Other poultry such as turkeys, as well as pigeons, English sparrows, and other birds, may be infested. While man is commonly annoyed by crawling mites, instances of having been actually bitten appear to be quite rare. During the daytime, the mites remain hidden in crevices in the henhouses and roosts, under boards and debris. In these hiding places they deposit their eggs. At night the pests swarm out from these hiding places and attack the birds on the roosts. The damage done by these mites is considerable and may be summarized as follows: Egg production is greatly reduced or entirely prevented; setting hens are often caused to leave

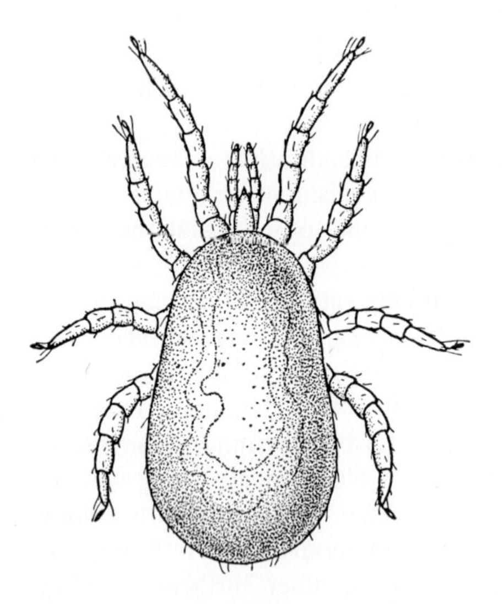

Fig. 160. The chicken mite, *Dermanyssus gallinae*.

their nests or perish; newly hatched chicks perish when attacked by a large number of these mites; chickens lose flesh, are unthrifty, and are unprofitable for marketing; loss of blood and reduced vitality cause birds to be easily susceptible to disease.

The Role of Bird Mites in the Epidemiology of Arthropod-borne Encephalitides. In 1942 Hammon *et al.*[26] demonstrated that a large percentage of wild birds as well as domestic fowl possess neutralizing antibodies for western equine and St. Louis encephalitis. The discovery gave impetus to an investigation already under way concerning the part that avian bloodsucking ectoparasites may have in the infection chain of these viruses. Discoveries that *Dermanyssus gallinae* and *Ornithonyssus sylviarum* could harbor encephalitis viruses and could transmit them experimentally led to the concept that, in the transmission of encephalitis, two bloodsucking vectors may be involved: one, the chicken mite, in which the virus is maintained in nature by transovarian passage, and the other, a *mosquito,* which transmits the infection from birds to other vertebrates, including man. For a number of years, many workers accepted this theory of the mite-mosquito vectorship of the mosquito-transmitted encephalitides.

Critical field and laboratory studies by Reeves *et al.*[48], Chamberlain and Sikes,[15] Sulkin *et al.*,[51] and Chamberlain *et al.*,[16] have failed to indicate any definite relationship between the infection of the mite with the viruses of St. Louis or western equine encephalitis and their transmission. It now appears that any mite transmission of these viruses that may exist is of very little importance. The recovery of the viruses from mites taken from wild or domestic birds is interpreted as meaning merely that the mites had fed upon the viremic birds shortly before they had been sacrificed for the detection of the virus.

The house mouse mite, *Allodermanyssus sanguineus* (Hirst), is probably the most important dermanyssid mite from the standpoint of medical entomology. It is the only one that has been definitely incriminated in the transmission of a human disease. This mite is known to occur in northern Africa, Asia, Europe, and the United States. The house mouse, *Mus musculus,* is the preferred host, but the mite will feed on rats and other rodents and will readily attack man.

Ewing[20] describes *A. sanguineus* as follows:

Palpi slender, reaching to the tips of anterior femora; chelicerae showing plainly the needlelike elements representing both arms. Dorsal shield divided; anterior shield broadest at the shoulders, lateral margins behind the shoulders concave; posterior shield circular, minute. Sternal plate squarish, lying entirely between the second coxae, with three pairs of subequal marginal setae. Anal plate egg-shaped in outline, anterior margin broadly rounded; anus situated centrally, rim very thin in front and on the sides, but enormously thickened behind; paired setae situated at the level of the center of the anus; media seta situated about two thirds its length behind anus; caudal area reaching about halfway to the base of median seta. Legs very long and slender. Length, 0.91 mm; width, 0.46 mm.

Life History. As in most dermanyssid mites, there are five developmental stages; unlike the tropical rat mite, both nymphal instars take a blood meal. Adult females feed several times, each feeding being followed by oviposition. The total period of time from deposition of the egg to emergence of the adult is 17 to 23 days. Unfed females are known to have lived as long as 51 days, and a female that had fed and oviposited twice is recorded as living 9 weeks. Engorged nymphs and adults may be found, sometimes in great numbers, in buildings, in the vicinity of rodent nests and runways.

The life history of this mite has been studied by Fuller[23] and Nichols *et al.*,[41] and a good summary is given by Baker *et al.*[6]

Rickettsialpox of man was first observed in New York City during the summer of 1946, the causal organism, *Rickettsia akari,* being isolated by

Huebner, Jellison, and Pomerantz.[32] Repeated recovery of different strains of the rickettsia has established the vector as *Allodermanyssus sanguineus* and the reservoir as the house mouse, at least in the United States. Rickettsialpox is usually a mild febrile disease, with no signs except a vesicular rash that follows the onset of the fever by 3 or 4 days; there is an eschar or initial lesion as in scrub typhus, caused by the bite of the mite. The disease occurs in the northeastern United States. A disease that seems to be the same, with the same vector and reservoir, has been described from the Soviet Union; and at least a similar disease, though probably with different vectors and reservoirs, is known from French Equatorial Africa and South America.

Control measures involve rodent control plus the use of miticides, similar to those used against the tropical rat mite.

Identification of Dermanyssid Mites. For the identification of the dermanyssid mites, the student is referred to the works of Baker *et al.*[6] and of Strandtmann and Wharton.[50] The following key, however, should serve to identify *properly cleared* specimens of the species of medical importance discussed here.

KEY TO SOME DERMANYSSID MITES OF MEDICAL IMPORTANCE

1. Chelicerae long, whiplike, the apical two-thirds or more much narrower than the basal portion (subfamily Dermanyssinae) 2
   Chelicerae shorter, stouter, of uniform diameter throughout their length (subfamily Macronyssinae) 3
2. With one dorsal plate; genitoventral plate broadly rounded posteriorly.... ....*Dermanyssus gallinae*
   With two dorsal plates, the posterior one very small; genitoventral plate tapering behind ....*Allodermanyssus sanguineus*
3. Dorsal plate of female broad; its central setae short, reaching only halfway to bases of setae of the following row 4
   Dorsal plate of female narrow, tapering posteriorly; its setae reaching to or beyond bases of setae of the following row ....*Ornithonyssus bacoti*
4. Sternal plate of female with three pairs of setae ....*Ornithonyssus bursa*
   Sternal plate of female with two pairs of setae ......*Ornithonyssus sylviarum*

THE HOLOTHYRIDAE

(*Suborder Onchopalpida*)

The Family Holothyridae includes the largest known mites, some of which reach a length of 7 mm. One species, *Holothyrus coccinella* Gervais, is of some medical importance. On the island of Mauritius this mite is said to cause the death of ducks and chickens that swallow it. The ill effects are due to a toxic secretion which the mite produces. Children are also affected through handling the mites and then touching their mouths with their fingers.

THE ITCH, MANGE, AND SCABIES MITES

(Suborder Sarcoptiformes)

Characteristics. Two groups of mites make up the Sarcoptiformes: the Acaridiae and the Oribatei. The latter are of little medical or veterinary importance, although Allred[1] has listed 40 species which serve as intermediate hosts for 13 species of tapeworm, including *Moniezia expansa* Rudolphi, a common parasite of ruminants. The vertebrate host can acquire the parasite through ingestion of the free-living oribatid mites which are common in pastures and may harbor the tapeworm cysticercoid. In the oribatids, the integument is leathery or strongly sclerotized; the tarsi have one to three claws but lack caruncles (delicate, transparent suckerlike structures between the claws); the sexes are similar; and the respiratory system consists of a complex of tracheae that open through stigmata or porous areas in many regions of the body.

The medically important Sarcoptiformes belong to the Acaridiae. These mites are weak-skinned, without tracheae and stigmata; caruncles usually are present on the tarsi; sexual dimorphism is often well marked, the males frequently having copulatory suckers on the tarsi or anal region. The following characteristics are shared with the Oribatei, according to the diagnosis given by Baker and Wharton: the coxae form characteristic plates (apodemes) beneath the skin on the venter of the body; the chelicerae are usually pincerlike or scissorslike, fitted for chewing; and the palpi are simple.

The sarcoptiform mites of medical importance belong to four families: the Acaridae, the Glycyphagidae, the Epidermoptidae, and the Sarcoptidae. To this list one should add a family of considerable veterinary importance, the Psoroptidae.

Family Acaridae (= Tyroglyphidae). This family includes a small group of very tiny mites, ordinarily about 0.5 mm or less in length. Several of the species attack grain, flour, meal, dried meat, hams, dried fruits, insect collections, etc. Their development is so rapid that literally millions of them may appear in a stored product in a few days.

The metamorphosis of this group involves a peculiar stage known as the *hypopus,* appearing in a number of species between the two nymphal stages, very unlike either of these and very different from the adult. This is a "wandernymph" stage in which the mites attach themselves, nonparasitically, to flies and other insects, which disseminate them.

Persons handling stored products of various kinds, cereal, flour, meal, etc., may be attacked temporarily by the mites and experience a severe dermatitis.

Acarus siro Linnaeus is the grain mite or cheese mite, found in grain, stored products, and cheese; this mite causes a rash known as "vanillism" in vanilla-pod handlers. *Tyrophagus castellanii* (Hirst) causes the "copra itch" among workers handling copra; dermatitis caused by this mite has also been described in dock workers who were handling cheese. The exact cause of the dermatitis is not known; it has been variously attributed to the "dust" caused by the feeding mites and the microorganisms present therein, to a hypersensitivity on the part of the patient, and to a substance present in the saliva of the mite.

Baker *et al.*[6] have summarized reports of mites involved in human pulmonary, urinary, and intestinal acariasis. *Tyrophagus longior* (Gervais), a free-living form, has been reported as occurring in both the digestive and urinary tract. Acarid mites, as well as representatives of other sarcoptiform families, have been recovered from the sputum of patients suffering from lung disorders; with one exception (*Dermatophagoides saitoi* Sasa, family Epidermoptidae), these were all nonparasitic mites and were probably inhaled casually.

Family Glycyphagidae. *Glycyphagus domesticus* (De Geer), often found in dried fruits and in such organic matter as skin and feathers, causes "grocers' itch" when highly infested material is handled. This mite may occur in enormous numbers in homes and stores. It has been reported as the intermediate host of the rodent tapeworm *Catenotaenia pusilla* (Goeze).

Family Epidermoptidae. These are very small mites, 0.17 to 0.39 mm in length, short-oval to nearly circular in shape, and flattened. The skin is soft and striated. All tarsi end in caruncles.

Several species of *Dermatophagoides* appear to be of some medical importance. *Dermatophagoides scheremetewskyi* Bogdanow is known to attack bats, rodents, and sparrows in the eastern United States; during recent years several human cases of infestation have been reported, in some instances resulting in a severe and persistent dermatitis. Baker *et al.*[6] have summarized human infestations known prior to 1956, and Traver [54] has published a very detailed account of two cases.

Sarcoptic Itch Mites. All members of the family Sarcoptidae, commonly known as the itch mites or scabies mites, are very small (just about visible to the naked eye), whitish, and somewhat hemispherical in form. They are skin parasites of warm-blooded animals. The propodosoma (the part of the body that bears the two fore pairs of legs) is not separated from the hysterosoma (the rest of the body, posteriorly) by a suture; it frequently bears a propodosomal shield, and it always bears a pair of vertical setae. In other areas the skin bears fine striae which may be interrupted by scaly areas or areas bearing small points or spines. The legs are very short; claws or caruncles may be present or absent.

The Sarcoptidae include three important genera, *Sarcoptes, Notoedres,* and *Knemidokoptes* (*Chemidocoptes*), each producing a particular type of acariasis. There are several other genera of no medical or veterinary importance.

Sarcoptes. The mange or itch mites belong to the genus *Sarcoptes;* they have very short legs, the posterior pair not extending beyond the margin of the nearly circular body; caruncles with nonsegmented pedicels are present on the first and second pairs of legs. The sarcoptic mites burrow in the skin, where they produce definite burrows in which the females deposit their eggs.

The forms of *Sarcoptes* inhabiting the skin of mammals are ordinarily regarded as varieties of *Sarcoptes scabiei* (De Geer) (Fig. 161). They differ very slightly from one another, and many of them exchange hosts to a certain degree, e.g., *S. scabiei* var. *suis* Gerlach is parasitic on swine and may be temporarily parasitic on man; *S. scabiei* var. *equi* Gerlach of the horse is also temporarily parasitic on man. The forms, properly physiologic races, appropriate to a given host, however, ordinarily exist only for a limited time on a different host species.

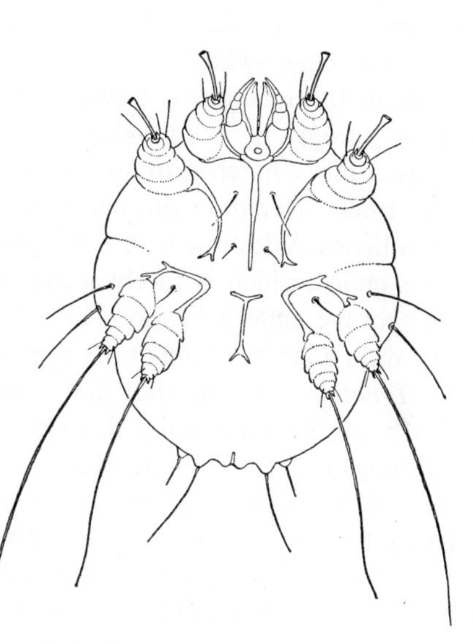

Fig. 161. The itch mite, *Sarcoptes scabiei.*

Human Scabies or Itch. The itch mite attacking man is known as *Sarcoptes scabiei* (De Geer), typical form [=var. *hominis* (Hering)]. The infection is known as "scabies," "seven-year itch," or "Norwegian itch." The mite is universal in distribution. The female measures 330 to 450μ in length and 250 to 350μ in breadth; the male is slightly more than half as large. The mite attacks by preference the thin skin between the fingers, the bend of the knee and elbow, the penis, the breasts, and the shoulder blades, although any part of the body is subject to attack. It appears as though newly infested persons do not experience any itching, and consequently the infestation may progress to a considerable extent before the patient is aware of it. Sensitization begins after about a month, when a rash appears in the neighborhood of the burrows, and an itching, so intense that it may interfere with sleep, is felt. The itching, caused by toxic secretions and excretions, is associated directly with the burrowing. The sinuous burrows which the mite makes in the epidermis may reach 3 cm in length (Warburton[56]), and tiny vesicles and papules are formed on the surface. Scratching may dislodge the mite; it also causes weeping and bleeding, which favor the spread of the mites. It is also a means of secondary infection. Transmission is due to intimate personal contact, usually through sleeping in the same bed with an infested person. It is usually effected by the adult fertilized female. By tracing a mite burrow to its end with a hand lens, the adult female mite can usually be removed with a needle or scalpel and, after treatment with potassium hydroxide on a glass slide, can be readily seen under a microscope. Long-standing chronic cases show few parasites.

Life History of the Itch Mite. The gravid female mite, adhering to the skin by means of the suckers on her tarsi, burrows in and deposits her rather large oval eggs ($150 \times 100\mu$) at intervals in the tortuous tunnel which she makes in the epidermis. Usually she remains in the burrow for her lifetime, depositing eggs at 2- to 3-day intervals for a period of about 2 months. The hexapod larva hatches in sometimes 3 or 4, but usually 5, days. The larvae move freely over the skin, and they, like the nymphs, are frequently found in hair follicles. Within 4 to 6 days after the egg hatches, the nymph transforms into a male (which is rarely seen) or an immature female; the female makes a temporary gallery in the skin before she mates. Maturity is reached in 10 to 14 days after hatching of the egg.

Treatment for Human Itch. Inasmuch as the mites are protected in their tunnels in the epidermis, the skin must either be softened thoroughly by scrubbing vigorously with green soap before a remedy is applied, or else a remedy with suitable penetration properties must be used. Sulfur ointments (10 to 15 per cent precipitated sulfur) give very good results, but overnight applications must be repeated at intervals of 3 to 4 days. Benzyl benzoate, in a 25 per cent emulsion painted on the body from the neck down, gives very good results; one treatment is sufficient and does not necessitate sterilization of underwear and bed clothing, as does sulfur treatment. All individuals of a family or living group should be treated at one time in order to prevent reinfestation. Baker *et al.*[6] mention two other methods of treatment: (1) lindane at 1 per cent in an ointment or vanishing cream, the preparation to be left on the patient 3 or 4 days, and bedding and clothing treated; (2) tetraethylthiuram monosulfide, three or more treatments 24 hours apart, or incorporated in bath soap at 5 to 10 per cent strength, for use as a combination treatment and prophylaxis.

Sarcoptic Mange of Domestic Animals. Mange of swine is caused by *Sarcoptes scabiei* var. *suis* Gerlach (Fig. 162). Mange attacks swine commonly about the top of the neck, shoulder, ears, and withers, and along the back to the root of the tail. A microscopic examination of deeper tissue from beneath scabs will usually reveal the mites. Suckling pigs and young shoats suffer most. The affected animals scratch and rub vigorously, which may, however, be due to lice, but if the skin is cracked and thickly encrusted with heavy scabs, and the hair stands erect, an examination for scab mites should be made.

Sarcoptic acariasis in horses, mules, and asses is caused by *Sarcoptes scabiei* var. *equi* Gerlach. This species is also transmissible to man and is said to be the chief cause of a transitory itch in individuals who handle horses extensively.

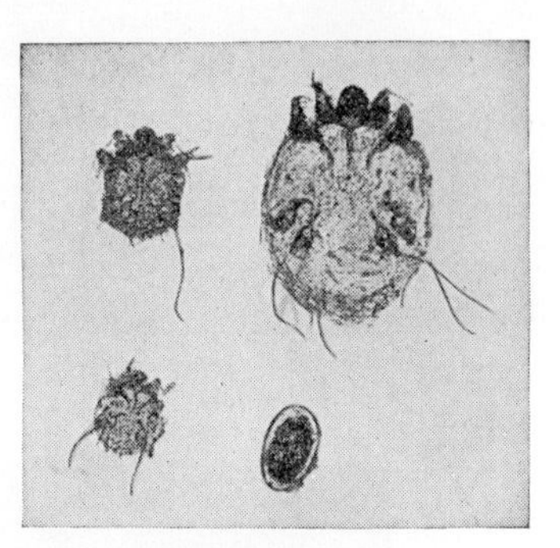

Fig. 162. Life history and general characteristics of a typical sarcoptid mite, *Sarcoptes scabiei* var. *suis,* the itch mite of swine: (*lower right*) egg; (*lower left*) larva; (*upper left*) adult male; (*upper right*) adult female. × 57.

Sarcoptic acariasis, or mange, in cattle caused by *Sarcoptes scabiei* var. *bovis* Robin is not so common as the psoroptic form (scabies) but is far more difficult to cure. It usually attacks the parts of the body where the hair is short, namely the brisket and around the base of the tail.

The common mange of dogs is caused by *Sarcoptes scabiei* var. *canis* Gerlach, closely resembling the swine parasite. Mange of the dog appears first on the muzzle, around the eyes, on ears, and breast, and later spreads to the back, abdomen, and elsewhere.

Sarcoptes scabiei var *ovis* Megnin of sheep occurs on the face primarily and causes "black muzzel." In more severe cases the limbs and rarely the body, but not the wooly parts, may be affected. *S. scabiei* var. *caprae* Furstenburg attacks goats and may be fatal.

Notoedric Mange. Mange of cats is caused by *Notoedres cati* Hering, smaller and more circular than *Sarcoptes* but otherwise quite similar. Notoedric mange of cats begins at the tips of the ears and gradually spreads over the face and head. This mite will attack dogs and certain rodents, but apparently not man. *Notoedric cati* var. *cuniculi* Gerlach causes a severe mange of rabbits, beginning at the muzzle and in severe cases spreading over the whole body.

Scaly Leg on Poultry. The legs of domestic fowls (chickens, turkeys, pheasants, etc.) are frequently attacked by a microscopic burrowing mite, *Knemidokoptes mutans* (Robin and Lanquetin) (Fig. 163), which causes

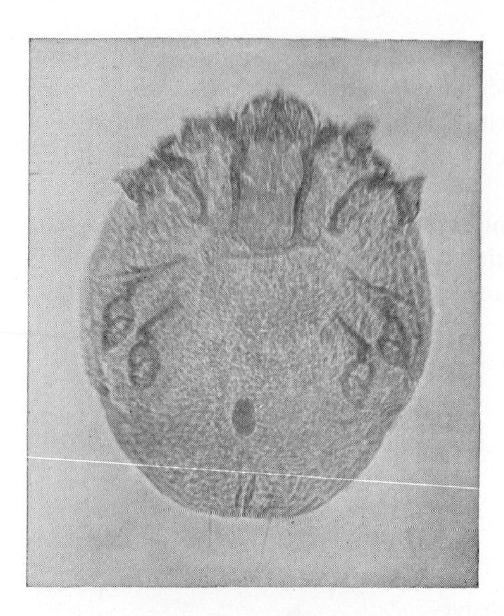

Fig. 163. The scaly leg mite of poultry, *Knemidokoptes mutans,* greatly enlarged. × 170.

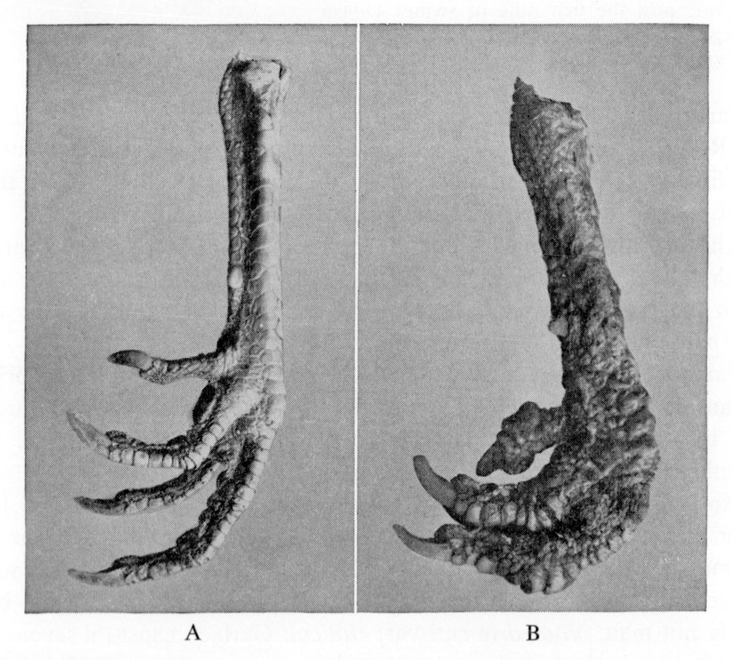

Fig. 164. (*A*) Normal leg and claw of a fowl; and (*B*) one affected with the scaly leg mite, *Knemidokoptes mutans,* causing scaly leg.

a lifting of the scales and a swollen condition of the shank with deformity and encrustation. The mites burrow and live in the skin, depositing their eggs in channels as do the mange mites. Scaly leg (Fig. 164) is easily transmitted from fowl to fowl; hence, segregation is important in effecting control.

The Depluming Mite, *Knemidokoptes laevis* var. *gallinae* (Raillet), is closely related to the scaly leg mite, but attacks the skin of the fowl near the bases of the feathers. These mites themselves do not cause the bird to lose plumage, but the intense itching caused by the mites impels the host to pluck its feathers in an attempt to reduce the itching.

Control of Sarcoptid Pests of Domestic Animals. As in most other fields of medical and veterinary entomology, the control of sarcoptids on domestic mammals and poultry has undergone great changes since the 1940's. Lindane particularly, among the newer insecticides, has been replacing less effective and harder-to-apply materials. For a concise discussion of control measures and references, the student is referred to Baker *et al.*[6]

Psoroptid Mites. Mites of the family Psoroptidae attack domestic animals in a variety of ways. These mites may be distinguished from the sarcoptids in that the propodosoma lacks vertical setae, although a dorsal shield may be present. The important genus *Psoroptes* may be distinguished from *Sarcoptes* (as well as from other genera of Psoroptidae) in that the tarsal suckers (caruncles) are borne on long, segmented stalks. The legs of the Psoroptidae are longer than those of the Sarcoptidae.

Chorioptic or *Symbiotic Mange.* Mites belonging to the genus *Chorioptes* produce a mange which is restricted to certain parts of the body such as the feet, tail, and neck. *Chorioptes bovis* (Gerlach) attacks cattle; other species of some veterinary significance are *C. equi* (Hering) on horses, *C. caprae* (Delafond) on goats, *C. ovis* (Raillet) on sheep, and *C. cuniculi* (Zurn) on rabbits. These "species" may, like those of *Sarcoptes* and *Psoroptes,* be merely physiologic races.

Psoroptic Mange Mites. These mites (Figs. 165, 166) are distinguishable from *Sarcoptes* in that the legs are long and slender, all four pairs extending beyond the margin of the body, which is elongate; the pedicel of the suckers (caruncles) is segmented; and the chelicerae are styliform, serrate near the tip. The psoroptic mites do not burrow, as do the sarcoptic mites, but live at the base of hairs of the host, piercing the skin and introducing a toxic saliva which causes inflammation. An exudate follows which partially hardens, forming a scab. As the mites multiply, bites increase as well as itching; more serum oozes out to form a crust of loose humid matter. The parasitized area increases, and the skin becomes hardened and thickened. This condition is known as *scab.* Owing to the loose condition of the scabs and the hardiness of the mites, this form of acariasis becomes quickly and easily distributed from animal to animal by contact and by rubbing against fences, trees, and the like.

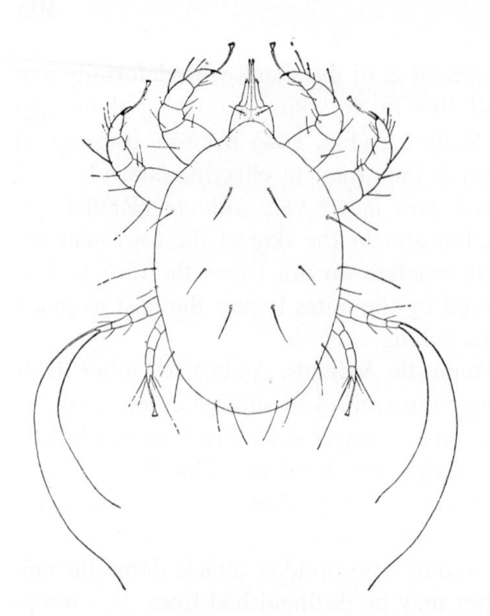

Fig. 165. The scab mite, *Psoroptes equi.*

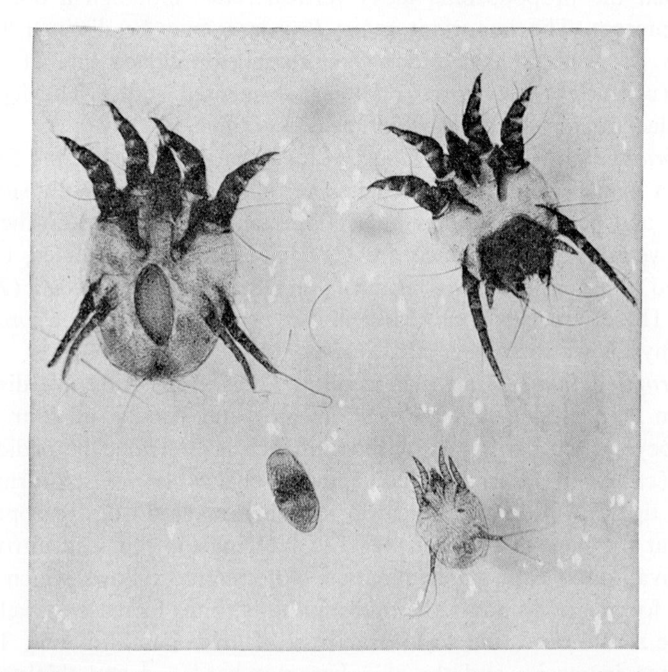

Fig. 166. Showing life history and general characteristics of the scab mite, *Psoroptes equi.* (*Lower left*) Egg; (*lower right*) larva; (*upper left*) adult female; (*upper right*) adult male. × 85.

Psoroptes equi (Hering) is the causative organism of psoroptic mange or scab in domestic animals. *Psoroptes equi* var. *equi* causes psoroptic mange of horses. It generally makes its appearance near the root of the tail or mane and is regarded as a serious disease. Bovine scabies in cattle is caused by *P. equi var. bovis* (Gerlach) and is a comparatively common disease; *P. equi* var. *caprae* (Delafond) is found on goats but is confined to the pinnae of the ears.

Psoroptes equi var. *ovis* (Hering) is the causal organism of sheep scab or scabies. This is by far the most important of the scab mites. However, with the widespread use of dips and rigid quarantine regulations, scabies in sheep is gradually being controlled.

Unlike the sarcoptic mange mite, the sheep scab mite is found on the parts of the body most thickly covered with wool. Scabies is indicated by a "tagging" of the wool; the coat becomes rough, ragged, and matted at the points affected. Tags of wool are torn away by the sheep or are left attached to rubbing posts and other objects against which the animal rubs. The sheep scratches vigorously and shows signs of intense itching. The infestation is spread by contact with infested sheep.

Auricular Mites (Otoacariasis). A comparatively common infestation of cats, dogs, and foxes, known as *otoacariasis* or *parasitic otitis,* is traceable to *Otodectes cynotis* (Hering), which resembles *Psoroptes* very closely. These mites literally swarm in the ears of the host causing much discomfort, tenderness of the ears, auricular catarrh, loss of appetite, wasting, torticollis, "fits," etc.

Control of Psoroptid Mites. Control methods vary as to the mite and its host, but in general, as in the case of control of the sarcoptid mites, lindane is replacing less effective insecticides. For control, the student is referred to Baker *et al.*[6]

KEY TO SOME IMPORTANT GENERA OF ACARIDIAE

1. Free-living; tarsi terminating in clawlike empodia, which are sometimes minute; female genital openings longitudinal, with flaplike plates and two pairs of internal genital suckers 2
   Parasitic; tarsi terminating in caruncles which lack clawlike empodia; female genital openings transverse, without genital suckers 3
2. Caruncles not stalked, the clawlike empodia large; propodosoma separated from the hysterosoma by a suture (Acaridae). ....*Acarus*
   Caruncles stalked, the empodial claws minute; propodosoma not separated from the hyterosoma by a suture (Glycyphagidae) .....*Glycyphagus*
3. Propodosoma with a pair of vertical setae (except in *Knemidokoptes*); stalks of caruncles not segmented; female without genital apodemes (Sarcoptidae) 4
   Propodosoma without a pair of vertical setae; stalks of caruncles segmented or not; female with genital apodemes 6

4. Dorsal striae interrupted by strong spinelike serrations; tarsi I and II of female with long-stalked caruncles .... *Sarcoptes*
   Dorsal striae not interrupted by strong spinelike serrations 5
5. Anus dorsal; tarsi I and II of female with long-stalked caruncles . . *Notoedres*
   Anus terminal; caruncles of tarsi of female not stalked ...... *Knemidokoptes*
6. All tarsi with short-stalked caruncles; all legs of equal size (Epidermoptidae) .... *Dermatophagoides*
   Caruncles of tarsi III of female not stalked, those of I, II, and sometimes IV long- or short-stalked; legs of unequal size (Psoroptidae) 7
7. Stalks of caruncles long, segmented .... *Psoroptes*
   Stalks of caruncles short, not segmented 8
8. Tarsi I, II, and IV of female with short-stalked caruncles, tarsus III with a pair of long terminal setae; leg IV of female not smaller than leg III .... *Chorioptes*
   Tarsi I and II of female with short-stalked caruncles, tarsi III and IV each with a pair of long terminal setae; leg IV the smallest in both sexes .... *Otodectes*

THE CHIGGER MITES, FOLLICLE MITES, AND THEIR RELATIVES

(*Suborder Trombidiformes*)

Characteristics. The trombidiform mites form a large and diverse group of mites of different habits. Many of them are aquatic, mostly fresh-water, but some marine; some of the terrestrial forms are parasitic, and some of the free-living forms are parasitic in the larval stage. The classification, as accepted by Baker *et al.*,[5] is rather complicated, but the suborder includes the wormlike, four-legged Tetrapodili, composing the plant-feeding family Eriophyidae; the water-inhabiting Hydrachnellae; and many others. Families of demonstrated medical importance are the Pyemotidae, the Demodicidae, the Tetranychidae, and particularly the Trombiculidae.

The Pyemotidae are soft-bodied mites with greatly reduced mouth parts; the chelicerae are tiny, styletlike, and the palpi are reduced, lying close to the rostrum. The females have a prominent clavate organ of uncertain use between the first and second pairs of legs. The third and fourth pairs of legs are separated from the first and second by a long interspace. Sexual dimorphism is usually marked.

Pyemotes ventricosus (Newport) (Fig. 167) is a widely distributed predaceous mite which attacks the larvae of a number of species of insects such as the Angoumois grain moth, *Sitotroga cerealella* (Olivier); the wheat straw-worm, *Harmolita grandis* (Riley); the peach twig borer, *Anarsia lineatella* Zeller; the boll weevil, *Anthonomus grandis* Boheman; the bean weevil, *Acanthoscelides obtectus* (Say); the pea weevil, *Bruchus pisorum*

(Linnaeus); and others. It is therefore normally a beneficial mite, but unfortunately it also attacks man, producing a very disagreeable dermatitis known as straw, hay, or grain itch.

While the male mite is very tiny, barely visible to the naked eye, the female when gravid becomes enormously swollen, measuring nearly a millimeter in length, the abdomen presenting a globular appearance and resembling a tiny pearl.

Within the enlarged abdomen of the female may be found rather large eggs which hatch internally, and the young mites develop to maturity within the body of the mother before being extruded. The number of offspring pro-

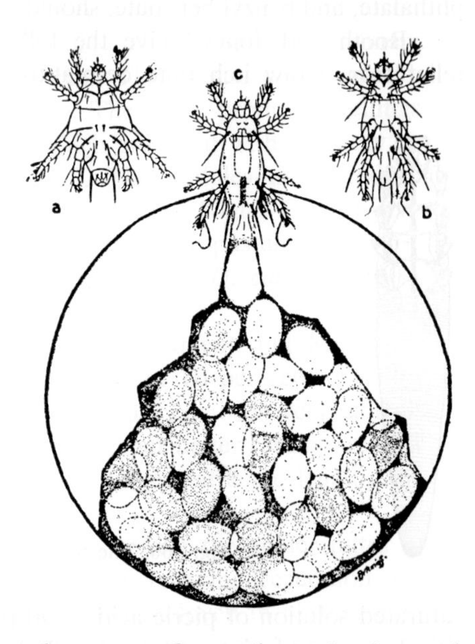

Fig. 167. *Pyemotes ventricosus.* (*a*) Adult male; (*b*) adult female; (*c*) gravid female, showing developing eggs. (Redrawn after various authors.)

duced by a female is 200 to 300. The males emerge first and remain clustered around the genital opening of the mother, fertilizing the young females as they emerge.

A number of epidemics of dermatitis have been traced to these mites, and it is probable that, because of the temporary nature of the dermatitis, many cases have never been reported to doctors. Infestation is brought about by sleeping on straw mattresses, laboring in grain fields at harvest time, or otherwise coming in contact with or handling grains, straw, hay, grasses, or even beans, peas, cottonseed, or other materials that may be infested with larvae that are attacked by these mites. The dermatitis has been confounded with hives, scabies, and even chickenpox; the neck, chest, abdomen, back, arms, and legs—in fact, the whole body—may be involved, and the itching is intense. The wheals caused by the bites of the mites vary with different individuals, but they form around a vesicle marking the site of the puncture;

The chelicerae have two segments; the basal segment is stout and muscular while the distal segment is a sclerotized, curved blade with or without projections called teeth. The palps have five segments; the basal segments are fused along the midline and have a median, anterior, laminar projection that extends beyond the basal segment of the chelicerae and a pair of lateral wings or galeae that curl dorsal about the chelicerae and bear a seta on each side; each basal segment also bears a seta posterior to the junction with the palpal femur. The second palpal segment or femur bears a single seta; the third or genu bears a single seta; the fourth, or tibia, has three setae; one is dorsal, one lateral, one ventral, and there is a terminal palpal claw. The fifth, or tarsus, articulates ventrally with the tibia and opposes the palpal claw in thumblike fashion. It bears several setae (usually eight), the basal one of which is a striated sensory seta. The body is usually red but may be almost colorless; it bears a dorsal plate or scutum at the level of the anterior two pairs of legs, usually two pairs of eyes that flank the scutum, several rows of dorsal setae, several rows of ventral setae, occasionally a posterior plate or a posterior group of specialized setae, a ventral anus, three pairs of legs, an urstigma or sclerotized pit associated with the posterior distal angle of coxa I, and at times a pair of tracheal trunks that open through stigmata in the region of the gnathosoma. The scutum bears from three to six marginal scutal setae or infrequently more, and a pair of pseudostigmata from which the sensillae or pseudostigmatic organs arise. The legs are composed of six segments if the femur is undivided and of seven if the femur consists of a basifemur and telofemur.

The adults are about 1 mm long, oval or, more usually, figure-8–shaped. The cuticle is clothed with filiform, densely pilose setae, giving it a velvety appearance. The color is often bright red.

Wharton and Fuller[57] divide the Trombiculidae into four subfamilies, of which most chiggers belong to the Trombiculinae. These authors characterize this subfamily as follows: "Trombiculids whose larvae have a median, scutal seta, lack submedian scutal setae, have seven segments in all legs, at least four sternal setae, no median, anterior projection on the scutum, and no stigmata or tracheal trunks." A diagnosis based on larvae is more useful for our purposes than one based on nymphs or adults, since it is the larval form which is of medical importance, and which is more frequently submitted for identification.

The taxonomy of the chiggers presents some difficult problems, as pointed out by Fuller.[24] Chief among these are, first, the fact that a great many chigger mites have been described from the larval stage only and that adults and nymphs are either unknown or uncorrelated with the larvae; and, secondly, that the taxonomist is faced with the problem of evaluating the statistical and biological significance of variation, which, in some important groups of chiggers, is but poorly known and understood.

The literature pertaining to the Trombiculidae, their taxonomy and medical importance, has grown enormously during recent years. The bibliography published by Williams[58] in 1944 consisted of 375 references, and

Wharton and Fuller's[57] *Manual of the Chiggers* (1952) contains nearly 700. For identification and taxonomic studies of the family, the student should start with the manual of Wharton and Fuller; this work carries these mites through keys only to genera and subgenera, although detailed bibliographic, distributional, and host information is given for the species. Fuller[24] cites a number of references to taxonomic papers in the Pacific area and Asia. For determination to species, the student is referred to the keys of Brennan and Jones,[12] to the studies of Jenkins,[35] and Brennan and Wharton,[13] respectively, for the North American species of the subgenera *Eutrombicula* and *Neo-*

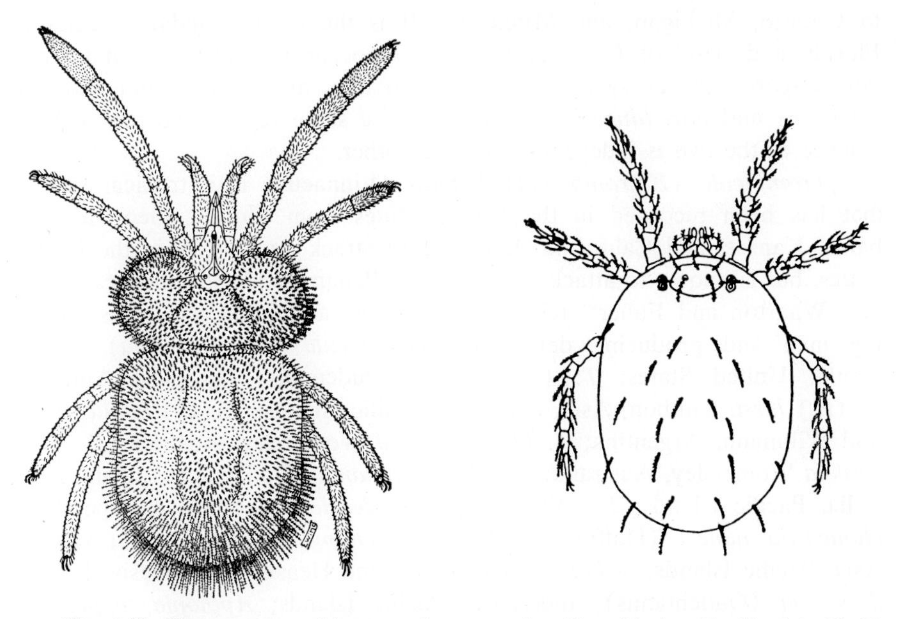

Fig. 169. The common chigger or harvest mite, *Trombicula alfreddugèsi.* (*Left*) Adult; (*right*) larva. (From Ewing's *Manual of External Parasites.* Courtesy of Charles C Thomas, Publishers.)

trombicula of the medically important genus *Trombicula,* and to Farrell[21] for the genus *Euschöngastia*. For a regional study, consult the study of the chiggers of Kansas by Loomis[37] and that of the chiggers of California by Gould.[25]

Important Species of Chiggers.[34] Among the chigger mites that cause a severe dermatitis is the European species *Trombicula* (*Neotrombicula*) *autumnalis* (Shaw), known as the *harvest mite, aoutat,* or *lepte automnal.* It differs from the American chiggers of the subgenus *Eutrombicula* in that its larvae have trifid, rather than bifid claws.

Trombicula (*Eutrombicula*) *alfreddugèsi* (Oudemans) (*Leptus irritans* of much of the earlier literature) is the common chigger (Fig. 169) of the

United States, ranging from New England and eastern Canada to Nebraska, south to Florida and Texas, and west to California; it also occurs in Mexico, Central America, and South America. It is known by a wide range of names, including *tlalzahuatl, bicho colorado,* and *bete rouge.* It is abundant in second growth cut-over areas, especially blackberry patches, forest edges, and river valleys. Its hosts include man, a wide range of domestic and wild animals, birds, reptiles, and even a few amphibians.

Trombicula (*Eutrombicula*) *splendens* Ewing [= *masoni* (Ewing)] is distributed along the Atlantic Coast from Florida to Massachusetts and along the Gulf Coast to Texas, then northward and westward in suitable habitats to Ontario, Michigan, and Minnesota. It is the most abundant species in Florida and parts of Georgia. It seems to occur in moister habitats than *alfreddugèsi,* such as swamps, bogs, rotten logs, and stumps, and although *splendens* and *alfreddugèsi* may occur in the same region, the seasonal incidence of the two is independent of each other.

Trombicula (*Eutrombicula*) *batatas* (Linnaeus) is a tropical species that has been recorded in the United States from Florida, Georgia, Alabama, Kansas, and California. It is said to attack man rarely in the United States, but is known to attack man freely in Panama and other tropical areas.

Wharton and Fuller[57] report the following additional species as attacking man and producing dermatitis: *Trombicula* (*Eutrombicula*) *belkini* Gould, United States; *T.* (*E.*) *goldii* (Oudemans), Tropical America; *T.* (*E.*) *hirsti* Sambon, Asia, Australia, Pacific Islands; *T.* (*E.*) *lahillei* Thor and Willmann, Argentina; *T.* (*E.*) *samboni* Womersley, Australia; *T.* (*E.*) *sarcina* Womersley, Australia; *T.* (*E.*) *wichmanni* (Oudemanns), Asia, Australia, Pacific Islands; *T.* (*Neotrombicula*) *desaleri* Methlagl, Europe; *Euschöngastia nuñezi* (Hoffmann), Mexico; *Schöngastia schüffneri* (Walch), Asia, Pacific Islands; *S. katonis* Womersley and Heaslip, Micronesia; *S. vandersandei* (Oudemanns), Indonesia, Pacific Islands; *Apolonia tigipioensis* Torres and Braga, Brazil; and *Acomatacarus australiensis* (Hirst), Australia, Indonesia, Pacific Islands. *Apolonia* and *Acomatacarus* do not belong to the subfamily Trombiculinae; *Apolonia* differs from the trombiculine chiggers in that it has four scutal setae; in *Acomatacarus* all legs have only six segments. *Schöngastia vandersandei, S. schüffneri,* and *Trombicula wichmanni* are the principal causes of scrub itch of man in New Guinea. *Acomatacarus australiensis* is known as the grass itch mite in Australia, New Guinea, and the Celebes; it infests a variety of domestic animals and readily attacks man.

Trombicula (*Leptotrombidium*) *akamushi* (Brumpt), one of the two common vectors of scrub typhus, occurs from Japan and China southward through Indonesia to New Guinea. It inhabits partially cultivated land which is inundated by the floods of spring and early summer, the mite reaching a peak during July and August. *Trombicula* (*L.*) *deliensis* Walsh, the other important scrub typhus vector, occurs from Pakistan and India through Indonesia to New Guinea and Australia. It occupies the grassy places characteristic of *T. akamushi,* but may occur in primary jungle.

Life Cycle. The bright red adult mites are found on the surface of moist ground or to a depth of 2 or 3 in. in dried soil, being often seen in the bases and root stocks of clumps of grass, in sphagnum moss, and under logs. Adults feed on insect eggs and the early instars of insects and other arthropods. Just prior to oviposition, the color of the adult becomes more yellowish; food can also influence its color.

With few exceptions, eggs are laid singly in the soil. Females are ready to lay eggs within a few days (7 days for *Trombicula splendens* and *T. alfreddugèsi*)[33] after the adult stage has been reached, and once egg laying is begun, it continues as long as conditions are satisfactory. Jenkins[33] counted 4764 eggs produced in the laboratory by 23 females within 1 month—an average of 7 per day per female. After a 4- to 6-day incubation period, the eggs hatch to produce a quiescent stage, the *deutovum,* which remains within the eggshell fragments. In about a week, after having completed the deutoval stage, the fully formed red hexapod larva emerges and crawls about rapidly in search of a host. The larva can live for a considerable period (probably 2 weeks or longer) without feeding. The opportunity to find a suitable host should be good since the range of species attacked is so broad; for *T. alfreddugèsi* more than a hundred hosts, including mammals, birds, amphibians, and reptiles, are known. The larval chigger feeds but once and requires 1 to 3 or 4 days (sometimes up to a month) for engorgement.

The chigger then drops to the ground, burrows into the upper layers of soil, and becomes quiescent. Within the larval skin, a *nymphocrysalis* develops. After about a week, the active, eight-legged nymph emerges. It feeds on insect eggs and the early instars of insects and other arthropods, as does the adult, for about a week; then it goes into another inactive stage, the *imagocrysalis,* which lasts about a week. This form then molts into the adult. The minimum time required to complete the life cycle is, according to Jenkins,[33] 50 days for *T. splendens,* 55 for *T. alfreddugèsi,* and 71 for *T. batatas.* The number of generations per year will vary from one or sometimes two in northern latitudes (one for *T. autumnalis* in Europe) to continuous breeding in the tropics and subtropics. Hibernation probably takes place in the adult stage.

Chigger Dermatitis. In many parts of the world, particularly in the warmer portions and during the late summer months in temperate climates, persons who have walked among tall weeds and grass, brambles, and low scrub often suffer an intolerable itching, which begins 3 to 6 hours after exposure and is followed by a severe dermatitis consisting of pustules and wheals. When, after a trip through tall weeds or grass or a berry brambles, itching begins around the ankles, the knees, and the waist, a careful examination will pretty surely reveal at least one (there will be others) bright red mite barely visible to the naked eye either traveling fast or about to attach itself to the skin. A microscopic examination will show that it has three pairs of legs, and no doubt it is the larva of a trombiculid mite—a chigger.

Chiggers do not burrow into the skin as is commonly believed. Ewing[19] observed and studied daily 26 chiggers on his own skin; 21 were attached to the smooth surface of the skin, while 5 were attached at the bases of hairs, each having the capitulum thrust into the mouth of the hair follicle; not a single one had penetrated a pore or hair follicle. The chigger does not suck blood; when firmly attached it injects a digestive fluid which causes a disintegration of the contents of cells with which it comes in contact, the result being a disorganized cytoplasm and fragmented nuclei (Jones[36]). The resulting material is utilized as food by the chigger. The skin of the host becomes hardened, and there is formed a tube (stylosome) in which the chigger lies and continues to ingest the nourishment until it is replete; then it retreats and drops to the ground. According to Michener and Michener,[38] it is presumably the action of the digestive fluid which causes the "bite" to itch after a few hours. Williams[59] points out that histologic preparations of chigger bites on rabbit ears show that the epidermis is completely penetrated. A tube lined with stratum germinativum is formed which extends to the derma and subcutis. This tube appears to represent a reaction of the host to the secretion of the chigger, and its inner layer of cells is necrotic and gives evidence of digestion.

Tsutsugamushi disease or *scrub typhus,* also known as Japanese flood fever, Japanese river fever, kedani fever, and other names, is an ancient disease[10] first described from Japan. It was long said that the infection is transferred to man by the "akamushi" (Japanese for "dangerous bug"), the larval trombiculid (chigger) mite, *Trombicula akamushi,* from rodent reservoirs (voles, *Microtus montebelli* Sado). It was not, however, until 1916 that positive experimental evidence was secured by Miyajima and Okumura[40] in tests with monkeys. Hayashi,[27] reporting on the etiology of tsutsugamushi disease, gave the name *Theileria tsutsugamushi* to what he believed to be the causal agent. The accepted name for this organism at the present time is *Rickettsia tsutsugamushi* (Hayashi) Ogata.

The disease has an incubation period of 6 to 21, usually 10 to 12, days. During the first 5 to 7 days, it is characterized by Blake *et al.*[10] as follows: "headache (postorbital), apathy and general malaise, fever (chills), relative bradycardia, anorexia, conjunctival congestion, lymphadenitis, often regional, and an eschar." The eschar is the primary lesion which originates at the point of chigger attack (ankle, shin, groin, waistline, or axilla) in the great majority of cases. It is a painless papule at first, usually unnoticed by the patient (and usually absent in Asians). It slowly enlarges to a diameter of 8 to 12 mm, the center becoming very dark and necrotic; a shallow ulcer may result eventually, leaving a scar. Between the fifth and eighth days in nearly all cases, a dull red macular or maculopapular rash appears on the trunk and may spread to the extremities involving the palms, soles, face, and scalp. This may persist for several days, or it may disappear within a few hours. Enlargement of the spleen, nervous disturbances, delirium, and prostration are common symptoms; in many cases there is deafness. The majority recover by lysis in 3 to 5 weeks. In extremely severe cases "symptoms and signs of more severe pneumonitis and encephalitis are constant. Evidences of peripheral circulatory collapse are common and signs of myocarditis may appear. . . . Thromboses and cerebral or gastrointestinal hemorrhage may take place." (Blake *et al.*[10])

Mortality ranges from 1 to 60 per cent in different localities and among different populations; death results from secondary bacterial penumonia, encephalitis, or circulatory failure, in approximately equal numbers, at about the end of the second week. The rickettsiae may readily be recovered from the blood of patients during the acute stage of the disease by the intraperitoneal inoculation of 0.2 to 0.3 ml of blood in white mice.

Although the greatest number of cases occur at low elevations (sandy bottom land overgrown with grasses and scrub), infections occur at elevations of 2000 to 3000 ft and, in Taiwan, as high as 6500 ft. The chigger mites have been reported as high as 8000 ft in India. The infection is endemic in many parts of southeastern Asia and adjacent islands in the Indian Ocean and southwest Pacific (Ceylon, Japan, Philippines, Indonesia, Taiwan) and the coastal area of North Queensland, Australia.

The importance of scrub typhus as a "medical casualty producer in some areas during the Asiatic-Pacific operation, 1941–45," according to Philip,[44] "was second only to malaria and was more dreaded by the men." Interference with actual combat operations was greatest, Philip states, on the Assam-Burma front where:

> . . . eighteen per cent of a single battalion got scrub typhus in two months and in that time 5 per cent of the total strength had died of it.
>
> American Task Force operations in the Schouten Islands resulted in a thousand cases in the first 2 months on Owi and Biak, reaching a total of 1,469 casualties in 6 months time, while at Sansapor beach head the curve for weekly admissions on a thousand-per-year basis shot up to over 900 at the end of the second week, a rate higher for an individual episode than any yearly rate for all causes in the entire American Army in all theatres. . . . These two disasters alone provided a potential estimated loss of over 150,000 man days to the American Sixth Army.

The Vectors. Two closely related mites of the subgenus *Leptotrombidium,* namely *Trombicula akamushi* (Brumpt) and *T. deliensis* Walch, are the two proven vectors of scrub typhus. Until recently, they were thought to be the only species involved in the transmission of this disease. The two species are differentiated from each other chiefly on the number and arrangement of the dorsal setae.

The adult mites measure from 1 to 2 mm in length, are generally reddish in color, often pale. In cultures, they feed readily on collembola and mosquito eggs. The winter is spent in the adult stage, except in equatorial climates where there is no hibernation. Eggs are deposited in the soil, under leaves or in damp places. The hexapod larvae, at first measuring about 0.22 mm in length, emerge in about 10 to 12 days at 30° C and wait the coming of a suitable host—mammal or bird (man is an accidental host). They attack in clusters, often packed together in the ears of a field rodent. Numerous hosts are available, the chigger being habitat-specific rather than host-specific;[4] but continuous propagation of the infection is dependent upon susceptible so-called reservoir animals, the first of which was demonstrated to be a vole, *Microtus montebelli*. Wartime studies as reported by Philip and Kohls[46] indicate that rats play an important widespread role in the disease cycle in nature. "Six kinds of rats (among them *Rattus concolor browni* and *R. flavipectus yunanensis*) indigenous to New Guinea, Burma, or India, plus a species each of field mouse and tree shrew (*Tupaia belangeri versurae*) have been added to two murid species already demonstrated to carry natural infection in Japan and Malaya, and to others under strong indictment in Formosa, Sumatra, and Australia." Infection has been demonstrated in the circulation of English sparrows, pigeons, and turkeys.

The larval mite ("*akamushi*") remains on the host from 1 to perhaps 10 days. It measures about 0.55 mm when fully engorged. It then drops to the ground, spends some time seeking suitable shelter, and then, after the nymphocrysalis stage, emerges as an adult. The life cycle, from egg to egg-laying, under laboratory conditions, is completed in "under 40 days" for *T. deliensis* in Malaya and "in under 70 days" for *T. akamushi* in Japan, according to Audy.[4]

Transmission of scrub typhus has been shown to be transovarian in both *T. akamushi* and *T. deliensis*. No other method would be possible in a mite that takes but one blood meal during its lifetime.

The discovery that chiggers other than the two important vectors of scrub typhus may carry the rickettsia and transmit it with more or less success has led to some interesting implications. Traub *et al.*[52] recovered *R. tsutsugamushi* from the chigger *Euschöngastia audyi* (Womersley) taken from tree squirrels. The presence of the rickettsia in different hosts, both acarine and mammalian, and under jungle conditions, led Traub and his associates to the conclusion that "the natural cycle of scrub typhus in the jungle and the explosive local outbreak of the disease in man following exposure in hyperinfected areas of scrub terrain may prove to have a number of similarities to jungle and urban yellow fever." Subsequent studies by Audy and others support this theory and add to the complication of the epidemiology of scrub typhus. The relation of various vectors to the epidemiology of the disease is summarized by Audy[4] when he divides mammal-infesting chiggers capable of transmitting the rickettsia into the following categories: (1) major vectors of general importance to man (*T. akamushi, T. deliensis*); (2) major vectors of local importance (apparently confined to certain palaearctic species of *Leptotrombidium,* such as *T. pallida* Nagayo *et al.* and *T. scutellaris* Nagayo *et al.*); (3) efficient vectors which may attack man but do not occur in sufficient numbers or in suitable habitats to infest man sufficiently, although they may be responsible for sporadic cases or rare anomalous outbreaks; and (4) species which do not attack man but may be responsible for enzootic infection.

Audy[4] has pointed out that the tick-borne and flea-borne rickettsioses are world-wide in distribution, whereas the mite-borne rickettsiosis, scrub typhus, occurs only in eastern Asia, the East Indies, and northern Australia. He offers as an explanation the "hypothesis that scrub typhus has evolved in the broad area of evolution of both the genus *Rattus* and the chigger subgenus *Leptotrombidium,* where extensive deforestation by man has encouraged dense populations of field rats infested particularly by the major vectors." It is interesting to note, for whatever implications it may have, that one species of *Leptotrombidium, T.* (*L.*) *myotis* Ewing, occurs in the United States, and another, *T.* (*L.*) *mexicana* Ewing, occurs in Mexico.

Control of Chiggers. In controlling chiggers, one must first locate the infested areas. It is not always possible to detect chigger-infested terrain by looking at it; a given area may be inhabited by large numbers of chiggers in one year and deserted by them in another. Chiggers may be detected if one will place at various intervals pieces of black cardboard edgewise on the ground.[2] If chiggers are present, they will, within a few minutes, crawl up the cardboard and congregate at its top edge. In doing the survey work, one must remember that he is hunting chiggers and that he should, therefore, protect himself adequately with repellents.

Chigger infestations in lawns, gardens, and the general premises can be wiped out by applying suitable chemicals either as a spray or a dust to the infested areas. Chlordane, toxaphene, and lindane are recommended against American chiggers. A knapsack sprayer or a cylindrical compressed-air sprayer will be satisfactory for application to a limited area, such as a lawn or a campsite, but power equipment is required for larger areas. An emulsifiable solution or wettable powder, 1 per cent, should be applied at the concentration of 2 lb per acre for chlordane or toxaphene or 1/4 lb per acre for lindane. Poultry should be kept out of the treated areas for at least 2 days following treatment. Dust may be used instead of the liquid spray. Repetition of the application at intervals of 4 to 8 weeks may be necessary. Traub *et al.*[53] found that the application of dieldrin or aldrin, preferably dieldrin, applied at the rate of 2 1/4 lb per square acre virtually eliminated *Trombicula deliensis* in test plots in Borneo.

Diethyltoluamide is the best repellent against chiggers so far developed. The following are also effective: dimethyl phthalate, dimethyl carbamate, ethyl hexanediol, and benzyl benzoate. The repellent may be applied to clothing (caution: some synthetic fabrics may be harmed by contact with it). Apply particularly to openings in the clothing, inside and out, to cuffs and waistbands of trousers and slacks, to cuffs, sleeve hems, neckbands, armholes, and waistbands of skirts, shirts, and blouses, and dresses. It may be applied lightly to arms or legs that are not covered by clothing.

If one has been in a chigger-infested area without the protection of repellents, one should bathe as soon as possible after returning. Apply a thick lather, then rinse it off, and repeat several times. The bath will kill at least most attached chiggers, plus any others which may not be attached. If welts have formed, a dab of antiseptic applied to each will kill the chigger, if it is still alive, and will prevent infection. To get temporary relief from the itching, application of a local anesthetic will be useful, or the following formula may be taken to a druggist for compounding: Benzocaine, 5 per cent; methyl salicylate, 2 per cent; salicylic acid, 0.5 per cent; ethyl alcohol, 73 per cent; water, 19.5 per cent. Application of this material to each welt with a piece of cotton should give relief for an hour or more; treatment may be repeated as often as necessary.

THE PENTASTOMIDS

Tongue-worms

The Class Pentastomida, also known as the Linguatulida, comprehends the so-called tongue-worms, parasites of numerous species of vertebrate animals, from fishes to man. Because of certain resemblance to the phytoptine mites (Eriophyidae) the tongue-worms have been classed with the Acarina (Sambon[49]). Heymons[28] points out that the difference between the pentastomids and the annelids is far less than the difference between them and the arthropods.

These endoparasites, in the adult stage, inhabit primarily the lungs and air passages of their hosts. The body consists of a head or cephalothorax and a not distinctly separated abdomen. The head possesses five ventral openings: the median opening is the mouth, and the remaining two pairs lead to hollows from which sclerotized hooks protrude. They are legless, vermiform, and pseudo-annulated. Development is indirect, in that an intermediate host is required. The larvae live either free or encysted in the viscera of the intermediate host. A good account of a life history [*Porocephalus crotali* (Humboldt), a parasite of muskrats (intermediate) and rattlesnake (definitive host)] has been given by Penn.[43]

The class Pentastomida is divided into two orders: (1) Cephalobaenida, and (2) Porocephalida. The order Porocephalida consists of two families: (1) Porocephalidae, which includes among others the genus *Porocephalus* and the genus *Armillifer;* (2) Linguatulidae, which includes the genus *Linguatula,* to which the tongue-worm *Linguatula serrata* Frölich belongs.

Pentastomiasis of man is commonly encountered, the cause being either linguatulids (linguatulosis) or porocephalids (porocephaliasis).

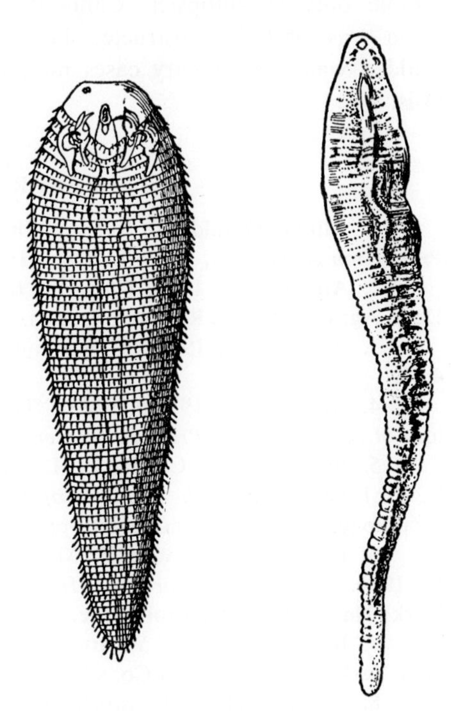

Fig. 170. *Linguatula serrata.* (*Left*) Larva; (*right*) adult. (Redrawn after Brumpt.)

Linguatulosis is primarily due to ingestion of the eggs of *Linguatula serrata* Frölich (= *L. rhinaria* Moniez), the adult of which normally inhabits the nasal and frontal sinuses of the dog and wolf, occasionally those of the fox. The adult female reaches a length of 80 to 120 mm and a breadth of 8 to 10 mm (Fig. 170). The males are hardly half this size. The eggs are discharged from the nostrils and mouth of the parasitized animal and are ingested by the intermediate host with food and water. Intermediate hosts under natural conditions are, as a rule, wild rabbits in whose body the larvae travel freely, invading the liver and lungs; if infested rabbits are eaten by a dog, wolf, or fox, the larvae develop into the mature form in these animals. Faust[22] has reported upon the presence of the immature form (encysted nymph) in the liver and lungs of a laboratory rabbit in Peking. He states that the material from the Peking rabbit averages 4 mm in length by 0.8 mm in breadth.

Another linguatulid of man reported by Faust is *Armillifer moniliformis* (Diesing) from the liver of a Tibetan. This species, as described by Hill,[29] is parasitic as an adult in the respiratory tract of pythons and has for nymphal host, among many others, such animals as mongooses, monkeys, ground squirrels, and rats.

Man is frequently parasitized by *Linguatula serrata* and *Armillifer moniliformis,* but most cases of parasitism are asymptomatic and are recognizable only at autopsies. Cannon[14] has reported one case in which the colon was partially obstructed because of the thickening of its parasite-studded walls. Pulmonary cases may show symptoms suggestive of tuberculosis.

REFERENCES

1. Allred, Dorald M., 1954. "Mites as intermediate hosts of tapeworms," *Proc. Utah Acad. Arts, Sc., & Letters,* **31:**44–51.

2. Anonymous, 1956. *Chiggers, How to Fight Them.* Washington, D. C.: Dept. Agric. Entomol. Research Branch, in Leaflet, no. 403.

3. Anonymous, 1957. "Clover mites invading homes," *Calif. Vector Views,* **4:**30.

4. Audy, J. R., 1958 (1956). "The rôle of mite vectors in the natural history of scrub typhus," *Proc. 10th Internat. Cong. Entomol.,* **3:**639–49.

5. Baker, E. W.; Camin, J. H.; Cunliffe, F.; Woolley, T. A.; and Yunker, C. E.; 1958. *Guide to the Families of Mites.* College Park, Maryland: Institute of Acarology, Contribution no. 3. 242 pp.

6. Baker, E. W.; Evans, T. M.; Gould, D. J.; Hull, W. B.; and Keegan, H. L.; 1956. *A Manual of Parasitic Mites of Medical or Economic Importance.* New York: National Pest Control Assoc. 170 pp.

7. Baker, E. W., and Wharton, G. W., 1952. *An Introduction to Acarology.* New York: The Macmillan Co. xiii + 465 pp.

8. Bertram, D. S.; Unsworth, K.; and Gordon, R. M.; 1946. "The biology and maintenance of *Liponyssus bacoti* Hirst, 1913, and an investigation into its role as a vector of *Litomosoides carinii* to cotton rats and white rats, together with some observations on the infection in the white rats," *Ann. Trop. Med.,* **40:**228–52.

9. Bishopp, F. C., 1923. *The Rat Mite Attacking Man.* Washington, D. C.: Dept. Agric., in Department Circular, no. 294. 4 pp.

10. Blake, Francis G.; Maxcy, Kenneth F.; Sadusk, Joseph F., Jr.; Kohls, Glen M.; and Bell, E. John; 1945. "Studies on tsutsugamushi disease (scrub typhus, mite-borne typhus) in New Guinea and adjacent islands: Epidemiology, clinical observations and etiology in the Dobadura area." *Am. J. Hyg.,* **41:**243–373.

11. Booth, Boynton, H., and Jones, Roland W., 1952. "Epidemiological and chemical study of grain itch," *J.A.M.A.,* **150:**1575–79.

12. Brennan, James M., and Jones, Eleanor K., 1959. "Keys to the chiggers of North America with synonymic notes and descriptions of two new genera (Acarina: Trombiculidae)," *Ann. Entomol. Soc. Amer.,* **52:**7–16.

13. Brennan, James M., and Wharton, G. W., 1950. "Studies on North American chiggers no. 3. The subgenus *Neotrombicula*," *Amer. Midland Naturalist,* **44:**153–97.

14. Cannon, D. A., 1942. "Linguatulid infestation of man," *Ann. Trop. Med. & Parasitol.,* **36:**160–66.

15. Chamberlain, R. W., and Sikes, R. K., 1955. "Laboratory investigations on the role of bird mites in the transmission of eastern and western equine encephalitis," *Am. J. Trop. Med. & Hyg.,* **4:**106–18.

16. Chamberlain, R. W.; Sikes, R. K.; and Sudia, W. D.; 1957. "Attempted laboratory infection of bird mites with the virus of St. Louis encephalitis," *Am. J. Trop. Med. & Hyg.,* **6:**1047–53.

17. Chumakov, M. P., 1957. "Etiology, epidemiology, and prophylaxis of hemorrhagic fevers," Public Health Service: Public Health Monograph, no. 50. pp. 19–25.

18. Dove, W. E., and Shelmire, B., 1932. "Some observations on tropical rat mites and endemic typhus," *J. Parasitol.,* **18:**159–68 (3 plates).

19. Ewing, H. E., 1921. *Studies on the Biology and Control of Chiggers.* Washington, D. C.: Dept. Agric., in Bull., no. 986. 19 pp.

20. Ewing, H. E., 1929. *A Manual of External Parasites.* Baltimore: C. C. Thomas. 225 pp.

21. Farrell, Charles E., 1956. "Chiggers of the genus *Euschöngastia* (Acarina: Trombiculidae) in North America," *Proc. U. S. Nat. Museum,* **106:**85–235.

22. Faust, E. C., 1927. "Linguatulids (Order Acarina) from man and other hosts in China," *Am. J. Trop. Med.,* **7:**311–22 (2 plates).

23. Fuller, H. S., 1954. "Studies of rickettsialpox. III. Life cycle of the mite vector, *Allodermanyssus sanguineus,*" *Amer. J. Hyg.,* **59:**236–39.

24. Fuller, H. S., 1956. "Veterinary and medical acarology," *Ann. Rev. Entomol.,* **1:**347–66.

25. Gould, Douglas J., 1956. "The larval trombiculid mites of California," *Univ. Calif. Pub. Entomol.,* **11:**1–116 (26 plates).

26. Hammon, W. M.; Lundy, H. W.; Gray, J. A.; Evans, F. C.; Bang, F.; and Izumi, E. A.; 1942. "A large scale serum neutralization survey of certain vertebrates as part of an epidemiological study of encephalitis of western equine and St. Louis types," *J. Immunol.,* **44:**75–86.

27. Hayashi, N., 1920. "Etiology of tsutsugamushi disease," *J. Parasitol.,* **7:**53–68.

28. Heymons, R., 1935. *Pentastomida. Dr. H. G. Bronns. Klassen und Ordnungen des Thierreichs.* 5. Band: Arthropoda. iv. Abteilung, Arachnoidea. 1. Buch, Pentastomida. 268 pp.

29. Hill, H. R., 1934. "The occurrence of linguatulids in pythons," *Bull. South. Calif. Acad. Sc.,* **33:**117–22.

30. Hirst, S., 1913. "On three new species of gamasid mites found on rats," *Bull. Entomol. Research.,* **4:**119–24.

31. Hopla, Cluff E., 1951. "Experimental transmission of tularemia by the tropical rat mite," *Am. J. Trop. Med.,* **31:**768–83.

32. Huebner, Robert J.; Jellison, William L.; and Pomerantz, Charles; 1946. "Rickettsialpox—a newly recognized rickettsial disease. IV. Isolation of a

rickettsia, apparently identical with the causative agent of rickettsialpox from *Allodermanyssus sanguineus,* a rodent mite." U. S. Public Health Service, *Pub. Health Rep.,* **61:**1677–82.

33. Jenkins, Dale W., 1947. "A laboratory method of rearing chiggers affecting man (Acarina: Trombiculidae)," *Ann. Entomol. Soc. Amer.,* **40:**56–68.

34. Jenkins, Dale W., 1948. "Trombiculid mites affecting man. I. Bionomics with reference to epidemiology in the United States," *Amer. J. Hyg.,* **48:**22–35.

35. Jenkins, Dale W., 1949. "Trombiculid mites affecting man. IV. Revision of *Eutrombicula* in the American Hemisphere," *Ann. Entomol. Soc. Amer.,* **42:**289–318.

36. Jones, B. M., 1950. "The penetration of the host tissue by the harvest mite, *Trombicula autumnalis* Shaw," *Parasitology,* **40:**247–60.

37. Loomis, Richard B., 1956. "The chigger mites of Kansas (Acarina, Trombiculidae)," Univ. Kansas, in *Sc. Bull.,* **37** (part 2):1195–1443.

38. Michener, Mary H., and Michener, Charles D., 1947. "Chiggers!" *Natural History,* **56:**231–35.

39. Miskjian, H. G., 1951. "Demodicidosis (*Demodex* infestation of the scalp)," *Arch. Dermat. & Syph.,* **63:**282–83.

40. Miyajima, M., and Okumura, T., 1917. "On the life cycle of the 'akamushi,' carrier of Nippon River fever," *Kitasato Arch. Exper. Med.,* **1:**1–14.

41. Nichols, E.; Rindge, M. E.; and Russell, G. C.; 1953. "The relationship of the habits of the house mouse and the house mite (*Allodermanyssus sanguineus*) to the spread of rickettsialpox," *Ann. Int. Med.,* **39:**92–101.

42. Oudemans, A. C., 1937. *Kritisch Historisch Overzicht der Akarologie.* Tijdschrift voor Entomologie intzegeven door de Nederlandsche Vereeniging, Jan. 1926 (850 v.c. tot 1758), vol. G. (1805–1850), Leiden: E. J. Brill. 3379 pp.

43. Penn, George H., 1942. "The life history of *Porocephalus crotali,* a parasite of the Louisiana muskrat," *J. Parasitol.,* **28:**277–83.

44. Philip, Cornelius B., 1948. "Tsutsugamushi disease (scrub typhus) in World War II," *J. Parasitol.,* **34:**169–91.

45. Philip, Cornelius B., and Hughes, Lyndahl E., 1948. "The tropical rat mite, *Liponyssus bacoti,* as an experimental vector of rickettsial pox," *Am. J. Trop. Med.,* **28:**697–705.

46. Philip, Cornelius B., and Kohls, Glen M., 1948. "Mites and scrub typhus," *Proc. 4th Internat. Cong. Trop. Med. & Malaria.* (Abstracts). Washington, D. C.

47. Radford, C. D., 1943. "Genera and species of parasitic mites (Acarina)," *Parasitology,* **35:**58–81.

48. Reeves, W. C.; Hammon, W. M.; Doetschman, W. H.; McClure, H. E.; and Sather, G.; 1955. "Studies on mites as vectors of western equine and St. Louis encephalitis viruses in California," *Am. J. Trop. Med. & Hyg.,* **4:**90–105.

49. Sambon, L. W., 1922. "A synopsis of the family Linguatulidae," *J. Trop. Med.,* **25:**188–206, 391–428.

50. Strandtmann, R. W., and Wharton, G. W., 1958. *A Manual of Mesostigmatid Mites Parasitic on Vertebrates.* College Park, Maryland: Institute of Acarology, Contribution no. 4. xi + 330 pp. (69 plates).

51. Sulkin, S. E.; Wisseman, C. L., Jr.; Izumi, E. M.; and Zarafonetis, C.; 1955. "Mites as possible vectors or reservoirs of equine encephalitis in Texas," *Am. J. Trop. Med. & Hyg.*, **4:**119–35.

52. Traub, R.; Frick, L. P.; and Dierks, F. H.; 1950. "Observations on the occurrence of *Rickettsia tsutsugamushi* in rats and mice in the Malayan jungle," *Amer. J. Hyg.*, **51:**45–76.

53. Traub, R.; Newson, Harold D.; Walton Bryce C.; and Audy, J. R.; 1954. "Efficiency of dieldrin and aldrin in area control of the chigger vectors of scrub typhus," *J. Econ. Entomol.*, **47:**429–35.

54. Traver, J. R., 1951. "Unusual scalp dermatitis in humans caused by the mite, *Dermatophagoides,*" *Proc. Entomol. Soc. Washington,* **53:**1–25.

55. Vitzthum, H. Graf, 1943. *Acarina, 7 Lieferung. Dr. H. G. Bronns' Klassen und Ordnungen des Thierreichs,* **5:**913–1011. Akademische Verlagsgesellschaft, Becker und Erler Kom. Ges.

56. Warburton, Cecil, 1920. "Sarcoptic scabies in man and animals," *Parasitology,* **12:**265–300 (1 plate).

57. Wharton, G. W., and Fuller, H. S., 1952. *A Manual of the Chiggers.* Washington, D. C.: Entomol. Soc. Washington, Memoir, no. 4. 185 pp.

58. Williams, Roger W., 1946. "A contribution to our knowledge of the bionomics of the common North American chigger, *Eutrombicula alfreddugèsi* (Oudemans), with a description of a rapid collecting method," *Am. J. Trop. Med.,* **26:**243–50.

59. Williams, R. W., and Brown, H. W., 1945. "The development of *Litomosoides carinii,* filariid parasite on the cotton rat in the tropical rat mite," *Science,* **102:**482–83.

Chapter 21

VENOMOUS AND URTICARIAL ARTHROPODS

Arthropod Venoms. Arthropod venoms, like other animal venoms, are toxic principles probably not greatly unlike the bacterial toxins, but about which we know comparatively little. Unlike many of the bacterial toxins which reach toxic proportions only after a period of elapsed time subsequent to the introduction of the infection into the body, the animal venoms take effect almost instantly, i.e., as soon as introduced and without incubation.

The venoms act in one or more ways when introduced into the body: (1) they may act directly on the blood corpuscles (hemolytic); (2) they may act directly on the nervous system, producing shock or inhibiting reflexes (neurotoxic); (3) they may produce an infiltration and congestion of blood (hemorrhagic) often in the vicinity of the wound or in deeper tissues, such as the mesenteries; (4) they may produce an anaphylactic reaction which may be much more important than the direct result of the toxin itself. A given arthropod venom may act in one or more of these ways. Its effects may be localized and of no more importance than the temporary production of a sensitive or painful area; or they may be general and may terminate fatally. Secondary infection may also accompany arthropod bites and stings.

The importance of envenomization by arthropods has been, at least in temperate areas, exaggerated in the public mind. Many persons are unjustifiably afraid of spiders, centipedes, millipedes, and, in fact, many arthropods which are completely powerless to harm one; and a report that black widow spiders occur in a given area may be enough to throw the neighborhood into panic. On the other hand, the danger from venomous arthropods is greater than most entomologists have realized. In an interesting report based on examination of death certificates from all parts of the country, Parrish[58] has shown that deaths resulting from arthropod bites and stings, over a five-year period (1950–54), far outnumber those resulting from snake bite. Of 215 deaths caused by venomous animals, 71, or 33 per cent, were attributed to venomous snakes (55 of these to rattlesnakes); 14 to miscellaneous or unknown causes; 5 (2.3 per cent) to scorpions; 39 (18.1 per cent) to spiders, either definitely the black widow or to unknown spiders, presumably the black widow; 52 (24.2 per cent) to bees; 33 (15.3 per cent) to wasps, including "yellow jackets" and "hornets"; and 1 (0.5 per cent) to ants. It is noteworthy that centipedes, tarantulas, and, of course, millipedes, are absent from the list. A total of 130 deaths were attributable to arthropod venom in the United States during this five-year period.

It is well known that different persons react in much different ways to the bite or sting of an arthropod. Also, it is a matter of common knowledge verified by various investigators that repeated inoculation of minute or attenuated quantities of a venom may lead to a degree of immunity; this is true of the venoms or poisons of bees, bed bugs, mosquitoes, fleas, conenose bugs, etc. Newcomers to a flea-infested country may suffer great misery until they have acquired an "immunity"; this may require many months or may never be acquired by some individuals. Promising results have been obtained by administering a course of immunization consisting of injections (six) of a flea antigen[23] (extract of *Pulex irritans,* 75 per cent, and *Ctenocephalides canis,* 25 per cent) given subcutaneously 1 week apart.

How the Venom Is Introduced. Arthropod venoms are introduced into the body of man and other animals in one of three ways: (1) by the *bite,* thrust of piercing mouth parts, as in the conenoses, or penetration of the chelicerae of spiders; (2) by the *sting,* as in the ants, bees, and wasps (aculeate Hymenoptera), and the scorpions; (3) by *contact,* e.g., by means of urticarial hairs of certain caterpillars, such as the brown-tail moth, producing a condition similar to nettling, or with vesicating fluids of the blister beetles (Meloidae), resulting in a *vesicular dermatitis,* or through wind-blown parts of insect bodies, such as cast mayfly skins, resulting in allergic reactions.

STINGING INSECTS

The stinging insects belong to the order Hymenoptera; they include the ants, bees, and wasps, in which the females are usually provided with a specialized ovipositor known as a sting, more or less well adapted for piercing the skin of higher animals or of other insects. The sting is used either as an organ of defense or offense; in the latter case it is often used to procure food for the young. The venom apparatus of the so-called "aculeate," or stinging Hymenoptera, such as bees, wasps, hornets, and bumble bees, does not vary greatly in structure.

The principal aculeate Hymenoptera, according to the classification followed by Borror and DeLong,[15] are divided into the following seven superfamilies, all of which, except the first, contain representatives which can at times be dangerous or annoying: (1) the Chrysidoidea, the cuckoo wasps and their relatives; (2) the Bethyloidea, the bethyloid wasps; (3) the Scolioidea, the scoliid wasps, velvet ants, and their relatives; (4) the Formicoidea, the ants; (5) the Vespoidea, the hornets, yellow jackets, spider wasps, and their relatives; (6) the Sphecoidea, the sphecoid wasps; (7) the Apoidea, the bees.

Morphology of the Bee Sting. The sting of the worker bee is regarded as a specialized ovipositor; it originates from the seventh and eighth abdominal segments and lies between the ovipositor and the rectum above. The darts of the sting follow the ventral line of the abdomen and are held in place by the sheath situated above, while the barbs of the darts point downward and outward. In the space above the sheath lie the fleshy palpi (Fig. 171). The delicate attachment between the sting and the organs of the abdomen account for the ease with which the sting of the honey bee is torn from the abdomen when the barbs become embedded after the darts are thrust into the skin. The sting can easily be extracted either by separating the segments of the abdomen from it by means of dissecting needles, or by squeezing the live bee between forceps, which causes it to protrude the sting. The sting can be grasped with other forceps and drawn out. After extraction the sting can be examined best when the parts are floated out in a few drops of glycerin.

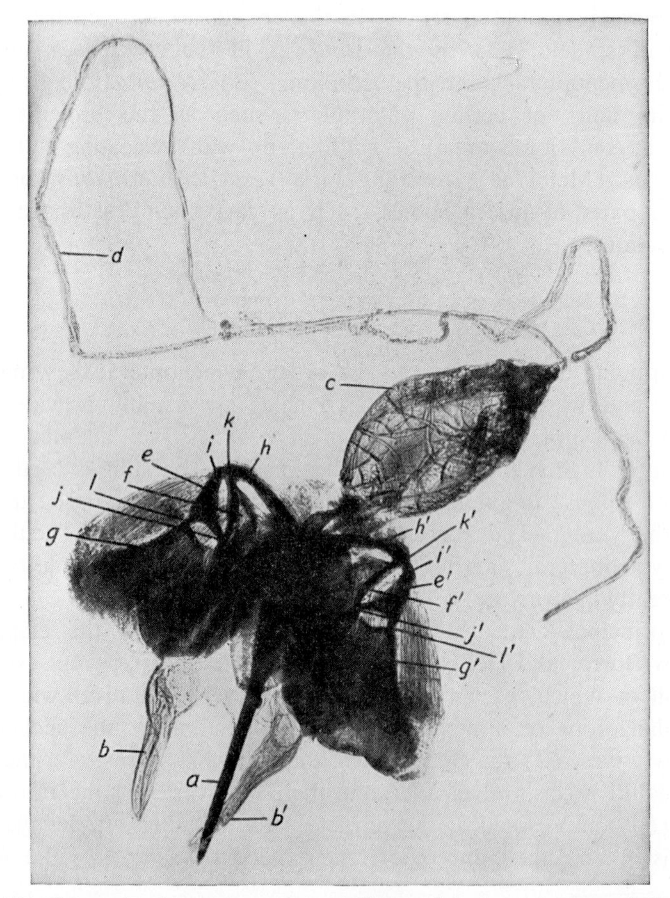

Fig. 171. Sting of a honey bee, *Apis mellifera:* (*a*) the two serrated darts; (*b, b'*) sting palpi; (*c*) venom (poison) sac; (*d*) venom gland; (*e, e'*) triangular plates or levers; (*f, f'*) semilunar plates or levers; (*g, g'*) lateral plates or levers; (*h, h'*) Y-shaped darts; (*i, i'*) points of attachment for darts to levers; (*j, j'*, also *e, e'*) points around which levers rotate; (*k, k'*) points of attachment for lever (*f, f'*). × 17.5.

The sting may be divided into three parts, viz.: the piercing apparatus; the lateral plate and appendages; the poison sac and glands.

The piercing apparatus itself consists of three parts, one the stylet-sheath, the other two lying within the sheath and partially surrounded by it. In appearance, the sheath is yellowish and translucent. The darts or stylets, which present concave surfaces to each other, are heavily sclerotized. The distal one-third of the dart possesses a series of sharp, recurved barbs, about ten in number. Toward the base the darts diverge to form a "Y" (Fig. 171, *h, h′*); the arms of the "Y" gradually bend laterally. Plates are attached to the upper edges of these laterally bent arms (see the *lateral appendages*). One of the most remarkable portions of the darts is the poison valve with which each is provided. At the point of separation of the darts each presents a delicate cup-shaped valve, whose closed portion is directed downward toward the tip of the sting. This is formed of the same material as the darts, and each is free to move with the movement of the dart. In order to accommodate this enlargement of the darts, the sheath in this region expands to about five times its smaller diameter, which is toward the tip of the sting. For at least one-third of its length the sheath at this portion is expanded into a symmetrical oblong body providing ample room for the movement of the darts and valves within.

The *lateral appendages* are of three kinds: semilunar, triangular, and lateral, according to shape or position. Both the *semilunar* (Fig. 171, *f, f′* and *triangular* (*e, e′*) *plates* are attached to the bent ends of the Y-shaped darts. The triangular plates are attached to the arms of the darts almost at their extremities, while the semilunar ones are connected for about one-third of the distance from the ends of the arms. The apex of the triangle is attached to the extremity of the dart. The other two points are directed outward and downward, and serve as points of attachment for two elevated edges on the *lateral plates* (Fig. 171, *g, g′*), which hang thus suspended. As they hang, half of their surface lies above and covers the dorsal surface of the semilunar plates just beneath them. Continuing in the same straight line with the semilunar plates and attached at their extremity to them, lie the fleshy *palpi* covered with delicate hairs.

The third set of structures which completes the sting is the *venom sac* and *glands*. In order to understand these, it is necessary to know that the stinging Hymenoptera are divided into two groups, those which kill their prey by stinging, and those which only paralyze it. The former are the more complicated, for they possess two poison glands; the acid gland, which opens directly into the great poison sac (the larger of the two), and the alkaline gland, which is comparatively small and is situated at the base of the poison sac. It is the combination of the acid and alkaline fluids from the two glands that results in the death of the attacked insect, or that causes the extreme pain and resulting reactions in man.

The formic acid gland alone is found in those Hymenoptera which only paralyze their prey by the sting. This fact has led various observers to make chemical tests of both the formic acid and alkaline substance. The result, according to Carlet and others, has been to show that neither substance by itself is effective except to paralyze, but when combined, the substances have deadly effects upon other insects. Carlet's experiments to prove this were made on house flies and blow flies by injecting each substance singly and then introducing both into the body of the fly.

Operation of the Sting. The sting may be observed in operation by confining the bee on its back and then prodding it until its sting is angrily thrust in and out. This process shows three things, viz.: that the sharp-pointed sheath always appears first when the thrust is made; second, that the darts inside the sheath work back and forth alternately and quite independently of the sheath or of one another; third, that the poison exudes in droplets from the tip of the sting between the darts.

The sheath has three functions: to open the wound; to serve as the dorsal wall of the poison canal; and to hold the stylets in position. The sheath does not wholly enclose the darts; rather, it forms the dorsal wall of the canal which is formed when the two concave surfaces of the darts are brought together. Two delicate, but strong, sclerotized, tracks or "rails" of the sheath dovetail into a corresponding groove in each dart, thus permitting no other than an up-and-down movement. By a series of short, quick thrusts, the sting can be driven in to its hilt.

The three pairs of plates composing the lateral appendages function as levers. Powerful muscles attached to the triangular and semilunar rotate these plates, thus driving the sheath and darts into the flesh of the victim. The two components of the venom then mingle and flow down the canal formed by the sheath and the darts. The rapid series of movements is entirely reflex, being governed by the fifth abdominal ganglion and its radiating nerves. This explains why the severed abdomen of a bee may still be able to sting severely for a period of several hours after separation from the rest of the body.

The Stinging Hymenoptera. *Bees* constitute the superfamily Apoidea. They may readily be distinguished from the wasps, with which they may sometimes be confused, by the presence, especially on the bee thorax, of hairs which under the microscope are distinctly plumose. Many bees live in solitary or subsocial existence, that is, each female will develop her own nest, lay eggs, and lay in provisions for her brood, without the aid of a worker caste. Many such bees possess stings. Occasionally a person is stung mildly by a bee belonging to the genus *Halictus,* the sweat bees, as he attempts to brush them from his skin where the bee has settled for the purpose of obtaining moisture. Serious cases of bee-sting envenomization, however, are usually due to bumble bees or honey bees.

Both bumble bees, *Bombus* spp., and the honey bee, *Apis mellifera*

Linnaeus, are social bees, with a worker caste in addition to the sexually fertile males and females. The bumble bees form temporary colonies, only the fertilized young queen surviving the winter. In the spring, the queen searches for a place to found her colony. Her nest is on the ground, in some protected place, or in the ground, often in a deserted rodent burrow. A person working or hiking in a field where bumble bees are nesting may unwarily step into a nest and be stung, sometimes severely. The honey bee forms permanent colonies that may survive from year to year indefinitely. Worker honey bees will readily sting an invader in defense of their colony.

Yellow jackets or hornets are members of the family Vespidae, superfamily Vespoidea. Representative members are the European hornet, *Vespa crabro* Linnaeus; the giant hornet of Europe and eastern North America, *Vespa crabro germana* (Christ); the bald-faced hornet of North America, *Vespula maculata* (Linnaeus); the North American *Vespula pennsylvanica* (Saussure); and the widespread Holarctic *Vespula vulgaris* (Linnaeus). All of these species build nests (Fig. 172) of pulp made by masticating wood fiber. Nests are built in hollow trees (e.g., *Vespa crabro*), among the branches of trees, under eaves of houses, etc. (e.g., *Vespula maculata*), or in holes in or near the ground (e.g., *Vespula pennsylvanica, V. vulgaris*). The somewhat elongated aerial nests may reach 9 to 10 in. in diameter. Old colonies die out in the summer or fall; the young fertilized queens hibernate and start a new nest in the spring.

Species of *Polistes* likewise form paper nests; but they are not as massive as those of *Vespa* and *Vespula,* and they are not enclosed in a paper envelope. They consist each of a single horizontal comb of hexagonal cells attached to a support by a pedicel. In cold climates the queens, which are difficult to distinguish from the workers, hibernate. They may hide away in houses and may be quite troublesome toward spring, when they begin to emerge from hibernation.

Persons are rarely stung by other members of the superfamily Vespoidea, although Bromley[16] describes pain and swelling, involving the entire hand and forearm, which he, an admittedly susceptible individual, experienced from being stung in the finger by the tarantula wasp, *Pepsis formosa* (Say) (Family Pompilidae).

Mud daubers or thread-waisted wasps (superfamily Sphecoidea), such as *Chalybion californicum* (Saussure) (= *C. caeruleum* Johannson and Linnaeus), make their nests, usually quite small, of mud, and provision them with insects and spiders to serve as food for the larvae. These nests are frequently found in attics and outbuildings.

Ants belong to the family Formicidae, superfamily Formicoidea. Many ants are incapable of stinging, but, on the other hand, some species sting viciously. Parrish[58] lists one human death, during the study period of 1950–54, due to ant stings.

The subfamily Myrmicinae includes several formidable stinging groups of pugnacious nature. Because of their numbers, a mass attack may result seriously. Some of the more dangerous species belong to the following two groups:

1. The fire ants, genus *Solenopsis,* are so-called because of the sharp, fiery pain of their sting. Of especial importance is the imported fire ant,

Fig. 172. (*Top, left*) Aerial nest of yellow jacket; (*top, center and right*) side and top view of the insect, *Vespula diabolica;* and (*bottom*) longitudinal section of nest.

Solenopsis saevissima richteri Forel, which was introduced probably as cargo stowaways into the United States some time prior to 1930, and which has become a scourge throughout the southeastern states.[1] It builds large hard-crusted earthen mounds. It stings by first sinking its powerful mandibles into the flesh for leverage, and then driving its sting into the victim. This ant not only attacks crops but also will kill and devour newly hatched quail and poultry, or enter pipped eggs to reach the unhatched chicks; it will also attack young pigs, newly born calves, etc. Persons may be severely stung.

Other fire ants of some importance are the common fire ant, *Solenopsis geminata* (Fabricius), and the southern fire ant, *S. xyloni* McCook.

2. The genus *Pogonomyrmex,* the harvester ants, have a vicious sting and readily attack man and animals. They are of concern in agricultural entomology because their low, bare mounds, with their destruction of adjacent vegetation, can cause quite a little waste of land. The red harvester ant, *Pogonomyrmex barbatus* (F. Smith), occurs at lower altitudes from Kansas and Louisiana to Utah and California, and into Mexico; the California harvester ant, *P. californicus* (Buckley), occurs from Texas and Utah to California and Mexico; the western harvester ant, *P. occidentalis* (Cresson), is widespread, from North Dakota and British Columbia southward to Arizona and Oklahoma; and the Florida harvester ant, *P. badius* (Latreille), the only species known from east of the Mississippi, occurs in the southeastern states.

Fig. 173. A velvet ant, family Mutillidae, also known as a "cow killer." × 2.2.

These ants will readily attack man and small animals. Young pigs may be killed by the stings of these species. A small pig may walk leisurely upon an ant mound and suddenly begin to kick and squeal, as a result of the terrific attack of ants rushing forth from the nest. The animals commonly topple over with legs outstretched, and death may ensue.

Ants play a very minor role in the mechanical dissemination of pathogenic organisms. Smith[71] has pointed out that *Solenopsis* workers may carry viable dysentery germs on their bodies for at least 24 hours, and Donisthorpe[27] has recorded mechanical transmission of smallpox by ants in a hospital in Egypt. Krull and Mapes[46] recorded *Formica fusca* (Linnaeus) as being an intermediate host of the little liver fluke of sheep, *Dicrocoelium dendriticum* (Rudolphi).

Mutillid Wasps. Among the less known stinging insects are the wasps belonging to the family Mutillidae, superfamily Scolioidea. Members of this family are commonly known as velvet ants, woolly ants, cow killers, mule killers, etc. (Fig. 173). Most mutillids are covered with a velvety pubescence;

many are brightly colored with orange or red or yellow. The females are apterous, good runners, and may inflict a painful sting. They are parasites of bees and other wasps. There are many species, some of the commoner forms measuring from 1/2 to 1 in. in length. Our knowledge concerning these interesting insects has been greatly advanced by Mickel.[51] A very common species in the central United States is *Dasymutilla occidentalis* (Linnaeus), a rather large black species clothed largely with scarlet hairs dorsally. This species is very common on the beach sands of Lake Erie, causing barefoot bathers much distress.

The bethylid wasps, Superfamily Bethyloidea, are, so far as known, parasitic on hymenopterous, lepidopterous, and coleopterous larvae, although comparatively little is known of their bionomics. Three genera, *Cephalonomia, Scleroderma,* and *Epyris* have been reported as stinging man. These small wasplike insects may become abundant in houses as a result of a persistent infestation by one of their hosts.

Guiglia[37] describes two cases of bethylid sting that occurred in Genoa, Italy, and gives considerable general information concerning the stinging propensities of these insects. A woman, stung, while in bed, on many places on her body by *Scleroderma domesticum* Latreille, showed not only localized results of the stings, but also general symptoms of the anaphylactic type, with malaise, nausea, and headaches. The second case involved multiple stings of three members of a family by a species of *Cephalonomia.* Muesebeck and Walkley[54] state that there are many reports of the North American *C. gallicola* (Ashmead) stinging man.

In 1927 von Geldern[33] reported a tiny wasp from Yolo County, California, identified as a species of *Epyris,* which inflicts a severe sting.

> The wasps appear in fairly great numbers in the fall after a warm spell and invade the house where they get into the bedding and clothing, and sting when brushed or crushed by clothing or sheets against the skin. . . . The sting is distinctly felt as a fairly sharp prick, decidedly less intense than a bee sting. . . . In the oldest and youngest child no further manifestations occur, but in the parents and second child a decided systematic disturbance follows. A few minutes after being stung, there is felt a numbness, often at the site of the sting, but at other times beginning at the finger tips. It remains localized for a few minutes and then gradually spreads and involves the entire body. In the mother there is an intense itching of the vulva and in the father of the pubes. This is followed by a marked diarrhoea, not painful in the father, but resembling severe uterine cramps in the mother. The diarrhoea and cramps last for about ten minutes. The mother, who is an asthmatic, experiences no respiratory difficulty, but with the father, who has never had an attack of asthma, wheezing occurs occasionally. Accompanying these symptoms there is marked prostration, weakness and sweating. The duration of the attack is about half an hour. The second child becomes drowsy and is awakened with difficulty and wheezing occurs. He also recovers in about the same time as the parents.

Essig[28] in 1932 reported a number of instances, in the same county (Yolo), of stings by *Epyris californicus* (Ashmead). This wasp is barely over 5 mm in length and is black in color.

Reaction to Bee and Wasp Stings. The painful effect of the stings of bees and wasps is not due to the simple thrusts of the sting, but more particularly to the introduced venom. The severity is greatly increased in the case of multiple stings. Pawlowsky, according to Martini,[50] estimates 500 bee stings within a short time as a lethal dose for man. Tolerance to bee stings appears to be developed in beekeepers, long exposed to stings; however, this tolerance seems to be lost when exposure to stings is discontinued.

The more severe effects of bee and wasp stings, however, are due not to the venom itself, but to the associated antigens. Sensitizing antigen may be present in the entire insect, independent of venoms or pollen, although some is contained in the venom; in fact, particles from an insect's body or dried extract may produce asthmalike symptoms in some individuals.

A sting in a nonsensitized person will produce local pain, swelling, and redness which will pass harmlessly within a few hours. In susceptible individuals, however, it is quite a different matter. Mueller,[55] on the basis of a study involving 84 patients who showed allergic reactions to insect stings, groups susceptible individuals into four classes, according to the severity of the reaction. (1) In those with a slight general reaction (12 patients), general urticaria, malaise, and anxiety develop on an average of 24 min (range, 2 to 60) after the occurrence of the sting. (2) In those with a general reaction (36 patients), in addition to the above, the signs and symptoms include any two or more of the following: generalized edema; constriction in the chest; wheezing; abdominal pain, nausea, and vomiting; and dizziness. (3) In cases with a severe reaction (23 patients), any two or more of the following are added to the above: dyspnea; dysphagia; hoarseness and thickened speech; confusion; and feeling of impending disaster. (4) Finally, in patients with a shock reaction (13 patients), at least two of the following may be added to any of the above signs or symptoms: cyanosis; fall in blood pressure; collapse; incontinence; and unconsciousness. The onset of the symptoms becomes progressively more rapid with the increasing severity of the case, being on an average only 5 min (range, 2 to 15) in cases involving shock reaction.

Various case histories have indicated that a person sensitive to bee sting may not be sensitive to wasp sting, and vice versa. Foubert and Stier[32] have shown that for the honey bee, *Apis mellifera,* and the vespid wasps *Polistes fuscatus aurifer* Saussure, *Vespula arenaria arenaria* (Fabricius), *V. maculata* (Linnaeus), and *V. pennsylvanica* (Saussure), common antigenic fractions are present, along with antigenic fractions which are characteristic of the individual species. A person may become sensitized to certain antigenic fractions to the complete or partial exclusion of the others.

It must be emphasized that to some persons a single bee or wasp sting may be very dangerous.[52] If a person shows severe allergic reactions to insect stings, he should undergo a course of desensitization. Treatment is similar to desensitization to grasses, but it is much more important; it may save a life.[55] If the insect causing the reaction is known *accurately and specifically,* desensitization using the extract of that particular insect alone may be safe. If the offending insect is not known, or if there is a possibility of sensitivity to other stinging insects, desensitization with a combined antigen, including at least bee, wasp, yellow jacket, and hornet extracts would seem advisable.[32] The physician should be aware of what species of dangerous stinging Hymenoptera are represented in his area.

If no antigenic complications are present, the sting may be treated by (1) applying an icepack to the area of the sting, and then (2) applying a paste of bicarbonate of soda and water.

Control of Stinging Insects. In the control of hornets,[2] one should seek out the new nests under construction and destroy them by night when the queen and her progeny are at home and when activity is at a low ebb. If the entrance to the nest is plugged with cotton soaked in carbon tetrachloride, the hornets will be stunned by the fumes and the nest can be dislodged more easily and safely. The aerial nests may then be quickly enveloped with a tight drawstring bag and then soaked with kerosene, scalding water, or burned. In some cases aerial nests are hard to dislodge with safety. These may be treated with a 5 or 6 per cent chlordane dust or a 5 or 10 per cent DDT dust applied with a hand duster. A few puffs at the entrance of the nest will filter through it, usually killing the colony within 24 hours. A spray made from wettable powders or emulsifiable concentrates may also be used.

Underground nests should be located by day, then treated by pouring several ounces of carbon tetrachloride into the hole at night and plugging it with absorbent cotton. Also, DDT or chlordane may be used, as for the aerial nests.

The small nests with exposed cells made by *Polistes* may be removed at night by placing a tin can or box with open end over the nest and then slipping a sheet of tin between the surface and the open end of the can so that it can be cut away. The surface from which the nest has been removed may be daubed with creosote to repel other females from starting a nest on the same site.

In the control of ants,[10] as in the social wasps, it is necessary to kill the queen along with the rest of the colony. Treatment is most effective at times when most of the workers are in the nest (e.g., in the cooler months of the early spring, for control of the imported fire ant) and at times when there are no young. Chlordane, dieldrin, aldrin, and heptachlor, used either as a dust or in liquid form, are effective in the control of harvester ants or fire ants. The mounds may be drenched with the spray, or the foraging areas covered with spray or dust. When one or a few mounds or nests are to be treated, the problem is relatively simple, but when areas, such as lawns where children may be playing or where extensive dusting may threaten wildlife, special caution must be taken. Nests of harvester ants may be destroyed by injecting carbon disulfide (4 oz for a colony that has cleared an area 4 ft in diameter) into the entrance hole and stamping it shut with the heel of the shoe. Such treatment should be applied at times when most or all of the workers are in the hole. Control of ants, particularly of fire ants, should be carried out in such a way that other interests, e.g., those relating to wildlife, are not unnecessarily harmed.

BITING AND VESICATING INSECTS

Insects that pierce the skin with their mouth parts are normally bloodsuckers as a rule, and the act of biting or piercing is simply a part of the act of food-getting. There are noteworthy exceptions, as later explained. The pain caused by the mechanical insertion of such tiny mouth parts would be, no doubt, relatively benign, particularly if only one or a few individual insects were concerned in the attack; however, in perhaps every instance an irritating salivary enzyme is introduced. This enzyme apparently differs among the various species, as evidenced by the resulting reactions, local and systemic, which are generally specific enough so that one who is experienced may be able to determine the cause, i.e., whether the offender was a bed bug, a flea, a mosquito, or a black fly.

To understand the operation of the bloodsucking mechanism of the various offending insects one should consult the earlier chapter on mouth parts and the other chapters appropriate to the subject. The student will profit much by a careful study of *Zoonosen der Haut in warmeren Landern* by Martini.[50]

Some individuals apparently suffer no ill effects from bed bug bites, not even a swelling at the site of the bite; others react violently to even one bite. These differences in tolerance to a given species are not fully understood. Martini remarks that doubtless allergic processes play a role in these reactions.

Insects that inflict a very painful bite, such as the stable fly and most salt-marsh mosquitoes, e.g., *Aedes dorsalis* (Meigen), are apparently seldom vectors of disease, while species with benign bites, such as *Anopheles maculipennis* Meigen, are commonly potent vectors. It seems as though successful adaptation to feeding upon a given host, to the extent that the arthropod may become a successful vector of disease, is dependent upon a modification of the severity of the bite.

Biting bugs (Order Hemiptera) have already been discussed in Chapter 7. The assassin bugs, aside from the Triatominae, attack species of insects, particularly soft-bodied forms from which they suck the body fluids. Attacks upon man are made principally, if not wholly, in self defense. Persons picking up boards, sticks, or stones, etc., may accidentally pick up one of these insects; likewise, in plucking a leaf or flower from a tree or other plant, the fingers may close upon the insect as well, with the result that a very painful bite may be suffered.

The order Hemiptera contains a number of families of aquatic forms, several of which include biting species; among these are the Belostomatidae and Notonectidae.

The giant water bugs *Lethocerus, Belostoma,* and *Benacus,* belonging to the family Belostomatidae, are among the largest of the water bugs, the larger species measuring 2 1/2 in. or more in length and possessing formidable beaks. They feed on other aquatic insects, also young frogs, fish, etc., and since they are winged and readily attracted to lights, they are commonly known as electric light bugs. They have been known to attack birds, fatally in at least one instance. Ewing[29] describes the bite as follows:

> . . . at 9:30 A.M. a giant water bug *Benacus griseus* (Say) was allowed to bite the back of the right index finger. The beak was left inserted for a few seconds. Immediately a burning sensation followed. Two minutes later the same bug was allowed to puncture the back of the left index finger for several seconds. A burning sensation was produced. Soon some swelling was noted, and a reddened area developed around the point of the puncture. Pain continued but diminished during the forenoon and by noon the reddened area had become reduced. By 1:30 P.M. a small red spot was all that was left at the puncture. . . . When *Benacus griseus* bites it emits a milky fluid from the tip of the beak, and the back adheres to the skin after penetration, so that the skin is pulled up when the beak is withdrawn.

Back swimmers belonging to the family Notonectidae may also inflict a painful bite. These predaceous bugs swim on their backs, hence the common name "back swimmers." The bite is nearly as severe as a bee sting.

Numerous instances of bloodsucking among phytophagous Hemiptera have been reported. Much information concerning these cases has been assembled by Usinger and Myers.[78] Among the species exhibiting this fortuitous bloodsucking behavior are members of the following families: Membracidae (treehoppers), such as *Stictocephala bubalus* (Fabricius); Cicadellidae (leafhoppers and sharpshooters), such as *Circulifer tenellus* (Baker) and *Erythroneura comes* (Say); Miridae, such as *Irbisia solani* (Heidemann) and *Lopidea marginata* Uhler; Coreidae, *Leptocoris trivittatus* (Say). Tingids have also been reported as biting man.

Thrips Biting Man. Thrips (Order Thysanoptera) are minute, mostly plant-feeding (sapsucking) insects (see Chapter 5 for description of mouth parts); however, there have been numerous reports of their attacking man and their ability to suck blood. Bailey[8] states that while working in experimental plots, he experienced bites from the onion thrips, *Thrips tabaci* Lindeman. He felt slight pricks on the arm, face, and neck, both when perspiring and when not. He observed that the larvae (second instar) were more prone to bite than the adults and that the alimentary canal took on a reddish-brown appearance after feeding. Small pinkish dots appeared on the skin and disappeared in 1 or 2 days. No swelling occurred, but there was a slight itching sensation. He had similar experiences with the pear thrips, *Taeniothrips inconsequens* (Uzel).

According to personal communication to the author (James) from Stanley F. Bailey, *Chirothrips aculeatus* Bagnall and *Limothrips cerealium* (Haliday), species which normally breed in the heads of oats, rye, foxtail grass, and similar plants, are often annoying to man. Reports of annoyance have come from many areas in Europe and the United States. The immature thrips feed on the kernels of the grass when they are in the milky or dough stage. As the grass or grain dries up, the winged thrips develop and migrate, often in large numbers, particularly if the grass is mowed or harvested. If there is a local prevailing wind, the insects will migrate with it during late afternoon, if it is warm and clear. Military installations, commercial plants, and populated areas in the wake of the migrations may suffer serious annoyance at such times. The insects are so small that they pass through ordinary window screen, but they may be killed by treating the screens with DDT or lindane. Fine cloth placed over the screens will also aid in keeping them out. If feasible, the fields in which the infestation develops should be treated or burned before the migration takes place. Serious infestations of regular occurrence may thus be avoided.

Several other species of thrips have been reported in a similar connection, e.g., *Heliothrips* sp., recorded as *indicus* Bagnall, but probably either *H. fumipennis* Bagnall and Cameron or *H. sudanensis* Bagnall and Cameron, in the Sudan; *Thrips imaginis* Bagnall, reported from Australia; *Limothrips denticornis* (Haliday), for Germany; *Gynaitkothrips ficorum* (Marchal), for Algiers; and other species. It would appear that many species of thrips are thus involved, and that this behavior is not restricted to one or two species.

Urticarial Hairs. The caterpillars, or larvae, of many species of Lepidoptera (at least 10 families and more than 50 species) possess urticating hairs. Among the families which have urticarial larvae is the Saturniidae of which the genus *Hemileuca* is especially offensive. *Hemileuca oliviae* Cockerell, the range caterpillar, is reported to be a menace to cattlemen in New Mexico.[20] The io moth, *Automeris io* (Fabricius), produces a sharp, stinging dermatitis similar to that produced by some species of nettles. A rash known as "brown-tail rash" is traceable to the caterpillar of the brown-tail moth, *Nygmia phaeorrhoea* (Donovan) (Family Lymantriidae), a common and very destructive shade tree pest in Europe and in America, especially in New England. When the caterpillars of this species molt, numerous tiny barbed hairs are shed with the skin. The cocoons of the pupated caterpillars as well as the adult moths possess these hairs. These hairs are blown about by the wind, and when they come into contact with the skin of the neck, face, hands, and other exposed parts of the body, they produce a severe dermatitis. These hairs are hollow, and they contain a toxin, as do those of other nettling moth larvae, which is injected into the skin by the sharp-pointed hair as it comes into contact with the skin. An especially sensitive dermatitis is produced when the hairs come into contact with the conjunctiva of the eye. Ingestion or inhalation of the hairs may cause serious internal disturbances.

Certain flannel moths, family Megalopygidae, are among the most serious urticarial forms. *Megalopyge lanata* (Stoll) is a constant cause of a painful dermatitis in the Panama Canal Zone. Randel and Doan[61] observed 18 cases at the Albrook Air Force Base in 1949–1951; they briefly describe five case histories. All cases were characterized by sudden burning pain at the point of contact, erythema, swelling, lymphangitis, leucocytosis, and eosinophilia. Numbness, lymphadenopathy and vesication sometimes occurred. All cases were self-limiting. These authors point out the need for the physician to be alert to the hazard, in order to relieve the symptoms and to distinguish the condition from insect bites (and even snake bite) which may need more specific treatment. The caterpillar is yellow, about 5 cm long and 1 1/2 cm in diameter; the body is covered with tufts of black hairs emerging from papillae. Contact with the caterpillar, in the Canal Zone, is made during March and April.

The puss caterpillar, *Megalopyge opercularis* (J. E. Smith), produces a painful and sometimes serious dermatitis in the southern United States. Bishopp[11] describes the symptoms produced by contact with it as follows:

> Almost immediately after any portion of the body comes in contact with one of these caterpillars an intense burning pain is felt, described by some as similar to a severe nettle sting. This usually becomes worse accompanied by itching for several minutes and persists from 1 to 12 hours and sometimes longer. Almost immediately after a sting the area touched by the caterpillar shows minute raised whitish spots or papules which soon become red, followed by spreading of the inflammatory area for several inches and often accompanied by general swelling of the portion of the body stung. Stings on the wrist have been followed by a swelling of the entire arm to almost double its normal size. A feeling of numbness which assumes the characteristics of paralysis accompanies the swelling. This is usually confined to the member attacked but may be generalized. Apparently stings on the neck are even worse, as the writer has one record of a man who was stung severely on the neck and completely incapacitated, being confined to the hospital for 6 days. These paralytic symptoms are often accompanied by nausea and sometimes vomiting. The stings are especially severe among young children, who often develop considerable fever and nervous symptoms. These sometimes last for a day or two and are accompanied by nausea, especially during the first few hours. Usually within two or three hours after a sting, the reddened pimple-like swellings at the site assume the appearance of small vesicles or blisters. These

usually persist for a few hours and then apparently harden through absorption, leaving a roughened area. In some instances the discoloration of the skin surrounding the point of attack is rather marked, varying from a deep red to almost black. The paralytic symptoms usually subside with the pain, but the local lesions often persist for several days.

Students concerned with the study of urticarial hairs will need to consult Weidner's[81] work which includes a bibliography on poisonous insect hairs. Among the more recent papers that have been published on the subject are those of Kemper, particularly his report to the Tenth International Congress of Entomology.[45] Some of the more important nettling and urticating Lepidoptera are the following: **Morphoidae,** *Morpho hercules* Dalman (South America); **Arctiidae,** *Lithosia caniola* Hübner, *L. griseola* Hübner, and *Arctia caja* (Linnaeus), Europe, and *Euchaetias egle* (Drury) and *Halisidota caryae* (Harris), the hickory tussock moth, North America; **Lymantriidae,** *Nygmia phaeorrhoea* (Donovan), the brown-tail moth, *Stilpnotia salicis* (Linnaeus), the satin moth, and *Porthetria dispar* (Linnaeus) the gypsy moth, Europe and the United States; *Lymantria monacha* (Linnaeus), the nun moth, *Euproctis similis* (Fueszly), and *Dasychira pudibunda* (Linnaeus), Europe, *Hemerocampa leucostigma* (J. E. Smith), the white-marked tussock moth, United States, and *Euproctis flava* (Bremer), China; **Thaumetopoeidae,** *Thaumetopoea processionea* (Linnaeus), the processionary caterpillar, *T. pinivora* Treitschke, and *Anaphe infracta* Walsingham, Europe; **Lasiocampidae,** *Macrothylacia rubi* (Linnaeus), *Dendrolimnus pini* (Linnaeus), *Lasiocampa quercus* (Linnaeus), and *Gastropacha quercifolia* (Linnaeus), Europe; **Noctuidae,** *Acronicta lepusculina* Guénée, *A. oblinita* (J. E. Smith), and *Catocala* spp., United States; **Nymphalidae,** *Nymphalis antiopa* (Linnaeus), the mourning-cloak butterfly, North America and Europe, and *Nymphalis io* (Linnaeus), Europe; **Saturniidae,** *Automeris io* (Fabricius), the io moth, *Hemileuca oliviae* Cockerell, the range caterpillar, *H. maia* (Drury), the buck moth, *H. nevadensis* Stretch, *H. lucina* Edwards, *Coloradia* spp., *Pseudohazis eglanterina* (Boisduval), and *P. hera* (Harris), United States, and probably many other species, including other species of *Automeris* and *Hemileuca;* **Megalopygidae,** *Lagoa crispata* Packard, the white moth, *Megalopyge opercularis* (J. E. Smith), the puss moth, *Lagoa pyxidifera* (J. E. Smith), and *Norape crenata* (Grote), United States, and *Megalopyge lanata* (Stoll), tropical America; **Limacodidae,** *Sibine stimulea* (Clemens), *Adoneta spinuloides* (Herrich-Schaeffer), *Parasa chloris* (Herrich-Schaeffer), *Parasa indetermina* (Boisduval), *Phobetron pithecium* (J. E. Smith) and others, United States, *Parasa hilarata* (Staudinger), east Asia, and *Parasa latistriga* (Walker), South Africa. Undoubtedly many Saturniidae, Megalopygidae, and others should be added to the list. On the other hand, some of the species listed, such as those of Noctuidae, are very mild in their nettling effects and would have no effect at all on any but the most highly sensitized individuals.

Blister beetles belong to the family Meloidae, order Coleoptera. They are so designated because of their vesicating properties, i.e., the application of the pulverized bodies or even simple contact with the insect may produce a blistering of the skin.

The Meloidae are described by Comstock*:

> The blister beetles are of medium or large size. The body is comparatively soft; the head is broad, vertical, and abruptly narrowed into a neck; the prothorax is narrower than the wing covers, which are soft and flexible; the legs are long and slender; the hind tarsi are four-jointed, and the fore and middle tarsi are five-jointed.

The blister beetles deposit their eggs on the ground; the larvae are active; some species feed on the eggs of grasshoppers and in the nests of solitary bees, others are predaceous. They undergo a number of changes not usual to insects, in that there is a multiplicity of larval stages which differ structurally and in habits from one another; this development is termed "hypermetamorphosis." The adults are plant feeders.

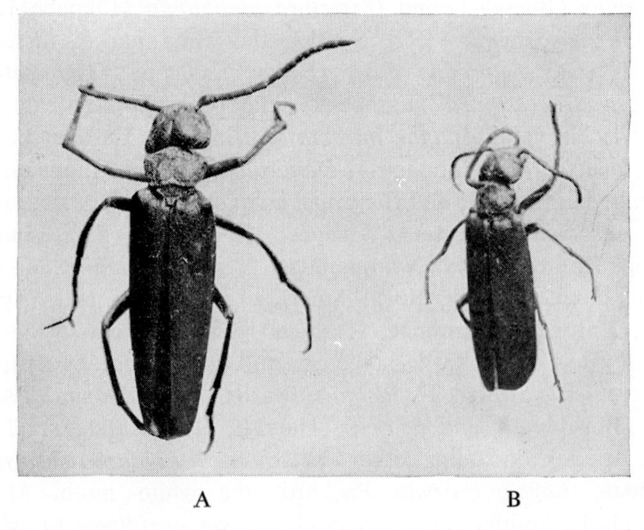

A B

Fig. 174. The Spanish fly, *Lytta vesicatoria;* (*A*) female; (*B*) male.

Spanish Fly. The Spanish fly, *Lytta vesicatoria* (Linnaeus), is a European species of beetle found most abundantly during the early summer in Spain, southern France, and other parts of Europe (Fig. 174). It is golden green or bluish in color, and ranges from 1/2 to 3/4 in. in length. It makes its appearance quite suddenly in early summer, when it may be collected by the hundreds, clinging principally to such vegetation as ash, privet, and lilac. The

* 1948, *An Introduction to Entomology,* Ithaca, N. Y.: Comstock Pub. Co., 9th ed., revised, p. 495.

peculiar hypermetamorphosis of these insects and their subterranean predaceous larval habits give to them some obscurity during their early development; the sudden appearance and equally sudden disappearance, owing to short adult life, give rise to the belief that they are migrating forms.

Cantharidin, a crystalline principle, the anhydrid of cantharidic acid, was isolated by Robiquet in 1812 from the Spanish fly. Cantharidin penetrates the epidermis quite readily and produces, even in very small quantities (0.1 mg), violent superficial irritation, resulting in vesication (blistering) in a few hours. Even when applied to the skin, cantharadin irritates the kidneys so that "fly blisters" are contraindicated in nephritis. It was formerly used as an aphrodisiac, but its effects may be dangerous to life; hence, its use for that purpose has been largely discontinued.

The collection and preparation of beetles for medical purposes provide an occupation for many persons for a brief period. Collecting and preparing the insects require special precautions owing to their vesicating properties. The best quality of cantharidin produced from the pulverized beetles results from special care in the drying, which must be gradual.

Other blister beetles, causing severe vesicular dermatitis in Africa, are *Zonabris nubica* (de Marseul), *Epicauta tomentosa* Maeklin, and *E. sapphirina* Maeklin, according to Chalmers and King.[21] Also *Paederus crebripunctatus* Eppelsheim is reported to be a severe vesicating beetle of East Africa[63] affecting Europeans and Africans similarly, although less severely on habitually exposed parts of natives. The term "Nairobi eye" applies to the conjunctivitis caused when the juices of crushed beetles are rubbed into the eye. The active principle is cantharidin. Roberts and Tonking[63] recommended a cold compress of saturated solution of magnesium sulfate.

Other Vesicating Beetles. At least two species, *Sessinia collaris* (Sharp) and *S. decolor* Fairmaire, belonging to the family Oedemeridae, cause severe blistering on some of the mid-Pacific islands where they are called coconut beetles.[40] These beetles fairly swarm about the newly opened male flowers of the coconut where they feed on pollen. They are readily attracted to light. Contact with one of these beetles causes a sharp momentary pain, like a burn from hot oil, but the large blister which forms in a few hours causes little pain.

SPIDERS

Class Arachnida—Order Araneida

General Characteristics. Spiders are arachnids in which the prosoma is uniform, bearing not more than eight eyes, and joined to the opisthosoma by a pedicel. The opisthosoma is usually unsegmented and bears not more than four, usually three, pairs of spinnerets. There is no telson. The chelicerae are two-segmented, moderately large, and unchelate and contain or are connected with a poison gland. The pedipalps are six-segmented, leglike, and tactile in function. In some forms they are so large that they might be mistaken for an extra pair of legs. The legs consist each of seven segments; the tarsi have two or three claws. Respiration is by book lungs or tracheae or, normally, both. The pedipalps of the male are modified as intromittent organs (see Savory,[65] p. 95). A good account of spider anatomy is given by Kaston[43] and, in more detail, by Snodgrass.[72]

Although spiders are universally feared, no doubt because of the knowledge that they are able to kill insects and other small animals by introducing a venom with the bite, it is nevertheless true that out of the more than 2000 genera in more than 60 families only a very few species are actually dangerous to man.

TARANTULAS

The term *tarantula* was first applied to a European species, *Lycosa tarentula* (Linnaeus), a member of the family Lycosidae (wolf spider). It is of interest to note that the American tarantulas belong to an entirely different group of spiders, and that the arachnid that goes by the generic name *Tarantula* is not a spider at all, but a tailless whipscorpion (Order Phrynichida). In Italy in the vicinity of Taranto, there occurred a spider scare during the seventeenth century which gave rise to a condition known as "tarantism," resulting from the bite of the European tarantula, *Lycosa tarentula.* To rid the body of the venom those bitten engaged in a frenzied dance known as the "tarantella."[76]

The following account of *tarantism* is from the *Cambridge Natural History,* Vol. 4, p. 361:

> The bite of the spider was supposed to induce a species of madness which found its expression—and its cure—in frantic and extravagant contortions of the body. If the dance was not sufficiently frenzied, death ensued. In the case of survivors, the symptoms were said to recur on the anniversary of the bite. Particular descriptions of music were supposed to incite the patient to the exertion necessary for his relief; hence the name "Tarantella."
>
> In the middle ages epidemics of "tarantism" were of frequent occurrence and spread with alarming rapidity. They were seizures of an hysterical character, analogous to the ancient Bacchic dances, and quite unconnected with the venom of the spider from which they took their name. The condition of exaltation and frenzy was contagious, and would run through whole districts, with its subsequent relapse to a state of utter prostration and exhaustion. The evil reputation of the Tarantula appears to have exceedingly little basis in fact.

In the United States the term "tarantula" is applied to the very large spiders belonging to the family Theraphosidae. They are also known as "bird spiders," as *carangueigeiras* or "crab spiders" (in Brazil), or as *arañas de caballo* or *matacaballos* (in Central America). Many of these spiders measure 6 or 7 in. in the spread of legs. About 30 species live within the limits of the United States, mostly in the Southwest,[34] and many others occur in the New World tropics. They are greatly feared and are erroneously supposed to have prodigious jumping power, up to 10 to 25 ft.

The supposedly venomous nature of tarantulas has been investigated at length by Baerg, whose studies, involving 35 years of research and numerous publications, have been summarized in an interesting and very readable little book entitled *The Tarantula.*[6] Baerg tested the effects of the venom on guinea pigs, white rats, rabbits, and, in some cases, upon himself. He concludes that most species from Mexico, Central America, and Trinidad, as well as all from the United States, so far as has been determined, are harmless to man. The bite "is as painful as a couple of pin stabs and has essentially the same effect." The Arkansas tarantula, *Dugesiella hentzi* (Girard), can kill rats; but usually, after a rat is bitten, it "runs about excitedly, and in a jumping and jerking manner. Then it becomes more quiet and appears to have considerable pain in the wounded leg. For much of the time the eyes are closed. In about four or five hours the rat shows evidence of recovery and in another hour it is normal."[5]

On the other hand, some tropical tarantulas, such as the southern Mexican species *Aphonopelma emilia* (White), may be poisonous to man; and the large black tarantula of Panama and the Canal Zone, *Sericopelma communis* Cambridge, is definitely poisonous to man, but the effects of its bite, though severe, are local, not general. Baerg[5] allowed a spider of this species to bite him on the finger. He allowed only one fang to puncture the skin. The finger felt numb in a few minutes, and in 10 minutes the pain was quite severe. There followed considerable swelling of the finger, hand, and wrist. After 2 hours Baerg put the hand in hot water for 30 minutes, when the pain and swelling subsided. A lame feeling in the small and third fingers remained for several days.

The supposed pugnacious attitude of tarantulas has been greatly exaggerated. Baerg records that the bird spider of Trinidad, *Avicularia velutina* Simon, is very pugnacious, but most tarantulas need to be teased considerably in order to induce them to bite. The tarantulas of our Southwest should be considered as beneficial in that they destroy many harmful insects and are themselves harmless to man.

GENUS LATRODECTUS

Dangerous spiders belonging to the genus *Latrodectus* are found throughout the world. The genus belongs to the family Theridiidae, the comb-footed spiders. They have eight eyes and three tarsal claws; the hind pair of legs is comb-footed. They spin irregular webs in which the female spiders hang belly upward.

Arachnologists do not agree as to the classification of the spiders of this genus. Levi[48,49] recognizes only six species in the world: *Latrodectus mactans* (Fabricius), the black widow, widespread from the southern United States, through much of tropical America, and through the tropical and warmer temperate regions of all continents; *L. curacaviensis* Müller, widespread from southern Canada and the northern United States through the lesser Antilles, southward in America to Chile and Argentina; *L. geometricus* Koch, the brown widow, widespread in the tropics, particularly in Africa, but occurring in the United States only in Florida; *L. pallidus* Cambridge, occurring from the Turkmen Soviet Republic through Iran and Asia Minor to Libya and Tripolitania in North Africa; *L. hystrix* Simon, known only from Yemen; and *L. dahli* Levi, from Iran and the island of Sokotra. If this classification is accepted, one must consider the black widow of Canada and most of the northern United States as distinct from the predominant species in the South (although both may coexist in the same area); also, one must consider *L. mactans* as occurring throughout the tropics and as being the important venomous member of the genus in the Old World as well as the new. Arachnologists who do not accept this synonymy consider the following, at least, as important venomous species: *L. bishopi* Kaston, from Florida; *L. tredecimguttatus* Rossi, from the Mediterranean region and the European and Asiatic steppes, the *karakurt* of Russia and the *malmignatte* of Italy; *L. cinctus* Blackwell (= *L. indistinctus* Cambridge), the *Knoppiespinnekop* or "shoe-button spider" of South Africa; *L. hasselti* Thorell, occurring from Australia and New Zealand northward to India; and *L. menavodi* Vinson, from Madagascar.

The black widow spider, *Latrodectus mactans* (Fabricius),* was first described from America in 1775, under the name *Aranea mactans*. Many common names are in use. In the United States, in addition to "black widow," the names "hourglass spider" and "shoe-button spider" have been used. "Pokomoo" was a name used by the California Indians, who referred to this species as "a small black spider with a red spot under his belly."

The adult female is glossy black to sepia and densely clothed with short, almost microscopic hairs which give it a naked appearance. As it occurs in the United States, it is usually wholly black dorsally, although an irregular red (or rarely white) stripe or pattern is sometimes present. The characteristic crimson hourglass marking on the underside of the abdomen (Fig. 175), rarely altogether absent, varies among individuals from the distinct hourglass marking to a design comprising two or more distinct triangles or blotches or sometimes only an irregular longitudinal area. The abdomen is globose and often likened to a shoe button. The average width of the abdo-

* Because of the uncertainty of the status of *L. curacaviensis* and because as interpreted by Levi, it has not been separated from *mactans* in biological studies, the American black widow is here considered as one species, *L. mactans*.

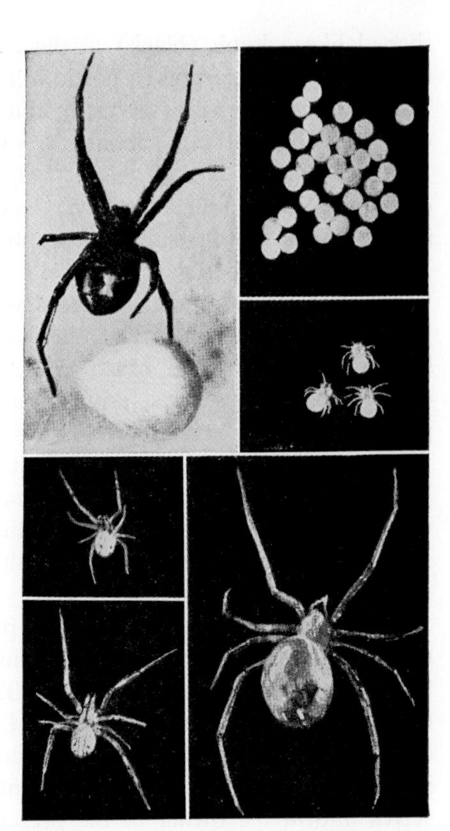

Fig. 175. The black widow, *Latrodectus mactans;* (*upper left*) mature female with egg sac; (*upper right*) eggs and first instars; (*lower left*) second and third instars; (*lower right*) fourth instar.

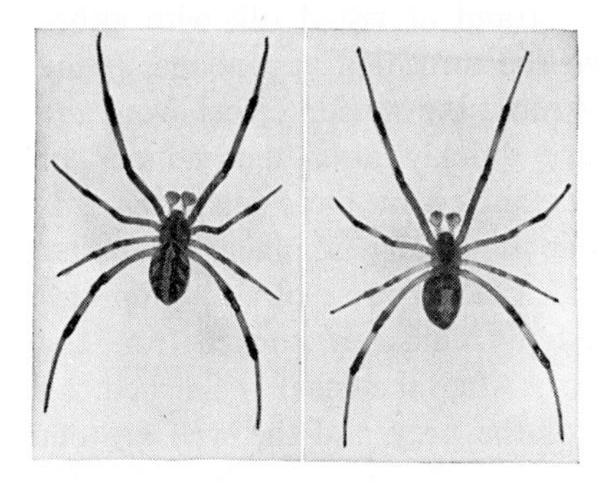

Fig. 176. Male black widow spider, *Latrodectus mactans.* Dorsal view (*left*); ventral view (*right*).

men is 6 mm, or 1/4 in.; and the length over-all (legs extended) is about 40 mm, i.e., about 1.5 in. The abdomen of gravid females often measures 9 to 13 mm.

The color pattern of the adult male (Fig. 176), while exhibiting considerable variation, approaches that of the immature female spider. Occasionally mature males are almost black but retain some of the abdominal markings of the immature form. The terminal segment of each palpus is shaped like a knob (black) at the front of the head and contains the ejaculatory sexual apparatus, a portion of which resembles a coiled watch spring. The abdomen measures about 3 mm (1/8 in.) in diameter, and the length over-all is about 30 mm (about 1 1/8 in.).

Distribution and Habitat. Latrodactus mactans (including *L. curacaviensis* as interpreted by Levi) is known to occur in virtually every state in the United States, with the exception of Alaska, and in southern Canada. It has been recorded at an altitude of 8000 feet in Colorado.[26] In her natural habitat the female spider is found with her web and egg sacs in protected places, such as vacant rodent burrows, under stones, logs, and long grass, in hollow stumps, and in brush piles. Convenient abode is found in darker corners of barns, stables, privies, pump houses, garages, fruit drying sheds, piles of boxes and crates, wood piles, stone piles, etc.

As a rule the females are not aggressive unless agitated or hungry. When guarding the egg sac, the female is particularly prone to bite. Once a web is established in a suitable location, the female spends the rest of her life feeding on the prey ensnared in this crude but effective web and guarding such eggs as she may deposit.

Feeding Habits. Whether the prey be a nocturnal moth, cricket, or domestic fly, the technique of capturing, killing, and finally sucking the fluids from the victim is very consistent. The spider depends largely upon vibrations of the web as an indication of a trespasser or prospective meal. The coarse, permanent web is not particularly viscid in nature, but inadvertent insect visitors become temporarily entangled and in struggling to free themselves inform the owner of the presence. The spider always approaches the victim backwards, extending a freshly spun strand of viscid silk with either or both hind legs, and attempts to tie down the thrashing appendage. If the captured prey appears particularly obstreperous, the spider ejects from the spinnerets large viscous droplets which dry quickly after the manner of rubber cement, and if the victim becomes entangled by these jets, escape is impossible. At about this point, a lethal bite is usually administered. After being bitten the victim struggles violently and, in the course of a few minutes of progressively weaker tremors, dies. The body fluids are sucked from the trussed-up victim at the leisure of the captor. After the meal is finished, all points of attachment between the remains of the prey and the web are cut loose, allowing it to drop from the web.

The diet of the black widow consists largely of insects of the locality, small spiders, and even centipedes and sow bugs. Whatever is caught in the web is likely to be eaten. Beetles, such as ground beetles, lady beetles, and June beetles, along with flies, grasshoppers, and, if the web is near to the entrance of a bee hive, honey bees, are taken. It is surprising how many insects an individual spider can consume during its lifetime. Accurate records of the food of isolated specimens have shown a total, in the life of an individidual spider, as high as 250 house flies, 33 vinegar flies (*Drosophila*), 2 crickets, and 1 small specimen of *Latrodectus mactans*. In considering the economic status of this spider, its large diet of prevailing pests is a matter which should not be put aside lightly. It is interesting to note in connection with the diet that one individual (a male) was reared on a diet of its own species exclusively.

Mating Habits. After molting the last time, the male leaves its web and seeks a mate. In this active, wandering state the male makes no attempt to capture prey but will occasionally suck up a small amount of water or liquid food if the opportunity is offered. If fortunate in finding a likely mate, the male vibrates his abdomen rapidly, causing the entire web to vibrate; the female may produce reciprocating movements. Cautiously the male approaches and strokes the female with his forelegs. It is a dangerous game the suitor plays for, if the female is not ready for his advances, death may result. On the other hand, if the female accepts his advances, the wooing begins. If agreeable, the female remains quiet and allows herself to be spun up in a delicate web. Once the web is successfully spun, the male effects coitus by applying the springlike apparatus of either palpus to the female genital opening. Occasionally this is repeated. It is interesting to note that, in this and other spiders, the intromittent organ is separate from the rest of the reproductive system. After coitus, the female easily frees herself and sometimes, although not as often as is commonly supposed, ensnares and feeds upon her mate. The infrequent observance and recognition of the male of *Latrodectus mactans,* together with the matricidal tendency of the female, have given rise to the name "black widow." However, if other food is immediately available, often the male is not killed, and in due course of time dies a natural death. In the laboratory, the males will readily mate a second time, but the females do not show such a tendency.

Life History. There seems to be a variation in regard to the stage in which the black widow hibernates. The studies of Lawson[47] and of Herms *et al.*[41] indicate that the adult female hibernates, but Baerg[7] cites Frank R. Smith as saying that in Pennsylvania the black widow winters in the immature stage.

The life history of the black widow spider from egg to maturity requires about 4 months under laboratory conditions with ample food.[41] The gravid female, when ready to deposit her eggs, forms a loosely woven cup of silk which hangs downward and, while clinging invertedly to its rim, emits the eggs singly with rapid but regular upward flexures of the abdomen. The eggs, which appear to be forced into an expanding, gelatinlike film, gradually fill and adhere to the silken cup. The open end of the cup is then covered with loose strands of silk, and the whole enclosed in a tough, watertight covering of silk. The entire process consumes from 1 to 3 hours. Shortly after the egg sac is completed, the film surrounding the eggs disappears, and the eggs are free to roll about within the envelope. Egg-laying usually takes place during the night.

The white or buff-colored egg sacs may be found suspended in webs out of doors from midsummer to late August, according to Baerg;[7] Herms has observed them in California from March to October, inclusive. Egg-laying may take place in the laboratory where food is plentiful throughout the year. The egg sacs measure 12 to 15 mm in diameter, are usually oval in shape, and usually contain from 250 to 750 eggs (25 to 917, according to Lawson[47]), each of which is about 1 mm in diameter. In the field one frequently finds a female guarding 4 to 6 egg sacs, and in the laboratory females have been observed to spin from 1 to 9 sacs a season. Fertile, mature females in isolation have produced egg sacs in the fall, survived the winter, and produced additional egg sacs the following spring, both groups of eggs being fertile.

The time between the deposition of successive groups of eggs varies from about 1 week to about 4 months. The incubation period depends on the temperature, and at normal summer temperatures requires about 20 days in the interior of California, the observed extreme range being from 14 to 30 days, according to the studies of Herms; these figures compare favorably with the range of 14 to 30 days reported by Lawson in Kansas and the four weeks reported by Frank R. Smith in Pennsylvania.

The spiderlings after hatching spend some time—varying from 4 days in the summer to about 1 month in cooler weather—within the egg sac before emerging from one or more holes which they make in the tightly woven envelope. The first molt, previous to which the spider cannot feed, occurs from 1 to 2 weeks after hatching. Usually the first instar (and sometimes the second) remains within the egg sac, and at emergence the molted skins are left behind together with the egg remnants. There is a tendency on the part of the spiderlings to cluster for a few days after emerging from the egg sac, and cannibalism rules during this time. The spinnerets appear to be capable of functioning at the time of emergence, but the extremely delicate web is capable of holding only the smallest of prey, such as gnats, mosquitos, and other tiny spiders. The mother, if confined with her young, will not feed upon them even though extremely hungry.

Shortly after emerging and after a period of clustering, the nymphal spiders disperse by means of nearly invisible strands of silk. For several weeks they move about in the vicinity of their birthplace and suffer a high mortality from other predaceous spiders, and, as already stated, from their own species. When about one-third grown, the female spiders establish themselves in some protected niche, constructing small, loosely woven webs of their own, lacking in specific design, or, rarely, take possession of an abandoned funnel, sheet, or irregular web. Once settled, they remain in the chosen lair, capturing progressively larger prey and extending the web as they approach maturity.

The number of molts that the black widow has varies, and the length of the intervening periods is even more inconstant, seemingly conditioned by the season and the amount of food assimilated. The average number of skins cast by the male is five. At optimum temperatures and with plenty of food this number is often reduced to three; under less favorable conditions, resulting in slower growth, a series of six or seven skins may be shed. The sexes may be distinguished by the palpi, which in the male are swollen or knoblike (Fig. 176), while in the female they are slender. Subsequent to acquiring this secondary character, the male molts once (sometimes twice) before attaining maturity, at which time the web is abandoned, and his search for a mate begins.

The female takes longer to mature and has an average of 7 molts, with a range from 6 to 9. When preparing to molt, she eats nothing for several days. The old skin splits around the margin of the carapace, slips off the abdomen, and the spider then gradually pulls its legs free from its old sheaths, leaving the "ghost" of itself on or near the web. The entire process requires about an hour. The newly molted spider is rather delicate and usually remains at rest for a day or so after molting. Individuals occasionally die during the molting process.

The Immature Stages. First Instar. The abdomen of the newly hatched spiderling is opalescent white with no markings. The cephalothorax and appendages are white to pale yellow; short hair covers the body, becoming dark at the tips of the legs. The tarsi, or last segment of the legs, have each two notched claws and a supplementary third between. Eight simple eyes are on the anterior margin of the cephalothorax in two rows of four, and the anterior medians are comparatively dark.

Second Instar. All eyes become darker and a black band extends down the center and around the margin of the carapace. Also the mouth parts and the appendages become darker as well as the margin of the sternum of the cephalothorax. A double row of black dots extends down the mid-region of the dorsum of the abdomen, which remains whitish. On the underside of the abdomen the white area takes on a broad hourglass design outlined by a dark-brown border.

Third Instar. From this stage to maturity a wide variation in color pattern occurs. Distinct lateral stripes begin to appear on the dorsum of the abdomen, in the region of the dots of the second instar. Intervening areas take on a pale greenish-yellow cast, and the legs acquire four black bands, one at each end of the patella, one near the center of the tibia, and one at the junction of the tibia and the metatarsus. The longitudinal white area on the underside of the abdomen becomes tinged with crimson.

Fourth Instar. Dark stripes or bands become distinct and faintly bordered with buff. The spinnerets take on a mottled appearance. Black bands at the leg joints become more distinct.

Fifth Instar. The center dorsal white stripe on the abdomen tends to be constricted at intervals and acquires a reddish tinge near the tip. All white areas become lightly colored with brown. Males usually mature at this point.

Sixth and Seventh Instars. Usually only the females go through these two stages. All coloration is much darker, and the more variable remaining white areas become more and more restricted. Often a series of reddish spots is formed along the middorsal region of the abdomen.

Eighth Instar. Only the females pass through this stage, which is often difficult to distinguish from the mature form. They are usually all black or sepia with the exception of the characteristic crimson markings and an occasional white band on the anterior margin of the abdomen.

Longevity. The length of life of individual spiders, as one might expect, depends on such factors as food supply, natural enemies, including man, etc. Under optimum conditions of food, temperature, humidity, protection, etc., the complete life cycle from egg to maturity requires at least 4 months. Spiderlings which emerge from eggs laid in July and hatched in August will, of course, pass the winter in an immature stage which thus materially extends the length of time required to complete the life cycle. Activity on the part of both the spiders and the insect prey is greatly reduced during the winter months which largely accounts for the retardation in development.

When a brood emerges in late spring or early summer, the females generally reach maturity before cold weather sets in, but egg-laying is held over until the following spring; hence, the life cycle is extended over a complete year. Mature males have not been found overwintering. Under laboratory conditions a few females have lived through the second and third summers, giving a life span of nearly 2 years.

Arachnidism (Black Widow). While spiders in general have been considered poisonous, though largely erroneously, for centuries, the group to which the black widow belongs in particular has been classed as poisonous for little more than a century. Many of the early reports of spider bite traceable to the black widow came from the southern states, and from 1889 to 1894 were frequently mentioned in *Insect Life* (Riley and Howard, 1889–94). After the rapid increase in the population of California during the latter part of the nineteenth century, reports of poisonous spider bites began to be received from that state. In 1932 Bogen[13] listed a total of 380 cases from 18 states, of which 250 were from California.

The chain of symptoms resulting from the bite of the black widow spider is so striking that once recognized there is little danger of confusing it with that of other venomous forms or with abdominal conditions. Cases of arachnidism, or spider-bite poisoning, suggest numerous acute abdominal conditions such as a ruptured peptic ulcer, acute appendicitis, renal colic, enteritis, food poisoning, etc.

The bite itself (similar to a pinprick) is not always felt, and often there is but little evidence of a lesion. However, a slight local swelling and two tiny red spots may occur, and local redness is usually in evidence at the point of attack.

Pain, usually in the region of the bite, is felt almost immediately and increases in intensity, reaching its maximum in 1 to 3 hours and generally continuing for 12 to 48 hours, gradually subsiding. Rigidity and spasm of most of the larger muscle groups of the body (particularly those of the abdomen) are constant symptoms. The abdominal muscles become "boardlike," but local tenderness as in appendicitis is almost always absent. There are a slight rise in body temperature, increased blood pressure, a definite leucocytosis, and usually an increase in the pressure of the spinal fluid. There are usually profuse perspiration and often a tendency to nausea. The degree to which these symptoms are present varies in individual cases, and other symptoms, such as chills, urinary retention, constipation, hyperactive reflexes, priapism, and a burning sensation of the skin are frequently reported. Baerg[5] cites a case in which a young housewife suffered amnesia for a period of several weeks following spider bite, long enough to cause considerable alarm.

Clinical case records published by Baerg,[4] Herms *et al.*,[41] Sampayo,[64] Tinkham (for *L. bishopi*),[77] and others, agree in that there is severe muscular pain, a rigid ("boardlike") abdomen, tightness in the chest and usually difficulty in breathing and speech, and nausea, with usually profuse sweating. The condition is self-limiting, and in most cases symptoms wane without treatment after 2 to 3 days. However, the patient is in such pain that therapy must be administered to give him relief. A representative case has been described as so severe that the patient doubled up and rolled on the floor.[41]

Of 37 persons with cases of arachnidism treated at the Woodland, California, Clinic during a period of 10 years, about one-half were bitten on the genitalia while using a privy.[38] Four of the patients were females and the remainder males, the majority of whom were laborers and farmers between the ages of 20 and 50 years. Five school children were among those treated. Although spider bite cases were admitted to this hospital every month in the year except December and January, the greater number were admitted during June, July, and August. There was no correlation between the time of day and the bites. The spider was seen in 11 cases. None of the patients reported any aftereffects on the follow-up inquiry.

Mortality from black widow spider bite is usually considered as running 4 to 5 per cent. Of the 37 Woodland cases, two terminated fatally; one of these was a 78-year-old male with heart and syphilitic complications. Thorp and Woodson[76] list 1291 cases of black widow spider bite in the United States from 1726 to 1943, with 55 fatalities, or 4.26 per cent; these figures have led several authors to conclude that the death rate of 4 to 5 per cent is too high, on the assumption that all deaths, but not all cases, of arachnidism have been reported. However, Parrish[58] lists 39 deaths from spider bite in the United States in the five-year period from 1950–1954. It is not reasonable to suppose that three-fourths as many people died from arachnidism in this *five-year period* as did during the entire previous history of our country. The only reasonable conclusion is that many cases of black-widow poisoning have been misdiagnosed and that the death rate is higher than Thorp and Woodson's figures would indicate.

The danger of black widow bite is exaggerated in the public mind, however. The spider is ordinarily shy and retiring. She does not bite "without provocation," but she will defend her eggs and will bite when cornered. If one attempts to put on a shoe in which a spider is concealed, or if one grasps hold of a spider while picking tomatoes, or if one comes into contact with a spider that is trapped in the bed sheets, one is apt to be bitten. Spiders may be very abundant in a field and may never attack a person. Most bites occur in open toilets, the spider apparently responding to the vibration in the web caused by the presence of a foreign object. Spider bites decrease in numbers in areas where outdoor privies have been eliminated.

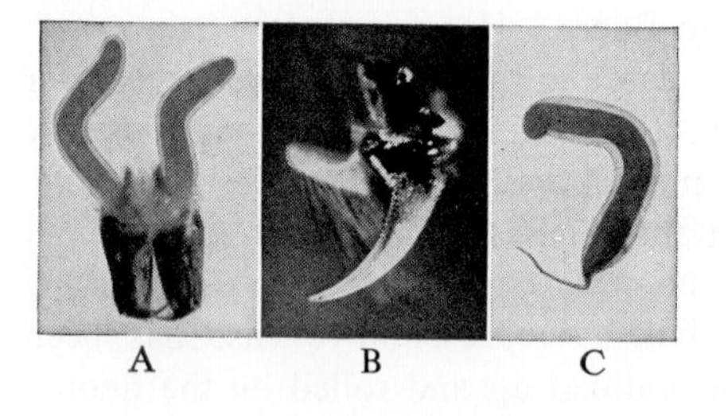

Fig. 177. (*A*) Chelicerae and venom gland of female black widow spider, *Latrodectus mactans;* (*B*) separated chelicerae; and (*C*) a freed gland. (Photograph by Charles Ladenheim.)

Venom Apparatus. Spiders are equipped with a poison apparatus for purposes of killing prey. The venom apparatus of *Latrodectus mactans* consists of poison sacs, each with an attached duct leading into the heavily sclerotized chelicerae (horny fangs) from which the poison is expelled at the time of biting (Fig. 177). The venom apparatus is present in both the male and the female spider. In the male the venom is primarily of use in the immature stages. The mature male does not attack its prey, and the poison apparatus appears to become inactive with maturity and remains small in size. In the case of the female spider, the venom apparatus increases in size and strength with maturity. The large quantity of the venom present in the poison glands of the female black widow spider makes her presence perilous. The poison glands of the mature female average about 0.40 mm in diameter and 2.70 mm in length, and in the mature male they average 0.16 mm in diameter and 0.66 mm in length.

The poison glands are located in the cephalothorax extending posteriorly about two-thirds of the way to the junction of the cephalothorax with the abdomen. The long narrow glands curve outwardly around the *fovea media,* that is, the indentation in the center of the cephalothorax for muscular attachment; this is due to the position of the sucking stomach directly below. If the glands were over the sucking stomach, they would be squeezed together every time the sucking stomach filled with food and cause a loss of venom. In the female (all stages) the glands are opaque and filled with venom, while in the mature male they are rather translucent but, according to experimental evidence, contain sufficient venom to produce symptoms of arachnidism in white mice.

Nature of the Venom. There is good evidence showing that the poison glands are not exclusively glandular in nature, but also function as absorptive organs which take up the poisonous constituents from the body fluid of the spider. Proteolytic or hemolytic substances variously known as *epeiralysin, arachnotoxin, arachnolysin,* and *epeiratoxin,* have been found in the eggs, newly hatched spiderlings, and gravid females,[43] as well as in the venom of the adult female.

The venom produced in the poison glands is a neurotoxin. The severe muscular pain and rigidity following the bite of the spider are due to a heightening of the muscular tonus to an excess degree and to the contraction of the intercostal muscles. Death results from asphyxia produced by respiratory paralysis. The venom of the black widow spider is far more potent than that of the prairie rattlesnake (about 15 times as potent, on the basis of dry weight), but the amount of venom injected into a wound, even when the spider injects the full contents of her poison glands into the bite, is relatively very small. Consequently, the mortality resulting from spider bite is far less than that from rattlesnake bite. Nevertheless, as Blyth and Blyth[12] point out in the case of the Russian karakurt: "The fatal dose of the poison, injected subcutaneously or intravenously, is extremely small. Cats are killed by quantities equal to 0.2 to 0.35 milligram per kilogram body weight." The effect on infants and small children is much more serious than that on older persons, presumably because the amount of poison is large in comparison with their small bodies or low resistance.

Treatment. Even though arachnidism of this type is usually self-limiting, the intense suffering of the victim justifies considerations of therapy. When bitten by the black widow spider, the patient should be treated with local antiseptics, such as alcohol or hydrogen peroxide, at the point of injury to prevent secondary bacterial infection, and should be kept as quiet as possible; a physician should be summoned at once. Since, among other properties, the venom appears to be neurotoxic and its effects little short of instantaneous, first-aid measures for snake bite are of little value; in fact the use of a tourniquet, incision and scarification at the site of the bite, and the use of suction and corrosive chemicals such as potassium permanganate will only tend to increase local necrosis and add to the patient's discomfort.

Treatment of latrodectism (black widow arachnidism) is discussed concisely by Bogen,[14] and the following account is taken mainly from his discussion. Gilbert and Stewart[36] had pointed out that, since the toxin stimulates the myoneural junctions or acts on the nerve endings, calcium salts, which apparently depress the neuromuscular junctions, would have a desirable therapeutic effect. Calcium gluconate was used instead of calcium chloride because of the necrotic effect of the latter on tissue outide a vein, particularly in the case of children. Bogen states that the value of the use of intravenous injection of calcium gluconate has been "abundantly confirmed." The treatment may be repeated as required. Relief is rapid.

The use of depressant drugs is usually not indicated. Analgesics and sedatives such as opiates and barbiturates are usually not sufficient to overcome the muscular pain. Hydrotherapy in the form of warm baths or applications may aid in lessening the pain resulting from muscular spasms and some of the undesirable aftereffects.

An antiserum is available against the venom of the black widow, and in some areas it is being used widely. In South Africa, the *L. cinctus* (= *indistinctus*) antiserum has been shown to be equally effective against the venom of *L. geometricus*.[31] Experimentally, the results obtained with the use of *L. mactans* antiserum are impressive, and clinically the antiserum is useful, but the results are not so dramatic as those obtained from the intravenous injections of the calcium salts.

Control and Prophylaxis. The black widow spider is frequently found in garages, basements, in living quarters, in old outbuildings (particularly privies, barns, pump houses, stables), and woodpiles. Frequently disturbance of spider webs with a broom or brush is suggested, and the spiders should be killed in any convenient way. General cleanliness, light, and the painting of the walls of infrequently used buildings discourages the spider from remaining in such places. Workers in dried-fruit industries in California find numerous black widow spiders under and in the drying trays when handling these. Other agricultural workers, such as tomato pickers, may readily come in contact with the spiders. The use of gloves is suggested in such instances. Out-of-doors the spider may be found in vacant lots and open fields on hillsides, building their webs in rock piles, heaps of rubbish, under logs, under protecting banks, in deserted squirrel or rabbit holes, under low wooden or concrete bridges, culverts, etc. The worker who needs to put his hand into such harboring spots should use due caution and, when possible, should wear protecting gloves.

Since the egg sacs are conspicuous and are not carried about by the spider, they may be readily collected and destroyed. Great care should be exercised when collecting egg sacs because the female spider guards the sac closely. The public should be encouraged to collect and burn or otherwise *destroy* the egg sacs of the black widow spider. Where accessible, the adult spider can be brushed from her web with a broom or stick and stamped upon, or a suitable fly swatter may be used to knock the spider to the floor, where it should then be crushed. The use of a blowtorch *when no hazard is involved* is effective in the destruction of spiders and eggs as well. Because of the danger from spider bites when using privies in rural sections, such habitats should be especially guarded. Tightly constructed privies that will exclude flies will also tend to exclude the spiders and will deprive of their food any that happen to gain entrance. Thorough and liberal spraying of all parts, particularly under the seats, with DDT, chlordane, or lindane in kerosene or petroleum distillate is recommended. These insecticides may also be used in other places where the spiders are common. Periodic inspection should be made in order to detect signs of reinfestation.

Natural Enemies. Under natural conditions the black widow spider is held at least moderately in check by its natural enemies. Baerg[7] found that 36 out of 60 nests of the yellow-marked mud dauber, *Sceliphron caementarium* (Drury), contained from 1 to 12 black widows. Irving and Hinman[42] discovered that the blue mud dauber, *Chalybion californicum* (Saussure), captures great numbers of this species. They found 285 black widow spiders had been stored in 15 nests, an average of 19 per nest. Egg predators such as the scelionid wasp, *Baeus latrodecti* Dozier, the ichneumonid *Celis* sp., and the chloropid, *Pseudogaurax signata* (Loew), play an important role.

The chloropid fly, *Pseudogaurax signata* (Loew), which can be reared successfully in captivity, has been studied by George Elwood Jenks (*Popular Science Monthly,* August, 1936) and Kaston and Jenks.[44] The larvae of this fly lie free in the egg sac and completely consume the eggs of the spider.

Baerg[7] has shown that the spiders *Agelenopsis naevia* (Walckenaer), a funnel-web weaver, and *Lycosa carolinensis* Walckenaer, a wolf spider, as well as the scorpion *Centruroides vittatus* (Say) and certain ground beetles, will, under experimental conditions, kill and devour black widow spiders (and, in turn, sometimes be devoured by them). Baerg concludes that none of these predators are of any importance as natural enemies of the black widow.

The large San Diegan alligator lizard, *Gerrhonotus multicarinatus webbi* (Baird), in southern California, has been suggested by Cowles[25] as probably an important factor in cutting down the incidence of this spider on his property. Cowles points out that the elimination of cats is essential because they will eat the lizard.

With protection afforded by man-made structures which exclude the natural enemies, the spider thrives and multiplies rapidly.

The brown widow, *Latrodectus geometricus* Koch is a little smaller than *L. mactans.* In color it varies from gray to light brown to almost black. The dorsal abdominal pattern is rather intricate and variable, and the hourglass on the venter is brownish yellow. The spider occurs in most of the tropical areas of the world, particularly in Africa, where it is supposedly endemic. It enters the United States only in Florida.

The brown widow is much less aggressive than the black widow, and records of its biting man are rare. Baerg[7] describes two cases, one involving himself while studying this spider in Jamaica and the other involving a visiting scientist in his laboratory. The spider was very reluctant to bite, but, when finally induced to do so, it produced a definite syndrome of arachnidism. The pain was restricted to the hand, in one case, and to the arm, in the other, but was sufficiently sharp to make sleep impossible without sedation for 2 or 3 subsequent nights. In South Africa, *L. geometricus* poisoning, according to Finlayson,[31] occurs among workers in vineyards in the Western Cape Province. Workmen are bitten while harvesting grapes. No fatal cases have been reported.

THE GENUS LOXOSCELES

At least two species of this genus are of medical importance, one in the United States and one in Central and South America. The genus *Loxosceles,* family Loxoscelidae, contains spiders of medium size, the body being 10 to 15 mm in length, and yellow to brown in color. The carapace is flattened, with six eyes (most spiders have eight) in a strongly curved row; the legs are long and lack the unpaired claws on all tarsi. The genus as it occurs in North America, Central America, and the West Indies has been reviewed by Gertsch.[35]

Loxosceles reclusa Gertsch and Mulaik (Fig. 178) has been responsible for a number of cases of necrotic spider poisoning in Arkansas and Missouri. It is a common house spider in Missouri. According to Wingo (cited by Baerg[7]), it has been collected in "bathrooms, bedrooms, closets, cellars, basements, smoke-houses, barns, and in any kind of seldom disturbed storage place in houses and outbuildings. In areas where it is common, it has been taken in folds of seldom used clothing hanging in closets or other storage space." It spins a loose, very insignificant web.

Unlike the bite of the black widow, that of *L. reclusa* is localized, but it produces considerable local necrosis which may ultimately produce an unsightly scar. Atkins *et al.,*[3] who have studied the bite of this spider in Missouri, describe the pathology as follows:

> A thick wheal usually forms with necrosis of tissue at the immediate site of the punctures made by the chelicerae. The necrotic area soon turns violaceous, then black and dry. The area sloughs in a few days or a week, leaving a deep sharply defined granular area surrounded by the raised edge of healthy tissue. The sloughed area, frequently quite large, may persist for several weeks, and healing takes place very slowly. In a few patients, systemic disturbances of a general nature have been indicated by a rash resembling that of scarlet fever.

Baerg cites one case in which the wound failed to heal and in which a skin graft was ultimately necessary. In another case, the patient became very ill, but the patient herself suggested that the illness might have been psychosomatic. The record of one fatal case in a four-year-old boy is to be published by the attending physician (personal communication, Gertsch to James).

South American Loxoscelism. Numerous cases of arachnidism in Peru and Chile (also Argentina and Uruguay) have been attributed to *Loxosceles,* chiefly *L. laeta* (Nicolet), although another species, erroneously referred to as *L. rufipes* (Lucas), apparently was the spider involved in the one case (a fatal one) authentically reported from Argentina.[68] *Loxosceles laeta,*

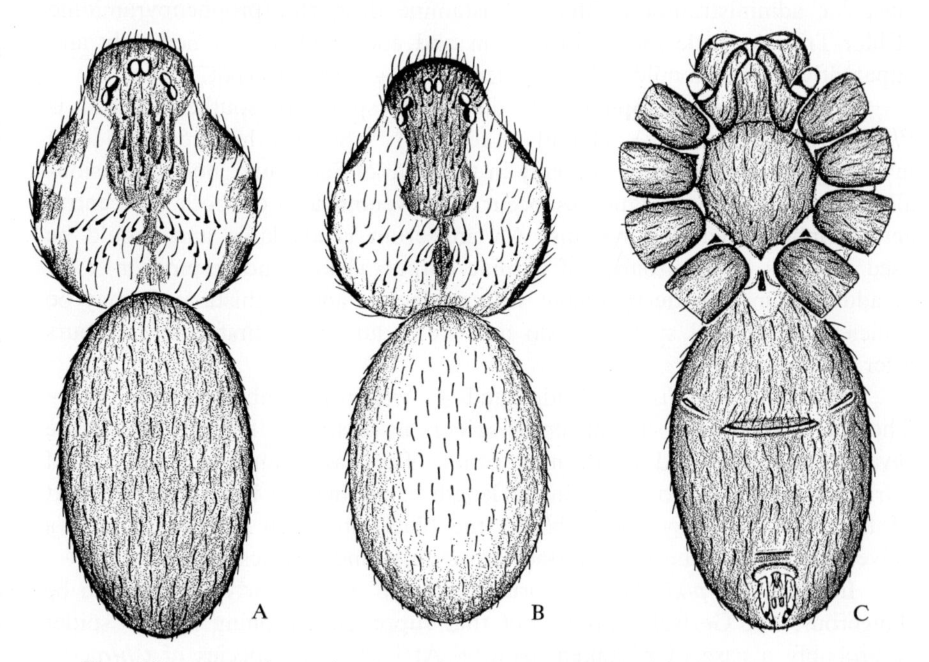

Fig. 178. *Loxosceles reclusa,* sometimes known as the brown spider. (*A*) Dorsal view of well-marked female; (*B*) dorsal view of male; (*C*) ventral view of female. (After Gertsch, 1958; courtesy of W. J. Gertsch.)

known as the *araña de los rincones, araña de detras de los cuadros* (spider of the corners, spider of behind the pictures), is similar in size and appearance to *L. reclusa* and is, like that species, a domestic spider, being found on walls, especially in the corners, behind pictures, in cracks, and sometimes in clothing that has been hung on the walls. Most cases of spider bite occur in homes, while the victims are sleeping or dressing themselves. Case histories indicate a much higher incidence of spider bite among women than among men.

Two forms of loxoscelism occur: a *cutaneous* form, localized and benign, involving local necrosis (*mancha gangrenosa,* skin gangrene) similar to that usually produced by *L. reclusa;* and a *cutaneovisceral* form, generalized and often fatal. The latter is fortunately uncommon; in it the kidneys and liver are involved; symptoms are general, and there is considerable passage of hemoglobin and albumin in the urine; death results, in the fatal cases, within a few days as a result of internal hemorrhages and renal blockage due to the accumulation of hemoglobin in the renal tubules.[66] If general symptoms (fever, jaundice, hematuria) do not appear within the first 24 hours, the prognosis is good.[67]

Schenone[67] has presented a valuable summary of 27 cases, 25 cutaneous and 2 cutaneovisceral (1 fatal), occurring in Chile. Subcutaneous or intramuscular administration of the antihistamine drug chlorprophenpyramidine (Chlor-Trimeton) decreased local pain and edema almost immediately and apparently effected a milder development of the gangrenous spot.

Other Venomous Spiders. A dangerous spider in southern Brazil is *Phoneutria fera* (Perty) (Family Ctenidae).[17] Several hundred accidents involving this spider occur annually in the state of São Paulo alone; occasionally in young children fatalities occur. The venom acts on both the central and peripheral nervous systems. An antiserum is available and should be used in cases of disturbance of cardiac output, vision, and respiration, even in adults. Symptomatic treatment with analgesics and antihistamines may be sufficient, if general symptoms do not occur during the first 3 to 12 hours after the accident.

Atrax formidabilis Cambridge and *A. robustus* Cambridge are cited by Thorp and Woodson[76] as dangerous spiders in Australia. The bite may cause severe symptoms, and death may result. They are funnel-web spiders of fairly large size, up to 1 1/2 in. in length excluding the legs. The fore part of the body is glossy ebony black, the black abdomen is covered with a velvety pile, while the undersurface bears tufts and brushes of red hair.

In Peru, the *pododora* or "pruning spider" is popularly supposed to be dangerous, but Gertsch[34] points out that supposed poisoning by this spider is probably a case of mistaken identity. At least three species of *Chiracanthium,* family Clubionidae, are venomous. *Chiracanthium inclusum* (Hentz), a widespread species in the United States, has been known to bite man, producing a temporarily painful localized effect, and *C. diversum* Koch, in Hawaii, has on a number of occasions bitten persons in the Honolulu area, in some cases requiring hospitalization and supportive treatment with calcium gluconate (Hardy, cited by Baerg[7]).

SCORPIONS

Class Arachnida, Order Scorpionida

General Characteristics. Scorpions are easily recognized by their more or less crablike appearance, but particularly by the long fleshy five-segmented tail-like postabdomen terminating in a bulbous sac and prominent sting (Fig.

179). The pedipalps are greatly enlarged, and the last two segments form strong chelae or pincers. The true jaws, chelicerae, are small and partly concealed from above by the front edge of the carapace. There are four pairs of terminally clawed legs.

The cephalothorax bears a pair of conspicuous eyes near the middorsal line (median eyes) and several smaller ocelli in groups of from two to five, on the lateral margins (lateral eyes). Some species are eyeless. Scorpions breathe by means of book lungs. They are ovoviviparous, and when the young are born they are carried attached by their pincers to the body of the mother. Although the sexes are very similar in appearance, the males have a longer cauda and broader chelae. An excellent account of the morphology as well as characters used in classification of scorpions is given by Moreno[53] in "Scorpiologia Cubana."

Scorpions are found most commonly in warmer climates. They are nocturnal, remaining hidden during the day beneath loose stones, loose bark

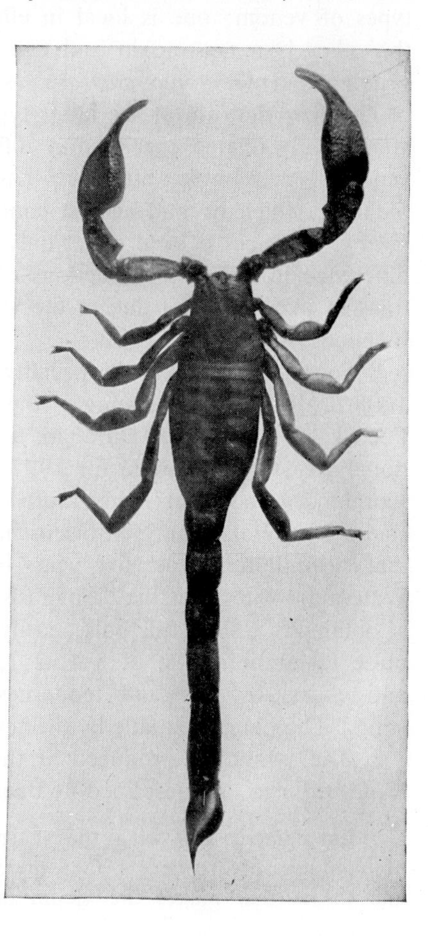

Fig. 179. A scorpion, *Hadrurus hirsutus*. × 0.6.

of fallen trees, boards, piles of lumber, floors of outbuildings, and debris; some bury themselves in sand or loose earth. They feed upon insects, spiders, millipedes, and even small rodents;[79] they seize their prey with their chelae and strike with the powerful sting, which is thrust forward in a characteristic fashion over the scorpion's head.

Scorpion Sting. The aculeus or sting of the scorpion is situated terminally on the final bulbous segment. This segment contains a pair of venom glands, which are separated by a muscular septum. From the glands are given off fine efferent ducts opening at the apex of the sting.[59] The sting curves upward when the "tail" is extended but downward when the scorpion poises for attack or defense, the entire tail-like postabdomen being curved dorsally and forward. The victim is struck quickly and repeatedly, the thrust being made forward over the scorpion's carapace.

Although published information is not consistent as to the nature of scorpion venom and its effect upon its victim, it seems that there are two general types of venom: one is local in effect and comparatively harmless to man; the other is a neurotoxin and can be fatal.[24] Scorpions such as the highly venomous *Androctonus australis,* as well as the dangerous American species of *Centruroides,* are of the latter type. It is of interest to note, however, that very closely related species may differ markedly in the effectiveness of their venom; for example, Stahnke[74] has shown that *Centruroides pantheriensis* Stahnke, which he had at first confused with the dangerous *C. sculpturatus* Ewing, produces a local effect only. Del Pozo[60] believes that, in spite of the difference in toxicity, the actions of all scorpion venoms are similar, variations in toxicity being due to the variable content of several active chemical functions.

Scorpion stings are especially dangerous to children. Baerg[5] records 1608 deaths due to the sting of the Durango scorpion, *Centruroides suffusus* Pocock, in the state of Durango, Mexico, from 1890 to 1926, with an additional 40 deaths recorded for 1927 and 17 for 1928. According to Balozet,[9] scorpions account for many more deaths in French North Africa than does snake bite. Waterman,[80] in discussing the scorpion problem in Trinidad, says that "in children under five years of age the sting frequently causes death." Waterman states that the "diagnosis is generally easy if a history of the sting is obtained, a slow full pulse easily compressible, with rapid respirations, a pulse respiration ratio of 3:1, 2:1, or 1:1; salivation, vomiting, glycosuria and epigastric pain and tenderness—a characteristic picture of scorpion sting." The puncture made by the aculeus may be visible.

The symptoms produced by the sting of the Durango scorpion, *Centruroides suffusus,* are described by Baerg[5] as follows:

> Immediately following the sharp pain produced by the sting is a feeling of numbness or drowsiness, then there is an itching sensation in the nose, mouth, and throat that makes the victim distort the face, rub nose and mouth, and

sneeze. There is at first an excessive production of saliva; this and a curious feeling that is described as the sensation of a ball of hair in the throat, induce the victim to swallow as rapidly as possible. The tongue is sluggish, so that communication is often by signs. The muscles of the lower jaw are contracted so that it is difficult, or impossible, to give medicine through the mouth. There is a disorder of movements in arms and legs. The temperature rises rapidly to 104° or 104.8° F., the salivary secretion now diminishes and there is a scarcity of urine. The senses of touch and sight are affected, objects appear large on touching them, hair feels rigid, face feels bulky, a veil seems to be interposed between the eyes and various objects, strong light is unpleasant to patients. Luminous objects, such as a candle, are surrounded by a red circle. Frequently there is a pronounced strabismus. There may be a hemorrhage of the stomach, intestine, and lungs. The convulsions come in waves and increase in severity for an hour and a half to two hours, or in severe cases until a fatal result. When the case ends in death, respiration stops a full minute before the pulse ceases to beat. When the patient survives for three hours he is usually considered out of danger; yet death may occur six to eight hours after the patient was stung. It is then probably due to nervous exhaustion following the long periods of convulsions.

Stahnke,[75] characterizing the effects of the stings of the two dangerous species of scorpions that occur in Arizona, *Centruroides sculpturatus* and *C. gertschi,* emphasizes the fact that the venom does not produce a swelling or discoloration at the site of the sting; the spot may become quite painful, however, and is hypersensitive so that bumping it will cause additional tingling sensations. On the other hand, the sting of the less venomous species of *Centruroides* and some species of *Vejovis, Diplocentrus, Hadrurus,* and others, may produce local swellings, with or without discoloration. These swellings, if a person is bitten on the hand or fingers, may move up the arm and even to the armpit, but there will be little or no systemic reaction, and, unless there are anaphylactic reactions, there will be no danger of death. Consequently, the *lack of swelling,* following scorpion sting in areas where dangerous *Centruroides* species may occur, should be taken as a warning indication of possibly serious or even fatal poisoning.

Stahnke's bulletin entitled *Scorpions*[75] is of inestimable value to persons living in areas where dangerous *Centruroides* species might occur and who might be in danger of coming in contact with these animals. This bulletin is available through the Poisonous Animals Research Laboratory, Arizona State University, Tempe.

If at all in doubt, one should take the victim of scorpion sting to a physician, preferably one who has had experience in dealing with them, particularly if the victim is under 5 years of age, has a heart ailment, has been stung on a number of widely distributed places, or has been stung on the face, back of the neck, or genitalia. Antiscorpion serum is available for most of the dangerous scorpions, and, when administered early and in sufficient quantities, it saves many lives. Failure of antiserum results from three causes, according to Balozet:[9] delay in administration, rapid development of bulbar intoxication, or a sudden relapse following the disappearance of symptoms and the discontinuation of treatment.

After applying a tight tourniquet as close as possible beyond the site of the sting, scorpion stings may be given first-aid treatment according to Stahnke[73] as follows:

> A piece of ice should be applied as soon as possible against the site of the sting; then more ice should be finely crushed and placed in water, using more ice than water. With a piece of ice against the site of the sting place the hand in the ice mixture. . . . Where a large dose of venom has been received the hand should be kept in this mixture for about two hours . . . . a large ice pack of finely crushed ice in a thin cloth may be placed over the site of the sting.

The function of the ice is to decrease absorption or to localize the venom; it has no effect on the venom itself. The patient should be kept as cool and calm as possible, but morphine or Demerol should not be used to relieve the pain as these increase the killing power of the venom. It is useless to make incisions at the site of the sting; bleeding will probably not eliminate the small amount of venom injected into the wound, and complications may result from the incision wound.

The order Scorpionida is divided into six families (some authorities recognize seven); these are the Scorpionidae, Buthidae, Vejovidae, Chactidae, Bothriuridae, and Diplocentridae. The Buthidae are by far of most importance from the medical standpoint. According to Ewing,[30] four of these families occur in the United States and northern Mexico, and are separated as follows:

1. Sternum subpentagonal, with sides almost parallel.................... 2
   Sternum triangular, the sides being strongly convergent anteriorly; membrane at the base of the last tarsal segment of most of the legs with two unbranched spurs; fixed arm of chelicerae without ventral tooth..Buthidae
2. Membrane at base of last segment of most of the legs with a single spur; postabdomen frequently reduced........................Diplocentridae
   Membrane at base of last tarsal segment of most of the legs with two spurs 3
3. With two ocelli on each lateral margin of carapace..............Chactidae
   With three to five ocelli on each lateral margin of carapace........Vejovidae

More than 600 species of scorpions in about 70 genera are known. Of the approximately 40 species found in the United States, according to Stahnke[73] only two are dangerously virulent to man.

Family Buthidae. The most important venomous scorpions of the world all belong to this family. The dangerous scorpions of Mexico and the southwestern United States belong to the genus *Centruroides* (Fig. 180). The Durango scorpion, *C. suffusus* Pocock, is the common scorpion of the State of Durango. Its sting is frequently fatal to children, particularly those under 7 years of age. At least four other Mexican species are dangerous, including *C. limpidus* Karsch and *C. norius* Hoffmann; the latter is reported to be about six times as venomous as *C. suffusus.*

Centruroides sculpturatus Ewing, said by Stahnke[73] to be confined at present to Arizona, is a small species, about 2 1/2 in. in length; it is generally of a solid yellow-straw color. It is a dangerously virulent species and is reported to be abundant. *Centruroides gertschi* Stahnke, so far as is known,

Fig. 180. Three *Centruroides* scorpions. (*Left to right*) *C. sculpturatus, C. gertschi,* and *C. vittatus.* (Reprinted with permission from Stahnke, Herbert L.: *Scorpions,* Figure 6, page 16, 1956; through courtesy of Dr. Stahnke and the Poisonous Animals Research Laboratory, Tempe, Arizona.)

according to Stahnke, is also confined to Arizona, but is much less abundant than *C. sculpturatus.* It is about the same size as the latter but has two irregular black stripes down its entire back; its basic color is yellow. This is also a dangerous species.

Centruroides vittatus (Say) is the common striped scorpion of the United States. It is widely distributed, having been reported from Georgia, Florida, Kansas, Texas, Arkansas, Louisiana, New Mexico, and South Carolina. Concerning the sting of this species, Ewing[30] writes:

> The writer has induced this species to sting him and has observed the effect of its sting on others. At the time of the stinging there is a sharp pain, but

this soon subsides. A small swollen area, or wheal, usually develops around the puncture point. This soon disappears. There are no permanent effects of the sting reported for the species as far as known to the writer.

Stahnke also regards this species as relatively harmless.

Buthus quinquestriatus Hemprich and Ehrenberg is a common Egyptian and North African species, more especially in upper Egypt, according to Wilson,[82] who states that it is of a sandy-yellow color tending to brown and that it measures about 10 cm in length. He also states that it is undoubtedly the commonest species in that region and is generally believed to be the most dangerous; it is frequently found in houses, and is the species, in all probability, giving rise to the numerous cases of scorpion sting said to be most commonly fatal in upper Egypt. Shulov[69] reports having traced four fatal cases in children between the ages of 6 and 13 years in Palestine.

Androctonus australis (Linnaeus) is the most important of several venomous species (genera *Androctonus, Buthus, a*nd *Buthacus*) occurring in North Africa west of Egypt. Balozet,[9] citing the work of Sergent, says that this scorpion was responsible for 142 out of 183 stings in which the guilty scorpion was identified. It is widespread in Algeria, Morocco, and Tunisia. In the Near East, *Prionurus crassicauda* (Oliver) is the most dangerous species.

Tityus serratulus Lutz and *T. bahiensis* Perty are dangerous species in Brazil. In South Africa certain species of *Parabuthus* are dangerous.

Family Diplocentridae. *Diplocentrus whitei* (Gervais) is a very dark reddish-brown scorpion from 5 to 7 cm in length; it occurs in southern Texas and rarely westward to Arizona and possibly California.

Family Vejovidae. This is the best represented family in North and Central America. It contains a number of very large species. *Hadrurus hirsutus* (Wood) (Fig. 179), the giant hairy scorpion of southern California and adjacent regions, measures 11 to 12 cm in length. Two other species of *Hadrurus* occur in the United States.

Vejovis spinigerus Wood, the stripe-tailed scorpion, is a typical desert species of the southwest. Baerg[5] reports that its sting caused only a slight pain which disappeared in less than half an hour; its poison had no appreciable effect on white rats. *Vejovis boreus* (Girard), the northern scorpion, is a yellowish-brown species, 3.5 to 5 cm in length occurring from Saskatchewan, Alberta, and Washington southward to higher elevations in California and Arizona. Its sting, though painful, is benign in effect. The mordant scorpion, *Uroctonus mordax* Thorell, a dark-brown, medium-sized species of the Pacific Coast, produces a sting about as painful as that of a yellow jacket, but causes as a rule less swelling; its effects soon disappear.

Scorpion Control. The scorpion hazard on premises may be reduced to a great extent by eliminating favorable hiding places, such as boards, rubbish, loose rocks, bricks and lumber, and the like. Dwellings built of adobe brick may have cracks and crevices that harbor scorpions. Scorpions may hide deep in recesses, however, and they may go without food or water for as long as 6 months. Consequently, their eradication may prove a difficult matter, particularly in the light of the fact that their development to maturity may require 3 to 5 years.

Stahnke[75] gives some concise and practical suggestions for control. Trapping under a damp burlap or heavy cloth, in cases of heavy infestation, may bring scorpions together to a place where they may be destroyed. Cats are effective predators; so are ducks and chickens, although the latter are more apt to be stung, sometimes with fatal results. Old crankcase oil, fuel oil, tractor oil, kerosene, applied to places suitable for scorpions to hide, may make such places unattractive, and the addition of a little creosote will discourage their prospective prey.

DDT has proven effective against *Centruroides* species in the West Indies, as have isodrin and chlordane in southern Mexico. Stahnke recommends insecticides containing several of the chlorinated hydrocarbons (such as DDT, chlordane, lindane, and dieldrin), plus pyrethrum. A residual insecticide should be such that it will remain effective for a minimum of 4 months. It should be applied as a paint spray to woodwork, plumbing, closet interiors, under floors, and elsewhere scorpions may hide or travel.

WHIPSCORPIONS

Class Arachnida, Order Pedipalpida

Characteristics of the Pedipalpida. The Pedipalpida (also known as the Uropygi or Thelyphonida) are widespread through the tropics and subtropics, although very unevenly distributed. They are scorpionlike in appearance but differ in the form of the pedipalps, the antennalike first legs, and the whip-bearing abdomen. Whipscorpions feed chiefly on insects, worms, and slugs, which they seize quickly with their sharp pedipalps. They are nocturnal, and in the daytime they may be found under stones, in burrows, and in other protected places. They protect themselves by means of their pedipalps and an acid, with the odor of acetic acid, which they eject from near the base of the tail.

The giant whipscorpion, *Mastigoproctus giganteus* (Lucas) (Fig. 181), locally known as the vinegarone, vinegaroon, grampus, or mule killer, occurs commonly in Florida, Texas, other parts of the South, and westward to California. It feeds on almost all kinds of larger insects and other arthropods, if not too hard or active; it has been known to kill small frogs and toads.[24] Although it is greatly feared, there seems to be little justification for this. Ewing[29] states that on no occasion was there more than a trivial mechanical effect from the bite, similar to that of a slight pinprick. He states that when handled it gives off a repellent fluid which has the odor of vinegar. This fluid may produce some irritation to persons with a tender skin.

Flower (cited by Cloudsley-Thompson[24]) described the scorpionlike behavior of *Thelyphonus skimkewitchii* Tarnani in Thailand and the resulting "sting" which pained him for several hours and which required medication. If the irritating fluid secreted by the whipscorpion should come into contact with a prick or scratch on a person's hand, possibly one made by the chelicerae or pedipalps of the arachnid, it is quite possible that a smarting sensation which might be mistaken for the result of a sting may occur. Cloudsley-Thompson also cites one case of a blacksmith experiencing blisters as the result of a vinegarone being crushed on his chest.

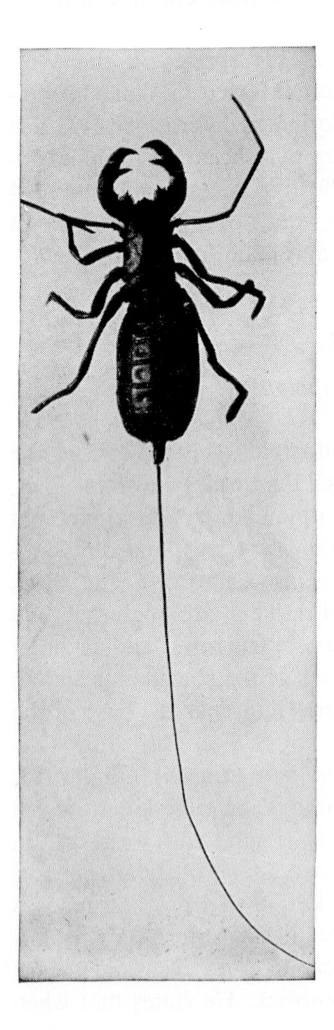

Fig. 181. Whipscorpion, *Mastigoproctus giganteus.* × 0.8.

SOLPUGIDS

Order Arachnida, Class Solpugida

Characteristics of the Solpugida. The solpugids (Fig. 182), commonly known as "sun spiders" and "wind scorpions," are in general appearance largely spiderlike, although there is no pedicel; they are rather hairy, occurring mainly in the desert, tropical, and subtropical regions. The chelicerae are large and powerful and are two-segmented. The second segment is movable and articulates in such fashion as to work in a more or less vertical plane. Food is crushed to a pulp, the fluid is swallowed, and the hard parts are usually ejected. The first pair of legs is long and rather feeble, and they are used as tactile organs. Respiration is tracheate.

Fig. 182. (*Left*) A solpugid, commonly called "sun spider"; (*right*) eggs.

Solpugids are commonly but erroneously regarded as exceedingly venomous. There is not the slightest foundation for the supposition, sometimes expressed, that any animal drinking from a water trough in which a solpugid was present would die. The question as to the venomous nature of these animals cannot be dismissed summarily, however. Cloudsley-Thompson[24] has given a concise account of the subject. No poison glands associated with the jaws have been found, but it has been suggested that poisoning might result from toxic excretions through the setal pores which could be traced along the tips of the jaws (Bernard, 1897). Apparently authentic cases of aftereffects resulting from solpugid bite have been recorded, some of them even fatal. Cloudsley-Thompson concludes, however, that "on the few occasions that poisoning does occur, it is most probably due to infection of the wound."

The solpugids of the United States have been monographed by Muma,[56] who recognizes about 75 species (in addition to several of uncertain status) distributed through two families, four subfamilies, and ten genera. Most species are found in the southwest, from Texas to California, but *Ammotrechella stimpsoni* (Putnam) inhabits Florida, and *Eremobates pallipes* (Say) is widespread throughout the western half of the United States.

VENOMOUS TICKS

Class Arachnida, Order Acarina

Ticks belonging to both families, Ixodidae and Argasidae, may cause local as well as systemic disturbances by their bites (see Chapter 19).

Ordinarily little or no injury results from the mere bite of an ixodine tick; *Dermacentor occidentalis* Neumann and *D. variabilis* (Say) have been known to remain attached to a person for days without causing any great inconvenience and occasionally are quite unobserved by the host. However, Nuttall[57] records a number of cases cited by other authors in which the bite of *Ixodes ricinus* (Linnaeus) has caused serious consequences, notably a case described by Johannessen of a "boy where the tick's body was removed but the capitulum remained embedded in the skin at the back of the head. Swelling followed at the point of injury, accompanied by headache, stiffening and cramps in the muscles of one side, partial loss of memory and polyuria; the pupils became dilated, etc. The boy made a slow recovery." The bite of *Ixodes pacificus* commonly results in more or less marked systemic disturbances.

Quite a number of species belonging to the family Argasidae are known to cause more or less serious consequences by their bites alone, notably *Ornithodoros moubata* (Murray), *O. coriaceus* Koch, *O. talaje* (Guérin-Ménéville), and *O. turicata* (Dugès).

Ornithodoros moubata has been reported repeatedly as causing marked disturbances by its bite. Wellman, as quoted by Nuttall *et al.*[57] (p. 98), "states that the bite is very painful, the swelling and irritation (especially in Europeans) not subsiding for days. The wheals are hard, raised and swell most disagreeably if scratched, and this even a week after being bitten. The bite of young ticks (nymphae) is said by the natives to be more severe than that of the adults."

Ornithodoros coriaceus Koch. This species (Fig. 183) occurs commonly in the more mountainous coastal counties of California, having been first described from Mexico where it is known as the "tlalaja." In California it is known as the "pajaroello." On Mount Hamilton, it flourishes in the deer beds among the scrub oaks. The following description of the species is a translation by Nuttall from the original:

Shaped like the sole of a shoe, thick margined, roughly shagreened, yellowish-earthy color, spotted rusty-red, legs toothed dorsally. Length 9.3 mm. Body about twice as long as wide, width fairly uniform, indented on the sides, pointed above the mouth parts, rounded posteriorly, a thick turned-up border all around; the whole surface above and below thickly granulated like fish skin

Fig. 183. Showing *Ornithodoros coriaceus* just backing away from her eggs recently deposited in the sand. Note protective coloration of the tick.

(shagreen), the granules flat above, consequently, the whole leathery, on the back unequal folds and grooves. Beneath in the front of the body a deep groove running to the stigmata and on the inner protrusion the rather large round quite clearly marked eyes. The coxae gradually thickened toward the distal extremity and are somewhat bent; the other articles somewhat compressed and clearly notched or round toothed. The whole surface, above and below, dirty yellowish-earthy color, rusty-red spots irregularly distributed throughout. Capitulum and palps light yellow. Legs gray-brown. Female.

The pajaroello is more feared than the rattlesnake by persons living where it exists, and many harrowing tales are told regarding the loss of an arm or leg, or even death resulting from its bite. Much of this is, of course, gross exaggeration. However, the following is an account of two bites suffered by a University of California student some years ago in July. He experienced sharp pain on the left arm and upon rolling up his sleeve discovered a large tick, partly engorged, attached to the upper arm in front. He dislodged the tick and sucked the lesion. The lesion when first discovered showed a small dark purple ring surrounding a bright red spot, the point of attachment. The discoloration disappeared in a short time, but the arm was "highly irritable for two or three days and at the point of attachment a minute clear scab formed." The tick proved to be a pajaroello.

The second bite took place 2 weeks later while he was seated in a thicket of willows (the first bite had occurred while he was riding over a brush-grown hill), and in this case the sharp pain involved the left leg. An almost fully engorged tick (again a pajaroello) measuring about 3/4 in. in length and about 1/2 in. in width was removed from just above the shin. Once more a bright red spot was visible at the point of attachment, surrounded by an irregular ring about 3/4 in. in diameter. In about an hour the leg began to swell in the vicinity of the lesion, and in about 3 hours the entire leg was tremendously swollen. The coloration about the point of attachment had widened considerably, was puffy, and a clear lymph exuded freely from the lesion. The young man lanced the wound, causing blood to flow freely, and treated it with crystals of potassium permanganate, binding the leg with cotton and gauze. During the following night he reports experiencing a general disagreeable feeling, the entire lower leg "irritable and numb." On the following day the bite on the arm became "irritable" again and was treated as had been the leg as he feared bad results. For several weeks both lesions exuded a clear lymph from beneath an "oily-looking, transparent, red mottled scab" which remained in evidence for 2 or 3 months.

Life History of Ornithodoros coriaceus. The pajaroello deposits large plum-colored spherical eggs (Fig. 184). In the laboratory these are deposited on sand in slight depressions. There are commonly 4 to 7 layings at intervals of from several weeks during the months of May to July, inclusive (as early as February under laboratory conditions), and the female is known to deposit eggs for at least two successive seasons. The greatest number of eggs observed at one laying was 802, with a total of 1158 for one season. The incubation period at a maintained temperature of from 24° to 26° was from 19 to 29 days, with an average of about 22 days.

The larvae (Fig. 184) are very active, scattering quickly and attaching readily to a host, particularly rabbits in the laboratory. Experimentally man may also serve as a larval host. The ear of a rabbit apparently affords a most satisfactory point for attachment. The larva remains attached to the host for a period of about 7 days, becoming quite globular and much engorged. Under favorable conditions, the larval stage lasts 10 to 12 days.

Sexually differentiated ticks appear after about the fourth molt. Others did not become sexually differentiated with five molts. There may be six or seven nymphal stages. Ordinarily the tick molts once for each engorgement, but there may be two molts between feedings. Smith[70] reports that reared females begin ovipositing 4 to 6 months after the first feeding. He records the adult longevity of reared, fed ticks as ranging from 8 months to more than 3 years and 7 months for males and from 13 months to more than 5 years for a female.

Fig. 184. Eggs of *Ornithodoros coriaceus;* larvae in the act of emerging; and two fully emerged individuals. × 14.

CENTIPEDES

Class Chilopoda

Centipedes. Centipedes are wormlike in form, with a distinct head that possesses a pair of antennae, and with many fairly similar body segments, each with one pair of segmented appendages. Like the insects, they are tracheated and, for the most part, terrestrial. The individual body segments are somewhat flattened so that a cross section through one of them is oval. The legs are at least moderately conspicuous; in number they vary from 15 pairs to more than 100 pairs. Notwithstanding the confusing number of walking appendages, centipedes crawl very rapidly.

Most centipedes are predaceous, feeding mainly on insects. They are provided with powerful poison claws, the maxillipeds, located immediately ventral to the mouth and connected by means of a hollow tube to large poison glands. These maxillipeds are the appendages of the first body segment behind the head. Large insects are quickly killed when the poison claws of a large centipede close upon them. Centipedes have been reported as feeding on flesh of living toads and small snakes and as killing mice, small birds, and geckoes.[24]

The larger centipedes (Fig. 185) are commonly regarded as venomous and are generally much feared. Much of this fear is without justification, although it is true that the larger species of *Scolopendra,* some of which reach a length of 8 to 10 in. or more, and even the smaller house centipede, *Scutigera cleopatra* (Linnaeus) [= *S. forceps* (Rafinesque)], are able to pierce the skin and cause severe pain with some swelling at the site of the bite. Accounts of centipede bites in the literature are somewhat confusing, but it would seem that the worst a centipede can be expected to do is to produce severe local pain, which, like the sting of a hornet, will gradually disappear. Büchcrl,[18] experimenting with five of the largest and commonest Brazilian

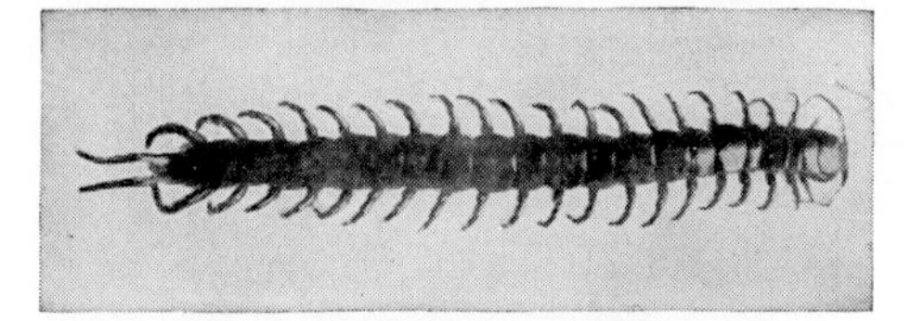

Fig. 185. A centipede, *Scolopendra heros.* × 0.66.

species, with mice, guinea pigs, and pigeons as experimental animals, concluded that the poison was too feeble to endanger the life of man, even of young children. Remington[62] has reviewed the literature on centipede bites, and, coupling his studies with personal experience, he concludes that "the soundest conclusion from the published records appears to be that no centipede bites are potentially deadly to man and that the immediate pain diminishes rapidly, much like the sting of a honey bee." There is only one record, he points out, of centipede bite fatal to man, and that was a seven-year-old child bitten on the head, who died 29 hours later.

Remington makes one interesting observation in respect to treatment of centipede bite. A medical aid man in the Philippine Islands conceived the idea of treating the symptoms by injecting local anesthetics, such as were used by dentists, in the vicinity of the bite. Many suffering from centipede bite received prompt relief from this treatment.

MILLIPEDES

Class Diplopoda

Millipedes. These arthropods differ from the centipedes in that most of the apparent body segments possess two pairs of appendages instead of one. Millipedes are vegetarians and lack the poison fangs characteristic of centipedes. In most species the body is cylindrical, and the numerous legs, as well as the antennae, are relatively short and inconspicuous.

The Diplopoda are commonly separated into two groups depending upon the presence or absence of repugnatorial glands. In the *Chilognatha,* to which all North American genera except one, *Polyxenus,* belong,[22] these glands are present and are capable of producing irritating effects.[19] Certain species are able to squirt irritating fluids a distance of several inches; the Haitian species *Rhinocrichus latespargor* Loomis is reported as discharging its secretion a distance of 28 to 33 in. This fluid is dangerous to the eyes and is responsible for occasional blindness in poultry in the West Indies and elsewhere. Halstead and Ryckman[39] report a conclusively proven case of vesicular dermatitis in Montemorelos, Nuevo Leon, Mexico, caused by a diplopod of the genus *Orthoporus.*

REFERENCES

1. Anonymous, 1954. *The Imported Fire Ant and How to Control It.* Washington, D. C.: Dept. Agric., in Leaflet no. 350. 8 pp.

2. Anonymous, 1954. *Wasps—How to Control Them.* Washington, D. C.: Dept. Agric., in Leaflet no. 365.

3. Atkins, J. A.; Wingo, C. W.; Sodeman, W. A.; and Flynn, J. E.; 1958. "Necrotic arachnidism," *Am. J. Trop. Med. & Hyg.,* **7:**165–84.

4. Baerg, W. J., 1923. "The effects of the bite of *Latrodectus mactans* Fabr.," *J. Parasitol.* **9:**161–69.

5. Baerg, W. J., 1929. "Some poisonous arthropods of North and Central America," *Tr. 4th. Internat. Cong. Entomol.,* Ithaca, 1928, **2:**418–38.

6. Baerg, W. J., 1958. *The Tarantula.* Lawrence: Univ. Kansas Press. 88 pp., 19 figs.

7. Baerg, W. J., 1959. *The Black Widow Spider and Five Other Venomous Spiders in the United States.* Fayetteville: Univ. Arkansas Exp. Sta., in Bull., no. 608. 43 pp.

8. Bailey, S. F., 1936. "Thrips attacking man," *Canad. Entomologist,* **68:**95–98.

9. Balozet, Lucien, 1956. "Scorpion venoms and antiscorpion serum," in Buckley and Porges, *Venoms.* Washington, D. C.: Amer. Assoc. Adv. Sc., publ. no. 44, pp. 141–44.

10. Barnes, O. L., and Nerney, N. J., 1953. *The Red Harvester Ant and How to Subdue It.* Washington, D. C.: U. S. Dept. Agric., in Farmers' Bull., no. 1668. 11 pp.

11. Bishopp, F. C., 1923. *The Puss Caterpillar and the Effects of Its Sting on Man.* Washington, D. C.: Dept. Agric., in Circ., no. 288. 14 pp.

12. Blyth, A. W., and Blyth, M. W., 1920. *Poisons: Their Effect and Detection,* 5th ed. London: Chas. Griffin Co. 745 pp.

13. Bogen, E., 1932. "Poisonous spider bites: newer developments in our knowledge of arachnidism," *Ann. Int. Med.,* **6:**375–88.

14. Bogen, E., 1956. "The treatment of spider bite poisoning," in Buckley and Porges, *Venoms*. Washington, D. C.: Amer. Assoc. Adv. Sc., publ. no. 44, pp. 101–05.

15. Borror, Donald J., and DeLong, Dwight M., 1954. *An Introduction to the Study of Insects*. New York: Reinhard and Company. ix + 1030 pp.

16. Bromley, Stanley W., 1933. "The sting of a tarantula wasp," *Bull. Brooklyn Entomol. Soc.*, **28:**192.

17. Bücherl, Wolfgang, 1956. "Studies on dried venom of *Phoneutria fera* Perty 1833," in Buckley and Porges, *Venoms*. Washington, D. C.: Amer. Assoc. Adv. Sc., publ. no. 44, pp. 95–97.

18. Bücherl, Wolfgang, 1946. "Acçao do veneno dos escolopendromorfos do Brasil sobre algunas animais de laboratorio," *Mem. Inst. Butantan,* São Paulo, **19:**181–97.

19. Burt, E., 1947. "Exudate from millipeds, with particular reference to its injurious effects," *Trop. Dis. Bull.,* **44:**7–12.

20. Caffrey, D. J., 1918. "Notes on the poisonous urticating spines of *Hemileuca oliviae* larvae," *J. Econ. Entomol.,* **11:**363–67.

21. Chalmers, A. J., and King, H. H., 1917. "Blister beetles as a public nuisance," *New Orleans M. & Sci. J.,* **70:**445–55.

22. Chamberlin, Ralph, and Hoffman, Richard L., 1958. *Checklist of the Millipeds of North America.* Washington, D. C.: U. S. National Museum, Bull. 212. 236 pp.

23. Cherney, L. S.; Wheeler, C. M.; and Reed, Alfred C.; 1939. "Flea-antigen in prevention of flea bites," *Am. J. Trop. Med.,* **19:**327–32.

24. Cloudsley-Thompson, J. L., 1958. *Spiders, Scorpions, Centipedes and Mites*. New York: Pergamon Press. xiv + 228 pp.

25. Cowles, R. B., 1937. "The San Diegan alligator lizard and the black widow spider," *Science,* **85:**99–100.

26. D'Amour, F. E.; Becker, F. E.; and Van Riper, W.; 1936. "The black widow spider," *Quart. Rev. Biol.,* **2:**123–60.

27. Donisthrop, H., 1945. "Ants as carriers of disease," *Entomol. Monthly Mag.,* **81:**185.

28. Essig, E. O., 1932. "A small insect which stings severely," *Science,* **75:**242–43.

29. Ewing, H. E., 1928. "Observations on the habits and the injury caused by the bites and stings of some common North American arthropods," *Am. J. Trop. Med.,* **8:**39–62.

30. Ewing, H. E., 1928. "The scorpions of the western part of the United States, with note on those occurring in northern Mexico," *Proc. U. S. Nat. Museum,* **73** (Art. 9):1–24 (2 plates).

31. Finlayson, M. H., 1956. "Arachnidism in South Africa," in Buckley and Porges, *Venoms*. Washington, D. C.: Amer. Assoc. Adv. Sc., publ. no. 44, pp. 85–87.

32. Foubert, Edward L., Jr., and Stier, R. A., 1958. "Antigenic relationships between honeybees, wasps, yellow hornets, black hornets, and yellow jackets," *J. Allergy,* **29:**13–23.

33. Geldern, Charles E. von, 1927. "Systemic effects following the sting of a species of *Epyris*," *Science*, **65:**302–03.

34. Gertsch, Willis J., 1949. *American Spiders*. New York: Van Nostrand Co., Inc. viii + 285 pp (64 plates).

35. Gertsch, Willis J., 1958. "The spider genus *Loxosceles* in North America, Central America, and the West Indies," *Amer. Mus. Novitates*, **1907:**1–46.

36. Gilbert, E. W., and Stewart, C. M., 1935. "Effective treatment of arachnidism by calcium salts, a preliminary report," *Am. J. Med. Sc.*, **189:**532–36.

37. Guiglia, D., 1958. "Les sclerodermines par rapport à l'homme," *Proc. 10th Internat. Cong. Entomol.*, Montreal, 1956, **3:**883–87.

38. Halter, B. L., and Kuzell, W. C., 1943. "Black widow spider bites in the adult male," *Mil. Surgeon*, **92:**427–32.

39. Halstead, B. W., and Ryckman, R. E., 1949. "Injurious effects from contacts with millipedes," *Med. Arts and Sciences*, **3:**16–18.

40. Herms, W. B., 1925. "Entomological observations on Fanning and Washington Islands," *Pan-Pacific Entomol.*, **2:**49–54.

41. Herms, W. B.; Bailey, S. F.; and McIvor, Barbara; 1935. *The Black Widow Spider*. Berkeley: Univ. Calif., in Agric. Exper. Sta. Bull., no. 591. 30 pp.

42. Irving, W. G., and Hinman, E. H., 1935. "The blue mud-dauber as a predator of the black widow spider," *Science*, **82:**395–96.

43. Kaston, B. J., 1948. *Spiders of Connecticut*. Hartford: State of Connecticut, State Geol. and Nat. Hist. Survey, Bull. no. 70. 874 pp.

44. Kaston, B. J., and Jenks, G. E., 1937. "Dipterous parasites of spider egg sacs," *Bull. Brooklyn Entomol. Soc.*, **32:**160–65.

45. Kemper, Heinrich, 1958. "Experimentelle Untersuchungen über die Wirkung von Raupenhaaren auf die Menschliche Haut," *Proc. 10th Internat. Cong. Entomol.*, Montreal, 1956, **3:**719–23.

46. Krull, Wendell H., and Mapes, Cortland R., 1952. "Studies on the biology of *Dicrocoelium dendriticum* (Rudolphi, 1819) Loos 1899 (Trematoda: Dicrocoeliidae) including its relationship to the intermediate host, *Cionella lubrica* (Müller). VII. The second intermediate host of *Dicrocoelium dendriticum*," *Cornell Veterinarian*, **42:**603–04.

47. Lawson, P. B., 1933. "Notes on the life history of the hour-glass spider," *Ann. Entomolog. Soc. Amer.*, **26:**568–74.

48. Levi, Herbert W., 1958. "Number of species of black-widow spiders (Theridiidae: *Latrodectus*)," *Science*, **127:**1055.

49. Levi, Herbert W., 1959. "The spider genus *Latrodectus* (Araneae, Theridiidae)," *Trans. Amer. Microscop. Soc.*, **78:**7–43.

50. Martini, E., 1932. *Zoönosen der Haut in wärmeren Ländern*, in Handbuch der Haut- und Geschlechtskrankheiten (**12:**575–707). Berlin: Julius Springer. 133 pp.

51. Mickel, C. E., 1928. *Biological and Taxonomic Investigations on the Mutillid Wasps*. Washington, D. C.: Smithsonian Inst., in U. S. Nat. Museum Bull., no. 143. 352 pp.

52. Miller, D. G., 1956. "Massive anaphylaxis from insect stings," in Buckley and Porges, *Venoms*. Washington, D. C.: Amer. Assoc. Adv. Sci., publ. no. 44, pp. 117–21.

53. Moreno, Abelardo, 1940. "Scorpiologia Cubana," *Rev. Univ. Habana,* nos. 23, 26, 27. 75 pp.

54. Muesebeck, C. F. W., and Walkley, Luella M., 1951. "Bethyloidea," in Muesebeck, Krombein, and Townes, *Hymenoptera of America North of Mexico —Synoptic Catalog.* Washington, D. C.: Dept. Agric., monograph no. 2.

55. Mueller, Harry Louis, 1959. "Further experiences with severe allergic reactions to insect stings," *New England J. Med.,* **261:**374–77.

56. Muma, Martin H., 1951. "The arachnid order Solpugida in the United States," *Bull. Amer. Mus. Nat. Hist.,* **97:**35–141.

57. Nuttall, G. H. F.; Warburton, Cecil; Cooper, W. F.; and Robinson, L. E.; 1908–1911. *Ticks, a Monograph of the Ixodoidea. Part I, Argasidae.* x + 104 + 35 pp. (1908). *Part II, Ixodidae.* xix + 105 + 348 pp. (1911). London: Cambridge Univ. Press.

58. Parrish, Henry M., 1959. "Death from bites and stings of venomous animals and insects in the United States," *A.M.A. Arch. Int. Med.,* **104:**198–207.

59. Pawlowsky, E. N., 1924. "Studies on the organization and development of scorpions," *Quart. J. Micros. Sci.,* **68:**615–40 (3 plates).

60. Pozo, E. C. del, 1956. "Mechanism of pharmacological action of scorpion venom," in Buckley and Porges, *Venoms.* Washington, D. C.: Amer. Assoc. Adv. Sci., publ. no. 44. pp. 123–29.

61. Randel, H. W., and Doan, G. B., 1956. "Caterpillar urticaria in the Panama Canal Zone: Report of five cases," in Buckley and Porges, *Venoms.* Washington, D. C.: Amer. Assoc. Adv. Sci., publ. no. 44. pp. 111–16.

62. Remington, Charles L., 1950. "The bite and habits of a giant centipede (*Scolopendra subspinipes*) in the Philippine Islands," *Am. J. Trop. Med.,* **30:**453–55.

63. Roberts, J. I., and Tonking, H. D., 1935. "Notes on an East African vesicant beetle, *Paedurus crebripunctatus* Epp.," *Ann. Trop. Med.,* **29:**415–20.

64. Sampayo, Rafael R. L., 1942. *Latrodectus mactans y Latrodectismo.* Buenos Aires: Inst. de Fisiologia de la Faculdad de Ciencias Medicas.

65. Savory, T. H., 1935. *The Arachnida.* London: Edward Arnold & Co. xi + 218 pp.

66. Schenone, Hugo, 1953. "Mordeduras de arañas," *Bol. Chileno de Parasitol.,* **8:**35–37.

67. Schenone, Hugo, 1959. "Estudio de 27 casos de loxoscelismo," *Bol. Chileno de Parasitol.,* **14:**7–13.

68. Schenone, Hugo; Rosales, Segundo; and Garcia, Emilio M.; 1957. "Caso de loxoscelismo cutáneo visceral en Mendoza," *Bol. Chileno de Parasitol.,* **12:**56–59.

69. Shulov, A., 1939. "The venom of the scorpion *Buthus quinquestriatus* and the preparation of an anti-serum," *Tr. Roy. Soc. Trop. Med. & Hyg.,* **33:**253–56.

70. Smith, Carroll N., 1944. "The life history of the tick *Ornithodoros coriaceus* Koch (Argasidae)," *Ann. Entomol. Soc. Amer.,* **37:**325–35.

71. Smith, M. R., 1951. "Formicidae," in Muesebeck, Krombein and Townes, *Hymenoptera of America North of Mexico—Synoptic Catalog.* Washington, D. C.: Dept. Agric., monograph no. 2 (cf. p. 812).

72. Snodgrass, R. E., 1952. *A Textbook of Arthropod Anatomy*. Ithaca, New York: Comstock Publ. Co. viii + 363 pp.

73. Stahnke, Herbert L., 1944. "Scorpions of the United States," *Turtox News,* **22:**20–22.

74. Stahnke, Herbert L., 1956. "A new species of scorpion of the Buthidae: *Centruroides pantheriensis,*" *Entomol. News,* **67:**15–19.

75. Stahnke, Herbert L., 1956. *Scorpions.* Tempe, Arizona: Poisonous Animals Research Laboratory, Arizona State (University). 35 pp. Revised edition.

76. Thorp, Raymond W., and Woodson, Weldon D., 1945. *Black Widow, America's Most Poisonous Spider.* Chapel Hill: Univ. North Carolina Press, xi + 222 pp.

77. Tinkham, Ernest R., 1956. "Bite symptoms of the red-legged widow spider (*Latrodectus bishopi*)," in Buckley and Porges, *Venoms.* Washington, D. C.: Amer. Assoc. Adv. Sci., publ. no. 44. pp. 99–100.

78. Usinger, R. L., and Myers, J. G., 1929. "Facultative bloodsucking in phytophagous Hemiptera," *Parasitology,* **21:**472–80.

79. Vachon, Max, 1953. "The biology of scorpions," *Endeavour,* **12:**80–89.

80. Waterman, J. A., 1938. "Some notes on scorpion poisoning in Trinidad," *Tr. Roy. Soc. Trop. Med. & Hyg.,* **31:**607–24.

81. Weidner, Herbert, 1936. "Beiträge zu einer Monographie der Raupen mit Gifthaaren," *Zeits. f. Angewandte Entomol.,* **23:**432–84.

82. Wilson, W. H., 1904. "On the venom of scorpions," *Records Egyptian Govt. School Med.,* **2:**1–44 (3 plates).

INDEX

[**Bold face** figures indicate primary discussion of topic in text.]